THE TREE BOOK

BIG TREES IN THE GIANT FOREST OF THE SEQUOIA NATIONAL PARK
CALIFORNIA (*Sequoia Wellingtonia*)

THE TREE BOOK A POPU-LAR GUIDE TO A KNOWLEDGE OF THE TREES OF NORTH AMERICA AND TO THEIR USES AND CULTIVA-TION

BY
JULIA ELLEN ROGERS

WITH SIXTEEN PLATES IN COLOUR
AND ONE HUNDRED AND SIXTY IN
BLACK-AND-WHITE FROM PHOTOGRAPHS
BY A. RADCLYFFE DUGMORE

NEW YORK
DOUBLEDAY, PAGE & COMPANY
1905

THE WORLD'S WORK PRESS, NEW YORK

TABLE OF CONTENTS

PART I

HOW TO KNOW THE TREES

Table of Contents

Part I—*Continued*

PART II
FORESTRY

PART III
THE USES OF WOOD

PART IV
THE LIFE OF THE TREES

LIST OF COLOURED PLATES

LIST OF OTHER ILLUSTRATIONS

List of Other Illustrations

xiv

List of Other Illustrations

xvi

GLOSSARY OF TECHNICAL TERMS

Abortive. Not developed.

Acuminate. Tapering to apex.

Acute. Pointed.

Adventitious. Out of the natural order, as buds that are formed where the bark is bruised, or about a stub.

Anther. The pollen-producing part of the stamen.

Apetalous. Without petals.

Apex. The tip.

Arbourescent. Having tree form.

Arboretum. An assemblage of living trees of many kinds.

Aril. Loose bag around the seed.

Axil. Angle between leaf and twig.

Axillary. Arising from the angle between stem and leaf.

Baccate. Berry-like.

Bast. Inner fibrous layer of bark.

Bloom. A pale film covering some ripe plums, grapes, etc.

Bract. Modified leaf in flower cluster.

Budding. Setting a bud upon a stock so it shall grow fast.

Burs. Woody, irregular excrescences upon trunks and roots. Spiny husks of nuts.

Calyx. The outer whorl of a flower.

Cambium. The mucilaginous living layer between wood and bark.

Capsule. A dry, debiscent seed case of more than one compartment.

Carpel. A single pistil, or a division of a compound pistil.

Catkin. A slender spike of minute, crowded flowers, as in willows.

Chlorophyll. The green colouring matter in leaves.

Ciliate. Fringed with hairs.

Cion. See *Scion*.

Coalesce. To grow together.

Collar. The place where trunk and roots meet.

Compound. Of several units on a common stem, as the leaflets of a locust leaf.

Cone. A fruit made up of overlapping scales, as of pines.

Coppice. Woods made up of sprouting stumps.

Cordate. Heart-shaped.

Coriaceous. Leathery.

Corolla. The whorl of petals.

Cotyledons. Seed leaves.

Crenate. Scalloped.

Cross. To produce seed by fertilizing the ovules of one flower with pollen from flowers of another species.

Crustaceous. Dry; horny.

Cutting. A piece of root or twig by which certain species are able to reproduce themselves.

Cyme. A flat flower cluster.

Deciduous. Falling in autumn.

Dehiscent. Opening when ripe, as the husks of hickory nuts.

Deltoid. Triangular.

Diffuse. Loosely spreading.

Diœcious. Bearing pistillate and staminate flowers on separate trees.

Disk. Base of flower to which all floral parts are attached.

Drupe. A stone fruit, as a plum.

Duct. A tube.

Elliptical. Evenly and narrowly oblong with rounded ends.

Entire. Without teeth or lobes, as leaves of magnolias.

Exotic. Not native.

Falcate. Sickle-shaped.

Fascicle. A crowded cluster, as seen in the leaf arrangement of larches.

Fertilisation. The union of pollen grain and ovule. The setting of seed.

Filament. The slender thread that supports the anther.

Fungi. Low vegetable organisms, including mushrooms, mildew, rust and decay in wood.

Genus (Pl. *genera*). Subdivision of a family.

Germination. The sprouting of seeds.

Glabrous. Smooth.

Glaucous. Covered with a pale, powdery film.

Grafting. Inserting a cion in a stock so it will grow fast.

Habitat. Chosen situation of growth.

Heartwood. The dead wood in the trunk under the sapwood.

Humus. Vegetable mould.

Hybrid. A seedling resulting from a cross.

Indehiscent. Not opening to discharge seeds at maturity. See husks of walnuts.

Glossary of Technical Terms

Involucre. Whorl of green leaves or bracts below flower or flower cluster.

Leader. A terminal shoot or bud.

Lateral. On the side.

Lenticels. Corky slits or dots on bark for admission of air.

Liber. The inner, fibrous layer of bark.

Linear. Long and narrow, like a grass blade.

Membranaceous. Thin and pliable.

Monœcious. Bearing both staminate and pistillate flowers on one tree.

Monotypic. Having but one representative. as the genus Cladrastis.

Nutlet. Small, hard seed case, as in haws.

Oblanceolate. Lance-shaped, but broadest toward apex.

Obovate. Ovate, with broadest part toward apex.

Obtuse. Blunt.

Osmosis. The passing of liquids and gases through cell walls and other continuous membranes.

Ovary. Base of pistil containing ovules. Becomes the seed vessel.

Ovule. A rudimentary seed.

Palmate. With leaflets all arising from the end of the petiole, as in the horse chestnut leaves.

Panicle. Spreading, conical flower cluster as in yellow-wood.

Parasite. Any organism that is supported and nourished by another one.

Pedicel. Secondary flower-stalks; branches of the peduncle.

Peduncle. Main flower-stalk.

Perfect. Having both stamens and pistils, as the flowers of apple and magnolia.

Pericarp. The matured ovary.

Persistent. Remaining longer than ordinary. Evergreen.

Petiolate. Provided with a petiole.

Petiole. Stem of a leaf.

Pinnate. Feather-like. With leaflets along sides of main leaf-stalk, as in ash and walnut leaves.

Pistil. Central, seed-producing part of the flower, consisting of ovary, style and stigma.

Pistillate. Having pistils.

Pollen. The fertilising dust formed in the anther.

Polygamous. Bearing (1) staminate, (2) pistillate, and (3) perfect flowers on the same tree, as in hackberry.

Pome. Fleshy fruit with a core.

Procumbent. Sprawling.

Pubescent. Covered with fine, short hairs.

Raceme. Loose flower cluster with flowers arranged on short pedicels along peduncle, as wild black cherry.

Receptacle. Base to which parts of the flower are attached.

Resin. Viscid exudation of the wood of conifers.

Rhombic. Diamond-shaped.

Rosin. Hard, brittle substance left after distilling turpentine from the resin of certain pines.

Rufous. Red or tawny.

Samara. Key fruit; a winged seed case, as of elm, ash and maple.

Sapling. Any young tree.

Sapwood. The living wood near the bark.

Scion (Cion). The budded twig that is set in the stock in grafting.

Seedling. A tree that has come from a seed.

Serrate. Saw-toothed.

Sessile. Without a stalk.

Simple. Of one part, as the pistils and leaves of elms and cherries.

Sinuate. Winding.

Sinus. Bay between lobes, as in black oak leaf.

Slash. Branches and defective material discarded in lumbering.

Species. Subdivision of a genus.

Spike. Pencil-like receptacle crowded with small flowers.

Stamen. Pollen-producing organ of the flower, consisting of filament and anther.

Staminate. Having stamens.

Stellate. Star-shaped in branching.

Stigma. The tip of the pistil which receives the pollen.

Stipule. Leaf-like growth, at base of petiole.

Stomates. Breathing holes on under side of leaves.

Stratified. Spread out in layers, alternating with sand and gravel.

Strobile. A cone.

Style. Slender part of pistil between stigma and ovary.

Subterminal. Near the tip.

Sucker. Sprout from root or stub of branch.

Suture. A seam where parts are united until maturity. See burs of chestnut and beech.

Symmetrical. Well proportioned.

Terete. Cylindrical.

Tomentose. Velvety.

Umbel. Flat flower cluster in which many pedicels rise from the end of the peduncle.

Unisexual. Lacking either pistils or stamens.

Valves. Divisions, as of a pod or husk.

Variety. Subdivision of a species.

PART I.

HOW TO KNOW THE TREES

THE TREE BOOK

CHAPTER I: HOW TO KNOW THE TREES

"And surely nobody can find anything hard in this; even the blind must enjoy these woods, drinking in their fragrance, listening to the music of the winds in their groves, and fingering their flowers and plumes and cones and richly furrowed boles. The kind of study required is as easy and natural as breathing."
—*John Muir.*

OCCASIONALLY I meet a person who says: "I know nothing at all about trees." This modest disclaimer is generally sincere, but it has always turned out to be untrue. "Oh, well, that old sugar maple, I've always known that tree. We used to tap all the sugar maples on the place every spring." Or again: "Everybody knows a white birch by its bark." "Of course, anybody who has ever been chestnutting knows a chestnut tree." Most people know Lombardy poplars, those green exclamation points so commonly planted in long soldierly rows on roadsides and boundary lines in many parts of the country. Willows, too, everybody knows are willows. The best nut trees, the shagbark, chestnut and butternut, need no formal introduction. The honey locust has its striking three-pronged thorns, and its purple pods dangling in winter and skating off over the snow. The beech has its smooth, close bark of Quaker grey, and nobody needs to look for further evidence to determine this tree's name.

So it is easily proved that each person has a good nucleus of tree knowledge around which to accumulate more. If people have the love of nature in their hearts—if things out of doors call irresistibly, at any season—it will not really matter if their lives are pinched and circumscribed. Ways and means of studying trees are easily found, even if the scant ends of busy days spent indoors are all the time at command. If there is energy to begin the undertaking it will soon furnish its own motive power. Tree students, like bird students, become enthusiasts. To understand their enthusiasm one must follow their examples.

3

The beginner doesn't know exactly how and where to begin. There are great collections of trees here and there. The Arnold Arboretum in Boston is the great dendrological Noah's Ark in this country. It contains almost all the trees, American and foreign, which will grow in that region. The Shaw Botanical Garden at St. Louis is the largest midland assemblage of trees. Parks in various cities bring together as large a variety of trees as possible, and these are often labelled with their English and botanical names for the benefit of the public.

Yet the places for the beginner are his own dooryard, the streets he travels four times a day to his work, and woods for his holiday, though they need not be forests. Arboreta are for his delight when he has gained some acquaintance with the tree families. But not at first. The trees may all be set out in tribes and families and labelled with their scientific names. They will but confuse and discourage him. There is not time to make their acquaintance. They overwhelm with the mere number of kinds. Great arboreta and parks are very scarce. Trees are everywhere. The acquaintance of trees is within the reach of all.

First make a plan of the yard, locating and naming the trees you actually know. Extend it to include the street, and the neighbours' yards, as you get ready for them. Be very careful about giving names to trees. If you think you know a tree, ask yourself *how* you know it. Sift out all the guesses, and the hearsays, and begin on a solid foundation, even if you are sure about only the sugar maple and the white birch.

The characters to note in studying trees are: leaves, flowers, fruits, bark, buds, bud arrangement, leaf scars and tree form. The season of the year determines which features are most prominent. Buds and leaf scars are the most unvarying of tree characters. In winter these traits and the tree frame are most plainly revealed. Winter often exhibits tree fruits on or under the tree, and dead-leaf studies are very satisfactory. Leaf arrangement may be made out at any season, for leaf scars tell this story after the leaves fall.

Only three families of our large trees have opposite leaves. This fact helps the beginner. Look first at the twigs. If the leaves, or (in winter) the buds and leaf scars, stand opposite, the tree (if it is of large size) belongs to the maple, ash or horse-chestnut family. Our native horse chestnuts are buckeyes. If

4

the leaves are simple the tree is a maple; if pinnately compound, of several leaflets, it is an ash; if palmately compound, of five to seven leaflets, it is a horse chestnut.   In winter dead leaves under the trees furnish this evidence.   The winter buds of the horse chestnut are large and waxy, and the leaf scars look like prints of a horse's hoof.   Maple buds are small, and the leaf scar is a small, narrow crescent.   Ash buds are dull and blunt, with rough, leathery scales.   Maple twigs are slender.   Ash and buckeye twigs are stout and clumsy.

Bark is a distinguishing character of many trees—of others it is confusing.   The sycamore, shedding bark in sheets from its limbs, exposes pale, smooth under bark.   The tree is recognisable by its mottled appearance winter or summer.   The corky ridges on limbs of sweet gum and bur oak are easily remembered traits.   The peculiar horizontal peeling of bark on birches designates most of the genus.   The prussic-acid taste of a twig sets the cherry tribe apart.   The familiar aromatic taste of the green twigs of sassafras is its best winter character; the mitten-shaped leaves distinguish it in summer.

It is necessary to get some book on the subject to discover the names of trees one studies, and to act as teacher at times.   A book makes a good staff, but a poor crutch.   The eyes and the judgment are the dependable things.   In spring the way in which the leaves open is significant; so are the flowers.   Every tree when it reaches proper age bears flowers. Not all bear fruit, but blossoms come on every tree.   In summer the leaves and fruits are there to be examined.   In autumn the ripening fruits are the special features.

To know a tree's name is the beginning of acquaintance— not an end in itself.   There is all the rest of one's life in which to follow it up.   Tree friendships are very precious things. John Muir, writing among his beloved trees of the Yosemite Valley, adjures his world-weary fellow men to seek the companionship of trees.

"To learn how they live and behave in pure wildness, to see them in their varying aspects through the seasons and weather, rejoicing in the great storms, putting forth their new leaves and flowers, when all the streams are in flood, and the birds singing, and sending away their seeds in the thoughtful Indian summer, when all the landscape is glowing in deep, calm enthusiasm—for this you must love them and live with them, as free from schemes and care and time as the trees themselves."

5

CHAPTER II: THE NAMES OF TREES

Two Latin words, written in italics, with a cabalistic abbreviation set after them, are a stumbling block on the page to the reader unaccustomed to scientific lore. He resents botanical names, and demands to know the tree's name "in plain English." Trees have both common and scientific names, and each has its use. Common names were applied to important trees by people, the world over, before science was born. Many trees were never noticed by anybody until botanists discovered and named them. They may never get common names at all.

A name is a description reduced to its lowest terms. It consists usually of a surname and a descriptive adjective : Mary Jones, white oak, *Quercus alba*. Take the oaks, for example, and let us consider how they got their names, common and scientific. All acorn-bearing trees are oaks. They are found in Europe, Asia and America. Their usefulness and beauty have impressed people. The Britons called them by a word which in our modern speech is *oak*, and as they came to know the different kinds, they added a descriptive word to the name of each. But "plain English" is not useful to the Frenchman. *Chêne* is his name for the acorn trees. The German has his *Eichenbaum*, the Roman had his *Quercus*, and who knows what the Chinaman and the Hindoo in far Cathay or the American Indian called these trees? Common names made the trouble when the Tower of Babel was building.

Latin has always been the universal language of scholars. It is dead, so that it can be depended upon to remain unchanged in its vocabulary and in its forms and usages. Scientific names are exact, and remain unchanged, though an article or a book using them may be translated into all the modern languages. The word *Quercus* clears away difficulties. French, English, German hearers know what trees are meant — or they know just where in books of their own language to find them described.

The abbreviation that follows a scientific name tells who

6

first gave the name. "Linn." is frequently noticed, for Linnæus is authority for thousands of plant names.

Two sources of confusion make common names of trees unreliable: The application of one name to several species, and the application of several names to one species. To illustrate the first: There are a dozen ironwoods in American forests. They belong, with two exceptions, to different genera and to at least five different botanical families. To illustrate the second: The familiar American elm is known by at least seven local popular names. The bur oak has seven. Many of these are applied to other species. Three of the five native elms are called water elm; three are called red elm; three are called rock elm. There are seven scrub oaks. Only by mentioning the scientific name can a writer indicate with exactness which species he is talking about. The unscientific reader can go to the botanical manual or cyclopedia and under this name find the species described.

In California grows a tree called by three popular names: leatherwood, slippery elm and silver oak. Its name is *Fremontia*. It is as far removed from elms and oaks as sheep are from cattle and horses. But the names stick. It would be as easy to eradicate the trees, root and branch, from a region as to persuade people to abandon names they are accustomed to, though they may concede that you have proved these names incorrect, or meaningless, or vulgar. Nicknames like nigger pine, he huckleberry, she balsam and bull bay ought to be dropped by all people who lay claim to intelligence and taste.

With all their inaccuracies, common names have interesting histories, and the good ones are full of helpful suggestion to the learner. Many are literal translations of the Latin names. The first writers on botany wrote in Latin. Plants were described under the common name, if there was one; if not, the plant was named. The different species of each group were distinguished by the descriptions and the drawings that accompanied them. Linnæus attempted to bring the work of botanical scholars together, and to publish descriptions and names of all known plants in a single volume. This he did, crediting each botanist with his work. The "Species Plantarum," Linnæus's monumental work, became the foundation of the modern science of botany, for it included all the plants known and named up to

7

the time of its publication. This was about the middle of the eighteenth century.

The vast body of information which the "Species Plantarum" contained was systematically arranged. All the different species in one genus were brought together. They were described, each under a number; and an adjective word, usually descriptive of some marked characteristic, was written in as a marginal index.

After Linnæus's time botanists found that the genus name in combination with this marginal word made a convenient and exact means of designating the plant. Thus Linnæus became unknowingly the originator of the binomial (two-name) system of nomenclature, now in use in all sciences. It is a delightful coincidence that while Linnæus was engaged on his great work, North America, that vast new field of botanical exploration, was being traversed by another Swedish scientist. Peter Kalm sent his specimens and his descriptive notes to Linnæus, who described and named the new plants in his book. The specimens swelled the great herbarium at the University of Upsala.

Among trees unknown to science before are the Magnolia, named in honour of the great French botanist, Magnol. Robinia, the locust, honours another French botanist, Robin, and his son. Kalmia, the beautiful mountain laurel, immortalises the name of the devoted explorer who discovered it. Linnæa, the little twin flower of the same mountains, is the one which the great botanist loved best.

It is inevitable that duplication of names attend the work of the early scientists, isolated from each other, and far from libraries and herbaria. Anyone discovering a plant he believed to be unknown to science published a description of it in some scientific journal. If someone else had described it at an earlier date, the fact became known in the course of time. The name earliest published is retained, and the later one is dropped to the rank of a *synonym*. If the *name* has been used before to describe some other species in the same genus, a new name must be supplied. In the "Cyclopedia of Horticulture" the sugar maple is written : " *Acer saccharum*, Marsh. (*Acer saccharinum*, Wang. *Acer barbatum*, Michx.)" This means that the earliest name given this tree by a botanist was that of Marshall. Wangheimer and Michaux are therefore thrown out; the names given by them are among the synonyms.

Our cork elm was until recently called "*Ulmus racemosa,* Thomas." The discovery that the name *racemosa* was given long ago to the cork elm of Europe discredited it for the American tree. Mr. Sargent substituted the name of the author, and it now stands "*Ulmus Thomasi,* Sarg." Occasionally a generic name is changed. The old generic name becomes the specific name. Box elder was formerly known as "*Negundo aceroides,* Mœnch." It is changed back to "*Acer Negundo,* Linn." On the other hand, the tan-bark oak, which is intermediate in character between oaks and chestnuts, has been taken by Professor Sargent in his Manual, 1905, out of the genus Quercus and set in a genus by itself. From "*Quercus densiflora,* Hook. and Arn.," it is called "*Pasania densiflora,* Sarg.," the specific name being carried over to the new genus.

About one hundred thousand species of plants have been named by botanists. They believe that one-half of the world's flora is covered. Trees are better known than less conspicuous plants. Fungi and bacteria are just coming into notice. Yet even among trees new species are constantly being described. Professor Sargent described 567 native species in his "Silva of North America," published 1892–1900. His Manual, 1905, contains 630. Both books exclude Mexico. The silva of the tropics contains many unknown trees, for there are still impenetrable tracts of forest.

The origin of local names of trees is interesting. History and romance, music and hard common sense are in these names —likewise much pure foolishness. The nearness to Mexico brought in the musical piñon and madroña in the Southwest. *Pecanier* and *bois d'arc* came with many other French names with the Acadians to Louisiana. The Indians had many trees named, and we wisely kept hickory, waahoo, catalpa, persimmon and a few others of them.

Woodsmen have generally chosen descriptive names which are based on fact and are helpful to learners. Botanists have done this, too. Bark gives the names to shagbark hickory, striped maple and naked wood. The colour names white birch, black locust, blue beech. Wood names red oak, yellow-wood and white-heart hickory. The texture names rock elm, punk oak, and soft pine. The uses name post oak, canoe birch and lodgepole pine.

The tree habit is described by dwarf juniper and weeping spruce. The habitat by swamp maple, desert willow and seaside alder. The range by California white oak and Georgia pine. Sap is characterised in sugar maple, sweet gum, balsam fir and sweet birch. Twigs are indicated in clammy locust, cotton gum, winged elm. Leaf linings are referred to in silver maple, white poplar and white basswood. Colour of foliage, in grey pine, blue oak and golden fir. Shape of leaves, in heart-leaved cucumber tree and ear-leaved umbrella. Resemblance of leaves to other species, in willow oak and parsley haw. The flowers of trees give names to tulip tree, silver-bell tree and fringe tree. The fruit is described in big-cone pine, butternut, mossy-cup oak and mock orange.

Many trees retain their classical names, which have become the generic botanical ones, as acacia, ailanthus and viburnum. Others modify these slightly, as pine from Pinus, and poplar from Populus. The number of local names a species has depends upon the notice it attracts and the range it has. The loblolly pine, important as a lumber tree, extends along the coast from New Jersey to Texas. It has twenty-two nicknames.

The scientific name is for use when accurate designation of a species is required ; the common name for ordinary speech. "What a beautiful *Quercus alba !*" sounds very silly and pedantic, even if it falls on scientific ears. Only persons of very shallow scientific learning use it on such informal occasions.

Let us keep the most beautiful and fitting among common names, and work for their general adoption. There are no hard names once they become familiar ones. Nobody hesitates or stumbles over chrysanthemum and rhododendron, though these sonorous Greek derivatives have four syllables. Nobody asks what these names are "in plain English."

CHAPTER III: THE TREE FAMILIES

It is quite possible for a person who has never had any particular interest in trees to acquire by himself a general knowledge of the tree families represented in our American forests, and to form an intimate and delightful acquaintance with particular species and individual trees, as his personal preferences dictate. And it is not to be undertaken as a herculean task, a duty to be performed, a means of grace, or an ill-tasting medicine that does one good. True, there are half a hundred families or more, and over six hundred distinct species of trees, if we wander from Key West to the far Aleutians, and from Maine to Mexico, and count every species any botanist has discovered and named. But the average forest contains comparatively few families. Different families have traits in common that indicate their relationship. Within the family closer kinship still is revealed.

The discovery of these family ties and family groups comes easy and as naturally as breathing, once it is begun. The necessary botany is unconsciously imbibed. One borrows that from the books as need is. Every acorn-bearing tree is an oak. The needle leaves set in scaly sheaths at the base distinguish the pines from all other evergreens. The hickories have close relatives in all the nut trees. The sycamores have no near relatives at all. The willows and poplars are alike in catkin flowers and fluffy seeds. All locusts bear pods.

The key that follows is a simple tool. It unlocks mysteries that are largely imaginary as to the common tree families by setting them forth in brief, descriptive terms, giving a bird's-eye view of them, and emphasising their chief points of similarity and difference. Botanical terms have been avoided, and such characters selected as shall be obvious to the inexperienced observer.

The plan of construction is easily grasped. A and AA are the two grand divisions into which trees naturally fall. Being co-ordinate, these have the same letter of the alphabet, and are set on the extreme left margin of the page. The second has an added letter; if there were a third division it would have three A's. The subdivisions of A are always B, BB, etc., according to their number. B is divided into C, C into D, and so on down the list. In every instance co-ordinate letters are set at the same distance from the left margin, forming a vertical line down the page. They are also grouped by their "catch words"—as will be seen.

A includes the chief families of the evergreens. Under A are two groups, B and BB, based upon the character of the fruit. Under B there are two subdivisions, based upon the general shape of the leaf. The cone-bearing evergreens, B, show two types of foliage, described under C and CC. The former is divided into three groups, D, DD, and DDD, on "Arrangement of leaves." The catch word of B and BB is "Fruit"; of C and CC, "Foliage."

D and DD each describes a family; DDD includes more, and must be subdivided. E and EE are the headings and "Leaves" the catch word. E contains F and FF, based on the cones and other characters. EE, CC, and BB are undivided, as each describes a single family.

The next step is to learn how to use the key. It is worthless unless it unlocks closed doors and reveals hidden things worth finding. Go out with the key and approach the first evergreen in sight. It belongs in the group A, your common sense tells you. Very well. Which B does it agree with? Look for signs of fruit on and under the tree. Are they cones or berries? Cones? Then this tree belongs in B. All right. Is its foliage needle-like, etc., or scale-like—C or CC? Needle-like. Now you must study the arrangement of leaves on the twigs, and decide which one of the three D's fits. Perhaps the leaves are solitary and scattered. Still closer study of them is necessary. If they agree with EE you know that the tree is a spruce.

Suppose at the start your tree has borne blue berries instead of cones. You would have dropped to BB at once and found your tree to be a juniper.

Now the beauty of a key is that you so soon outgrow the need of it. There are seven great families of the native ever-geens. To make it as simple as possible, the rare and local evergreens, like the sequoias, the bald cypress and the yews, have been omitted. It should take but a single encounter with

12

a tree to run it down to its family in the key. The intentness of this exercise will fix on the mind the characters that distinguish the family. You find yourself rolling a leaf between thumb and finger to see if it has the four sharp edges that set the spruces apart from all the others. Or you look intently for the tiny leaf stem of a pale-lined flat leaf, to know whether it is a hemlock or a fir.

In the grand division AA the broad-leaved trees are set in their proper families. There are more of these than of the evergreens. They are best studied while leaves are to be had for identification. Often the seeds remain in winter, and we can get on with only the evidence of dead leaves. There are few weeks in the year when the key may not be effectively used on any tramp in the woods.

As in the evergreens, the local and rare families of broadleaved trees have been omitted, that the key may not discourage beginners by its complexity. In all, the thirty-three families given include between four and five hundred species, and a large proportion of those left out are esteemed chiefly by the botanists. Many of these will be found described later in this book.

The key to the families introduces the reader to the more intricate distinctions between trees of various genera and species in the family. The keys to species are made on the same plan. Having determined that a certain tree belongs to the maple family, the inquirer is able to turn to "The Maples," and by the key to decide which of the various species this individual tree represents. This is the final end of any key—to lead the student to discover the name of the individual tree.

KEY TO THE PRINCIPAL TREE FAMILIES.

A. THE EVERGREENS, OR CONIFERS.
  B. Fruit, a cone.
    C. Foliage needle-like, conspicuous, spirally arranged.
      D. Arrangement of leaves, few in sheathed bundle.
                                      The Pines
     DD. Arrangement of leaves, many in unsheathed
         tufts, deciduous   *The Larches*
    DDD. Arrangement of leaves, solitary and scattered.
      E. Leaves flat, blunt, pale beneath, 2-ranked
         on twig.
        F. Cones erect, large; branches stiff; bark
            smooth, with resin blisters. *The Firs*
       FF. Cones pendant, small; branches sup-
          ple; bark rough; leaves on minute
          stalks.   *The Hemlocks*
     EE. Leaves 4-sided, sharp at tip, not pale be-
        neath; standing out in all directions.
                                  The Spruces
   CC. Foliage scale-like, minute, 4-ranked, close pressed
      to twig; cones small.   *The White Cedars*
  BB. Fruit, a blue berry; foliage spiny or scale-like, or
    both.   *The Junipers*, or *Red Cedars*
AA. THE DECIDUOUS, BROAD-LEAVED TREES.
  B. Position of leaves opposite.
    C. Leaves simple.
      D. Fruit winged, 1-sided keys in pairs. *The Maples*
     DD. Fruit clustered berries.
      E. Flowers 4-parted; berry 2-seeded; leaves
        not saw-toothed on margins. *The Dogwoods*
      EE. Flowers 5-parted; berry, 1-seeded; leaves
        finely saw-toothed on margins.
                            The Viburnums
    DDD. Fruit long, rod-like pods, with thin seeds.
                            The Catalpas
    CC. Leaves compound.
      D. Fruit slender, winged darts in thick clusters;
        leaflets set along central leaf stem. *The Ashes*
     DD. Fruit large nuts in leathery husks; leaflets
        clustered on end of leaf stalk. *The Buckeyes*
  BB. Position of leaves alternate.

14

C. Leaves simple.
  D. Bases of leaves symmetrical.
    E. Fruit fleshy, globular, more or less edible.
      F. Seeds solitary.
        G. Margins of leaves saw-toothed.
          The Plums and *Cherries*
        GG. Margins of leaves not saw-toothed.
          The Tupelos
      FF. Seeds several in walled cells.
        G. Cores papery.
          H. Fruit small, berry-like.
            The Juneberries
          HH. Fruit large.   *The Apples*
        GG. Cores bony; fruit thin fleshed.
          The Hawthorns
    EE. Fruits dry.
      F. Seeds borne in protecting cups or burs.
        G. Burs scaly, not opening when ripe; nut conical.   *The Oaks*
        GG. Burs spiny, 4-valved, opening when ripe.
          H. Nuts triangular, small. *The Beech*
          HH. Nuts conical, larger. *The Chestnut*
      FF. Seeds borne in swinging balls.
        G. Leaves star shaped; branches corky ridged.   *The Sweet Gum*
        GG. Leaves broad, 3 to 5-lobed, bark shed in sheets, leaving pale, irregular patches.
          The Sycamore, or *Buttonwood*
      FFF. Seeds borne in cone-like heads.
        G. Bark in horizontal sheets.
          The Birches
        GG. Bark smooth; leaves large, leathery.
          H. Leaves pointed at tip; seeds scarlet, berry-like, on elastic threads.   *The Magnolias*
          HH. Leaves truncate at apex; seeds dry, with long, flat wing.
          The Tulip Tree
      FFFF. Seeds borne in 2-valved pods on elongated catkins; minute and hid in cottony down.
        G. Leaves narrow; branches supple.
          The Willows
        GG. Leaves b r o a d; leaf stalks flat, branches stiff, angular. *The Poplars*

15

DD. Bases of leaves unsymmetrical.
  E. Fruit, a berry; leaves with three main
    veins; bark warty.   *The Hackberries*
  EE. Fruit dry with circular wing; leaves oval
    with prominent, straight veins.   *The Elms*
  EEE. Fruit a woody ball on leaf-like blade;
    leaves large, distinctly one-sided.
                    The Lindens, or *Basswoods*

CC. Leaves compound.
  D. Fruit, a flat pod.   *The Locusts*
  DD. Fruit, a nut.
    E. Husk opening when ripe by four valves.
                          The Hickories
    EE. Husk not opening when ripe.   *The Walnuts*

CHAPTER IV: THE CONIFERS

THE distinguishing feature of this great tree group is the cone-bearing habit. The overlapping scales of the cone are attached to a central stem, and each scale bears one or more naked ovules when the time of flowering comes. Pollen from the staminate flowers falls on the exposed ovules, fertilising them, and thus seed is set. The fertile scales are favourably situated near the middle of the cone. Here the best seeds are found. The terminal scales crowd at both ends of the cone, and their seeds usually fail utterly or are stunted in development.

The coalescence of scales to form soft berries characterises the junipers, but the cone-like flowers indicate that the modification in fruit is more apparent than real. The scale tips are there on the outside of the berry to indicate the close kinship of these trees with other conifers.

The yews are not conifers, but are set in a family by themselves. A single ovule stands erect in the pistillate flower, and becomes in fruit a 1-seeded drupe, or soft berry. Two genera of yews, with two species of trees in each, constitute the family in the United States. The conifers include thirteen genera and a great number of species, quite overshadowing the yews in importance. Together the two families form the botanical grand division of the Gymnosperms, resinous plants (mostly trees) whose flowers have no true pistils, but bear their ovules naked—on a cone scale in the conifers—without even a scale to lean upon in the yews.

The Ginkgo or Maidenhair Tree (*Salisburia adiantifolia*), of Japan and China, is a tree whose botanical affinities seem to be with the conifers on one side and the ferns on the other. The leaves are fan-shaped, usually cleft with one deep suture to the petiole. The venation is the strange character. Unbranched veins extend in radiating lines to the upper border of the fan, just as in the leaf of maidenhair fern. The texture is leathery, and the leaves are fascicled on the ends of very short side twigs. Bright yellow green in summer, they turn to gold, and fall in the autumn.

The ginkgo is a narrow, tapering tree when young, very trim and pretty, widening to pyramidal form with years. It grows rapidly and has been planted as a street tree, notably in Washington, D. C. A serious drawback appears in the fruit, which is a soft, plum-like, oily drupe with an unpleasant odour. While they are dropping they keep sidewalks in a bad state, disgusting people with the tree. The ginkgo has had a great vogue among planters, though until recently none have been old enough to bear fruit.

The Chinese esteem the pits a great delicacy. They roast the nuts as we do almonds and use them as a confection or an appetiser at dinners and banquets.

KEY TO THE GENERA

A. Fruit a woody cone.
  B. Cone scales each in axil of a bract; seeds 2, inverted, on each scale.
    C. Foliage needle-like, fascicled.
      D. Cones requiring 2 to 3 years to mature; leaves evergreen, 1 to 5 in papery basal sheath.
                               Genus PINUS, THE PINES
      DD. Cones annual; leaves deciduous.
                               Genus LARIX, THE LARCHES
    CC. Foliage linear, solitary, scattered.
      D. Leaves flat, borne on short petioles; cones pendant.
        E. Twigs set with projecting leaf bases.
                               Genus TSUGA, THE HEMLOCKS
        EE. Twigs smooth.
                        Genus PSEUDOTSUGA, THE DOUGLAS SPRUCE
      DD. Leaves 4-angled, or flattened, without petioles.
        E. Twigs rough; cones pendant.
                               Genus PICEA, THE SPRUCES
        EE. Twigs smooth; cones erect.
                               Genus ABIES, THE FIRS
  BB. Cone scales without bracts.
    C. Leaves linear, alternate; cone scales many.
      D. Seeds many under each scale; leaves evergreen.
                               Genus SEQUOIA, THE SEQUOIAS
      DD. Seeds 2 under each scale; leaves 2-ranked, deciduous.   Genus TAXODIUM, THE BALD CYPRESS
    CC. Leaves scale-like, usually of two forms; cones small.
      D. Cones elongated, thin scaled, annual, with 2 seeds under each scale.

E. Scales of cone 6; seed wings unsymmetrical.
Genus LIBOCEDRUS, THE INCENSE CEDAR
EE. Scales of cone 8 to 12; seed wings symmetrical.
Genus THUYA, THE ARBOR VITÆS
DD. Cones globular, thick scaled.
E. Seeds many under each scale; cones biennial.
Genus CUPRESSUS, THE CYPRESSES
EE. Seeds 2 under each scale; cones annual.
Genus CHAMÆCYPARIS, THE CYPRESSES
AA. Fruit a berry; by union of scales of the flower; leaves scale-like or awl shaped, 3 to 4 ranked.
Genus JUNIPERUS, THE JUNIPERS

CHAPTER V: THE PINES

FAMILY CONIFERÆ

Genus PINUS, Duham.

Leaves evergreen, of two forms: primary, short, broad at base, scattered; secondary, needle-like, in sheathed bundles. *Flowers* monœcious, naked; staminate, clustered; pistillate, lateral or subterminal, with spirally arranged scales; ovules, 2 on each scale. *Fruit*, a woody cone, maturing in 2 or 3 years.

"What the apple is among the fruits, what the oak is among broad-leaved trees of the temperate zone, the pines are among the conifers, excelling all other genera in this most important family in number of species, in fields of distribution in extent of area occupied, in usefulness and importance to the human race."
—*B. E. Fernow.*

Six hundred species and varieties have been described and named in the genus Pinus. They are distributed in vast forests over the northern half of the globe, reaching into the tropics by following mountain chains. The East and West Indian Islands have each their own pines. Out of the hundreds of named kinds about eighty distinct species are now recognised. Half of this number are found in North America. Forests of pine still cover mountain slopes in the western and northern parts of the continent. Lumbering has been going on for a century in the Eastern States; more recently the Great Lakes region and the pine forests of the Southern States have been exploited to supply the demand for pine.

The foremost lumber trees in this country, pines have still other important uses. They offer a great variety of trees for protective and ornamental planting. Windbreaks from the seashore to the semi-arid prairie, from the low seaboard plain to the mountain's crests, may all be of pine. Arid soil or rich, cold or warm climate, swamp and desert sand—all offer congenial conditions for some native pine. In the parks of cities, in private

20

grounds of the rich and the poor, pines are planted for shade and shelter and ornament. Only in very smoky cities, St. Louis and Pittsburg, for instance, do pines with other conifers decline after a few years of growth. It is believed that sulphur and other substances in the noxious gases that constantly pour from great chimneys choke the evergreens. Nobody is able yet to give a final answer to the question. It is now under investigation.

The by-products of pine trees include oil, pitch, turpentine, and rosin, products of the resin that impregnates the wood of pitch pines. Minor products are the seeds of the nut pines, used as food; pine wool, spun from the leaves of certain species; and pine shoots used for Christmas decoration.

All pines are evergreens and cone bearers. They are distinguished from other genera of the family Coniferæ by bearing their needle-like leaves in clusters of 1 to 5 leaves, each of which is enclosed at its base by a .sheath made of papery scales. No other conifer has this sheath. The soft pines, so called from their soft, light wood, shed their leaf sheaths as soon as the young leaves are fully developed. The pitch pines, so called because their heavy, dark-coloured wood is full of resin, retain the leaf sheath until the leaves are shed.

In the lumber trade there is a certain fine scorn of "technical names," and a consequent confusion in the use of local and trade names of the kinds of pines. This is unfortunate, for woods that resemble each other so closely as to deceive experienced men have often very different ways of behaving in use. Lumbermen and carpenters are misled by dependence on trade names, and so are engineers and architects, to the great disadvantage of those whose interests they are supposed to serve intelligently.

"Hard pine" is a carpenter's term applied to pines whose wood is heavy, close and resinous. It includes everything but soft pine among staple lumber pines.

The "hard pines" are *P. palustris*, *P. taeda*, *P. echinata* and *P. heterophylla* in the South ; *P. ponderosa*, and *P. ponderosa*, var. *Jeffreyi*, in the West, and *P. resinosa* in the East and North.

"Yellow pine," a very vague and general colour designation, includes the Southern hard pines named above, also *P. rigida* in the East, and *P. ponderosa* in the West.

"Pitch pine" is a term applied to species whose wood is

21

rich in resin. Chief among these is *P. palustria*. It includes the other Southern lumber pines and *P. rigida* in the Eastern States.

" Georgia pine " is *P. palustris*. " North Carolina pine " is *P. echinata*.

The " soft pines " have soft, light wood, with little resin, easy to work—the carpenter's delight. The principal ones are *P. Strobus*, in the North and East, *P. Lambertiana*, of the Pacific coast, and two Rocky Mountain species, *P. monticola* and *P. flexilis*.

" Jack pines," used locally for ties and timbers, but not in the regular lumber trade, are small or medium-sized trees : *P. rigida*, *P. Virginiana* and *P. divaricata* in the East and North ; *P. contorta*, var. *Murrayana*, one in the West.

THE SOFT PINES

Leaf bundles in loose, deciduous sheaths. *Cone scales* usually unarmed. *Wood* soft, light coloured, close grained.

KEY TO SPECIES

A. Leaves 5 in a bundle.
    B. Cones long stemmed; scales thin; leaves 3 to 4 inches long.
        C. Leaves slender, flexible; cones 5 to 8 inches long.
            D. Cone scales not recurved at maturity; leaves bluish green. (*P. Strobus*) WHITE PINE
           DD. Cone scales recurved at maturity; leaves pale green. (*P. strobiformis*) ARIZONA WHITE PINE
        CC. Leaves stout, stiff.
            D. Cones 5 to 12 inches long; limbs grey. (*P. monticola*) MOUNTAIN PINE
           DD. Cones 12 to 18 inches long; limbs green. (*P. Lambertiana*) SUGAR PINE
    BB. Cones short stemmed; scales thick; leaves 1 to 2 inches long.
        C. Leaf bundles scattered; cones 3 to 10 inches long, opening at maturity. (*P. flexilis*) ROCKY MOUNTAIN WHITE PINE
        CC. Leaf bundles in crowded clusters.
            D. Leaf clusters at ends of twigs; cones not opening; bark pale. (*P. albicaulis*) WHITE-BARK PINE

DD. Leaf clusters along sides of twig; cone scales
    with spiny beaks.
    E. Spines of cone scales minute, incurved.
                     (*P. Balfouriana*) FOXTAIL PINE
    EE. Spines of cone scales, long, slender.
                     (*P. aristata*) BRISTLE-CONE PINE
AA. Leaves 1 to 4 in a bundle, 1 to 2 inches long; cones
    globose; seeds nut-like.
    B. Bundles 4-leaved, pale, glaucous green.
                     (*P. quadrifolia*) NUT PINE
    BB. Bundles 2 to 3-leaved, dark green.
      C. Leaves slender.   (*P. cembroides*) NUT PINE
      CC. Leaves stout.   (*P. edulis*) NUT PINE
    BBB. Bundles 1-leaved, pale, glaucous green.
                     (*P. monophylla*) NUT PINE

White Pine (*Pinus Strobus*, Linn.)—A stately tree, 100 to 120 feet high, conical, with spreading, horizontal branches in whorls of five. *Bark* grey, furrowed, thick, with broad, scaly ridges. *Wood* light, soft, close grained, resinous, easily worked. *Buds,* a strong, terminal, set round by five lateral ones in whorl ; ¼ to ½ inch long, pointed, with thin, pale-brown scales. *Leaves* evergreen, needle-like, in fives, sheathed at base of bundle, 3 to 5 inches long, slender, 3-sided, flexible, blue-green. *Flowers* in June, monœcious; staminate, clustered at base of season's shoots, ⅔ to 1 inch long, catkin-like, yellowish ; pistillate, subterminal, single or in twos, stemmed, elliptical, pink or purplish, and scaly, 2 ovules on each scale. *Fruit* biennial, 5 to 10 inches long, slender, stalked, with thin, unarmed scales ; seeds winged. *Preferred habitat,* good soil, moist woodlands, or uplands. *Distribution,* Newfoundland to Manitoba; south through Iowa, Illinois and Ohio to northern Georgia ; southern Canada and Eastern States, along Alleghanies to eastern Kentucky and Tennessee. *Uses:* One of the best ornamental conifers and formerly the chief lumber tree in this country.

Pines bear their evergreen leaves in sheathed bundles set on little projecting shelves along the twigs. The sheaths are shed during the spring in all the white pines, and the number of leaves in a bundle is always five. Certain pitch pines have leaves in fives, but the sheaths will be found at the bases of the bundles throughout the season. These 5-leaved pitch pines are all Western trees. In Eastern woods a 5-leaved pine is a white pine, *P. Strobus*, whether it is a flourishing little sapling, with only three or four whorls of branches coming out from its central stem, or a great forest tree towering above its broad-leaved neighbours, noble and picturesque, though storms have destroyed the symmetry of its youth.

Stroke the leaves of a white-pine branch—they are soft and flexible. As they sway in the wind they are graceful and light; the tree seems decked with plumes of dark blue-green. The young shoots, pale yellowish green, lighten the sombre pine woods, and the clustering catkins, shaking out their abundant pollen, sift gold dust through the whole forest. The pistillate flowers show themselves clustered about the terminal bud, which keeps on growing, leaving them to ripen, through two seasons, into long, slender green cones. The pinkish purple of these tiny cone flowers adds a rich colour to the upper twigs, where they stand erect until autumn. Below them, hanging down with their weight, are the half-grown cones, slim, finger-like and green, with tight, smooth scales, that will turn brown and discharge their ripened seed at the end of their second summer.

This white pine of ours is built on a semi-decimal plan, which it is quite worth our while to notice. In the gracefully winged seed, that reminds us of the samara of a maple, there are ten cotyledons, or seed leaves, that mount the stem, and surround the precious terminal bud when the seed germinates. This bud is the "leader." If anything happens to it the central shaft is maimed for life, and either one side bud will have to bend upward and take the leader's place, or two will divide the honour, and a forked pine is the result.

The buds on the crown of a baby white pine cluster at the top—a circle of five around the central bud. In spring the leader grows upward, and at its base five branches radiate. Next year the crown repeats the same story, and the tips of the side branches divide and elongate in the same way. The best growth is generally made by the crown buds in the very top of the tree. So it happens that we may count the years of our sapling by the whorls of branches it bears. In the early years the growth is beautifully symmetrical, if there is room for sun and air to reach the little tree. Later the branches crowd each other, and some are killed. In deep woods where trees interfere, the stems are bare of living branches almost to the top.

This is the lumberman's pine, a tree whose limbs die so

WHITE PINE GROWN IN OPEN GROUND (*Pinus Strobus*)
Forest-grown trees have no branches on lower part and upper branches are shorter.

young that there are practically no big knots in the lumber. He cuts clear, beautiful boards out of such a tree, and there is very little waste. Or he squares the trunk for a big bridge timber whose value and strength would be greatly lessened by large knots.

The great pine forests of lower Canada and the Northern States seemed inexhaustible to the early settlers. New York and Pennsylvania had pineries that promised a lumber supply for generations to come. But alas! for human foresight. The avarice of lumber companies and the blindness of politicians have squandered the heritage of the people. The virgin forests are gone except in areas too scattered and small to tempt the lumbermen. Second growth covers some of the territory that was stripped, but it will be hundreds of years before another such crop can come to maturity. The wanton wastefulness in the original slaughter of the pines is the greatest pity of it all. Forest fires, once started, eagerly fed on the "slash" the loggers left behind, and devoured untold acres of virgin woods.

The soft, white, resinous wood of *P. Strobus* is remarkably easy to work. It was used in all kinds of construction—from masts of ships to matches—it was shipped over the country for house building, for furniture, fencing and the like. Now its scarcity has led to the substitution of other woods, notably the hard pines of the Southern States.

The white pine has considerable vigour, reseeding lumbered areas, where poplars or other short-lived trees come in and furnish shade for the young seedlings. Careful forestry will restore pines to many tracts too broken for agricultural use. In fact, work to this end is being carried on to a considerable extent in the Northeastern and Middle States. Much of this work is under the direction of the Bureau of Forestry. White pine is one of the most profitable timber crops to plant at the present time.

Horticulturally considered, *P. Strobus* is one of the best of the pines. It is quick growing, symmetrical, and handsome in its early years ; later it becomes more irregular, but full of character, and beautiful in clean limbs and the plume-like tufts of blue-green leaves. The tree is picturesque, even in decrepit age, towering in stately dignity over the heads of neighbour trees, adding distinction to all sylvan scenery A white pine grown in the open has a broad crown that often keeps its lower branches, and these are borne to the ground by their own weight. Such a tree is a joy the whole year through to all tree lovers, including people and birds and squirrels.

The **Arizona White Pine** (*P. strobiformis,*) Engelm., is scattered scantly over gravelly ridges and on cañon sides in the southern part of New Mexico and Arizona, and on into Mexico. Its pale-green leaves and glaucous, downy branchlets blend it with the semi-arid landscape. Its scarcity and the inaccessibility of its habitat and range defend this tree from the lumberman, though it occasionally reaches the height of 80 feet or more, and a trunk diameter of 2 feet.

Mountain Pine, Silver Pine (*Pinus monticola,*) D. Don. —A spreading, pyramidal tree with stout trunk and slender, pendulous branches. *Bark* light grey and thin, becoming checked into square plates, with purplish scales and cinnamon-red under bark. *Wood* light brown or red, soft, fine grained, easily split, weak. *Buds* pointed, scaly, large, hoary, clustered, terminal. *Leaves* 1½ to 4 inches long, thick, stiff, blue-green with pale bloom. *Flowers* similar to those of *P. Strobus.* *Fruit* biennial, cones slender, 10 to 18 inches long; scales thin, broad, tipped with abrupt beak; seeds winged. *Preferred habitat,* sub-alpine valleys of streams. *Distribution,* Vancouver Island and southern British Columbia to northern Idaho and Montana, and south into California. Elevations 7,000 to 10,000 feet. *Uses:* Not equal to *P. Strobus* in cultivation. Locally used for lumber in Idaho and Montana.

The mountain white pine is the Western counterpart of *P. Strobus,* which it resembles in general appearance and in the qualities of its wood. Its foliage is denser and its cones nearly twice as large as those of our Eastern white pine, with a beak on each scale that the latter species lacks.

It is unusual, even in the Sierras, to find a tree of gigantic size climbing mountains. This one at the elevation of 10,000 feet shows specimens 6 to 8 feet in diameter and 90 feet high, apparently "growing nobler in form and size the colder and balder the mountains about it." The tree companions of this pine crouch at its feet; whatever they may be at lower levels, here they are dwarfs, and only the white pine keeps its noble proportions unmindful of the blasting winds and cold.

P. monticola surprises and delights the Eastern lover of noble

26

THE WHITE PINE (*Pinus Strobus*)

This tree has plume-like tufts of blue-green leaves in bundles of fives. The twigs have five buds around the central one, so the trunk and limbs send out whorls of five branches each spring. The pistillate flowers are near the top of the twig and hidden among the leaves. The staminate cones cluster behind the new shoot and are yellow when ripe. The cones are slender, curved, pendant, with thin, unarmed scales. The tree is chief among the soft pines in the lumber trade

Winter buds (leaves cut to show buds)

THE MOUNTAIN PINE (*Pinus monticola*)

Silvery, stiff leaves in bundles of fives distinguish the white pine of the Western mountains

Winter buds
(leaves cut to show buds)

THE SUGAR PINE (*Pinus Lambertiana*)

"The largest, noblest and most beautiful of all the pine trees in the world." The leaves, in bundles of fives, are stiff and very dark green. The soft wood is creamy white

trees, for it submits gracefully to a complete change of altitude and location. Seedlings from veteran trees in their native fastnesses are growing to-day in Eastern nurseries, and thriving on lawns in New England villages. At the Arboretum in Boston the young trees form a narrower pyramid than saplings of *P. Strobus* at the same age. No Western pine makes as vigorous growth in the East as this one does. A tree 12 feet high bore several cones last year. The species has long been grown in Europe.

Great Sugar Pine (*P. Lambertiana*, Dougl.)—A majestic tree, 200 to 220 feet high, 6 to 10 feet through, pyramidal, becoming flat topped, with spreading, pendulous branches. *Bark* thick, furrowed, breaking into plates; dark grey, becoming purplish or cinnamon-red. *Wood* brownish, straight grained, soft, light. *Buds* pointed, scaly, clustered at tips. *Leaves* stout, stiff, 3 to 4 inches long, in fives, sheathed, serrate, needle-like, dark green. *Flowers* much like those of *P. Strobus*. *Fruits* 12 to 18 inches long, heavy, scales 2 inches long and 1½ inches wide; seeds ripe in second autumn, edible. *Preferred habitat*, mountain slopes and cañon sides. *Distribution*, coast region in mountains from Oregon into Lower California. *Uses:* Unsuccessful in cultivation; lumber used in carpentry, for doors, blinds, sashes, shingles and in cooperage. Sap yields sugar.

"The largest, noblest, and most beautiful of all the seventy or eighty species of pine trees in the world"—thus writes John Muir, who knows the sugar pine of the Sierras as he knows his other neighbours, the mountains and the glaciers, with which he has kept fellowship all his life. Fortunately these gigantic pines do not go down to the sea, nor overhang the banks of seaward-tending streams to tempt the lumberman. The hungry mills would have swallowed the best of them long ago had not Nature fenced them in by barriers too great to be overpassed, and the Government has now, by the reservation of the Yosemite National Park, insured the preservation of these mighty pines in sufficient number to remind those who visit the region of what all the Sierra forests were before they were laid waste.

The cones of the sugar pine are the longest known. In spring cone flowers an inch in length stand upright in clusters; they thicken, lengthen and turn down on the coming of the second spring. They are now 2 or 3 inches long, and quite

27

heavy. By September they are close to 2 feet in length and 3 or 4 inches in diameter, pale green, flushing to purple on the side exposed to the sun. High above the earth these cones hang like dangling tassels, none too large for the giant arm that holds them forth. Now the scales spread, and the cone's diameter is doubled. The seeds fall, and are frugally hoarded by squirrels, bears and Indians, for their food value is no secret to any creature that has tasted them. The empty cones hang on the trees until the new crop is ready to harvest, and hard on its heels are the half-grown yearlings, sealed tight to encounter the untried winter weather.

The wood of the sugar pine is the apotheosis of pine lumber. Soft, golden, satiny, fragrant—inviting the woodworker through every one of his senses to handle it. Crystals of sugar accumulate at the end of a stick when it is burning—the bleeding of the heart wood, which gives the trees its name. White masses, crisp and candy-like, gather at axe wounds. It tastes like maple sugar, but one is soon surfeited in eating it.

Up the mountain side, where these trees grow to greatest size, the shingle maker climbs and pitches his tent in spring. He fells the biggest tree he can find, never caring whose it is, saws out a few blocks of shingle length (often only one), above the stump, and splits it into shingles. Why should he discard the rest of that great trunk and fell another, leaving the first to rot and to invite forest fires? There might be a knot in the next section, and who is he that he should worry himself over knotty lumber? So he does not stay his axe and saw all through the season, and has bundles of shingles to sell in the valley, all made from straight-grained sugar pine from the butts of logs. For every bundle he has to sell he has destroyed thousands of feet of lumber. He and thieving mill owners are companions in crime, and should be in the state prison together. For each has been preying upon the public forest lands for years.

The sugar pine is various in form, spreading its slender arms like feathery drooping plumes. Like the crown of a palm tree, but far broader than the royalest of palms, it rises above a feathering of shorter branches, and above all neighbour trees. Or with more room, the tapering spire of a fir tree is imitated. The average tree tapers to the top, and is feathered half way down with short horizontal branches.

"The old trees are as tellingly varied and picturesque as oaks. No two are alike, and we are tempted to stop and admire every one we come to as it stands silent in the calm, balsam-scented sunshine or waving in accord with enthusiastic storms. No traveller, whether he be a tree lover or not, will ever forget his first walk in a sugar-pine forest."—*John Muir*.

Rocky Mountain White Pine.—(*P. flexilis*, James.)—A broad, stout-trunked tree, 40 to 75 feet high, with ascending branches in a diffuse head. *Bark* very dark, furrowed and broken into square plates; younger stems smooth, pale grey or white. *Wood* light, soft, close grained, yellow to red. *Buds* scaly, pointed, clustered at branch tips. *Leaves* in fives, thick, rigid, 1½ to 3 inches long, dark green, sheathed and tufted on end of branches; shed during fifth or sixth years. *Flowers* like *P. Strobus*, but rose coloured. *Fruit* annual, cones 3 to 10 inches long, purple; scales rounded and abruptly beaked at apex; seeds with narrow wings all around; ripe in September. *Preferred habitat*, mountain slopes, at altitude of 7,000 to 12,000 feet. *Distribution*, Rocky Mountains, Alberta (British Columbia), Montana to Mexico and California. *Uses:* Important timber tree of semi-arid regions. Used in construction as *P. Strobus* is.

It is a fortunate region that has its own white or soft pine for all sorts of construction. This "limber pine" is notable because it thrives where other pines fail. It grows on the sides of the desert ranges of mountains in Nevada and Arizona. It is the chief dependence of builders on the eastern slopes of the Rockies in Montana. Lacking this pine, the lumber problem in these regions would be serious. It is true that trees growing in scattered groups and open forests as these do produce knotty timber; but the important fact is that *P. flexilis* does grow in these regions, and the trees are appreciated, knots and all.

The best specimens grow in New Mexico and Arizona—sturdy trees, as broad as they are high, with trunks 5 feet through, and limbs of exceeding length, flexibility and toughness. From these characters the tree takes its specific name and the common name given above.

The Rocky Mountain white pine grows where the wind tests the fibre of its long arms, which reach out and up as if eager to meet the challenge and prove themselves. The foliage is thick and beautiful, even where the tree crouches a prostrate

29

shrub at the timber line. The tree's blossoms are its most striking feature. The staminate clusters are tinged with rose colour. On the tips of the branches the slim cones glow from their first appearance like tips of flame. The summer deepens them to purple, and as they turn down they fade to cinnamon-brown, before the springing of the scales releases the almost wingless seeds. In the most favourable locations the branchlets are stout and the cones approach a foot in length. Farther north, and at higher levels, the twigs are slim and the cones considerably shorter.

The **White-Bark Pine** (*P. albicaulis*, Engelm.) shouts its name at the traveller who climbs the snow-clad peaks where it rims the forests at the timber line. The snowy bark glistens in the sun as if it reflected the icy mantle that blankets the roots for a large part of the year. Its range is from British Columbia to Montana and Wyoming, south into California. It keeps near the timber line, but goes down to 5,000 feet level, becoming a tree 40 feet high in some places. Usually it is flattened and broad topped; its matted branches, cumbered with needles and snow, make a platform on which one may walk with perfect safety. Travellers sometimes spread their blankets upon the branches and sleep as comfortably as on a spring bed. These gnarled, shrubby trees are often astonishingly old. John Muir measured one carefully. It was

"Three feet high, with a stem 6 inches in diameter at the ground, and branches that spread out horizontally as if it had grown up against a ceiling; yet it was 426 years old, and one of its supple branchlets, about $\frac{1}{8}$ of an inch in diameter inside the bark, was seventy-five years old, and so tough that I tied it into knots. At the age of this dwarf many of the sugar and yellow pines and sequoias are 7 feet in diameter and over 200 feet high."

The **Foxtail Pines** include two species whose branchlets are clothed with crowded leaf bundles, while the branches are bare. *P. Balfouriana*, M. Murr., has stiff, stout, dark-green leaves lightened by pale linings. The tree forms an open pyramid of more or less irregularity when old, but picturesque, whether a tree of 40 to 80 feet on the higher foothills of the California mountains or a straggling shrub at the timber line.

P. aristata, Engelm., the other species, has the same brush-of-a-fox leaf distribution, and it is distinguished by the long, slender prickles which arm the scales of its cones, giving the tree its common name, "prickle-cone pine." The tree is bushy, with whorls of short branches, regular at first, but unsymmetrical when old. Its range extends from western Colorado to southern California and includes Nevada and Arizona. It keeps as close as possible to the timber line, and varies from a stocky tree 40 feet high to a prostrate shrub. In cultivation in the Eastern States it is a handsome, bushy shrub.

The **Nut Pine** (*P. quadrifolia*, Sudw.) is easily distinguished by its leaves, which are usually in fours. No other pine has this number of leaves in a bundle. The tree inhabits the mountains of southern and Lower California, growing to the height of 40 feet in favourable localities. It is a desert pine, furnishing the Indians an important article of food in its rich, nut-like seeds. Its cultivation is confined to southern California.

The **Nut Pine** (*P. cembroides*, Zucc.), a bushy tree of the cañon sides in Arizona and Lower California, may also be mentioned as an important source of food. The nuts are sold in most towns in northern Mexico. Its scaly bark distinguishes this tree from other nut pines.

The **Nut Pine,** or **Piñon** (*P. edulis*, Engelm.), of Colorado, New Mexico and Texas, is an important source of food to Mexicans and Indians. The tree grows in forests on the high Southwestern table lands, and follows the mountains into Mexico. Its leaves are very short, stiff, and in clusters of threes, its globular cones, scarcely over an inch in length, are woody, and the wingless seeds, two on each scale, about the size and shape of honey-locust seeds, are sweet and nutritious.

The one-leaved **Nut Pine** (*P. monophylla*, Torr.) is small and irregular, with the form of an old apple tree. Its single, cylindrical leaf, pale greyish green (in a cluster evidently intended to have two), sets it apart from other pines. Its plenteous little cones invest the tree with its greatest human interest.

"It is the commonest tree of the short mountain ranges of the Great Basin. Tens of thousands of acres are covered with it, forming bountiful orchards for the red man. Being so low and accessible, the cones are easily beaten off with poles, and the nuts procured by roasting until the scales open. To the tribes of the desert and sage plains these seeds are the staff of life. They are eaten either raw or parched, or in the form of mush or cakes

31

after being pounded into meal. The time of nut harvest is the merriest time of the year. An industrious squirrelish family can gather fifty or sixty bushels in a single month before the snow comes, and then their bread for the winter is sure."—*J. Muir.*

THE PITCH PINES

Leaf bundles in persistent sheaths. *Cone scales* thick, usually armed. *Wood* heavy, resinous, coarse grained, usually dark coloured.

KEY TO SPECIES

A. Leaves 5 in a bundle, stout, dark green.
   B. Cones 4 to 6 inches long; leaves 9 to 13 inches
      long.   (*P. Torreyana*) TORREY'S PINE
  BB. Cones 2 to 2½ inches long; leaves 5 to 7 inches
      long.   (*P. Arizonica*) ARIZONA YELLOW PINE
AA. Leaves 3 in a bundle.
   B. Length of leaf, more than 6 inches.
     C. Colour of foliage pale green.
       D. Cones 6 to 14 inches long; leaves 8 to 12
         inches long, bluish, stout, flexible.
                (*P. Sabiniana*) DIGGER PINE
      DD. Cones 3 to 5 inches long; leaves 6 to 9
         inches long, slender, stiff, twisted.
                (*P. Tæda*) LOBLOLLY PINE
    CC. Colour of foliage dark green.
       D. Cones 2 to 3 inches long; leaves 6 to 8
         inches long, yellowish, slender, flexible.
                (*P. serotina*) POND PINE
      DD. Cones 6 to 10 inches long; leaves 8 to 18
         inches long, slender, flexible.
               (*P. palustris*) LONGLEAF PINE
      DDD. Cones 10 to 14 inches long ; leaves 6 to 12
         inches long, bluish, stout, stiff.
              (*P. Coulteri*) BIG-CONE PINE
  BB. Length of leaf less than 6 inches.
    C. Leaves 3 to 5 inches long, stiff, yellow green;
      cones 1 to 3 inches long, opening when ripe.
               (*P. rigida*) PITCH PINE
    C. Leaves 4 to 5 inches long, slender, stiff; cones
      3 to 6 inches long, unsymmetrical, not
      opening when ripe.
            (*P. attenuata*) KNOB-CONE PINE
AAA. Leaves 2 or 3 in a bundle.

32

B. Length of leaf more than 6 inches; stout, dark green.
    C. Leaves 8 to 12 inches long; cones 3 to 6 inches
        long, lateral.   (*P. Caribæa*) CUBAN PINE
    CC. Leaves 5 to 11 inches long; cones 3 to 15 inches
        long, terminal.   (*P. ponderosa*) YELLOW PINE
BB. Length of leaf less than 6 inches; slender.
    C. Leaves 3 to 5 inches long, bluish green; cones
        $1\frac{1}{2}$ to $2\frac{1}{2}$ inches long, symmetrical.
                      (*P. echinata*) SHORTLEAF PINE
    CC. Leaves 4 to 6 inches long, bright green; cones 3
        to 5 inches long, unsymmetrical.
                     (*P. radiata*) MONTEREY PINE
AAAA Leaves 2 in a bundle.
    B. Length of leaf 4 to 6 inches; colour, dark green.
        C. Cones about 2 inches long, scales unarmed.
                     (*P. resinosa*) RED PINE
        CC. Cones about 3 inches long, scales armed with
          stout beaks. (*P. muricata*) PRICKLE-CONE PINE
    BB. Length of leaf 1 to 3 inches; cones 1 to 3 inches
        long.
        C. Leaves blue-green, stiff, twisted.
            (*P. pungens*) TABLE-MOUNTAIN PINE
        CC. Leaves dark green, slender.
            D. Cones oblique, set with stout, recurved
               prickles.
               E. Branches dark brown.
                 (*P. contorta*) SCRUB PINE
               EE. Branches ashy grey. (*P. clausa*) SAND PINE
            DD. Cones not oblique, set with minute prickles.
                 (*P. glabra*) SPRUCE PINE
        CCC. Leaves grey-green, stout, in remote clusters.
            D. Cones 2 to 3 inches long; scales armed with
               sharp prickles. (*P. Virginiana*) JERSEY PINE
            DD. Cones $1\frac{1}{2}$ to 2 inches long; scales unequal,
               unarmed.   (*P. divaricata*) GREY PINE

Torrey's Pine (*P. Torreyana*, Parry) grows on a strip of territory eight miles long and less than two miles wide along the mouth of the Soledad River in southern California, and on the neighbouring Island of Santa Rosa. It is a nut pine with large, thick, edible seeds upon which Indians and Mexicans formerly subsisted, eating them raw or roasted.

The tree is distinguished by its dark-green, tufted leaves, which are 9 to 13 inches long, and cluster in fives in close sheaths. The cones are abundant, oval, woody and heavy, the scales set with stout recurving beaks.

33

Though driven to the wall, as it were, this pine seems disposed to make the most of its chances. Seedlings are numerous and vigorous among the elder trunks, and as there is little demand for its wood, the species is likely to hold its own.

The **Yellow Pine** (*P. Arizonica*, Engelm.) is the Southern counterpart of its close relative, *P. ponderosa*. They are both lumber trees of importance in the Rocky Mountain regions. The Arizona yellow pine is often inaccessible, as it grows on steep declivities and in deep cañons from which the logs cannot be taken, even after the trees are felled. This tree is one of the 5-leaved pitch pines, with leaves 5 to 7 inches long, and small spiny cones. The bulk of the forests of this tree grow across the Mexican border, at elevations 6,000 to 8,000 feet above the sea.

The **Digger Pine** (*P. Sabiniana*, Dougl.), growing only on the sun-baked foothills of western California, deserves mention here on account of its peculiar sparse foliage, pale, bluish green, and 8 to 12 inches long, that in no wise conceals the angular limbs, and the great cones, 6 to 10 inches long, which fairly load the tree, and are carried for several years. The thickened scales protrude separately as two-edged, thick projections that end in a beak shaped like a shark's tooth.

The Digger Indians once gathered the seeds of this pine for food. The nuts are as big as lima beans, and rich in oils and other food elements.

Loblolly, or **Old-Field Pine** (*P. Tæda*, Linn.)—A tall, straight, deep-rooted tree, 80 to 100 feet high, with short, much-branched horizontal limbs. *Bark* bright red-brown, broadly ridged, scaly; branchlets smooth, yellow-brown, thickly set with the recurved inner scales of the branch buds. *Wood* resinous, weak, coarse grained, pale brown. *Buds* obovate-oblong, with pointed brown scales. *Leaves* in threes, slender, stiff, twisted, pale green, glaucous, 6 to 10 inches long; sheaths close, thin, persistent. *Flowers:* staminate, crowded on short spikes, incurved, cylindrical, in scaly involucres; pistillate, lateral, one to three in a cluster, below apex of new shoot, with yellow scales, oval on short, scaly stalks, April. *Fruits* ovate-oblong, 3 to 5 inches long, 1½ to 2 inches broad; ridged, purplish knobs, with prickles on scales; seeds, rhomboidal, with wing ¾ inch long. *Preferred habitat*, swampy lands near tidewater; low ground, sterile and worthless. *Distribution* intermittent, New Jersey (Cape May), south along coast to Tampa Bay and Texas. Inland, from the Carolinas to Arkansas and Louisiana. *Uses* : Lumber not distinguished from longleaf or yellow pine—shipped north in quantities. Used in heavy construction—building of docks, ships, cars and houses. Valuable tree for reforesting waste land, and for fuel.

There is probably no pine tree that has more nicknames than this, nor one more variable in its habits of growth and in the quality of its wood. "Old-field" and "meadow pine" refer to its habit of invading land abandoned by farmers. "Sap," "frankincense" and "torch pine" mean that it is rich in resin. Several local names refer to its long leaves; others to the dark colour of its bark. Some names are meaningless.

The loblolly pine is one which Nature seems to have favoured in the race for life. It bears seed copiously every year. It has remarkable vitality of seed and seedlings. It chooses low, water-soaked ground, or rolling upland terraces where soil is light and sandy, though wet, and where there are comparatively few trees to contend with. The young trees grow with tremendous vigour for the first ten years, crowding so that animals cannot get in to harm them. After that they are beyond this danger, and their struggle is among themselves. Fires do little harm in the marshy regions, so that these forests have a great advantage over others. The trees are deep rooted, and in spite of fungus and insect attacks, thrive throughout the Southern States.

In Michaux's travels he noted that three-fourths of the houses of lower Virginia were built of loblolly pine. Giant trees grew there, and down in the rich marsh lands that reached back from Pamlico and Albemarle Sounds the finest specimens of these loblolly pines furnished the navies of many countries with masts unsurpassed in quality and size. These were of the famous "rosemary pine," heavy, hard, fine-grained heart wood, with a thin rind of sap wood. Now they are all gone, practically, and there are left the slash pines, coarse grained, with half their diameter sap wood. Virgin woods and second growth furnish the mills with lumber which is not distinguished in the trade from longleaf pine, though inferior to it. The third grade of lumber, with sap wood three times as thick as heart wood, and exceedingly coarse grained, is known to lumbermen as old-field

35

pine, and is locally consumed as lumber and fuel in the coast regions. Its poor quality is the result of very rapid growth.

"Kiln-drying" of the lumber has greatly improved its quality by adding to the durability and hardness of it. Heat kills a fungus which in ordinary seasoning turns the wood blue. Loblolly timbers are made durable by the "creosoting" process. Though rich in resin, the tree is not one which yields resinous substances, such as turpentine and pitch, for when tapped there is scarcely any flow, and contact with the air hardens the little resin that starts. As a fuel tree the cheap loblolly pine is unexcelled. It gives a quick, intense heat when dried, and is used in bakeries, kilns and in charcoal burning,

The **Pond**, or **Marsh Pine** (*P. serotina*, Michx.) is the water-loving, round-headed pine, with yellow-green leaves from 6 to 8 inches long, and sturdy cones that open only after they have hung, matured, for a year or two. In the flat, peaty and sandy swamps from North Carolina down the coast to the St. John's River in Florida, the traveller finds this pine with the longleaf. It supplies some turpentine and some lumber in North Carolina, but is not an important commercial tree.

Longleaf Pine (*P. palustris*, Mill.)—A tall, slender trunk, 90 to 120 feet high, with deep tap root and short, stout, twisted limbs, which form an elongated open head. *Bark* furrowed, and crossed by deep fissures into thin, scaly plates; colour reddish brown, with blue tinge. *Wood* heavy, strong, yellowish brown, resinous, durable. Excels that of all other pines. *Buds* elongated, large, silvery, with linear scales. *Leaves* in threes, in long, pale sheaths, tufted on ends of branches, 12 to 18 inches long, pendant, flexible, dark green, shining, persistent 2 years. *Flowers*: staminate, 2 inches long, cylindrical, crowded at base of new shoot, anthers purplish; pistillate, subterminal, clustered, oval, with broad purple scales. *Fruits* narrow, tapering, reddish brown; scales thickened, and keeled crosswise at tip, and set with small recurved spine; seed triangular, with long, lustrous wing. *Preferred habitats:* (1) low coast sands, imperfectly drained; (2) uplands, rocky and well drained, with marl and limestone deposits; (3) upland pine barrens. *Distribution,* Virginia to Florida (Tampa Bay), west to Mississippi River; a belt about 125 miles wide somewhat back from coast; isolated forests in northern Alabama, in Louisiana and Texas.

36

The average Northerner probably first sees this Southern yellow pine as lumber in the woodwork and floors of a dwelling house or in the arches that support the roof of a church. The rich orange wood, with its pale, soft spring wood and the darker, harder summer wood in alternating bands, produces patterns of exquisite beauty and variety, to which the "natural finish" is generally given. A coat of oil is all sufficient, and time deepens and enriches the colour of this wood. The "curly pine"—highest in value because of finest and most intricately waved grain— grows slowly in hard, sandy soils, on the damp, flat plains of the Gulf coast.

Within the past few years this Southern pine has come North in another form. The seedling trees just tall enough to show themselves above the forest floor are cut by thousands and shipped North for Christmas greens. No palm or *Ficus elasticus* is more effective in formal decoration than these tufted stems, standing erect with all their long, flexible leaves bending outward like a fountain of shining green. The enthusiasm with which the longleaf pine has been received by florists and the general public has already become a menace to the life of the species in sections of the South. Lumbering is going on at a terrible rate, taking the trees of merchantable size for an infinite range of uses. Now that the saplings 2 feet high have a price set on their heads, wherewithal shall the forests be renewed? It is a momentous problem, for a great part of the wealth of the South is in these hard-pine tracts.

The longleaf pine is second to none in the qualities that adapt lumber to building. Masts and spars, great timbers for trestles of bridges and aqueducts are made by simply squaring or dressing the slender, tall trunks. There are few knots, for the limbs are small and clustered at the top. In European dockyards there is an ever-increasing demand for these great timbers. Smaller "sticks," squared 10 x 12 inches and 36 to 42 feet long, free from blemish, are used in the building of railroad cars. Great quantities of small timber are used every year for railroad ties all over the country. Their durability in soil also commends these young trees for posts. Building and manufacture consume billions of board feet every year.

Quite independent of the lumber industry, the resinous products of the longleaf pine are of momentous importance to the

37

United States and to foreign countries. The colonists tapped these trees for resin (crude turpentine), and boiled it down for tar and pitch. Out of these beginnings grew the industries that supply naval stores to the world. The "orcharding" of long-leaf pines is reducing to a science the wasteful processes of earlier years. "Naval stores" include all the products of the resin of coniferous trees. The consumption of these is greatest in ship-yards and on shipboard. The products include turpentine, rosin, pine tar and pitch. Turpentine is extensively used in the arts and industries. The methods of "orcharding" the longleaf pine and preparing its products for market are described in the chapter, "The Uses of Wood."

Proper tapping does not injure the lumber nor shorten the life of the tree; but the resin-covered wounds feed the fires that so easily and frequently break out where careless workmen are deal-ing with inflammable substances. The terrible destructiveness of these fires raises one of the gravest problems of the forester. It is common to set fires to rubbish on the beginning of work among the pines so as to obviate dangers of later conflagrations. Fires often get beyond control, and sweep on till Nature puts them out. Settlers, burning underbrush to start the grass for their cattle, damage the woods irreparably in early spring. Seedlings and young growth which escape fire are injured by trampling, browsing cattle, sheep and goats. Squirrels gnaw the green cones and eat the unripe seeds. So between the care-less wastefulness of men and the inconsiderateness of lower ani-mals, the vast forests of longleaf pine dwindle.

The leaves of *Pinus palustris* yield by distillation an essential oil of balsamic odour that closely resembles oil of turpentine. The weaving of florists' baskets from the long, shining needles is just beginning, and is an industry that ought profitably to employ women and children in neighbourhoods. "Pine wool" is made by boiling the leaves in strong alkali, and then carding the fibres thus released. It is woven into a brown carpet somewhat like cocoa matting, and into other textile fabrics. It is an im-portant stuffing for upholstery, and is a natural antiseptic dress-ing for wounds.

The most conspicuous character of the longleaf pines is the great length of its flexible leaves. Next to this is the great sil-very "bud" at the tip of each shoot. This is the cluster of

THE FOXTAIL PINE (*Pinus Balfouriana*)

At the altitude of ten thousand feet and more this picturesque pine tree attains its noblest proportions. The trunk is often more than four feet in diameter. The short, irregular branches are tufted with thick, terminal brushes of leaves. In the same regions of the Sierra Nevada the species grows also as a prostrate shrub

Winter buds (leaves cut away to show buds)

THE TABLE MOUNTAIN PINE (*Pinus pungens*)

The leaves are in 2's, short, stout, twisted and blue green. The tree makes a scraggly growth on the barren slopes of the Appalachian mountains

Winter buds (leaves cut away to show buds)

THE PITCH PINE (*Pinus rigida*)

This picturesque pine of the swamps and arid coast plains of the East has leaves in 3's in persistent black sheaths. The bark is in reddish-brown plates

young leaves enclosed in their subtending scales, before these crowded scales fall.

Of late a new and profitable industry has sprung up in the wake of lumbering. Stumps are cut into small sticks for kindling wood, and sold in small bundles. These sticks are rich in resin, and bring good prices. Roots, branches and other waste pieces are gathered and converted into tar or into charcoal. The profits that come from gathering up the fragments after the lumbermen and turpentine distillers give one an idea of what enormous values are being squandered by wantonness and ignorance. The South is rich in natural resources, but its noblest patrimony, the pine forests, seems doomed soon to be spent.

The **Big-Cone Pine** (*P. Coulteri*, D. Don.) is chiefly remarkable for the size and weight of its cones, which are the heaviest of all the fruits of the pines. They hang like old-fashioned "sugar loaves" on the stout branches, which carry them with apparent ease, though they reach 15 to 20 inches long, and weigh 5 to 8 pounds. The scales are so thickened as to stand out from the central axis; the stout, curved beak and the thick part which it surmounts remind one strongly of the head of an eagle. The seeds, which reach $\frac{1}{2}$ inch in length, not counting the thin wing, are rich in oil and sugar. They are gathered for food by the Indians in southern California.

The leaves of this pine match the cones. They are stout and stiff, with saw-tooth edges, dark blue-green, and 6 to 16 inches long. The sheaths at the bases of the leaves are an inch or more long, and persistent. They are tufted on the twigs and are not shed for three or four years. This fact gives the tree a luxuriant crown, and though it does not grow over medium height, it is always a striking and picturesque figure on the western slopes of the California coast mountains.

The wood is indifferent in quality, and the tree is cut only for fuel. It is planted for its great golden-brown cones. In Europe it makes rapid growth, and fruiting trees of good size are not uncommon in France and Germany.

Pitch Pine (*P. rigida*, Mill.)—A gnarled, irregular tree 50 to 75 feet high, with short trunk and rigid, rough branches. *Bark* thick, broken into plates by deep, irregular fissures; scales thin; bark red or purple. *Wood* light red, soft, durable, brittle, coarse. *Buds* $\frac{1}{2}$ to $\frac{3}{4}$ inch long, reddish, with fringed scales.

39

Leaves in threes, **rigid**, stout, 3 to 5 inches long, dark yellow-green; sheaths becoming black, persistent. *Flowers* monœcious; staminate short, densely clustered at base of season's shoot; pistillate lateral, in clusters, rosy tinged, oval, short stalked. *Fruits* biennial, 1 to 3½ inches long, ovate, scales with sharp, recurving beaks. *Preferred habitat*, sandy uplands and cold swamps. *Distribution*, New Brunswick to Georgia; west to Ontario and Kentucky. *Uses:* Fuel and charcoal making. Reforesting worthless land. Sparingly used as lumber.

The pitch pine carries picturesqueness to extremes, and becomes in old age grotesque, even absolutely ugly. It has the look of a tree that has been hounded by untoward circumstances. In youth the tree has a rounded, symmetrical head, formed of successive whorls of branches. In its subsequent struggles symmetry is lost, and the contorted limbs, tufted with scant, sickly-looking foliage, and studded with the squat, black, prickly cones of many years, reach out with an expression of mute appeal that tempts one to cut the tree down and end its sufferings. If it is cut, however, it sends up suckers from the roots, a strange habit among the pines; and its winged seeds spread the species over barren and shifting sand dunes, and otherwise hopelessly treeless areas. This work is so well done on the island of Nantucket and the desert soil of Cape Cod, even those areas which are washed by the spring tides, that the pitch pines have earned the regard of men. The inferior lumber is forgiven.

Pitch pines are rich in resin; the knots especially accummulate it, and "pine knots" and "candlewood" are useful and familiar household words in the regions where this pine grows. Kindling wood and torches for midnight coon hunts are never lacking. The "pitchie kinde of substance" which makes handling of these sticks unpleasant business for tidy folks, gums the saws and makes trouble in the mills. Sills and beams of houses were formerly got of pitch-pine logs, but now other kinds are preferred, and these trees go into charcoal and fuel. The turpentine gatherer, too, has left these trees to seek the richer pineries of the South and West. There is small excuse for the pitch pine to stay on, were it not for the one thing it does better than any other—it makes glad the wilderness and the solitary place.

The **Knob-Cone Pine** (*P. attenuata*, Lemm.) is another

40

tree of striking habit. Its cones are woody, armed with stout beaks, and from 3 to 5 inches long. There is nothing peculiar in these cones, nor in the pale yellow-green foliage in its 3-leaved clusters. The tree is slim and tall, and grows on the hot, dry fire-swept foothills of California mountains. A stranger notes how dense and uniform in size is the growth of these trees, and how thickly studded are the limbs with clusters of cones. Close examination shows them sealed up tight—not a scale sprung on the oldest cone, though the branch that bears it may have actually swallowed the cone by the increase of its diameter.

A fire sweeps over the slope, and every tree gives up its cones. The scales are unsealed at last and the seeds, whose vitality has been preserved, apparently, in anticipation of this day, germinate at once, and soon a new forest takes the place of the old one. With such an abundance of seed, is it wonderful that the trees stand close and even like wheat in a field?

Cuban Pine, Swamp Pine (*P. Caribæa*, Morelet.)—Tree, 100 to 120 feet, with tapering trunk and dense, round crown, above large horizontal limbs. *Bark* in broad, scaly, irregular plates, reddish brown, showing orange in the shallow fissures. *Wood* heavy, very hard, strong, tough, durable, coarse, dark orange, with thick, nearly white sap wood. *Buds*, elongated, scaly, $\frac{3}{4}$ to $1\frac{1}{2}$ inches long, light brown; lateral buds smaller. *Leaves* in clusters of twos and threes; stout, dark green, 8 to 12 inches long, persistent 2 years; sheaths thin, brown. *Flowers* in January, before new leaves, subterminal; staminate clustered, incurving, purplish, 1 to $1\frac{1}{2}$ inches long; pistillate oval, 2 to 3 in cluster, pinkish, $\frac{1}{2}$ inch long. *Fruits* elongated, 3 to 7 inches long, narrowing to blunt apex, pendant, with beaked, thickened scales and winged seeds. *Preferred habitat*, damp, sandy soil of swamp borders, with even moisture supply. *Distribution*, coast region, South Carolina to Florida and Louisiana. Also Bahamas, Cuba and other islands, and Central America.

No more beautiful pine grows in the Southern States than this stately tree that skirts the swampy coast land, forming great forests and casting a goodly shadow under its thick, dark, lustrous foliage mass. Beside it the other pines seem to have very ragged and loose crowns. Here in the humid air that flows from sea or gulf, the Cuban pine promises to replenish our depleted forest areas even as the shortleaf does back from the coast. The same vigour characterises thousands which endure the shade and soon spring to a height that resists the fires that menace them.

The wood of the Cuban pine is not distinguished in the markets from longleaf pine, and it serves the same uses. Spars of the largest dimensions, straight and free from blemish, come out of these coast pineries. The wide, porous sap wood and the coarse grain once counted against this tree, but they are now considered distinct advantages, for this kind of wood more readily absorbs creosote and other preservatives by infiltration, and kiln-drying converts the sap wood into good lumber.

Turpentine of higher quality than that of longleaf pine is derived from these trees, which also abound in other resinous matters. Young trees are ready for tapping at forty years; and in this time a new forest has replaced the one stripped by lumbermen. A large part of the turpentine exported by Georgia and South Carolina to-day is from land thus spontaneously reforested. The future of our naval stores depends to a large extent on the perpetuity of the forests of Cuban pine.

Western Yellow Pine (*P. ponderosa*, Laws.)—Spire-like tree with stout, short horizontal branches; 100 to 230 feet high, with trunk 5 to 8 feet thick. *Bark* thick, cinnamon-red, sometimes black, becoming furrowed and broken into large plates. *Wood* light red, strong, hard, very heavy, not durable, fine grained. *Buds* ovate, brown, scaly, terminal the largest. *Leaves* in threes, or in twos and threes, stout, rigid, shiny, 3 to 15 inches long, yellow-green, tufted on ends of naked branches; last till third season; sheath persistent. *Flowers*: staminate yellow, in crowded spikes; pistillate dark red, oval, subterminal, clustered or paired. *Fruits* green or purple when full grown; scales conspicuously beaked, with recurved point. *Preferred habitat*, deep, well-drained soil on mountain slopes or elevated plains. *Distribution*, British Columbia and Black Hills south through Rocky Mountains and coast ranges to Texas and Mexico. *Uses:* Principal lumber tree of Northwestern and Southwestern states. Used in building, for railroad ties, fencing and fuel.

The most extensive pine forests in the world are those of the yellow pine in the mountainous West of our own country. The hardihood of this tree is the wonder of foresters and botanists, and the admiration of everybody who knows anything about it. Pines are particular trees, as a rule. They like one type of soil and climate, and out of their chosen range are unhappy and unhealthy. But here is a species which seems to have forgotten family traditions, and become a citizen of the world, as far as that is possible. It grows to great size in the arid foothills of southern Oregon, where the soil is volcanic in origin. In the Black Hills it roots itself solidly in sterile rocky soil, and is the dominant tree of these mountain forests. In the arid Southwest, on mountain and mesa, this tree is the principal source of lumber. It is the only pine tree native to Nebraska that thrives in the droughty western counties. This is the tree that inhabits the western slopes of the coast mountains from British Columbia to Lower California, as if the moisture-laden winds from the Pacific were the very breath of life to it. Finally, the same tree is found wading into swamps on the slopes of the Cascades. Its elevation ranges from 2,500 feet to the timber line.

A tree that clambers over mountains and meets so much variety of soil, elevation and climate must show variations in character to adapt it to its life. In the old lake basins on the Sierra slopes it reaches the height of 200 feet and more—with a trunk diameter up to 8 feet. These are the giants of the species, var. *Jeffreyi*. In swamps, and near the timber line the trees are stunted, and have black bark, in distinct contrast with the bright-red rind of the typical tree. Several species have already been made out of the forms this tree assumes in various situations. Closer study will doubtless lead to still finer distinctions. The common origin of these forms is not doubted; they are all *P. ponderosa*.

Knowing something of the extensive range of this tree, we are ready to appreciate the beauty of a single specimen. The central shaft rises like a spire, rugged if old, and massive at the base, lifting its head far into the blue and clothing itself with short, leafy branches most of the way down, if there is room. The young trees, under 100 feet high, are pictures of tree vigour, still " having the dew of their youth and the beauty thereof," waving their arms, that catch and reflect the light upon burnished needles. Against the dark-green mantle the ruddy flowers and purple cones glow in their season, and new leaves lighten the whole tree throughout the summer.

The habit of breaking off its cones and leaving the stem and the first few scales still hanging is one of the characteristics of the various forms of *P. ponderosa*. On this the botanists leaned content, until, alack! somebody breaks the reed by announcing an exception! The wood is so heavy that the logs have to dry for a while before they can be floated down stream to the mills. Hence, *ponderosa*.

The name is not the point of greatest interest. If there is to be a re-christening by the botanists we shall hear of it in good season. Let us take a hand, though, in blotting out the name, "bull pine," absurd and meaningless as it is misleading. It has been given variously by ignorant frontiersmen to *any* pine that attains large dimensions.

The yellow pine was first discovered by the members of the Lewis and Clark expedition, in 1804, while they were going up the Missouri River. Twenty-two later, David Douglas found the trees growing near the Spokane River. He suggested then the name they now bear, because of their ponderous bulk, and sent seeds and young plants to European gardeners.

In cultivation the tree does fairly well in the Eastern States and in Europe, though slow of growth and liable to disease. The best form in cultivation is var. *Jeffreyi*.

The Indians of the West long ago discovered that though the seeds of the yellow pine are inedible, yet the inner bark in spring is sweet and nutritious. So they stripped and scraped the bark for its mucilaginous living layer. The branchlets are fragrant, giving out when crushed an odour as of orange peel.

Shortleaf Pine (*P. echinata*, Mill.)—A slender trunk, with loose, round or pyramidal head, 80 to 120 feet high. *Bark* thick, cleft into square plates, with cinnamon-red scales. Young shoots violet. *Wood* orange or yellow-brown, hard, heavy, durable, strong, coarse grained, with broad bands of small summer cells in each annual layer. *Buds* plump, blunt, scaly. *Leaves* in clusters of twos or threes; dark blue-green; acute, slender, soft and flexible, 3 to 5 inches long, in silvery white sheath which turns brownish. *Flowers*: staminate crowded, subterminal, purplish; pistillate 2 to 4, stalked, subterminal or terminal on adventitious spurs; purplish or rose pink. *Fruit* biennial, abundant, $1\frac{1}{2}$ to $2\frac{1}{2}$ inches long, ovate, tapering, scales thickened, 4-angled at tip, with or without short, recurved prickle, seeds winged. Old cones persist several years. *Preferred habitat*, well drained, gravelly soil with clay intermixed;

(Winter bud some leaves cut away to show bud)

THE SHORTLEAF PINE (*Pinus echinata*)

The leaves are in 2's or 3's, dark blue-green, soft and flexible, 3 to 5 inches long, in silvery white sheaths which turn brown when old. The cones are biennial, about 2 inches long, tapering, of woody, 4-angled scales armed with or without recurved point. This is one of the important lumber trees of the East and South

THE RED OR NORWAY PINE (*Pinus resinosa*)

The leaves are slender and long, dark green and lustrous, in 2's, rising out of long sheaths.   The cones have thick, woody scales, destitute of prickles.   The pale-red wood is used for masts and bridge timbers

uplands of scant fertility. *Distribution*, Connecticut to Florida; west to Illinois, Kansas and Texas. Not continuous. *Uses:* Lumber used as *P. palustris* is. Young trees yield turpentine and pitch. Rarely planted. Reforests adjacent fields and lumbered areas by copious seeds and vigorous suckers.

The shortleaf pine is short leaved only in comparison with the exceedingly long needles of *P. palustris*. The leaves are about the length of those of the Austrian pine, so familiar in cultivation, and beside which the Scotch and white pines are short-leaved species.

Next to the longleaf in rank, the shortleaf pine is one of the most important lumber trees in the Eastern and Southern states. Just a shade inferior to the former in quality, this species is likely by its vigour and wide range to become greatest of them all in economic importance as the exploitation of the timber lands of the South progresses. Against the destructive agencies at work the longleaf cannot hold its own. Its ultimate extinction must follow present methods of lumbering and orcharding. But the shortleaf pine, less sensitive to injuries, more prolific of seeds, able to renew itself indefinitely by throwing up suckers from the stump, and to survive shading of its saplings better than the longleaf and Cuban pines, has a distinct advantage over these, its compeers in the South and East. The distribution of the species is over a vaster area, and each grove is the centre of a growing and widening territory. It industriously colonises adjacent land abandoned by the farmer or the lumberman. In a free fight with hardwood trees this pine is the winner, and the young forests it is planting will be marketable in 80 to 100 years.

The forest centre of this species is west of the Mississippi and below the Arkansas River. This great tract was practically untouched at the time the tenth Census Report, issued in 1880, estimated its merchantable timber then standing at 87,000,000,000 feet, board measure. This counted only the area in Texas, Louisiana and Arkansas, and left out the forests in Missouri and Oklahoma. There is little of the vast Eastern territory once covered by the shortleaf pine that has not been worked to some extent by lumbermen, especially where railroads make possible the distribution of the lumber. In the past twenty-five years astonishing inroads have been made upon the Southwestern forests.

While inferior to *P. palustris*, lumber of *P. echinata* is often

45

preferred, because it is less resinous and softer and so more easily worked. Doors, sash and blinds are made of it and interior finish of houses. It is the common "yellow pine" of the Middle West, brought north on the river. It is the "North Carolina pine" which the kiln-drying process cured of its "black sap" and made a beautiful finishing lumber.

The **Monterey Pine** (*P. radiata*, D. Don.), like its companion, Torrey's pine, is restricted to a very narrow range. They occur together in Santa Rosa Island, and each has a narrow strip of territory on the mainland of southern California. On Point Pinos, south of Monterey Bay, *P. radiata* is most abundant and grows to 100 feet in height, with trunks occasionally 5 or 6 feet in diameter. Its wood is soft and weak.

The bright rich green of the leaves, which never linger more than 3 years to dull the freshness of the new ones, and a silvery sheen the young growth wears, make this tree one of the handsome pines. Its quick growth also destines it for popularity with landscape gardeners wherever the climate is mild enough in winter. It is a favourite park tree from Vancouver Island down the coast to its natural range. It has long been planted in pleasure grounds of western and southern Europe, and occasionally in our Southeastern States.

Red or **Norway Pine** (*P. resinosa*, Ait.)—Large, broadly pyramidal tree, 75 to 120 feet high, branched to the ground, with stout twigs. *Bark* shallowly furrowed into flat, scaly ridges, reddish brown, rich in tannin; branches rough, glabrous. *Wood* pale red, light, hard, resinous; sap wood yellow or white. *Buds* conical, tapering, with loose, red scales. *Leaves* in clusters of twos, from close, persistent sheaths, ½ inch long; needle-like, dark green, 6 inches long, sharp pointed, flexible semi-circular in cross section, toothed near tip, with rows of pale dots lengthwise. *Flowers:* staminate red, abundant, clustered at base of season's shoot; pistillate 1 to 3, terminal, peduncled, reddish, oval. *Fruits* ovate, 1 to 3 inches long, standing at right angles with stem; biennial; scales thickened, 4-angled at apex, unarmed; seeds winged. *Preferred habitat*, dry, sandy plains and rocky ridges. *Distribution*, southern Canada, Northern States from Maine to Minnesota; south to Pennsylvania. *Uses:* Most picturesque and desirable of pitch pines for ornamental planting in the North; grows rapidly from seed; free from insect and fungous injuries.   Lumber used in heavy construction; for bridges, piles, docks, buildings, masts and spars.

The red pine is the only American member of a group of Old-World pines of which *P. sylvestris*, the Scotch pine of Europe, is a familiar example.   The paired leaves and red bark are signs of kinship.   Both are common in cultivation in America, and we shall distinguish the native tree by its longer leaf and the heavy tufting of its twigs; the short leaves of *P. sylvestris* are thinly and evenly scattered along its branches.

An early Spanish explorer erroneously described this tree as identical with the variety of the Scotch pine that grows in Norway.   In this way it came by its second name.

There is a lustiness and symmetry of growth and an expression of hardiness and health in the red pine which makes the other pitch pines look ragged and discouraged, and the graceful white pines delicate and unequal to the struggle of life.   No handsomer pine than this one is found in the Northeastern States.

The wood of red pine is not what we might expect from such a tree.   Rich in resin and fine grained, yet its durability is not to be depended upon.   Its height gave masts and spars of great size and free of blemishes.   It was once shipped in quantities to England out of the Canadian woods to be used at the dockyards, and for piles and bridge timbers.   Of late years better pine has been substituted.   Turpentine and tar are not derived from this tree, despite its name, *resinosa*, "full of resin." Less pitchy than *P. rigida*, soft like *P. Strobus*, the wood seems intermediate between the two.

The living tree is more valuable than its log; when the lumberman scoffs at the red pine the landscape gardener takes it up. It grows on exposed and sterile coasts, where it rapidly forms effective windbreaks and beautiful groves.   It adds a distinct type of beauty to parks and private grounds.   Its hardiness and rapidity of growth commend it to the colder states.   Not the least of its good points in the home grounds is that its two leaves in their close, deep sheaths furnish children exactly the right material for chains, the making of which is one of the most absorbing pleasures of childhood.

The **Prickle-Cone Pine** (*P. muricata*, D. Don.) is a handsome round-topped evergreen, covered with dense tufts of

47

stiff, yellow-green leaves. It is the dominant pine of the coast of Mendocino County, and follows down in sight of the ocean into Lower California. The oblique cones, whose thickened scales are armed with sharp, strong beaks, are conspicuous by their persistence for years unopened on the branch. It is rare for them to fall, even after they open and discharge the seed. They usually remain throughout the lifetime of the tree, but strangely are never swallowed up by the growth of the branch that bears them.

The **Table-Mountain Pine** (*P. pungens*, Michx.), with cones quite as formidable as those of the preceding species, and closely resembling them in appearance, has the same tardy habit of opening and casting its cones that marks *P. muricata*. But *P. pungens* is Eastern, growing on gravelly ridges oᶜ the Appalachian Mountains from Pennsylvania and New Jersey to North Carolina and Tennessee. It has clustered blue-green foliage of sombre hue, and forms a flattened, irregular head, its long, horizontal branches often drooping, but the twigs erect. The wood is used for fuel and for charcoal in some localities. Its dingy colour, barren habitat and scraggly growth earn it the name, "poverty pine." The thin bark, breaking into loose, scaly plates, is probably responsible for the name, "hickory pine." There is no quality of the brittle, coarse-gained wood to account for it.

It is interesting to note in Bulletin 10 of the Kansas Agricultural College, which is located at Manhattan in the western part of the state, that *P. pungens* is one of the hardiest and best pines for that region. The leaves are a decided yellow-green there, a cheerful contrast to the sombre Austrian pines so generally planted. The waywardness of the tree's habit is made a virtue. The terminal shoot bends strongly out of the vertical, producing a grotesque leaning tree, which breaks the monotony of the prim and formal European species with which it is successfully grouped in grounds of considerable extent. The following Western species and varieties were tried and failed on the college grounds: *P. contorta, edulis, Jeffreyi* and *ponderosa*. Besides *P. pungens*, other Eastern pines that were successfully grown were *rigida* and *echinata*. *P. Strobus* grew often into handsome, shapely specimens, but died young in the hot winds.

The **Scrub Pine** (*P. contorta*, Lond.) is one of four stunted, gnarly, round-shouldered trees that are prostrated by exposure to

48

the ocean winds. They are the beach pines. This one grows from northern California into Alaska in bogs and sand dunes, bearing its cones when only a few inches high in the bleakest situations. These trees form a windbreak behind which many sorts of tender plants thrive in quiet security. The bark is thin and pale and gummy on these dwarfs, and once a fire is started it devours all within reach. Now a very interesting habit of the tree comes into prominence. The cones hang on the trees for years without opening, but their seeds are safely sealed up and retain their vitality. The burned trees drop their cones, which, opening, free the seeds. From them young trees spring up to take the places of those wiped out by the fire.

It is hard to believe that the tall, slim lodge pole, or tamarack pine is but a variety—*Murrayana*—of *P. contorta*, but so it is considered on good authority. The mountains of Wyoming, Colorado and the states further west are clothed with dense forests of this tree. They grow as thick as wheat in a field, and so are all delicately tall, but in favoured situations isolated trees reach the height of 100 feet, and a trunk diameter of $1\frac{1}{2}$ feet. An average forest specimen is 5 inches through and 40 to 50 feet high. The Indians cut poles for their lodges or tepees. These pines, flexible, slender and always abundant, seemed designed by Nature to serve this need. The name remains, though the lodge of the Indian is rapidly disappearing.

There is great variation in this species and its variety, *Murrayana*, as the trees meet very different conditions. The leaves are in twos, and 1 to 3 inches long, dark green in *contorta*, yellow-green and quite wide in the variety. The wood of *contorta* is hard, brownish red, and strong; of *Murrayana*, soft, pale yellow, and weak. The latter is used for lumber to a limited extent, and both are cut for fuel. While it is not a prominent commercial tree, it is the main reliance of the pioneer in many regions. It supplies mines with supporting beams, fences the settler's homestead, and furnishes ties for the pioneer railroads.

The Indians cut the trees down and strip out the inner bark. This is broken into pieces by the patient squaws, who mash it in water into a pulp which they mould into large cakes. Then a hole is dug in the ground and lined with stones, and a fire kindled. When the stones are hot the embers are removed, and the cakes packed in with leaves of the Western skunk cabbage

49

between. A fire of damp moss is built on top, and the baking takes an hour or more. Then the cakes are laid on slat frames and smoked for a week in a close tent. Now they are ready to put away for future use, or to carry in canoes or on ponies ·to distant places.

This "hard bread" is prepared for use by breaking it in pieces and boiling them until soft. The pieces are skimmed out and laid on the snow to cool. "Ulikou" fat is used on this strange Alaskan bread as we use butter.

The Indians make berry baskets out of the bark of the lodge-pole pine. Nuttall, in his extension of Michaux's "Sylva of North America," calls this the twisted-branched pine. I well recall the curious rustic chairs and seats at the Dome Lake Club House in the Big Horn Mountains in Wyoming, made of the extravagantly twisted branches of this tree. They called it "screw pine," I remember. The name *contorta* may allude to this characteristic, too, although it is not constant in the species. It may rather be regarded as a freak of nature, the cause of which is not understood. However, the hard life of the species on the bleak, wind-swept coast and unprotected sand dunes may easily earn it the name there.

The **Sand Pine** (*P. clausa*, Sarg.) has a striking habit of swallowing its persistent woody cones by the growth of the stems that bear them. Chopping frequently reveals cones in the solid wood—a peculiar kind of modified knot. The tree is unimportant to the lumber trade, being inferior in quality and scant in quantity. It grows near the coast on either side of northern Florida and west into Alabama. It is used locally as masts for small vessels.

The **Spruce Pine** (*P. glabra*, Walt.) is a close relative of the shortleaf, *P. echinata*. It grows from South Carolina to Louisiana, in lowlands, solitary or in considerable groves. It attains the height of 120 feet, and spreads over a considerable territory in northwestern Florida. Little use is made of its light, soft wood beyond the local fuel supply. It is known as "cedar pine" in Mississippi. Its foliage is soft, and bright, dark green, being shed when but two years old.

The **Jersey** or **Scrub Pine** (*P. Virginiana*, Mill.) is another of those unfortunate trees whose lot seems to be to extort a meagre and miserable living out of worthless soil. A tortuous

A. Winter bud (some leaves cut away to show bud)

THE JERSEY PINE (*Pinus Virginiana*)

This also is a scrub pine; it grows on the pine barrens of New Jersey, a pendulous, discouraged tree. Its grey-green leaves are in bundles of twos. It does as well as a tree can on worthless soil. In Indiana it becomes a pyramidal tree forty feet high. The cones are dark-red, curved, and armed with sharp prickles

THE RED SPRUCE (*Picea rubens*)

Bright red downy twigs, red wood and reddish bark give this tree its name. Short, stiff, pointed, 4-angled leaves set all around the twig prove this tree a spruce. The wood is used for the sounding boards of musical instruments

Winter bud (some leaves cut away to show bud)

THE GREY PINE (*Pinus divaricata*)

Its flat, grey-green leaves are in clusters of 2's on the yellow twigs. The cones are strongly curved and taper to a long point. Among the pines this is a straggling good-for-little species, that clothes barren sand dunes and arctic bogs with a straggling tree growth

low tree, pendulous and discouraged looking, with grey-green leaves, that are yellowish as they first appear, stubby, 1 to 3 inches long, in clusters of twos. This is the tree of the Jersey pine barrens—the tree that clothes these waste places and gets little credit for it.

Peter Kalm observed that cattle, in the heat of the day, choose the shade of this tree rather than of any other, though its foliage be much thicker. He judges that this strange choice arises "from the gratefulness of the fragrance" of this tree. Another author comments on the delightful fragrance exhaled by the exuding balsam of the despised Jersey pine. The opportunity to point a moral here is almost irresistible. But I stay my pointer. The range of *P. Virginiana* is wide; from Long Island to Georgia and Alabama, and west to Indiana, where it rises to the height of 100 feet. Its average height is one-third of this maximum limit, with a trunk diameter rarely over 18 inches.

The wood has been locally used for making tar, and for pump logs, water pipes, for fencing and fuel. It is not an economic tree, unless considered so in its work of covering quickly large areas of sterile soils in the Eastern States.

The **Grey** or **Scrub Pine** (*P. divaricata*, Sudw.) is an outcast, strangely spurned and superstitiously feared in many places where it grows. It ventures farther north than any other pine. From the northern tier of states it ranges into the cold of frigid regions, following the Mackenzie River even to the Arctic circle. It grows only on barren ground—rocky slopes and in cold, boggy stretches. In Michigan it dips down to the southern point of the lake, scattering over the sand dunes, and clothing the barren stretches of the lower peninsula, which are known as the "Jack Pine Plains." The grey-green leaves, scant, stubby, in twos, and the crouching, sprawling habit of the tree, which wears its old cones for a dozen years or more—all tend to prejudice the casual observer against this pine. Only the thoughtful will consider what the desert and the cold North would be without it. North of Lake Superior it rises to the stature of a tree, reaching 70 feet in height, and spreading along the valley of the Mackenzie River, the only pine, it forms forests of considerable area, an immeasurable boon to the scant population of that region. The wood makes fuel and lumber, frames for the Indian's canoe, posts and railroad ties.

From Michigan to Minnesota the grey pine acts as a nurse tree to the seedlings of *P. resinosa* on denuded lands. Later the scrub "cleans" the young trees of lower limbs, greatly adding to their timber value.

Strange notions prevail in certain sections concerning this weird-looking pine tree. Women dare not pass within ten feet of a tree, and men also give it a wide berth. Cattle browsing near it are fatally stricken; the tree is believed to poison the ground it shadows. One who believes current reports of this tree will destroy every one growing on his land; but he dare not chop them down. Each must be burned like a witch, by making a funeral pyre all around it. Every misfortune that overtakes a family is laid at the foot of the grey pine, as long as there is one left on the place.

EXOTIC PINES

We are all European immigrants, once or twice removed. Our craving for things imported is an appetite inherited from our Colonial ancestors. Our horticulture owns its European parentage. The early settlers brought trees and flowers from the old country. They transplanted the old home, as far as could be, to the New World. European evergreens came in as a matter of course. Even species native to our west coast were brought into Eastern gardens first by way of European nurseries.

Oriental pines are coming in, making valuable contributions to the list in cultivation from Europe. Our native pines are being "discovered," horticulturally, and dissemination of species is widening the range of all. It is a small and unpretentious park indeed that does not show pines from every northern continent. The European pines most widely planted in the eastern United States are the Scotch and Austrian pines. They are dependable trees, hardy, vigorous, not particular as to soil and exposure—good for protective and ornamental planting even on the prairies where hot, dry winds blow and for weeks no rain may fall.

The **Austrian Pine** is a hardy variety, *Austriaca*, of the Corsican pine (*P. Laricio*, Poir.), of southern Europe. It is a sombre tree, darker green than any other evergreen except tne red cedar. In youth it is a compact cone or globe, resting on the ground. The leaves, two in a sheath, are 6 inches long, and inclined to twist stiffly. They persist several years. Cones ripen in the second autumn, and do not open until another crop is ripe. Large trees are transplanted safely, even in the height of the growing season.

The **Scotch Pine** (*P. sylvestris*, Linn.) is one of the most important timber trees of Europe. In this country it was frequently planted about homes, where it has grown to great size. By no means as handsome a tree as our own white pine, it has certain advantages over its companion, the Austrian variety. Its habit is less compact and formal, and its foliage (also in bundles of twos) is shorter, looser and more cheerful looking in spite of its blue tinge. It grows more rapidly, and neatly sheds its cones as soon as ripe, while the Austrian pine shows its bare limbs laden for years with empty cones.

The **Swiss Pines** (*P. Cembra* and *montana*) are all picturesque and hardy, as if they crouched under Alpine blasts, even in the most comfortable situations. Any flat-topped, irregular evergreen growing wild is attractive to the eye of the nurseryman who has a landscape-gardening department and facilities for moving large trees. He is able to get the tree at a bargain from the farmer in whose woodlot or pasture it stands. There is very little cordwood in it. The new owner cuts a big circle around the tree the depth of a spade, severing the roots outside this boundary. A year later a thick mat of rootlets has resulted from this root pruning, and in the winter the tree is easily taken up and planted in just the right place on Mr. ——'s new country place. He points out to his friends the striking "Swiss-pine effect" of this tree etched against the sky. It is a good thing, and worth the price, even if he never heard of a Swiss pine before in his life.

The **Mugho Pine** has a shrubby habit, spreading twice its height. It is one of several dwarf varieties of the Swiss mountain pine (*P. montana*, Mill.), and is very effective as a specimen tree or grouped with others to cover rocky hillsides.

The **Stone Pine** (*P. Pinea*) and the **Aleppo Pine** (*P. Halepensis*) are natives of southern Europe and so not hardy. The **Macedonian Pine** (*P. Peuce*) and the **Cluster Pine** (*P. Pinaster*) have the same climatic limitations in this country, though

53

hardy in England, where the Aleppo and cluster pines are much used for seaside planting.

China and Japan and Korea have furnished some exceptionally handsome pines that are hardy and vigorous in American parks and gardens. The **Korean Pine** (*P. Koraiensis*), is a handsome, narrowly pyramidal tree when young, becoming very picturesque when old. It is a slow-growing pine, well adapted to small gardens. The foliage is thick, and dark green with pale linings. From China comes the **Lacebark Pine** (*P. Bungeana*), with light-green foliage and white, intricately netted bark, slow of growth and hardy north.

From Japan we have three species. The little *P. parviflora*, often dwarfed by potting at home, is charming in its abundance of red cones in the dense pyramid of bluish-green leaves. It is one of Japan's forest trees, growing to 80 feet in height. The **Red Pine** (*P. densiflora*), also a great tree at home, attains a goodly size in cultivation, grows rapidly, with long branches spreading into a broad head. The foliage is bluish green. Many forms with variegated leaves have been derived from this species. The **Black Pine** (*P. Thunbergi*), another large tree from Japan, has bright green foliage, and grows in a handsome broad pyramid.

Himalayan Pines, two in number, both large trees at home, are cultivated here. Their other points of beauty are all secondary to the charm of their long, drooping leaves. The **Bhotan Pine,** *P. excelsa*, has blue-green leaves, 6 to 8 inches long, and cylindrical stalked cones of about equal length. It is hardy to the neighbourhood of Boston. *P. longifolia* is a tender species cultivated in California. Its leaves are pale green, 8 to 12 inches long, slender and pendulous. No more beautiful pine can be imagined than a young and vigorous Himalayan longleaf with the wind playing among its drooping leaf clusters.

The **Mexican White Pine** (*P. Ayacahuite*), a near relative of our Northern white pine, and resembling the Himalayan species in the pendulous leaf habit, is unknown to any but a few specialists. But it is sure to be recognised and widely planted where it is hardy. The tree is graceful and symmetrical, its whorls of slender branches held well apart and horizontal. The droop is in the leaves themselves, pale green, bluish and 4 to 6 inches long. The handsome cones are 9 to 15 inches long, tapering, often curved, and brownish yellow. Though not counted hardy in the North, this Mexican species grows behind the protecting Scotch pines on Mr. Dana's place, Dosoris, on Long Island.

The **Umbrella Pine** (*Sciadopitys verticillata*) is a Japanese conifer, a beautiful conical evergreen, whose glossy green leaves are needle-like, 3 to 6 inches long, and set in umbrella-like whorls of 15 to 35 leaves at the ends of all the twigs. The tree is a puzzle to botanists and a delight to horticulturists. It is hardy to Portland, Maine, grows slowly, but is thrifty in many soils, and is strikingly decorative at any age. A dwarf variety and one with variegated foliage are offered by dealers. The normal type of this species grows to the height of 100 feet, losing gradually its compact, spire-like form, its limbs becoming pendulous and more spreading.

NATIVE PINES VALUABLE AS ORNAMENTALS

HARDY

White	*P. Strobus* and vars.
Mountain	" *monticola*
Sugar	" *Lambertiana*
Rocky Mountain White	" *flexilis*
Pitch	" *rigida*
Shortleaf	" *echinata*
Norway or Red	" *resinosa*

NOT HARDY

Foxtail	*P. Balfouriana*
Digger	" *Sabiniana*
Big-cone	" *Coulteri*
Jeffrey's	" *Jeffreyi*
Yellow	" *ponderosa*
Cuban	" *Caribæa*
Monterey	" *radiata*
Prickle-cone	" *muricata*

EXOTIC PINES VALUABLE AS ORNAMENTALS

HARDY—*European*

Swiss Stone	*P. Cembra*
Austrian	" *Laricio*, var. *Austriaca*
Scotch	" *sylvestris*
Swiss Mountain	" *montana*
Mugho	" " var. *Mughus*

HARDY—*Asiatic*

Korean	- - - -	*P. Koraiensis*
Chinese Lace-bark	- - -	" *Bungeana*
Himalayan White	- - -	" *excelsa*
Japanese Black	- - -	" *Thunbergi*
" Red	- - -	" *densiflora*
" Small-flowered	-	" *parviflora*

NOT HARDY—*European*

Cluster	- - - -	*P. Pinaster*
Stone	- - - -	" *Pinea*
Aleppo	- - - -	" *Halepensis*
Macedonian	- - -	" *Peuce*

Mexican

White	- - - -	*P. Ayacahuite*

Asiatic

Himalayan Longleaf	- -	*P. longifolia*

PINES PICTURESQUE WHEN OLD

Native

Red	- - - - -	*P. resinosa*
Monterey	- - - - -	" *radiata*
White	- - - - -	" *Strobus*
Big Cone	- - - - -	" *Coulteri*
Pitch	- - - - -	" *rigida*
Nut	- - - - -	" *quadrifolia*
Table Mountain	- - - -	" *pungens*

European

Stone	- - - - -	*P. Pinea*
Swiss Stone	- - - -	" *Cembra*
Scotch	- - - - -	" *sylvestris*
Corsican	- - - -	" *Laricio*

Asiatic

Japanese Red	- - - -	*P. densiflora*
" Small-flowered	- - -	" *parviflora*

PINES VALUABLE FOR COVERING STERILE GROUND

Mugho	- - - -	*P. montana*, var. *Mughus*
Swiss Mountain	- - -	" "
Grey	- - - -	" *divaricata*
Pitch	- - - -	" *rigida*
Scrub	- - - -	" *Virginiana*
Foxtail	- - - -	" *aristata*

FOR SEASIDE PLANTING

Cluster - - - - -	*P. Pinaster*
Aleppo - - - - - -	" *Halepensis*
Pitch - - - - -	" *rigida*
Monterey - - - - -	" *radiata*

SLOW-GROWING HARDY PINES ADAPTED
TO SMALL GARDENS

Exotic

Korean - - - - -	*P. Koraiensis*
Macedonian - - - - -	" *Peuce*
Lace-bark - - - -	" *Bungeana*
Small-flowered - - -	" *parviflora*
Swiss Stone - - - -	" *Cembra*

Native

Nut - - - - -	*P. edulis*
Foxtail - - - -	" *Balfouriana*
Foxtail - - - -	" *aristata*
Rocky Mountain White - - -	" *flexilis*

57

CHAPTER VI : THE LARCHES

Family Coniferæ

Genus LARIX Adans.

Tall pyramidal trees, with few horizontal branches. *Leaves* linear, deciduous ; fascicled except on new shoots. *Flowers* solitary, monœcious, naked. *Fruit* annual, woody cones, solitary, erect and sessile on the twig. *Wood* hard, heavy, resinous.

KEY TO SPECIES

A. Cones less than 1 inch long, almost globular ; smooth ; leaves, 3-angled ; bracts not visible between scales.
(*L. Americana*) TAMARACK
AA. Cones more than 6 inches long, oblong, with prominent pointed bracts between scales.
B. Leaves 3-angled ; twigs downy at first.
(*L. occidentalis*) WESTERN LARCH
BB. Leaves 4-angled, blue-green ; twigs hairy.
(*L. Lyallii*) ALPINE LARCH

The distinction of the genus Larix is its deciduous habit. One other conifer sheds its leaves every autumn. The clustering of the leaves in fascicles on short lateral spurs is unique also. Only the terminal shoots bear scattered leaves.

Beside the three North American species there are six Old-World larches—all in the colder latitudes of the Northern Hemisphere, except a single Himalayan species. The native species are inferior to exotics in cultivation. The handsomest larch for lawns is *L. leptolepis*, Murr. (*L. Kœmpferi*, Sarg.), a Japanese species with pale blue-green, white-lined leaves. The common larch of Europe, *L. decidua*, Mill., is most frequently met with in cultivation here. It is a graceful, pyramidal tree, slender and supple limbed, with a fresh cover of feathery leaves every spring. In autumn the foliage turns yellow before it is shed. The Himalayan *L. Griffithi* is not hardy in the North. It is cultivated in its handsome pendulous forms.

58

Larches are cultivated as timber trees in Europe and to some extent in America. The European species is chosen for this purpose. Larch wood is very durable, heavy and hard. Rich in resin, yet not easily ignited. It does not splinter, and hence was preferred for the building of battleships before the day when steel came in to replace wood. Larch timbers built into the oldest of French castles are sound when the stones that support them are crumbling. It is believed that larch will outlast oak. The wood of *L. occidentalis* ranks higher than any other coniferous kind.

Larches are readily grown from seed and easily transplanted, even when quite large, if the work is done while the trees are dormant. They are admirable for windbreaks and shelter belts, to which uses they are put in the Middle West and along the coast in Massachusetts. They grow rapidly and profitably for posts, railroad ties and telegraph poles, as they are straight and free from large knots, being pruned by close contact with neighbours in the plantation rows.

In the fine arts larch wood has had its place. Raphael painted many of his earliest pictures on larch boards. Other painters of his time followed his example. Canvas had not then been generally adopted as a safe foundation for a painting. Old, dry larch wood from trees growing on the high Alps and Apennines looked almost transparent when polished. It was made into tables and cabinets of rare workmanship, and brought extravagant prices. From those superb larch forests it was not unusual to take out a ship's mast 120 feet high!

Minor products of larches are turpentine and an extract of tannin obtained from the European species.

Tamarack (*Larix Americana*, Michx.)—A slender, pyramidal tree, 50 to 60 feet high, with feeble horizontal branches, becoming pendulous. *Bark* thin, broken into reddish scales. *Wood* heavy, hard, light brown, strong, coarse grained, resinous, durable in wet soil. *Buds* small, globular, red, shining. *Leaves* soft, deciduous, fascicled on side spurs, scattered on terminal shoots; linear, triangular, $\frac{1}{4}$ to 1 inch long; autumn color, yellow. *Flowers:* monœcious, sessile, borne on short branchlets; pistillate rosy, ovate, with conspicuous finger-like points on bracts; staminate yellow, squat. *Fruit* small cones with concave, plain scales, bearing winged seeds; annual. *Pre-*

59

ferred habitat, cold swamps and northern slopes of mountains. *Distribution,* Newfoundland and Hudson Bay west across the Rocky Mountains ; south into Minnesota, Illinois, Indiana and Pennsylvania. *Uses :* Posts, telegraph poles, railroad ties and ships' timbers.

The tamarack loves the Northern mountain slopes and the cold swamps of Labrador and Canada and our Northern States. It is the bravest of all the conifers, standing erect, a pitiful miniature of its true self, on the very edge of the Arctic tundras, a line that no tree dares overstep. Its companions, the black spruce, Balm of Gilead and an Arctic willow, are prostrate at its feet. In American lawns trees 60 feet high are often seen. But compared with the European tree this one is not a horticultural success. The mark of its life struggle with adversity is on the species. Even seedlings coddled in nursery rows have sparse crowns of unsymmetrical growth. In rich soil and among luxuriant oaks and pines and thick-leaved maples the tamarack looks ragged and forlorn. It is homesick for the cold, wet soil and the bleak wind and the valiant company of its kinsmen. It is an artistic and an ethical mistake to set one of these trees by itself. Plantations of it are justifiable.

Mountain bogs too deep to measure are covered with tamarack. The fibrous roots were the Indian's thread ; tough and fine as a shoemaker's "waxed end," it sewed the canoe of birch, making a seam that scarcely needed the wax of the balsam to make it water tight. Hiawatha sang :

> "Give me of your roots, O Tamarack !
> Of your fibrous roots, O Larch Tree !
> My canoe to bind together
> So to bind the ends together
> That the water may not enter
> That the water may not wet me."

The flowers of the tamarack are not conspicuous, but they repay the one who looks for them. The yellow staminate clusters, like little powdery knobs, soon fall, but the pistillate ones, conical, with green bracts alternating with rosy scales, are beautiful along the twig against the lettuce green of the opening foliage clusters. Erect and with scales spread, they catch the flying pollen ; then close their scales and "hang their heads" throughout the summer. Under the rosy scales the seeds are

1 Winter bud   2 Flowering branch: A. Staminate flower; B. Pistillate flower   3 Fruit and leaves

THE AMERICAN LARCH (*Larix Americana*)

This conifer sheds its leaves in autumn. Cone flowers of two sorts come out of certain of the side buds; the staminate are knob-like, the pistillate borne on large scales. Other side buds produce crowded fascicles of leaves. The end shoots have leaves scattered along their whole length. The pistillate flower cones curve their stems so as to stand erect when pollen is flying. Then they turn down and close their scales all summer. In autumn they stand erect and loosen their scales, and the seeds are scattered

THE WHITE SPRUCE (*Picea Canadensis*)

Dark blue-green or pale blue foliage, leaves crowded on smooth twigs, cone slenderly cylindrical, 2 inches long, with thin, flexible, entire scales—these traits belong to this species. The white wood is now much in demand for making paper. The pale leaves and bark give the tree its name

THE BLACK SPRUCE (*Picea Mariana*)

This tree has pubescent twigs and spiny, blue-green foilage. The little oval cones, which become globose as their stiff scales spread, cling for years. There seems to be little justification for the word "black" in its name, for bark is greyish-brown, and the wood pale yellow. Yet a Northern bog clothed with acres of this growth is a sombre, monotonous stretch

growing. In autumn they wake up, turn themselves about (which seems quite unnecessary), and sitting quite erect on the twigs, part their brown scales, daring the wind to capture and carry off the winged seeds. There is plenty of time, for the ripe cones remain where they are until the second year.

Western Larch (*Larix occidentalis*, Nutt.)—A pyramidal tree, with naked trunk and sparse foliage at the top, 100 to 250 feet high. *Bark* cinnamon-red, broken into thick plates, with thin, scaly surface. *Wood* heavy, hard, strong, close grained, red, durable. *Buds* small, globose, brown, hoary. *Leaves* stiff, sharp, keeled below, triangular, pale green, turning yellow in autumn. *Flowers:* pistillate sessile, oblong; bracts needle pointed; staminate stalked, yellow, globose. *Fruits* large, oval cones; scales hoary at base; bract needle pointed, shorter than scale. *Preferred habitat,* low, wet soil, at 2,000 to 3,000 feet elevation. *Distribution,* southern British Columbia in Cascade Mountains to Columbia River; in Blue Mountains of Washington and Oregon; to western Montana. *Uses:* Best wood among conifers. Used for furniture and interior finish, railroad ties, fence posts.

The Western larch holds an enviable rank among American forest trees. It is counted superior to all other conifers in the value of its wood, which seems to have all good qualities. Its hardness, fine colour and brilliant polish commend it to the maker of furniture. As fence posts and railroad ties it lasts indefinitely, compared with other timber. Trees 6 feet in diameter and 200 feet high are quite common in this species. Of such mighty trunks a very small outer layer is sap wood.

For the first fifty years this larch is pyramidal, but thinly branched. From this age on the lower limbs die, and the tree at length presents a bare trunk with a mere wisp of a top. What wonder that growth is slow! One log 18 inches in diameter showed 267 rings. In its fiftieth year it was but 9 inches in diameter. The last inch of wood was eighty years in forming. No other tree has so inconsiderable a foliage mass to maintain so large a body.

The brown gum that exudes from wounds in the bark of this tree seems not to be resinous, though it smells like turpentine. It is sweet and resembles dextrine. As dextrine is a soluble form of starch, the Indians find this wax a very nutritious article of food.

The Western larch shows little merit as an ornamental tree on the eastern side of the continent. In Europe it does better, and is planted for timber as well as for ornament. I cannot grieve that this magnificent wild tree scorns to adapt itself, or even its seedlings, to the compass of a sunny suburban lawn in the East. People who truly wish to know it must go to the wild forest parks we own in the great Northwest. There waits for us with infinite patience (and an indifference quite as large), the grandest larch tree in the world!

The **Alpine Larch** (*Larix Lyallii*, Parl.) is a slender tree of the high tablelands of the Northwest, balancing itself on rocky ledges, and seeming to choose the most exposed and forbidding situations. It climbs to the very limit of tree growth, and presents a more irregular form than either of its relatives. The tough limbs divide at intervals, throwing out several branches at the same point. These differ in strength and size. The twigs are covered with white, hairy fuzz which is shed at the end of the second winter. The bark of the twigs then darkens for a period of several years and becomes almost black. On the trunk the bark is reddish and loosely scaly. The leaves are stiff and sharp, blue-green and distinctly 4-angled. The cones have their scales far surpassed in length by the tip of the bract. The hairiness of the cones is conspicuous.

The Alpine larch never grows below an altitude of 4,000 feet. It ranges from Montana west to the coast and north into the British possessions.

CHAPTER VII: THE SPRUCES

Family Coniferæ

Genus PICEA, Link.

PYRAMIDAL cone-bearing evergreens, with tall, tapering trunks and slender horizontal branches ending in stout twigs. *Roots* long, tough, fibrous. *Leaves* 4-angled, stiff, pointed, solitary, spirally arranged, each set on a prominent, woody projection. *Flowers* monœcious, solitary, in conical aments on new shoots. *Fruits* pendant, woody, annual cones. *Wood* soft, straight grained, valuable.

KEY TO SPECIES

A. Leaves distinctly 4-angled.
   B. Branchlets pubescent.
      C. Leaves blue-green, short.
         D. Cones ovate, $\frac{1}{2}$ to $1\frac{1}{2}$ inches long, persistent,
            foliage spiny.   (*Picea Mariana*) BLACK SPRUCE
        DD. Cones oblong, 1 to 3 inches long, deciduous;
            foliage soft and flexible.
                (*Picea Engelmanni*) ENGELMANN SPRUCE
      CC. Leaves yellow-green, spiny, cones 1 to $2\frac{1}{2}$ inches
         long, early deciduous. (*Picea rubens*) RED SPRUCE
   BB. Branchlets smooth ; leaves spiny, incurving, blue-
      green.
      C. Cones slender; scales entire, flexible, blunt; leaves
         strong smelling, $\frac{1}{2}$ to $\frac{3}{4}$ inch long.
                (*Picea Canadensis*) WHITE SPRUCE
      CC. Cones stout, scales, ridged, pointed; leaves $\frac{1}{2}$ to
         $1\frac{1}{4}$ inches long.
           (*Picea Parryana*) COLORADO BLUE SPRUCE
AA. Leaves more or less flattened; cones 2 to 5 inches long.
   B. Branchlets pubescent, pendulous; leaves blunt; cone
      scales entire, rounded.
           (*Picea Breweriana*) WEEPING SPRUCE
   BB. Branchlets smooth, erect; leaves pointed;.cone scales
      toothed, pointed.   (*Picea Sitchensis*) SITKA SPRUCE

63

THE BLUE SPRUCE (*Picea Parryana*)

This is the Colorado evergreen, whose blue or silvery foliage and the vigour and perfect symmetry of its early years have made it one of the familiar evergreens planted in the Eastern states. Its horticultural value quite dwarfs its significance as a lumber tree

Black as its name is, the wood is almost white, and the paper needs little or no bleaching.

The **Engelmann Spruce** (*P. Engelmanni*, Engelm.) is the white spruce of the Rocky Mountains and the Cascade range in Washington and Oregon. It crowns the lower and higher peaks, climbing to altitudes between one and two miles above the level of the sea. In the rocky sides of glacier-polished ravines these hardy trees find foothold, and set their spires like serried ranks of spearsmen to cover the bare cliffs. Snow loads them down for many months of the year ; they can survive that, but their destruction comes when a fire sweeps over them, killing all it touches, for the cambium of these trees is protected by a very thin bark. The seeds and seedlings go. There is no reproduction of forests thus destroyed. They give way to the lodgepole pine and other more fortunate species.

The Engelmann spruce is planted in the Eastern States, where it thrives. The disagreeable odour of the leaves counts against it. But the finest trees cannot be seen unless a journey be taken by the northernmost route to the Canadian Rocky Mountains, where snows protect the forests from devastating fires, and these spruce trees grow to 150 feet high, with diameters of 4 or 5 feet. In late spring the blue-green foliage is jewelled with the flowers, purple and scarlet. In autumn the showy cones, with their shining brown, pointed scales hang out on the highest twigs and fling down their black, winged seeds. Here is a vastly different tree from the tame little seedling that began life in a nursery row.

The lumber value of the Engelmann spruce is high. It is used for general building purposes, for fuel and charcoal. The bark is sometimes used in tanning.

The **Red Spruce** (*P. rubens*, Sarg.) is the most cheerful of our Eastern species, because its foliage is yellowish green and shining, the others blue-green. The colour in this tree's name is derived from the wood, so the lumberman gave it, without doubt. The slender, downy twigs are also bright red during their first winter, and there is a distinct tinge of red in the tree's brown bark. The flowers are rich purple and the cones glossy reddish brown. It wears its colour in plain sight the year round.

This tree forms considerable forests from Newfoundland through New England, and follows the Alleghany Mountains

65

into North Carolina. It has the spruce habit, but it rarely sacrifices its lower limbs even when crowded. In height these trees range from 75 to 100 feet, with trunks 2 to 3 feet in diameter. The wood is used for lumber and paper pulp. It is peculiarly adapted for sounding boards of musical instruments, and makes excellent flooring. It is occasionally cultivated, but other species are usually preferred. Its twigs are boiled to make spruce beer.

White Spruce (*Picea Canadensis*, B. S. & P.)—Broadly pyramidal tree, 60 to 150 feet high, with stout branches, smooth twigs and bad-smelling foliage. *Bark* greyish brown, breaking into scaly plates. *Wood* light, soft, yellow, brittle. *Buds* ovate, scaly. *Leaves* spread on upper side of twig, bluish, sharp, hoary when young, ½ to ¾ inch long. *Flowers* both kinds cone-like, pale red, turning yellow. *Fruit* oblong-cylindrical, stalked cones, blunt ; scales blunt or notched at broad apex, shiny, thin, falling soon after seeds ripen. *Preferred habitat*, rocky slopes, banks of rivers or lakes. *Distribution*, Labrador to Bering Strait ; south to Montana, northern Dakota, Michigan and Wisconsin, New York and New England. *Uses :* Lumber for building and interior finishing, and for paper pulp. Tree planted for ornament and shade. Variety *cærulea* most common in cultivation.

The pale bark and pea-green foliage of the white spruce enable one to account for its name without difficulty and to identify it in the woods. The whitish wood is not distinctly paler than that of the black spruce. The ill-smelling foliage and the smooth twigs better distinguish it, and the cones, which are twice as long as the black spruce's. They are shed almost as soon as they open, a tree habit that keeps the branches clean and thrifty in appearance.

White spruce is the pulp manufacturer's delight. He owns thousands of acres of it. As lumber the wood is used only in Alaska and Canada in lieu of better kinds. The inferiority of spruce lumber has saved it for the comparatively new enterprise of pulp manufacture.

Blue Spruce (*Picea Parryana*, Sarg.)—Handsome tree, 80 to 125 feet high, broadly pyramidal ; branches rigid, horizontal, in remote whorls. *Bark* grey, thick, broken into rounded, scaly ridges ; on young trees often reddish, in oblong plates. *Wood* light, fine grained, soft, weak, pale. *Buds* stout, blunt,

66

large, with reflexed scales. *Leaves* dull blue-green to silvery white, variable ; rigid, stout, curving, horny pointed, striped on both sides with white, ¾ to 1⅛ inches long, shorter on fruiting twigs. *Flowers:* staminate reddish yellow ; pistillate green, the scales square at end, and bracts pointed. *Fruit,* stalked cones, pendant on upper limbs, 2 to 3 inches long, oblong, brown, shining ; scales flat, narrowing to finger-like blunt point ; seeds winged. *Preferred habitat,* elevation 6,000 to 10,000 feet, banks of streams. *Distribution,* Colorado, Utah and Wyoming. *Uses :* Ornamental tree planted in Europe and United States. Hardy, and grows well in Middle West ; conspicuous in the East.

We have come to feel well acquainted with the blue spruce of Colorado through the beautiful blue or silver-leaved specimen trees so common on lawns everywhere we go. It is a cool, crisp-looking tree, of perfect symmetry, the whorls of branches well apart, insuring the full development of leaves and branchlets. It is a disappointment to its owner that the growing tree loses at length its lower limbs and the symmetry of its top. Yet this is a far-off event, and there are years of satisfaction ahead for the buyer of a handsome little blue spruce for his garden. Shrubbery can be tucked in around the tree when it begins to age, and other trees so placed as to hide its shortcomings.

Weeping Spruce (*Picea Breweriana,* Wats.)—Tree 75 to 125 feet high, with swollen base and tapering shaft; branches drooping and crowded, to the ground; twigs remarkably long and slender. *Bark* brick red, thin, scaly. *Wood* soft, close grained, satiny, pale brown, heaviest of native spruces. *Buds* conical, small, scaly, brown. *Leaves* flattened on the upper side only, blunt, pale above, dark green and lustrous beneath, ¾ to 1¼ inches long. *Flowers :* staminate rich purple ; pistillate oblong; scales broad, rounded, turning out at edge, with cut-toothed bract under each. *Fruit* slender cones, 2 to 4 inches long, tapering, stalked, purple turning to orange-brown, opening in autumn, but hanging a year empty; scales broad, entire, thin, turning backward; seeds winged. *Preferred habitat,* dry ridges on mountains near timber line. *Distribution,* elevation 4,000 to 7,000 feet, California and Oregon. In isolated groves in coast ranges.

It is somewhat embarrassing to the hard-working horticulturist in the East to be asked his opinion of the weeping spruce.

67

He regards it as one of the most distinct of the spruces, admirable in habit and beautiful in foliage—an ideal tree for ornamental planting—but he cannot make it grow! His most careful efforts have brought only failure. A tree that belongs to "dry mountain ridges and peaks near the timber line" has a good excuse for languishing in gardens on the wrong side of the continent. And such a range puts the species out of reach of lumbermen for a decade or two yet. The *uses* of this tree must be put down without reference to man's ineffectual yearnings to claim it for his own. It fulfils Nature's plan, lifting its graceful spire into the clouds and hanging out its purple flowers where there is no human eye to see.

Tideland Spruce, Sitka Spruce (*Picea Sitchensis*, Carr.)— Tree with tapering trunk and enlarged base, 100 to 200 feet high, with broadly pyramidal head of drooping branches. *Bark* reddish brown, thin, scaly. *Wood* light, soft, straight grained, satiny, light reddish brown. *Buds* lustrous, scaly, conical, $\frac{1}{4}$ to $\frac{1}{2}$ inch long. *Leaves* silvery white above, green beneath, $\frac{1}{2}$ to 1 inch long, flattened, twisted, pointed, horny tipped, all around the twig. *Flowers:* staminate on side twigs, abundant, dark red, conical, $\frac{3}{4}$ to $1\frac{1}{2}$ inches long; pistillate on terminal twigs of upper branches, smaller, oblong. *Cones* annual, stalked, pendant, 3 to 5 inches long, with elongated scales toothed at tips, fall in winter. *Preferred habitat*, moist, sandy soil; swamps. *Distribution*, coast region, Alaska to Cape Mendocino in California. *Uses:* Important lumber for interior woodwork in buildings, boat building, woodenwares, cooperage and fencing. Ornamental tree in Europe, and in the warmer parts of the eastern United States. Most important lumber in Alaska. Used for fuel, construction of buildings, boats, and fencing, wooden utensils and boxing.

The swamps of the tidewater regions of the Northwest, the rocky slopes (if well watered) of the Alaskan ranges of mountains facing the sea, are clothed with forests of this remarkable tree. Like the bald cypress of the Southeast and the pumpkin ash of the valley of the Arkansas, this lover of swamps is buttressed and much enlarged at its base. The indomitable hardihood of the species is shown where it climbs from sea level to an altitude of 3,000 feet, and follows the coast to the northernmost point reached by any conifer. The tree dwindles to a starveling shrub when the limits of its range are reached, but in the coast regions of Oregon and Washington it is one of the largest and most beautiful of the Western conifers. The graceful sweep of its wide-spreading lower limbs gives a constant and delightful play of light and shadow, owing to the lustrous sheen on the upper sides of the leaves.

In spite of all efforts to grow it in the East, it seems to suffer from summer heat and drought and winter cold. It grows in Boston if protected, but needs a great deal of coddling there.

Genus PSEUDOTSUGA, Carr.

Pyramidal trees with thick bark and hard, strong, durable wood. *Leaves* linear, flat, spreading at right angles from the twig; evergreen. *Flowers* solitary, cone-like, bright coloured. *Fruit* heavy, drooping annual cones, with thin unarmed scales.

KEY TO SPECIES

A. Leaves blunt, dark green; cones small, with long bracts.
   (*P. mucronata*) DOUGLAS SPRUCE
AA. Leaves sharp, blue-grey, cones large, with shorter bracts.
   (*P. macrocarpa*) BIG CONE SPRUCE

The genus Pseudotsuga stands intermediate between the hemlocks and firs, but the common name, as well as family traits, link it with the spruces, hence I have joined it to Picea under the common name spruce. The genus has two representatives in America and one in Japan. The name is a startling combination of the Japanese word *Tsuga* with a Greek prefix.

Douglas Spruce, Red Fir (*Pseudotsuga mucronata*, Sudw.) —Pyramidal or flat-topped tree, 150 to 250 feet high, with long, bare trunk in forest; in the open, a broad-based pyramid. *Branches* slender, crowded, long, drooping. *Spray* finely divided. *Bark* thick, deeply furrowed, with rounded irregular ridges coated with red scales. *Wood* pale red or yellow, durable in water and soil; variable in quality, usually tough and hard. *Buds* scaly, acute. *Leaves* straight, linear, blunt at apex, 1 to 1½ inches long, yellowish or bluish green, shed in eighth year. *Flowers* cone-like, staminate orange-red, pistillate red. *Fruit* a long-stemmed cone, 2 to 4 inches long, drooping, scales thin, with entire margins;

bracts ending in recurved, whip-like points. *Preferred habitat,* moist soil of coast plain. *Distribution,* Rocky Mountains from British America into Mexico; west to Pacific coast, except in the Great Basin (between Wasatch and Sierra Nevada Mountains). *Uses:* Valuable lumber tree for shipbuilding, piles, posts and railroad ties. Bark used to some extent for tanning.

He who would see for himself the most magnificent forests this continent holds to-day must go to the redwoods in California. When these groves have awed him with the tremendous bulk of timber in board feet they can yield in a single acre, let him move up the coast to where the moist Japan current breathes upon the evergreen forests of the Cascade's western slope. There are giant cedars and firs and hemlocks; and dominating all of them is the Douglas spruce.

"It is not only a large tree, the tallest in America next to the redwood, but a very beautiful one with bright green, drooping foliage, handsome pendant cones, and a shaft, exquisitely straight and round and regular."

The trees make a very even growth and stand together as closely as the stalks in a well-tilled field of grain. Excluding other kinds, these trees stand with their heads together, making the forest dark as night below. Far up the Alaskan coast the Douglas spruce extends, and eastward across mountain ranges, where it mingles with yellow pines in sunny, open forests, where the trees have opportunity to show the grace of their pendant limbs and the beauty of their red cone flowers and the ruddy cones adorned with pale green bracts. A small cone it is for so large a tree, yet one to remember for its beauty.

The Douglas spruce is known as "Oregon pine" in the lumber markets of the coast. The Puget Sound region furnishes spars of it to every great shipyard in the world. They are used as piles in wharves in Western harbours. Shipbuilders, bridge-builders—everybody who needs heavy timbers of great durability, toughness and hardness—desire this kind if it can be had. The best grades of it are stronger than the wood of any other large conifer in America. Its faults for general lumber purposes are its hardness and its tendency to warp in boards.

The Douglas spruce as seen in nurseries is the quickest-growing evergreen of all. Immense quantities of seed are sent to Europe, where the tree is grown both for ornament and for timber. The seed produces a large percentage of vigorous seedlings, and they transplant well. In the eastern and northern parts of the United States the trees do well from seed gathered in the Rocky Mountains. Failures in seedlings imported from European nurseries are traceable to the fact that seeds came from the Pacific coast plain, and the seedlings therefore are not hardy in the more rigorous climate of the East and North. In the seeds furnished by high mountain trees this difficulty is overcome. Even in the droughty regions of Kansas and Nebraska these trees planted in sheltered situations and in clumps grow into trees of exceeding beauty. Exposed in windbreaks the foliage is damaged, the trees lose their " leaders," and acquire bad shapes thereafter.

Big-Cone Spruce (*Pseudotsuga macrocarpa*, Mayr.)—A broadly pyramidal tree, 40 to 80 feet high, with stout trunk, pendulous lower limbs, and erect upper cones. Branchlets slender. *Bark* scaly, thick, reddish brown, furrowed, with rounded ridges. *Wood* brown, hard, heavy, strong, not durable. *Buds* ovate, small, scaly. *Leaves* linear, sharp pointed, spreading or 2-ranked, dark bluish grey, $\frac{3}{4}$ to $1\frac{1}{2}$ inches long. *Flowers* cone-like, staminate yellow in shining, scaly involucre; pistillate green tinged with red. *Fruit* usually on upper branches, 4 to 7 inches long, oblong-cylindrical, scales often 2 inches across, thin, entire; bracts scarcely as long as scales. *Preferred habitat*, mountain slopes. *Distribution*, southern California, in San Bernardino Mountains, at altitude of 3,000 to 5,000 feet. *Uses:* Wood used for fuel; sparingly for lumber.

71

CHAPTER VIII: THE HEMLOCKS

Genus TSUGA, Carr.

Tall, graceful trees of pyramidal form, with flexible tip shoots and pendulous, much-divided horizontal limbs. *Leaves* evergreen, petioled, flat and 2-ranked (except one). *Flowers* monœcious, solitary, in early spring. *Fruit* annual cones, small and oval (except one), with thin, entire scales. *Wood* soft, pale, cross-grained, stiff.

KEY TO SPECIES

A. Leaves flat, 2-ranked, pale beneath; cones about 1 inch long, oval.
  B. Cones stalked.
    C. Scales as wide as long, not flaring at maturity.
                    (*T. Canadensis*) HEMLOCK
    CC. Scales longer than wide, flaring at maturity.
                    (*T. Caroliniana*) CAROLINA HEMLOCK
  BB. Cones sessile, scales constricted in middle.
                    (*T. heterophylla*) WESTERN HEMLOCK
AA. Leaves 3-angled, whorled, pale blue-green; cones 2 to 3 inches long, oblong-cylindrical.
                    (*T. Mertensiana*) MOUNTAIN HEMLOCK

Hemlocks are distinctly graceful and symmetrical trees. Japan has two native species, the Himalayas one, our Eastern States one, the Western States three—seven in all—and *Tsuga* is the Japanese name for hemlock. The prostrate, shrubby "ground hemlock," familiar to many of us who have eaten its aromatic scarlet berry, is not a hemlock but a yew. The hemlock that Socrates drank was the deadly infusion of an herb, *Conium maculatum*, related to our wild carrot.

The best character by which to recognise the hemlocks is the tiny petiole of the leaf. No other cone bearer has leaf stalks. Of our native species, all have white lines on the under side of each leaf; the mountain hemlock has them above and below. The

72

Leaves and winter buds (some leaves cut away to show the buds)

THE DOUGLAS SPRUCE (*Pseudotsuga mucronata*)

The straight, blue-green leaves stand out at a wide angle with the twig. They persist for eight years, so the branches are leafy far into the crown. The bark becomes a foot thick, and woodpeckers hide acorns in it. The wood is light coloured, with white sap wood

B. C. Staminate flowers in two stages

THE HEMLOCK (*Tsuga Canadensis*)

This is the only conifer whose leaves are provided with petioles. The flat, blunt blades, have narrow lines of white beneath. The pistillate flowers are erect on the tips of twigs. The staminate flowers are many in the axils of leaves. Each is a yellow ball made up of globular anthers. The cones are purplish and small. Hemlock bark and wood are both important. Hemlock woods are sombre, but wonderfully lightened when seen from below. The leafy spray is light and graceful

first three species have leaves 2-ranked and flat and cones under an inch in length; the fourth has leaves 3-angled, whorled on the twigs, and cones 2 to 3 inches long. Cones are pendant, and thin scaled in all the species, and are borne annually.

Hemlocks are important ornamental trees. They come readily from seed, if shaded, and transplant safely, owing to their dense fibrous root system. They submit to severe pruning of roots or tops. They are not particular in regard to soil, if only it be moist. The two Japanese species are propagated from cuttings, or are grafted on our Eastern hemlock. All hemlocks have bark rich in tannin. The west American species are all large trees, except at high altitudes.

Hemlock (*Tsuga Canadensis*, Carr.)—A broadly pyramidal tree, 60 to 100 feet high, with tapering leading shoot and pendulous horizontal limbs. *Bark* cinnamon red to grey, thin, furrowed, scaly. *Wood* light, soft, coarse, cross-grained, not durable. *Buds* small, obtuse. *Leaves* flat, blunt, pale beneath, dark, shining above, on short petioles jointed to projecting bases, 2-ranked, shed in third year. *Flowers* in May, monœcious, solitary; pistillate terminal on short shoots. *Fruit* small, annual cones, falling in spring, oval, thin scaled, red-brown, turning to grey. *Preferred habitat*, rocky uplands near streams. *Distribution*, Nova Scotia to southern Michigan, central Wisconsin and Minnesota; southward to Delaware, and along Appalachian Mountains to Alabama. *Uses:* Wood, in building and for railroad ties; bark, in dyeing and in tanning leather. Cultivated as an ornamental tree and hedge plant.

"Hemlock Hill" in the Arnold Arboretum is a shrine at which the true tree-loving Bostonian worships at least once a year. It is a remnant of the forest primeval that clothes a steep promontory just inside one of the gates. In winter the hemlocks look black in contrast with the snow that hides the paths and smothers the brook into silence. It is awesome—this solitude of winter on the hill. But in summer all is different. The severity of its winter aspect is gone. Every twig waves in welcome a yellow-green plume, the new growth of the year, and up the hillside climb the well-remembered paths. The brook goes singing along between borders of laurel and rhododendron. The gloom of the hemlocks is wonderfully lightened, when one is actually under them, by the pale linings of the individual leaves. Just two parallel lines

73

of white on each narrow blade, but the aggregate makes a mighty difference in the atmosphere of the place.

Throughout New England one finds generous appreciation of this native hemlock. The slender terminal shoot, "the leader," lifted into the sky is a weather vane that never gets out of order. Where hemlocks of considerable size are scattered among pines or other trees, they are guideposts to the "timber cruiser" or the hunter in trackless woods. Each treetop has its own individuality —the scars of storms outridden, or other modifying influences at work.

The specimens of hemlock to be seen in parks and on private grounds exhibit the fitness of this species for ornamental planting. The symmetry and grace of the "dark green layers of shade," spreading into intricate sprays of remarkable delicacy, are familiar in forest and lawn. The pale bloom on the under sides of the leaves is punctuated by the little violet cones, pendant from every spray. There are many horticultural forms of this species, but, to my mind, none are as handsome as the wild species.

In winter the red squirrel finds a stable base of supplies in every fruitful hemlock tree. The litter of cone scales on the snow will convince any doubter, if, indeed, the squirrel does not himself appear and scold the intruder.

In hedges the young trees are thrifty, and even the shears cannot subdue the grace that renews every spring the delicate, flexible new shoots. They seem more like wavering tendrils of a vine than branches of a sturdy conifer.

The seeds of hemlock are slow to germinate on burned-over ground, but in the leaf mould, overshadowed by larger trees, they start in great numbers. For four or five years they average scarcely an inch a year, but they produce a good root system. After this they rapidly mount upward to independence. They supply a valuable protective cover for seedling white pines. The two species grow together often in large forests. Canada offers the best soil and climate for hemlock. It requires cool air with rich, loamy soil, moist but well drained. It is found plentifully in our Northern and Eastern States, and follows the mountains to Alabama.

Hemlock wood is coarse and splintery, likely to be cross-grained and full of knots. It warps in seasoning, and wears rough; moreover, it is brittle and weak. It has two cardinal virtues that adapt it for railroad ties and the large beams used in the frames of houses and barns. Hemlock timbers are stiff, and the wood has a firm grip on nails and spikes. The wood never loosens its hold upon the nail, nor does it split in nailing. Hemlock is used for the outside of cheap buildings, but it finds its greatest usefulness as the unseen props of a house, its faults covered up by woods of more uniform and attractive appearance.

The bark of hemlock abounds in tannin, which makes it a standard tan bark. It is not uncommon to see young hemlock woods felled and stripped for the bark alone. The waste of the wood is very bad forestry, but as hemlock is poor fuel, and ugly to saw and split, sometimes cordwood costs more to cut and haul than it brings in market. If the trees were left to attain proper age for mill stuff, the lumber would be salable, and there would be a much larger crop of bark.

The logs are cut for tan bark only in the summer. The bark "slips" from May until August. After that, peeling is impossible. The logs are girdled every four feet from the butt well up into the tops. Two or three cuts are made at equal distances apart, lengthwise of the trunk. This makes of each four-foot cylinder of bark two or three rectangular sheets, easily removed with a special bark-peeling tool. The sheets are stacked on end to dry, and are later laid in solid four-foot piles to be measured by the cord. The hemlock bark is usually mixed with some oak bark at the tanneries. A side of sole leather tanned with hemlock alone is a brighter red than is desired. The oak darkens it. Dye works consume some hemlock bark in making certain shades of brown.

Oil of hemlock is distilled from the leaves. "Canada pitch," formerly much used as a drug, is extracted from leaves and knots. In the practice of the Indians, the bark of young hemlocks, boiled and pounded to a paste, made a poultice for sores and wounds. Josselyn noted also: "The turpentine thereof is singularly good to heal wounds and to draw out the malice of any Ach, rubbing the place therewith." The antiseptic action of the oil and resin was recognised then as now.

The **Carolina Hemlock** (*Tsuga Caroliniana*, Engelm.) occurs most abundantly about the headwaters of the Savannah River in South Carolina. It grows on the mountains from Virginia into Georgia, and was long confused with the common

Northern hemlock by botanists and other observers. It has found favour with landscape gardeners, because it is more graceful though more compact than *T. Canadensis*. Its leaves are longer, darker green above, and a more pronounced white underneath. It rarely grows over 70 feet high, but has a better head when old than its Northern relative. It is a hardy, handsome tree in New England parks, and its popularity is growing.

Western Hemlock (*Tsuga heterophylla*, Sarg.)—Noble pyramidal tree, 100 to 200 feet high, 6 to 10 feet in diameter, with drooping, horizontal branches and feathery tip. *Bark* reddish brown, with broad, scaly, interrupted ridges and shallow fissures. *Wood* tough, durable, hard, light, strong, brown. *Buds* brown, ovate, small. *Leaves* grooved on top, lustrous, pale below, rounded at tip; petioles slender. *Flowers :* monœcious, terminal, solitary; staminate yellow; pistillate purple. *Fruit* oval, pointed cones 1 inch long; scales often constricted in the middle, broad, thin. *Preferred habitat*, moist valleys and uplands from tidewater to 6,000 feet elevation. *Distribution*, southeastern Alaska to Cape Mendocino in California; east to Montana and Idaho. *Uses:* Wood used chiefly in building; bark for tanning. Indians eat a cake made from the inner bark. Successfully used for ornamental planting in Europe. Not hardy in our Eastern States.

This greatest of all the hemlocks dominates the magnificent forests of the Pacific coast plain, in size as well as in numbers. It extends east into Idaho and Montana, and north into British Columbia. The tideland spruce is its companion in the lowlands. Superb trees are found on the mountains at an altitude of 6,000 feet, but only in moist situations. On dry, high ridges, the tree is stunted. But in the rich river valleys, with the breath of the Japan current to make the air humid, this hemlock is a giant— handsome, graceful, the delight of the artist and the lumberman; the most superb and the most useful of the hemlocks.

The root system of this tree is remarkably copious and aggressive. Mosses often a foot in thickness and saturated with moisture clothe the fallen trunks and other rubbish in those deep forests in the neighbourhood of Vancouver. The light seeds of the hemlocks often germinate on some elevated arm of a giant tree long dead. Such a mistake will first be discovered by the roots which go down until they anchor the tree in the earth. The dead trunk rots away, and the growing tree stands on stilts of its own sturdy roots, as confident and thrifty as any of its neighbours.

The little cones of the Western hemlock have scales like scallop shells, marked with radiating lines. This is before they loosen. Afterward each scale shows a narrow neck behind this "shell," and a long blade extending backward.

This tree has the strongest and most durable wood of all the hemlocks. It is a staple commercial lumber on the coast, lumber authorities claiming that it is harder, heavier and otherwise superior to the Eastern hemlock.

Mountain Hemlock (*Tsuga Mertensiana*, Sarg.)—A broad, open pyramidal tree, 75 to 100 feet high, with much-branched, often prostrate limbs. *Bark* cinnamon red, furrowed, scaly. *Wood* light, soft, brownish red, close grained, weak. *Buds* brown, small, pointed. *Leaves* not 2-ranked, rounded below, flat, often grooved above, petioles set on prominent bases, colour, blue-green. *Flowers :* staminate blue, pendant on stalk; pistillate erect, with purplish or yellow bracts. *Fruit* oblong cones 1 to 3 inches long, borne on upper branches; scales broad, entire, striate, yellow or purple, turning out and back at maturity. *Preferred habitat*, high, rocky ridges in exposed situations. *Distribution*, southeastern Alaska to British Columbia; south to central California, Montana and Idaho. *Uses:* Wood occasionally used in building and bark in tanning.

This hemlock, which has been variously called a spruce, a fir and a pine by botanical explorers, is not likely to be exterminated by lumber companies, for it grows in inaccessible mountain fastnesses, and battles with storms to the very timber line. "Between 5,000 and 7,000 feet above the sea on ridges and along the margins of alpine meadows in groves of exquisite beauty, and pushing the advance guard of the forest to the edge of living glaciers"—thus Sargent describes the habitat of the tree which he considers "the loveliest cone-bearing tree of the American forest."

During the larger half of each year the mountain hemlocks are buried in snow, their tough limbs cramped beneath their burden; but with summer comes freedom, and these limbs are flung out again with singular grace to brave the lashing of the winds. A tall tree in the humid lowlands, the trunk diminishes with the ascent of the mountains. At an altitude of almost

10,000 feet the treetop rests upon the ground, a flattened mass of graceful limbs, the trunk practically eliminated by natural selection.

John Muir, describing the forests of the Yosemite Park, tells how the young trees of the lower levels receive the light burden of the first snow in the early autumn, and gradually bending under the load left by succeeding storms, at length form graceful arches, and are buried from sight for five or six months. He has ridden for miles over a smooth snow bank that covered in this fashion trees 40 feet high. They return to their normal position, unharmed, when the snow goes off.

The blue-green foliage, the whorled leaf arrangement, the triangular leaf itself, pencilled with white on all sides, and the large cones—all set this hemlock in a class by itself. The spray, exceedingly beautiful, even for a hemlock, bears flowers that are unusual in their rich colouring. The pistillate blossoms are royal purple; the staminate, blue as forget-me-nots—"of so pure a tone that the best azure of the high sky seems to be condensed in them."—*Muir*.

Seeds of this alpine hemlock planted in England and in our Eastern States grow slowly, and show none of the grace and vigour of the wild sapling trees. It is the old story of the hardy mountaineer, languishing in luxury, dying of homesickness for the life of abstinence and struggle to which its race is born.

CHAPTER IX: THE FIRS

Genus ABIES, Link.

TREES of pyramidal habit with wide-spreading horizontal limbs bearing thick foliage masses. *Wood* weak, coarse grained. *Bark* smooth until quite old, pale, thin and blistered with over-flowing resin vescicles; later, deeply and irregularly furrowed. *Leaves* usually flat, blunt, 2-ranked, persistent for 8 to 10 years, leaving circular scars. *Flowers* in axillary, scaly cones, pistillate erect on upper branches; staminate on under side of branches lower down on the tree. *Fruit* annual, erect cones whose scales fall off at maturity; seed resinous.

KEY TO SPECIES

A. Leaves flat and grooved down the middle.
  B. Colour of leaves dark green, shining, with pale linings.
    C. Scales concealing the bracts of the cones.
      D. Cones purple.
        E. Leaves straight, 2-ranked, not crowded; bark smooth, brown.
          (*A. balsamea*) BALSAM FIR
        EE. Leaves curved, erect on twigs, crowded; bark rough, grey. (*A. amabilis*) WHITE FIR
      DD. Cones green; leaves about 2 inches long.
          (*A. grandis*) WHITE FIR
    CC. Scales not concealing the pale green, reflexed bracts of the purple cones. (*A. Fraseri*) BALSAM FIR
  BB. Colour of leaves pale blue-green.
    C. Cones purple. (*A. lasiocarpa*) BALSAM FIR
    CC. Cones purple, green or yellow.
      D. Bracts of cone scales concealed; leaves uniformly glaucous. (*A. concolor*) WHITE FIR
      DD. Bracts of cone scales extending into long, whip-like projections; leaves yellow-green, pale below. (*A. venusta*) SILVER FIR
AA. Leaves mostly 4-angled, thick, blue-green; cones purple.
  B. Cone scales covered by pale green, reflexed bracts.
      (*A. nobilis*) RED FIR
  BB. Cone scales covering bracts. (*A. magnifica*) RED FIR

Twenty-five species of Abies are widely distributed over the Northern Hemisphere, including the northern highlands of Africa. Nordmann's fir (*A. Nordmanniana*) has come from the Caucasus into extensive cultivation in our Eastern and Northern States. It is supplemented by four European and two Japanese species of recognised merit for ornamental planting. The beauty of our native firs has been pointed out in the names botanists gave them. But they do not thrive, as a rule, in cultivation. For the lawn, we wisely choose exotic species.

Balsam Fir (*Abies balsamea*, Mill.)—A broad, pyramidal tree, 50 to 60 feet high, with slender pubescent branchlets. *Bark* brown, thin, broken into scaly plates with dried balsam in white blisters. *Wood* soft, weak, coarse, brown with yellow streaks, not durable. *Leaves* blunt, dark green, lustrous above, with pale linings, $\frac{1}{2}$ to $1\frac{1}{2}$ inches long, spreading in 2-ranked order. *Flowers* axillary, staminate, yellow shaded to purplish; pistillate purple. *Fruit* erect, rich purple, oblong-cylindrical, 2 to 4 inches long, blunt at ends; scales broad, entire, closely overlapping. *Preferred habitat*, swamps or hilly slopes. *Distribution*, Labrador through Canada and New England, to Minnesota; south along mountains to southwestern Virginia. *Uses:* Wood used for box material; bark furnishes oil and Canada balsam, used in medicine and in the arts. Fresh leaves cut for balsam pillows.

In the North Woods the hunter cuts the fragrant boughs of the fir balsam to make his bed, and the ladies of every camping party industriously shear balsam twigs in order to fill sofa pillows later with the leaves. The native finds it profitable to collect the limpid balsam by draining the white resin blisters that occur plentifully on the smooth bark of young trees, and on the limbs of older ones. Wounding the tree produces increased flow. Whole families are often employed in this enterprise. The resin thus obtained is the "Canada balsam" employed in every laboratory for the mounting of microscopic specimens. It is used also in the practise of medicine and in other useful arts. "Oil of fir" is also obtained from the bark.

The erect cones of this tree distinguish it from the spruces with which it grows, and the hemlocks whose leaves are also pale beneath and 2-ranked in arrangement. Balsam fir leaves are blunt and stemless. Hemlock leaves have minute petioles.

The cultivation of balsam fir has been rather stupidly con-

THE BALSAM FIR (*Abies balsamea*)

Blunt, flat leaves, pale beneath and 2-ranked on the twig, characterise this species. On the old branches the leaves are more sparse and scattered. The oblong cones are erect on the stem. The bark of young trunks and branches are marked by pockets which discharge clear balsam when tapped

THE BALSAM FIR (*Abies balsamea*)

The leaves persist for eight years. Hence the twigs are covered. The blunt leaves are 2-ranked by the twisting of their bases. The lower figure shows leaves all around the twigs. It is so on fertile shoots. This picture also shows young, leafy shoots coming out below. A pistillate cone-flower is held erect

tinued in the Northeastern States, despite the fact that the tree is short lived and early loses its lower limbs. There are other firs that may be as easily obtained and grown, and these are chosen by wise planters for their greater beauty and longer life.

The **White** or **Lovely Fir** (*A. amabilis*, Forbes), of the high mountain slopes of British Columbia, Washington and Oregon, comes to its greatest estate in the Olympic range. Here it dominates other fir trees, a giant 150 to 250 feet high, with a trunk 4 to 6 feet through. The spiry pyramid is formed of limbs that strike downward and outward in curves of remarkable grace and symmetry. In open groves the trees are clothed to the ground. In dense forests the trunks are bare except for a tufted crown. The bark is thick and broken into irregular plates on very old trees; on younger ones it is silvery grey and smooth. The wood is light brown or white, weak, hard and close grained. It is occasionally used in interior finish of houses. In cultivation the tree forgets its wild beauty and becomes commonplace. It grows in Europe, but not in our Atlantic States. Only in its natural range is it truly the "lovely fir" of the mountains.

The **White Fir** (*A. grandis*, Lindl.) earns its name by the silvery linings of its leaves. It grows from Vancouver Island south to middle California, and eastward into Idaho. It climbs from the sea to elevations of 4,000 to 7,000 feet, mingled with other conifers, but keeping along the borders of streams. This white fir is *grand* indeed in the coast region, where it mounts upward with slender trunk to the height of 200 to 300 feet. Its limbs sweep outward in curves of the utmost grace, and the contrast of dark green with silvery white in the foliage makes the tree cheerful in the extreme. The flowers are yellow and the cones brilliant green, the broad, entire scales quite concealing the bracts.

The wood of this fir is pale brown, soft, light and coarse, used to a limited extent in interior house finishing, cooperage and boxing and for woodenwares. The tree grows rapidly in European parks.

The **Balsam Fir** (*A. Fraseri*, Poir.) is a tree 40 to 60 feet high which grows in forests at an altitude of 4,000 to 6,000 feet on the Appalachian Mountains from southwestern Virginia into Tennessee and North Carolina. It forms an open pyramid of rather stiff limbs, ending in twigs crowded with dark, lustrous foliage. The purple cones are ornamented by pale yellow-green bracts with toothed margins which turn back over the scales. The wood of this tree is rarely used as lumber. It has the faults of fir wood in general, and the trees are inaccessible to lumbermen. The tree is short lived and has little ornamental value.

The **Balsam Fir** (*A. lasiocarpa*, Nutt.) grows in the high, mountainous regions from Alaska south along the Cascades of Washington and Oregon, and follows the Rocky Mountains from Idaho to Arizona. The trees are tall, narrow spires with thickly crowded branches, the oldest of which droop slightly. They range from 80 to 180 feet high, with trunks 2 to 5 feet in diameter. The bark of the limbs changes from the reddish pubescence of the twigs to pale grey or almost white. Aged trees have shallow-fissured bark covered with cinnamon-coloured scales.

The blue-green of the leaves is intensified by the striking indigo colour of both kinds of flowers in their season. The cones are rich, deep purple, and plain, the broad scales quite concealing the ruddy bracts.

White Fir (*Abies concolor*, Lindl. & Gord.)—A narrow pyramidal tree, 125 to 250 feet high, with trunk 3 to 6 feet through; branches short, stout with long, stout, much-divided side branches extending forward; twigs stout, smooth. *Bark* 3 to 6 inches thick, broken into rounded ridges by deep, irregular furrows, and the surface into plate-like scales. *Wood* soft, light, pale brown to white, coarse and weak. *Buds* globular, $\frac{1}{4}$ inch thick. *Leaves* 2-ranked by crowding; erect, pale blue to whitish, becoming dull green when old; on fruiting branches often thickened into a keel above, curved and short; on lower branches flat, straight, 2 to 3 inches long. *Flowers:* pistillate on upper branches, with striking greenish bracts; staminate dark red, on middle limbs. *Fruit* erect oblong-cylindrical cones, 5 to 6 inches long, green, purple or yellow; scales broad, rounded at apex, concealing bracts; seeds $\frac{1}{3}$ to $\frac{1}{2}$ inch long with shining red wings. *Preferred habitat*, mountain slopes. *Distribution*, Colorado west to Oregon and California, south to New Mexico and Arizona, including the Great Basin. *Uses:* Wood for butter tubs and boxing. Best of Western firs for planting in the Eastern States. A favourite ornamental in Europe.

This white fir is known as a silver fir, from the pale foliage and from the grey bark of its branches. The forests of *A. magnifica* coming down the high slopes meet those of *A. concolor* coming up.

The trees are gigantic in the Sierras; scarcely of more than medium height and girth among the Rockies. The leaves are unusually long for a fir tree, on lower limbs often 2 to 3 inches. The flowers are conspicuous, the staminate rich red, the pistillate ornamented with backward-turning, finger-lobed bracts. The cones are stout, various in colours, with broad, short scales that quite cover the bracts. The seed wings are rose coloured and lustrous.

The tree is often planted in Europe; it is the most vigorous native fir tree met in cultivation on the Atlantic side of this continent. The best trees in Eastern nurseries come from seeds collected in the Rocky Mountains.

Another **Silver Fir** (*A. venusta*, K. Koch.) has leaves almost willow-like in form, so broad are the flat, pointed blades. They are 1 to 2½ inches long, yellow-green with silvery linings, especially bright on the newest shoots. The spray is flat by reason of the 2-ranked arrangement of the leaves, which stand out at right angles to the twig. The tree habit is peculiar. A slender trunk 100 to 150 feet high bears a broad pyramid of pendulous limbs, which is surmounted by a narrow spire for the last 20 feet of the tree's height. The cones are 3 to 4 inches long, and striking in ornamentation. The long, stiff whip of a pale yellowish brown bract extends an inch or two beyond each purple scale.

This fir is confined to elevated canon sides in the mountains of Monterey County, California, and has no commercial significance. Seeds sent to Europe produce handsome ornamental trees in North Italy and in warmer sections of England.

Red Fir (*Abies nobilis*, Lindl.)—A broad, round-headed tree 150 to 250 feet high, with trunk 6 to 8 feet through; branches stiff; twigs red velvety. *Bark* 1 to 2 inches thick, irregularly furrowed, red-brown. *Wood* hard, pale brown, streaked with red, light, strong, moderately close in texture; sap wood darker. *Buds* small, blunt, reddish. *Leaves* blue-green, often glaucous when young, flat, grooved above, crowded to upper side of twigs, and curved backward, 1 to 1½ inches long, on fertile shoots, 4-angled, sharp. *Flowers*: staminate reddish purple; pistillate scattered on upper limbs, bracts ornate with recurved tips. *Fruit* oblong, thick, blunt at apex and base, 4 to 5 inches long, purplish or brown, pubescent; scales covered with thin toothed bracts which end in recurving, pencil-like projections. *Preferred habitat*, mountain slopes at 2,500 to 5,000 feet elevation. *Distribution*, mountains of western Washington, Oregon and California. *Uses:* Lumber for interior finish of houses and for boxing. Rarely planted in Eastern States. Needs shelter at Boston. Cultivated in Europe.

The red fir, another giant of the Northwest, attains its best development in the Cascade Mountains of Washington and Oregon on elevated slopes facing the sea. An old tree is often 200 to 250 feet high, with a trunk 6 to 8 feet in diameter, crowned with a broad, round head, quite distinct from the spire form usual among firs. There are forests of this tree which furnish, at present in limited quantities, wood for boxing and house finishing. The wood is brownish red, with sap wood of a darker colour. The lumber dealer calls it "larch." As long as better lumber is to be had, these forests will be allowed to wait.

The distinctive features of this tree are its glaucous, blue-green foliage and the stout brown or purple cones, 4 to 5 inches long, and richly ornamented by the bracts which turn back like little pale green scallop shells over each scale.

Red Fir (*Abies magnifica*, A. Murr.)—A pyramidal tree which becomes round-topped with age, 150 to 200 feet high; trunk 6 to 8 feet through; limbs pendulous, *Bark* red-brown, 4 to 6 inches thick, scaly and broken into ridges and deep fissures that cross and join; twigs reddish, becoming silvery white. *Wood* soft, light, weak, durable, red. *Buds* scaly, ovate, red, lustrous. *Leaves* 4-angled, pale at first, then blue-green, crowded to erect position on the twig. *Flowers:* conspicuous; staminate reddish purple; pistillate green with red tips on scales. *Fruit* oblong-cylindrical cones, 6 to 9 inches long, purplish brown; scales plain, 1 inch broad at apex, closely overlapping and concealing the bracts. *Preferred habitat*, mountain slopes, at 5,000 to 7,000 feet elevation. *Distribution*, Cascade range in southern Oregon, throughout the western slopes of the Sierra Nevada Mountains. *Uses:* Wood makes packing cases and cheap buildings. Tree planted as an ornamental in western Europe. Scarcely hardy in our Eastern States.

"The magnificent silver fir," as John Muir calls it, is one of the noblest trees of the Northwest, a lover of the mountain slopes, which it climbs to two miles above sea level before it reaches its limit. On moraines, at an elevation of 7,000 to 8,000 feet, it grows to a height of 200 to 250 feet and a diameter of 5 to 7 feet.

Winter buds (some leaves cut away to show buds)

THE BALSAM FIR (*Abies lasiocarpa*)

The blue-green leaves and the pale or white bark of twigs give this tree a spectral expression. The leaves are long, blunt and curved so as to stand erect. This giant tree of the Northwestern mountains is comparatively worthless, except for fuel

Winter buds (some leaves cut away to show the buds)

THE BALSAM FIR (*Abies Fraseri*)

The lustrous dark leaves are pale beneath. They are blunt, even notched, at the tips. This is the fir of the Appalachian Mountains

Winter bud (some leaves removed)

THE WHITE FIR (*Abies concolor*)

This Colorado tree is often seen in Eastern gardens as a beautiful pale, bluish evergreen tree. In the mountains of California it becomes a mighty tree over 200 feet high. Its bark on old trunks is very thick and broken into broad ridges. The foliage is sometimes silvery white

Bark and wood of another Western white fir
(*Abies grandis*)

With these noble dimensions there is a richness and symmetry and perfection of finish not to be found in any other tree in the Sierras. The branches are whorled, in fives mostly, and stand out from the straight red-purple bole in level, or on old trees, in drooping collars, every branch regularly pinnated like a fern frond, and clad with silvery needles, making broad and singularly rich and sumptuous plumes.

The flowers are in their prime about the middle of June; the staminate, red, growing in crowded profusion on the under side of the branchlets, giving a rich colour to nearly all the tree; the pistillate, greenish yellow tinged with pink, standing erect on the upper side of the topmost branches; while the tufts of young leaves, about as brightly coloured as those of the Douglas spruce, push out their fragrant brown buds a few weeks later, making another grand show.

"The cones mature in a single season from the flowers. When full grown they are about 6 to 8 inches long, 3 to 4 inches in diameter, blunt, massive, cylindrical, greenish grey in colour, covered with a fine silvery down, and beaded with transparent balsam, very rich and precious looking, standing erect like casks on the topmost branches. If possible, the inside of the cones is still more beautiful. The scales and bracts are tinged with red and the seed wings are purple with bright iridescence."— *John Muir.*

A variety, *Shastensis,* Lemm., of *A. magnifica,* is distinguished from the type species only by the yellow bracts that protrude and partially cover the scales of the cones. This form inhabits high elevations in the region of Mount Shasta and also occurs at the lower end of the Sierra Nevada range.

CHAPTER X: THE BIG TREE AND THE REDWOOD

Genus SEQUOIA, Endl.

TREES of great size and age, resinous, aromatic. *Leaves* evergreen, alternate, of two shapes. *Flowers* in solitary cones, minute, monœcious, axillary. *Fruit* a pendant woody cone; seeds 5 to 7 under each scale.

KEY TO SPECIES

A. Leaves minute, ovate, usually compressed, buds naked; fruit biennial.　　　　(*S. Wellingtonia*) BIG TREE
AA. Leaves mostly linear, or lanceolate, spreading, 2-ranked; buds scaly; fruit annual.　　(*S. sempervirens*) REDWOOD

The **Big Tree** (*Sequoia Wellingtonia*, Seem.)—A pyramidal tree when young, becoming round-topped; 275 to 325 feet high; diameter 20 to 35 feet; fluted trunk. *Bark* reddish brown, fibrous, fluted; 1 to 2 feet thick. *Wood* red, soft, coarse, light, weak, durable. *Buds* naked. *Leaves* ovate, acuminate, spreading at tips, $\frac{1}{2}$ inch long. *Flowers:* monœcious, terminal, conical, scaly, profuse in late winter; staminate with broad scales and abundant pollen; pistillate with 25 to 40 needle-tipped scales, with 3 to 7 ovules under each. *Fruit* dark red-brown woody cone, biennial, 2 to $3\frac{1}{2}$ inches long, with thickened tips; seeds 3 to 7 under each scale, each 2-winged, small, light, eaten by squirrels. *Preferred habitat*, rich woodlands. *Distribution*, narrow area on western slope of Sierras in California. *Uses:* Most majestic tree in the world. Rare and dwarfed in cultivation. Lumber used for shingles, fencing and in general construction.

Sir Joseph Hooker and Asa Gray sat with John Muir around a campfire on Mount Shasta, and talked about the great forests of the Sierras they had just visited. Comparing them with Old-World forests, they agreed upon this statement: "In the beauty and grandeur of individual trees, and in number and variety of species, the Sierra forests surpass all others." Conifers are supreme in these forests and among conifers Sequoia is king. Of the two species, the Big Tree, *S. Wellingtonia*, stands first, and the redwood second.

The Old World has some trees of surprising girth and indefinite age—oaks, chestnuts, sycamores, and cedars of Lebanon—each with its history, the pride of the country it grows in. But these trees are derelicts—throwing out a wisp of foliage here and there, a truce to death, with each returning spring. The lime tree of Nürnberg and the chestnut at the foot of Mount Ætna are each famous; but these trees, with their tops dead and gone years before they were pronounced dead, their trunks honeycombed with decay, and leaning upon props and pillars, are scarcely to be compared with trees, hale, lusty-crowned, whose fluted trunks are a unit, and sound as a nut from the heart out. Granting a greater girth, if you please, to a few of these senile trees, and a greater height to one Eucalyptus that grows in Australia, we can truthfully declare that, excepting these, the Sequoias lead the world, past and present, in height and calibre. No other tree combines such massiveness of trunk with such height. And there is no doubt but that in age they can take rank with the oldest, for competent authorities estimate the age limit to be above 5,000 years. Muir thinks that some living trees have reached that age. Stumps now standing show 4,000 annual rings.

It would be great good fortune to visit one of the ten groves of Big Trees once a month and so get the story of the tree's life as the year rolls around. In the late winter the flowers appear, showering the whole region with their golden dust, and tipping the sprays with the pale green fertile flowers by thousands. The cones that follow are small for such a tree, and each scale bears from four to eight seeds at its base. Millions of them are scattered each year, thin, little winged discs, no larger than a baby's thumbnail, looking like half-grown elm seeds. It is incredible that such a tree should have come from such a seed. Not only have they vitality, but some store of nutriment, for the squirrels journey up the trees and cut off the cones in order to put away for winter the little seeds they contain. If fresh cones are falling, you may be sure the squirrels are at work, for the trees hold their empty cones for years.

It is strange that with such profuse seed production young

87

trees are so scarce in the Big Tree groves. Only in the southern range of this species do seedling trees appear to reassure us that the race will preserve itself, if only the three agencies of destruction, the axe, the saw and the forest fire, can be curbed.

The tourist, hurrying through the Sequoia National Park, gets very little but an awed sense of the magnificence of these trees. It is worth while to have had the glimpse his limited ticket permits. Big stories told by friends who had been there before, actual dimensions of noted trees, and all the guide-book extravagance of description, have not prepared him for the things he sees. He is speechless with astonishment. He walks across an ample platform which is the flat top of a Sequoia stump. He sleeps, perchance, in a house which is a hollow log. He rides in a coach and four through a tunnel over which a standing trunk arches, like a mighty occidental Colossus of Rhodes. He lifts a fragment of bark, and it is 2 feet thick. It took three long weeks of steady labour for two men to cut down one tree!

The living trees are green topped, but bare of limbs for two-thirds of their great fluted trunks. Our tallest Eastern oak, with the tallest sycamore or walnut atop of it, would not equal the height of one of these giants. Spruces and pines of majestic port standing around look like saplings. They are dwarfed by the company they keep. They look up, but the Sequoias look—not down but out, indifferent to all that is transpiring below them. They see only the limitless reaches of the eternal sky; their meat and drink, the sunshine and the leaf mould; their breath of life, the unwearying winds of heaven.

There were great forests of Sequoias once in central and northern Europe and in mid-continental North America. They stretched away, even to the Arctic circle. This was just before the great climatic Reconstruction Period, when magnolias flourished in Greenland and all the plants and animals of the temperate zone found congenial habitation in near proximity to the North Pole. Then came the Age of Ice, and only those species survived which were able to keep ahead of the glaciers, and establish themselves in regions not overwhelmed by the ice. The rocks of the Tertiary Period preserve the story of these times, and in the pages opened by the geologist's hammer, five distinct species of Sequoia are recorded. "Pressed specimens" indeed, these fossil trees are, two of which are identical with the California trees.

The other three species are extinct, and America has the only survivors of the noblest race of plants the world has ever produced. Trenches and ridges in the ground within the Sequoia belt contain the prostrate bodies of former generations of Big Trees. They are not found outside the range. This fact leads John Muir to believe that the area covered by these trees has not shrunken any since the Glacial Period—that Sequoia has held its own for 5,000 to 10,000 years.

The devastation of the Big Tree groves by lumbermen is now checked in a few locations by Government purchase and reservation. The lumber is put to such base uses as shingles and clapboards and fencing which lesser trees might better supply. It is the vast size and height of these trees, not the market value of the lumber per board foot, that make an acre yield such enormous profit.

Seedling Big Trees grow slowly, and do poorly in the Eastern States. In Europe they are more successful, and are popular everywhere. Weeping forms, which are much grown, originated in a French nursery.

The genus takes its name from Sequoiah, a wise Cherokee Indian, who made an alphabet of his tribal language by means of which the New Testament and a newspaper were published for his people.

Redwood (*Sequoia sempervirens*, Endl.)—Resinous, aromatic trees, with tall, fluted trunks and short, horizontal branches; 200 to 300 feet high, 12 to 28 feet in diameter. Head small, irregular. *Bark* thick, red, 6 to 12 inches thick, in ridges 2 to 4 feet wide, checked crosswise, showing brighter, close, inner layer. *Wood* light, soft, brittle, close, red, easily split, durable, satiny lustre. *Buds* oval, small, loosely scaly. *Leaves* of two forms: lanceolate and spreading, or awl shaped and shorter; evergreen, $\frac{1}{4}$ to $\frac{1}{2}$ inch long. *Flowers:* monœcious, in late winter, cone shaped, scaly; staminate on erect stems, scales 3-anthered, pollen copious; pistillate with 7 ovules on each scale. *Fruit* oblong, woody cone, $\frac{3}{4}$ to 1 inch long, scales thick and grooved at tip; 3 to 5-winged seeds on each. *Preferred habitat,* moist, sandy soil. *Distribution,* southern Oregon on coast range slopes to Monterey County, California. *Uses:* Most valuable timber tree of Pacific coast; successful in European gardens.

In many characters, the redwood is not different from the

Big Tree. Its spreading leaves on the terminal twigs give it a more graceful, feathery spray than do the awl-like blades of the other. The pistillate flowers have fewer scales, and the buds are scaly. The cones are smaller, and the seeds have more vitality. The redwood is only a trifle under the Big Tree in size, sometimes overtopping the highest of them, and reaching 400 feet. But the trunks are not so massive, and these trees average smaller than their cousins. In beauty the redwood is first; the lustrous leaves, the ruddy bark, and the gracefully curving branches of trees still in their prime will halt the passing stranger and compel his wonder and admiration. The forests throng with young trees in every stage of growth, showing that Nature left to herself would multiply and extend the range of this species. But the wood is beautiful, and light and easily worked. It is admirable in building, and durable beyond most woods. It receives a satiny polish, and it lasts indefinitely in the ground.

Curly grain is common in Sequoia lumber, and this, as in other species, is eagerly sought after by the makers of fancy furniture and bric-à-brac. People want redwood, so the lumberman is stripping the redwood forests as fast as possible. "They'll come on again!" And it is true to some extent. The trees send up suckers from the stumps, which the Big Trees cannot do. But lumbering is wasteful and greedy in its methods, and more is wasted than saved. Forest fires lick up the kindling the lumberman leaves, and young trees and old fall victims to this disaster.

Redwoods are more easily accessible than Big Trees. They come down to the coast and thus tempt the avarice of lumbermen. The extent of these woods seemed great, at first. But on the map the region is very small indeed, and immediate protective measures are demanded if any groves of big redwoods are to be saved from the sawmill.

In cultivation the redwood has followed the Big Tree into European gardens, and at length it has shown itself hardy and fairly content in the Southeastern States. Near Charleston, South Carolina, it is growing successfully.

THE BIG TREE (*Sequoia Wellingtonia*)

Spruces and pines of majestic port are dwarfed to saplings by the company they keep. They look up, but the sequoias look—
not *down*, but *out*—indifferent to all that transpires below them. They regard only the limitless reaches of the eternal sky

Flowering branch

THE ARBOR VITÆ (*Thuya occidentalis*)

Scale-like leaves are arranged to make a flat, frond-like spray. The cones are oval, erect and thin scaled. We know it as a hedge tree and an ornamental evergreen

CHAPTER XI: THE ARBOR VITÆS

Genus THUYA, Linn.

EVERGREEN resinous ornamental trees of slender, pyramidal habit, with intricately branched limbs, and flat, open spray. *Leaves* scale-like, 4-ranked, minute, closely appressed to twigs. *Flowers* solitary, terminal, small aments, monœcious, scaly. *Fruits* erect, loose, ovoid cones, of few thin scales; seeds few, usually two. *Uses:* trees especially adapted for formal gardens, clipped hedges and shelter belts. Wood variously employed.

KEY TO SPECIES

A. Cone with 4 fertile scales, as a rule; bark orange red.
(*T. occidentalis*) ARBOR VITÆ
AA. Cone with 6 fertile scales, as a rule; bark cinnamon red.
(*T. plicata*) GIANT ARBOR VITÆ

Four distinct species of Thuya are recognised. Two are native to Japan and China. The Chinese *T. orientalis*, one of the most popular decorative evergreens, is cultivated especially in Southern gardens. It is offered in several varieties. *T. Japonica* is a hardy species of lusty growth with white spots on the dark green of its leaf linings. A Japanese genus, Thuyopis, with one species, is one of the handsomest of Oriental evergreens introduced into cultivation here. It is hardy to Massachusetts, but suffers from drought. Its flat, frond-like spray resembles arbor vitæ, from which the genus is distinguished by having 4 to 5 ovules under each scale of the cone.

Arbor Vitæ (*Thuya occidentalis*, Linn.)—A conical, compact, resinous evergreen, 25 to 65 feet high, with short, ascending branches and flat, frond-like spray. *Bark* light brown, thin, cracking into ridges with frayed-out, stringy edges; branches smooth, red, shining. *Wood* soft, brittle, coarse, durable in the soil, light brown, fragrant. *Buds* naked, very small. *Leaves*, both keeled and flat, 4-ranked, to fit the flat twig, scale-like, blunt, or pointed, glandular, aromatic. *Flowers*, May, monœcious on tips of side twigs, but separate; staminate, a globose cluster of stamens; pistillate, a red cone of 8 to 12 scales with ovules on lower or central ones only. *Fruit* oval, pale brown, erect cone, annual, with 6 to 12 oblong scales. *Preferred habitat*, low, swampy ground near streams. *Distribution*, New Brunswick to Manitoba; Minnesota, Michigan and northern Illinois; south along Atlantic States into New Jersey, along Alleghanies to North Carolina and eastern Tennessee. *Uses:* Valuable ornamental and hedge tree. Wood used for telegraph poles, posts, railroad ties and shingles. Bark rich in tannin.

The flat leaf spray of the arbor vitæ of the Northern States sets it apart from other evergreens, and its use in hedges makes it familiar to most people. Children as well as grown people generally know it. Unfortunately the name, white cedar, has become attached to this tree, confusing it with another genus, Chamæcyparis, in which this name reappears.

Through years of cultivation this arbor vitæ has produced a great number of garden varieties. Their slow growth and compact habit adapt them to use in formal gardens. They are hardy, they submit to severe pruning and late transplanting, and they are easily propagated from seed—these traits of character commend them to nurserymen and planters. They are planted with profit for telegraph poles and posts, as the wood, though soft, is very durable in soil. As windbreaks they do good service, and have unique ornamental value when massed on stream borders or grouped on rocky slopes.

Giant Arbor Vitæ, or Red Cedar (*Thuya plicata*, D. Don.)—A pyramidal tree, 150 to 200 feet high, with a stout, often corrugated and buttressed trunk. *Bark* scaly in narrow strips, thin. *Wood* light, brittle, reddish brown, soft, coarse, durable. *Leaves* minute, close, blunt, scale-like, with pale markings, longer on leading shoots. *Flowers* dark brown, monœcious, very small. *Fruit* erect clustered cones, with 6 fertile scales, each bearing 2 to 3 winged seeds. *Preferred habitat*, rocky stream banks and rich bottomlands. *Distribution*, coast regions from Cape Mendocino in California north into Alaska; mountains east into Idaho and Montana. *Uses:* A handsome ornamental tree, grown in Europe and occasionally in the Middle and North Atlantic States. Wood used for interior finish of houses, sashes, doors, furniture and cooperage. Indians use it for totem poles, framework of lodges and war canoes. Inner bark furnishes fibre for blankets, ropes and nets; sheets of it thatch their cabins.

Beside this giant of the Northwest, our Eastern arbor vitæ is a pygmy. Solitary, or in small groves, it climbs the mountains to a level more than a mile higher than the rich river bottoms at sea level, where the noblest specimens and the greatest number are assembled. The Indian cuts the biggest specimen he can find for the totem pole that he carves into his family tree. The war canoes are dugouts made of the enormous butts which often measure 15 feet in diameter. Inside of the cabins the great rough-hewn rafters and joist of these primitive dwellings are of this arbor vitæ, whose soft wood the crude implements of the tribes can work with comparative ease. The walls that enclose the Indian's house, the blankets that keep him warm, and the ropes, indispensable in fishing, in the harnessing of his dog teams, and in various other enterprises—all come from the fibrous inner bark of this tree. Truly it is a "tree of life" to the Alaskan aborigines.

In cultivation, this species far exceeds the other native in beauty and rapidity of growth. It is coming into popularity in the United States.

CHAPTER XII: THE INCENSE CEDAR

Genus LIBOCEDRUS, Endl.

TALL, aromatic, resinous trees. *Leaves* scale-like, 4-ranked, in flat sprays. *Flowers* monœcious, solitary, minute, terminal. *Fruit* an annual cone, oblong, few-scaled.

(*L. decurrens*) INCENSE CEDAR

This single representative of its genus in America has seven sister species, chiefly in the Southern Hemisphere. Formosa and southwestern China, New Zealand, New Guinea, and South America from Chili to Patagonia—these have their incense cedars, distinguished by the flat, frond-like spray of bright green scale leaves. Our species is grown in parks in the neighbourhood of Philadelphia and New York, and in protected situations about Boston. In Europe it is often planted for ornament.

It is native to the slopes of the Cascade and other coast ranges and the Sierra Nevada. It extends from Oregon into Lower California, and reaches its best estate and greatest numbers in the central part of California, between 5,000 and 7,000 feet above the sea. Its lumber resembles that of arbor vitæ, and is used for furniture, fencing, lath and shingles, for interior woodwork, and for flume building.

John Muir's description of it is most illuminating:

"The incense cedar, when full grown, is a magnificent tree, 120 to nearly 200 feet high, 5 to 8 and occasionally 12 feet in diameter, with cinnamon-coloured bark and warm, yellow-green foliage, and in general appearance like an arbor vitæ. It is distributed through the main forest from an elevation of 3,000 to 6,000 feet, and in sheltered portions of cañons on the warm sides to 7,500 feet. In midwinter, when most trees are asleep, it puts forth its flowers. The pistillate are pale green and inconspicuous, but the staminate are yellow, about one-fourth of an inch long, and are in myriads, tingeing all the branches with gold, and making the tree as it stands in the snow look like a gigantic golden-rod. Though scattered rather sparsely amongst its companions in the open woods, it is seldom out of sight, and its bright brown shaft and warm masses of plumy foliage make a striking feature of the landscape. While young and growing fast in an open situation, no other tree of its size in the park forms so exactly tapered a pyramid. The branches, outspread in flat plumes and beautifully fronded, sweep gracefully downward and outward, except those near the top, which aspire; the lowest droop to the ground, overlapping one another, shedding rain and snow, and making fine tents for storm-bound mountaineers and birds. In old age it becomes irregular and picturesque, mostly from accidents— running fires, heavy wet snow breaking the branches, lightning shattering the top, compelling it to try to make new summits out of side branches, etc. Still it frequently lives more than a thousand years, invincibly beautiful, and worthy its place beside the Douglas spruce and the great pines."

CHAPTER XIII: THE CYPRESSES

CONIFEROUS trees having pyramidal habit. Very popular for ornamental planting. Some species have considerable lumber value. All have light, graceful leaf spray and small, globular, woody cones. Wood usually soft.

KEY TO GENERA

A. Leaves, minute, scaly, thick, evergreen.
   B. Seeds under each cone scale many.
                             1. Genus CUPRESSUS, Linn.
   BB. Seeds under each cone scale 1 to 5.
                    2. Genus CHAMÆCYPARIS, Spach.
AA. Leaves linear, deciduous.   3. Genus TAXODIUM, Rich.

1. Genus CUPRESSUS, Linn.

Resinous trees with naked buds, stout, ascending branches, which become horizontal. *Leaves* minute, scale-like, 4-ranked. *Flowers* minute, monœcious, yellowish. *Fruit* biennial, globular, woody cones.

KEY TO SPECIES

A. Branchlets stout.
   B. Foliage dark green. *(C. macrocarpa)* MONTEREY CYPRESS
   BB. Foliage pale green; twigs glaucous.
               (C. Arizonica) ARIZONA CYPRESS
AA. Branchlets slender; foliage dark green.
   B. Leaves obscurely glandular.   *(C. Goveniana)* CYPRESS
   BB. Leaves plainly glandular.   *(C. Macnabiana)* CYPRESS

Monterey Cypress (*Cupressus macrocarpa*, Gord.)—A broad pyramidal tree when young, 40 to 75 feet high, becoming gnarled and flat topped when old. *Trunk* short, 3 to 6 feet thick. *Bark* brown to pale grey, broken into irregular ridges, covered with elongated, persistent scales. *Wood* brown, hard, strong, heavy, durable, fine grained. *Leaves* ovate, minute, closely appressed to twigs. *Flowers* minute, monœcious, separated, terminal, yellow. *Fruit* clustered, erect, globular cones, of few woody scales,

96

seeds 18 to 20 under each middle scale. *Preferred habitat*, exposed coast bluffs. *Distribution*, around Bay of Monterey, California. *Uses:* Planted for windbreaks and hedges, and for ornament.

The Pacific coast forests thrill the heart of the Easterner, unless that heart be petrified by commercialism. Even then, the thrill is there, though it be a materialistic vibration, accompanied by a mental estimate in terms of board feet. The thrill changes from wonder to pity as the tree lover looks upon that small remnant of its race, the Monterey cypresses, that cling to the wind-beaten promontories about Monterey Bay. They look like battle-scarred veterans making a stubborn though hopeless stand in the last ditch. And that, literally, is the state of their fortunes. Wide as their gnarled roots range for foothold, the crumbling bluffs are gradually undermined by the waves, and one by one those in the front rank go down. The hungry waves will never give up the siege, and the last of the trees in their native soil will in time be swept out of existence.

Fortunately the species is hardy and happy in cultivation far from its native land. It is known in several horticultural forms as well as the type species in temperate South America, Australia and New Zealand. In southern and western Europe it is in great favour, and at home it is planted very generally for ornament and for hedges up and down the Pacific coast. Lately it is coming into use in the Southeastern States. Hence, the tree is saved to a larger life by man's intervention, although Nature ruthlessly lets extermination overtake it in the struggle for existence. It is to be hoped that age will bring these cultivated cypresses to something like the picturesque habit that distinguishes the trees that grow wild. No pine of the Alps ever took on such grotesqueness as marks the Monterey cypresses.

THE CYPRESSES OF MONTEREY

Staunch derelicts adrift on Time's wide sea,
  Undaunted exiles from an age pristine!
Your loneliness in tortured limb we see;
  Your courage in your crown of living green;
Your strength unyielding, in your grappling knee;
  Your patience in the calmness of your mien.
Enrapt, you stand in mighty reverie,
  While centuries come and go, unheard, unseen.
               —*Anna Botsford Comstock.*

The **Arizona Cypress** (*C. Arizonica*, Greene) extends as a small or medium-sized tree of pyramidal habit from Arizona into California and Mexico. Forests of it are found at 5,000 to 6,000 feet elevation. The trees are occasionally broad with flattened tops. The leaves are pale green, and a glaucous bloom covers them after the first year of growth. The cones are also glaucous, and each thick scale has a sharp beak at the top. The tree is rare in cultivation, and as yet has no importance in the lumber trade.

The **Cypress** (*C. Goveniana*, Gord.), of central and southern California coast mountains, has dark green foliage on spreading branches that form a loose, open head. The tree is not at all rare within its range, but varies from a shrub to a tree 50 feet high. Horticultural forms, usually dwarfs, are cultivated.

The **Macnab Cypress** (*C. Macnabiana*, Murr.), also a Californian limited to the northern mountainous part of the state, is a small spreading tree, rarely 30 feet high, often with many stems. Its leaves are dark green, sometimes whitened by a glaucous bloom, always distinctly set with glands. In cultivation the tree is the hardiest of the genus, although restricted to California and the Gulf States in this country and to the warmer parts of Europe.

The classic **Cypress** (*C. sempervirens*, Linn.) of the Old World gives distinction to Italian gardens to-day, and as the symbol of mourning has been planted in the burial places of Europe from the earliest recorded times. It is mentioned more frequently in classical literature than any other conifer.* Its sombre foliage was the badge of grief. It is one of the trees noted for longevity; its age limit is estimated at 3,000 years. Not hardy in our Northern States, it is cultivated in the South and in California. The species submits to severe pruning, so it is often planted for hedges.

2. Genus CHAMÆCYPARIS, Spach.

Trees of tall, narrow pyramidal habit, with short, spreading side branches, and flat branchlets spray. *Wood* pale, fragrant, durable. *Leaves* scale-like, sharp, opposite in pairs. *Flowers* monœcious, minute, globular, lateral. *Fruit* annual, erect, globular cones of few woody scales; seeds 1 to 5 under each fertile scale.

---

* " Nor, when you die, shall any of the trees you have planted, save only the mournful cypresses, follow their master."—*Horace.*

THE MONTEREY CYPRESS (*Cupressus macrocarpa*)

A small remnant of their race are the aged, flat-topped veteran cypresses that cling with gnarled and far-reaching roots to the crumbling soil of rocky promontories about Monterey Bay in California. The leaves are minute, but the foliage mass is thick and casts a sombre shade. In cultivation the species thrives, and makes a beautiful hedge tree and ornamental evergreen

THE WHITE CEDAR (*Chamaecyparis thyoides*)

This eastern cypress is unfortunate in its common name, for it is not a true cedar. The pistillate flowers are succeeded by woody little cones, globular but curiously carved, and showy in summer against the blue-green foliage. The wood is especially durable in contact with the soil. The stringy bark parts in narrow, interlacing strips

THE SITKA CYPRESS
(*Chamaecyparis Nootkatensis*)

This tree of the far Northwest has hard wood of exceeding durability. The bark is shed in loose, thin strips

THE LAWSON CYPRESS (*Chamaecyparis Lawsoniana*)

This handsome spire-like conifer inhabits the western coast mountains, and is common in cultivation. Its foliage is dense, for the short horizontal branches all bear twigs that end in a flat, frond-like spray. The cones are scarcely larger than peas

KEY TO SPECIES

A. Bark of tree thin; ridges flat; leaves blue-green.
  B. Twigs slender; leaves dull, glandular.
                        (*C. thyoides*) WHITE CEDAR
  BB. Twigs stout; leaves bright, not glandular.
                  (*C. Nootkatensis*) SITKA CYPRESS
AA. Bark of tree thick; ridges rounded, leaves bright green,
    glandular.   (*C. Lawsoniana*) LAWSON CYPRESS

This genus of six species is distributed in North America and Japan and on the Island of Formosa.

White Cedar (*Chamæcyparis thyoides*, Britt.)—A fast-growing, pyramidal tree, 40 to 80 feet high, with flat, graceful spray on erect, spreading branches. *Bark* pale, reddish brown, furrowed, stringy, often terminal. *Wood* light reddish brown, soft, light, weak, aromatic, close grained, easily worked, very durable in soil. *Buds* naked, very small. *Leaves* dull blue-green, minute, scale-like, opposite, 4-ranked, lateral pairs keeled, others concave, fitting compressed twigs. *Flowers*, April, monœcious, small, terminal, made of 4 to 6 scales; staminate red or yellow, abundant; pistillate few, greenish. *Fruit* woody, spherical cone, ¼ inch in diameter, annual, glaucous, blue-green, becoming brown; scales with beak in centre; seeds winged, 1 to 2 under each scale. *Preferred habitat*, deep swamps near seacoast. *Distribution*, seaboard states, Maine to Mississippi. *Uses:* Important ornamental evergreen. Wood used for interior finish of houses, for boats, fence posts, railroad ties, buckets, barrels, shingles, and small woodenware.

The Atlantic seaboard from Massachusetts Bay south has a cypress whose common name, "white cedar," is unfortunate. There ought to be distinct names enough to go around. All the species of a genus ought to have the same generic name in English as well as in Latin or Greek. However, white cedar is the trade name of the lumber, and there is little chance that the cedar muddle will be cleared by calling this tree a cypress.

The tree is a lover of swamps and doesn't get far back from the coast. In cultivation it thrives in any sandy loam, if not too dry. It is lumbered to some extent and devoted to uses that test its durability in contact with water and exposure to sun and wind.

The **Sitka Cypress** (*C. Nootkatensis*, Lamb.) grows over 100 feet tall, with a trunk over 5 feet through, near the coast of Alaska. Its yellow branchlets lighten the gloom of its blue-green

99

foliage, and the treetop is warmed by the ruddy colour of the oldest leaves, which remain for some time on the tree after they are dead. The range of the species is from Alaska into Oregon, climbing the mountains to the altitude of 3,000 feet, where the tree is reduced to a shrub.

The hard wood is very close of texture and pale yellow. It is durable and pleasantly aromatic. Carpenters employ it in the interior finishing of houses. It is made into furniture, and used in boat building.

Horticultural forms of this species are astonishingly numerous. Sudworth gives sixty-eight varieties in his "Check List."

Lawson Cypress (*Chamæcyparis Lawsoniana*, A. Murr.)— A spire-like tree, 150 to 200 feet high, with short horizontal branches ending in a flat spray. *Bark* very thick, with rounded scaly ridges, dark red. *Wood* hard, light, strong, pale yellow, close grained, resinous, fragrant, easily worked. *Leaves* minute, bright green, in opposite pairs. *Flowers:* minute, numerous; staminate bright red; pistillate dark coloured. *Fruit* clustered cones, pea sized, of few scales; seeds 2 to 4 under each scale. *Preferred habitat*, mountain slopes. *Distribution*, coast mountains of Oregon and California. *Uses:* A valuable ornamental tree. Wood used in house finishing, flooring, and in boat building and for railroad ties and fence posts. Matches are made of it.

Somewhat of the beauty of those Western cypresses can be appreciated by looking in gardens and nurseries at the multitude of varieties of each of them in cultivation in this country and abroad. In their own country the parents of these precocious ornamental offspring are to be seen. No horticultural substitute for the original will suffice the tree lover. To go to Oregon is his fondly cherished plan. To see that twenty-mile forest belt of Lawson cypresses that stretches from Point Gregory to the mouth of the Coquille River—only this will satisfy. There are men who name as "the handsomest of the conifers" trees outside of this genus, but the visitor to this splendid grove of Lawson cypresses will be inclined to deny it. It is hard to keep to a sliding scale and avoid superlatives in judging those Western trees.

The Japanese Retinosporas, beautiful evergreen of this type, widely cultivated in many horticultural forms, were assigned to a separate genus by Siebold and Zuccarini, but other authorities consider them all to be juvenile forms of the genus Chamæcyparis, or Thuya. These evergreens have in youth different foliage from that of the adult trees—a sufficient reason for confusion, especially before the trees bear cones. Whatever botanical affinities are eventually established, the trade name will probably remain Retinospora, and people will plant these handsome evergreens in increasing numbers. In his Manual, 1905, Professor Sargent includes two Japanese Retinosporas in the genus Chamæcyparis.

3. Genus TAXODIUM, Rich.

The bald cypress has two sister species in the genus Taxodium. One, a shrub, is native to China; the other, a large tree, to Mexico. Forests of bald cypresses covered large areas of Europe and central North America during the Tertiary Period, but they perished in the Glacial Era. The rocks tell the story.

Bald cypresses rank among the oldest and largest trees in the world. The Mexican species, *T. mucronatum*, is estimated to live 4,000 years. The far-famed "Cypress of Montezuma," in Chepultepec, is nearly 200 feet high and its trunk has a diameter of 15 feet. It is believed to be less than 800 years old—a tree still in the vigour of youth. The largest trunk known in this species is 40 feet in diameter at base. Beside this giant our own bald cypress seems small and short lived, but among our native trees it ranks high in size and age.

Bald Cypress (*Taxodium distichum*, Rich.)—A tall pyramidal tree, 75 to 150 feet high, with pendulous branches, becoming broad and round headed when old. Trunk lobed above, strongly buttressed and usually hollow at the base. Roots long, horizontal, with vertical anchor roots. *Bark* pale reddish grey, scaly, divided by shallow fissures. *Wood* soft, light, brown, easily worked, durable. *Buds* minute, globular, scaly, silvery. *Leaves* deciduous with the branchlets linear, $\frac{1}{2}$ to $\frac{3}{4}$ inch long, 2-ranked, spreading or scale-like, closely appressed. *Flowers:* monœcious, small; staminate in loose, drooping panicles, 4 to 6 inches long; pistillate globose, scaly, scattered near ends of twigs. *Fruit* annual, globular, woody cones, in pairs or solitary, 1 inch in diameter; seeds winged, 2 under each scale. *Preferred habitat*, swamps of coast or river bottoms. *Distribution*, Delaware to Florida; west into Texas; north along Mississippi to Missouri, Indiana and Illinois. *Uses:* Lumber for buildings, doors, shingles, cooperage, fencing and railroad ties. Planted as an ornamental tree in Northern States and in Europe.

Familiar to the traveller through our Eastern and Southern seaboard regions are the cypress swamps, dismal, but picturesque withal, and exhibiting characteristics that set this tree quite apart from others. A conifer is ordinarily an evergreen tree. This one establishes its family claims by the brave array of button-like cones it ripens every autumn. But it is deciduous, shedding not only its yew-like leaves, but, surprisingly, most of the little twigs also that bear the leaves. So the winter finds the trees bare and dead looking, the tall, corrugated trunks of old ones often supporting heads as broad as the height, and hopelessly unsymmetrical. In the soft muck of deep swamps the trees spread out abruptly at the base into flying buttresses, each becoming hollow in course of time, as the base of the trunk is long before. Out on all sides stretch long, thick roots whose branches go down and anchor the tree, while the main ones seem designed to balance it on its uncertain foundation. The "knees" that rise up at intervals from the main roots and are distinguished from stumps by their smooth, conical shapes, are still a physiological puzzle. Many people believe that they gather air for the submerged root system. Others declare that they strengthen it. The cypresses keep their secrets from the prying investigator, and the solemn cormorants that build in the treetops will never tell.

I shall not forget an excursion on foot into one of the large bald cypress swamps of southern Florida in May. The dangerous part of the jaunt was the passage forced through a jungle of young pines, palmettoes and scrubby live oaks interlaced with wiry vines and creepers. Here rattlesnakes hide, and show fight when disturbed. Emerging at length into comparatively open timber, we stood surrounded by young cypresses with pale grey trunks, smooth, slender, and flaring widely at the bases. Among the trunks were stumps, and also knees, the latter smooth, as if the fibres went up one side and on down the other. Overhead was a feathery canopy of pale sage-green leaves. On rugged old trunks air plants found ample roothold. Orchids of sorts I had admired afar off in florists' windows held out great cataracts of bloom which were ours for the plucking. Vivid amaryllis flowers were similarly growing out of the trunks of these trees, with delicate ferns to keep them company. Under foot, the dry, sandy soil bore a crop

THE BALD CYPRESS (*Taxodium distichum*)

The trees grow in swamps made by the spring overflow of rivers. Sage-green foliage against pale grey bark gives these stretches of cypress woods a weird look in summer or winter. The leaf-bearing side shoots fall with the foliage in autumn. In the Southeast a variety, *imbricarium*, occurs, having only spiny leaves that are appressed closely around the twigs. This form has pendulous branchlets. Lover of Southern swamps, yet this is one of the best of trees for parks in the North

THE BALD CYPRESS (*Taxodium distichum*)

The base of the trunk flares abruptly into lobed buttresses. Pointed "knees" rise from the long horizontal roots of old trees. They are supposed to be means of aëration to the inundated roots. The leafy, lateral twigs are deciduous. Cypress swamps are found in the maritime regions of the Southeastern states

of unfamiliar flowers. The rainy season which opens in May inundates this land for fully half of the year.

The wood of bald cypress is very important in the lumber trade, being soft, handsome, easily worked and durable in water and in the soil. Buckets and bowls are made by hollowing out knees of suitable sizes.

Lover though it be of Southern swamps, yet there is no handsomer spire of living green in any Northern upland park than this same bald cypress. In its early years the tree is perfectly symmetrical, trim and beautiful in the feathery lightness of its leafy spray. The roots keep out of sight and there is no hint of the outlandish hollow buttresses and bare knees that characterise the tree at home. Among strangers, the bald cypress puts on its best manners; there is no more conventional and fastidious tree in the park. The tree is cultivated also in a number of varieties, some dwarfs, some weeping forms, others of stricter spire forms that lend themselves to formal effects in gardens. The heads of cypress trees grow broad in moist soil, and assume narrower form in soil with scant moisture supply.

CHAPTER XIV: THE JUNIPERS

Genus JUNIPERUS, Linn.

EVERGREEN trees or shrubs with pungent sap, thin, ragged bark, and short, much-divided ascending branches. *Leaves* usually of two kinds, linear, spiny, free, in whorls of 3 at each joint, or scale-like, blunt, in pairs, 2-ranked, opposite, and closely appressed to twigs. *Flowers* in small, inconspicuous aments, diœcious or rarely monœcious. *Fruit* berry-like, by coalescence of fleshy scales; seeds 1 to 6, wingless, bony. *Wood* soft, close grained, durable.

KEY TO SPECIES

A. Leaves free, 3 in a whorl, awl shaped, spiny; flowers axillary; berry bright blue with pale bloom; seeds 3.
　　　　　　　　(*J. communis*) DWARF JUNIPER

AA. Leaves appressed to twig, in threes or opposite, scale-like, minute; flowers terminal; berry brown or dark blue; seeds 1 to 12.

　B. Berry large, brownish red, with dry, sweet flesh.

　　C. Seeds few or solitary.

　　　D. Fruit oblong, 1 to 2-seeded; leaves in threes; twigs stout. (*J. Californica*) CALIFORNIA JUNIPER

　　　DD. Fruit round, 1-seeded; leaves in twos or threes; twigs slender. (*J. Utahensis*) UTAH JUNIPER

　　CC. Seeds 4 to 12; berry with tubercles projecting.

　　　D. Bark shed in thin, red, papery scales.
　　　　　　　(*J. flaccida*) DROOPING JUNIPER

　　　DD. Bark shed in squarish plates.
　　　　　　(*J. pachyphlœa*) CHECKER-BARKED JUNIPER

　BB. Berry small (except *occidentalis*), dark blue or black, resinous, juicy; seeds 1 to 4.

　　C. Twigs slender, pendulous.

　　　D. Seed solitary, dark ashy grey.
　　　　　　(*J. monosperma*) ONE-SEEDED JUNIPER

　　　DD. Seeds 2; berry flattened, $\frac{1}{8}$ inch in diameter; bark light reddish brown; twigs 4-angled.
　　　　　(*J. Barbadensis*) SOUTHERN RED JUNIPER

　　　DDD. Seeds 1 to 4; berry round; bark brownish red, of loose scales. (*J. sabinoides*) MOUNTAIN JUNIPER

CC. Twigs slender, stiff, erect; berry bright blue.
  (*J. scopulorum*) ROCKY MOUNTAIN JUNIPER
CCC. Twigs stout; berry dark blue with pale bloom; seeds 2 to 3.
  D. Leaves in threes, grey-green; tree a broad, low crown of large horizontal branches.
  (*J. occidentalis*) WESTERN JUNIPER
  DD. Leaves in twos, blue-green; tree a tall, narrow pyramid.
  (*J. Virginiana*) RED JUNIPER—RED CEDAR

The junipers are distinguished from most other evergreens by the fact that they are not cone bearers. The flowers are inconspicuous, and similar to a true conifer's, but in course of development the scales thicken and grow together, forming a sweet, berry-like fruit. On many of these berries the tips of the cone scales may be distinctly seen on the outer surface. Junipers usually show two kinds of leaves: (1) stiff, spiny, narrow ones, channelled and free; (2) minute, scale-like ones, opposite in pairs and pressed close to the twig. The sap is resinous and aromatic. The wood is hard, reddish, durable and light—in certain species pleasantly fragrant.

Thirty-five species of junipers are distributed over the Northern Hemisphere, contributing to the wealth of the world valuable woods and ornamental trees and shrubs. Our own red juniper has over thirty cultivated varieties. The narrow, tapering spire, the globe of compact green and the pigmy forms—all are well adapted to formal gardening. The effects produced by the classic cypress in warmer climates may be reproduced in Northern gardens by the use of junipers.

The junipers are hardy over wide stretches of territory, and will grow on sterile soil. They resist unfavourable climates and thrive, as a rule, when transplanted. They love the sun and the wind. Better trees could not be provided for windbreaks against sea breezes, on a barren, exposed coast. They are multiplied by seeds, cuttings and layers, as well as by grafting. Seeds take two or three years to germinate.

Several Asiatic and European junipers are cultivated in America in various horticultural forms. Naturally, a tribe so submissive to the gardener's shears has long been under his care. Our native species are often seen in European gardens, and *J. communis*, Linn., of Europe is often planted here in its narrow, spiny form. A much-prized Himalayan species, *J. recurva*, D. Don., is a dwarf with long, spreading or trailing limbs. Of similar habit is *J. Sabina*, Linn., native of Europe and Asia, parent of many horticultural forms.

Dwarf Juniper (*Juniperus communis*, Linn.)—Shrub of sprawling habit, or small tree 20 to 30 feet, with short trunk and irregular, open head of erect branches. *Bark* loosely scaly, thin, reddish brown. *Wood* hard, fine textured, light brown, durable in soil. *Buds* loosely scaly, small, pointed. *Leaves* in threes, boat shaped, lined with a white bloom on the concave (upper) side, spiny, spreading, dark green, shiny below; $\frac{1}{3}$ to $\frac{1}{2}$ inch long; in winter, bronze green; persistent for many years. *Flowers* monœcious, axillary, in cone-like aments. *Fruits* ripe third autumn; berries bright blue with pale bloom, flesh mealy, soft; seeds 1 to 3. *Preferred habitat*, dry limestone hills; waste land. *Distribution*, Greenland to Alaska; south to Pennsylvania and Nebraska, in Rocky Mountains as far south as Texas, New Mexico and Arizona; Alaska to northern California. *Uses:* Planted for hedges, windbreaks and as a cover for waste land on seashore. Berries used to flavour gin.

This indefatigable little tree colonist has not only settled in most of the colder parts of this country, but it is found in the Eastern Hemisphere from the broad stretches of the North even to the mountains of southern Europe, northern Africa and the Himalayas. In America it assumes a definite tree habit only in southern Illinois. It would seem as if the limestone of these uplands gave the procumbent, incapable sprawler backbone enough to stand up and take its place among trees. In another particular this species lacks energy; it requires three years to ripen a crop of berries.

Out of *J. communis* has sprung a race of low junipers—important horticultural varieties, including graceful weeping forms, compact globose ones, some spire-like and some with golden foliage. The Irish juniper, one of the most popular varieties, has a tapering habit, very narrow, like a miniature Lombardy poplar. *J. communis* is the only species whose leaves are spreading throughout. On the remaining ten native species the leaves are minute and closely appressed to the stem, except a few whose new shoots imitate the dwarf juniper. In Europe, much more than in America, the berries are gathered and consumed in the making of gin.

From time immemorial the flavour of the juniper berry has been the *sine qua non* to quality in this beverage.

California Juniper (*Juniperus Californica*, Carr.)—Conical or broad and open-headed tree, 20 to 40 feet high, with irregular, fluted trunk and twisted limbs. *Bark* thin, pale grey, hanging in loose plate-like scales. *Wood* soft, fine grained, reddish brown, durable in soil. *Leaves* in threes, on older twigs, thick keeled, set close to twig, pale yellow-green; on new shoots, linear, pale lined, spiny, spreading. *Flowers*, January to March, monœcious, in scaly aments. *Fruits* ripe second season, oblong or round, $\frac{1}{2}$ to $\frac{3}{4}$ inch long, brown, with pale bloom; seeds 1 to 2, large. *Preferred habitat*, dry plains and slopes of mountains. *Distribution*, coast mountains from the lower Sacramento Valley to Lower California; east into Sierra Nevada. *Uses:* Wood for posts and for fuel. Fruit eaten by Indians. Locally planted to some extent on semi-arid land.

The **Utah Juniper** (*Juniper Utahensis*, Lemm.) takes the place of the California species in the arid regions between the Sierra Nevada and the Rocky Mountains. It is called the desert juniper, is gnarled like its Western relative, and has much the same habit, though its round berry, with a solitary seed, and its slender twigs distinguish it. This little tree serves the settler and the Indian just as the California species does.

The **Drooping Juniper** (*Juniperus flaccida*, Schlecht.) has long, flexible branchlets that give it grace beyond the portion allotted to its kindred. The bark of this little tree is bright cinnamon and is shed in papery scales. It is a pity that this dainty juniper, which is met in gardens of Algiers and in the south of France, should be unknown to horticulture in its own country. It wastes its beauty on uninhabited slopes of the Chisos Mountains in southwestern Texas, and is common at high altitudes across the Mexican border.

The **Checker-barked Juniper** (*Juniperus pachyphlœa*, Torr.) also inhabits southwestern Texas, following arid slopes between 4,000 and 6,000 feet in altitude, and invading New Mexico, Arizona, and Mexico. It is a considerable tree, 40 to 60 feet high, with short, stout trunk and broad, horizontal spread of limb—a lusty tree to be produced on arid soil. The peculiar checkered bark gives it distinction in the genus. It is often 3 to 4 inches in thickness, and the regularity of the deep, vertical furrowing seems strikingly artificial. The tree is called "alligator juniper" in Arizona. The thickness of the bark is exceptional among junipers.

The Indians gather the fruits, which are large and copiously borne by mature trees, and put them away for winter. Though resinous in taste, the cake made out of these berries ground into meal is by no means unpalatable to white folks. Baked in the sun, it is light, sweet and easily digested. The large and plentiful berries of the other mountain junipers are used in the same way.

The **One-seeded Juniper** (*Juniperus monosperma*, Sarg.) is easily distinguished by its ashy grey bark in seasons where the berry is not there to tell the tale. This thin bark is stripped into its fibres and woven into cloth and mats by Indians. Girths of their saddles are woven of it. The berries also furnish food.

The tree grows to 50 feet high, with a strongly buttressed trunk 8 or 10 feet in girth. The limbs are short, with clustering grey-green foliage of the minute, scale-like sort. This is a tree of the mountain slope or the high plateau, ranging from Colorado to Texas, and west to Arizona, forming forests in southern Colorado and Utah. Fencing and fuel consume some wood each year.

The **Rock Cedar** (*Juniperus sabinoides*, Nees.) is a considerable tree in the lowlands of the central counties of Texas, but dwindles in size as it ascends the mountains and arid regions to the west and south. This tree has distinctly quadrangular twigs by the paired, opposite arrangement of its strongly keeled leaves. The foliage mass is loose and irregular, with a dark blue-green cast. Young shoots bear linear, free, spiny leaves $\frac{1}{2}$ inch long. The bark is reticulated by an intricate network of furrows leaving flat plates between. This juniper furnishes much fuel as well as a considerable supply of fence posts, railroad ties and telegraph poles in a region where wood is not plenty.

Red Juniper, Red Cedar (*Juniperus Virginiana*, Linn.)— Conical tree, compact when young, becoming loose and cylindrical or irregular when old; from a shrub to a tree 100 feet high and 5 feet trunk diameter; branches short, slender, ascending, becoming horizontal. *Bark* red, stringy, persistent; branches smooth. *Wood* soft, weak, close grained, red, fragrant. *Buds* minute, green. *Leaves* opposite, on old stems, 4-ranked; scale-like, blue-green, closely appressed to twigs, which seem 4-angled; on new shoots, scattered, spiny, loose, awl shaped, $\frac{1}{2}$ to $\frac{3}{4}$ inch long, pale yellow-green. *Flowers* in April, May; terminal on side twigs, diœcious, rarely monœcious; staminate of 4 to 6 scales, each bearing several pollen sacs; pistillate of minute, paired, bluish, fleshy scales, bearing two ovules. *Fruit* a blue, glaucous berry, the size of a pea, ripening the first or second season and containing 1 to 4 seeds; flesh sweet, resinous. *Preferred habitat,* dry soil or peaty swamps. *Distribution,* east of the Rocky Mountains. *Uses:* Wood used largely for pails, pencils, chests and closets, sills and interior finishing, railroad ties and fence posts.

It is unfortunate that, whereas the true cedars are all in the Old-World genus Cedrus, the American genera, Thuya, Libocedrus, Chamæcyparis and Juniperus, each have one or more species to which the name is loosely applied. It would take a long while to unlearn the name "red cedar" for this familiar tree—to write with a *juniper* pencil; to put furs and woollens away in moth-discouraging *juniper* chests. So hard it is to break a habit. The logical thing is to call this tree a juniper, as well as the other species of Juniperus, and so far reduce the confusion involved now every time the word *cedar* is mentioned.

This vagabond tree, familiar in abandoned farms and ragged fence rows of New England, is the same that grows from Nova Scotia to Georgia, and west to where the hills lift and the arid ridges become the foothills of the Rocky Mountains. A stunted tree covering the limestone plateaus of Tennessee, it is a towering pyramid of luxuriant green in the lower Mississippi Valley. Seashores of the East and South, and sterile soil on foothills of Eastern mountains, all show these scattered trees, small and bushy, or tall and compact. The berries are borne in profusion and are distributed by birds.

The leaves are 2-ranked, spiny, channelled, lined with white on new shoots and on young trees. The older parts of twigs show closely appressed scale-like leaves. Both types are found on every tree. In winter a rusty brown comes over the dark blue-green of the foliage mass, but spring revivifies it.

The trunks are columnar and corrugated; they bare themselves by shedding the stringy brown bark in longitudinal strips. In lower Pennsylvania this is a shade tree of considerable popularity. It forms windbreaks in exposed situations, on the coast or inland, where most trees fail. The tree is planted profitably for posts and railroad ties in the Mississippi Valley States. Where trees can be had large enough for telegraph or telephone poles they command the highest prices, for the wood is one of the most durable. The Fabers have for generations maintained their own forests of this species in Germany to supply their pencil factories.

An interesting "fruit" of the red juniper, much larger and more luscious looking than the diminutive berries, is familiar to boys and girls under the name "cedar apple." A remarkable thing about these pulpy, jelly-like masses, with their yellow spurs, is that they come out on the twigs as suddenly as mushrooms. Still more astonishing is the fact that this parasitic fungus that makes itself at home on the red cedar utterly ignores all red cedars when its spores are germinating to produce the next generation. Only those that fall on apple trees live. They do not produce "apples" of any sort, but patches of yellow "apple rust" on leaves and fruit. Spores wafted away from these blotches germinate only when they fall on twigs of red cedar. They grow inside, and at fruiting time throw out the gelatinous cedar-apple mass whose spurs contain the spores.

This capricious "alternation of generations" is interestingly seen in wheat rust, whose alternate host is the common barberry. A third rust goes from birches to poplars and back again to birches each alternate year.

The **Red Juniper** of the South (*Juniperus Barbadensis*, Linn.) has long been considered by good authorities a variety of the preceding species. It furnishes the highest grade of "red cedar" for pencils. Western Florida has many swampy forests of these trees. The Fabers, of pencil fame, own vast tracts here. The West Indies and the Gulf States all contribute a considerable quantity to commerce each year. Growing naturally in swamps like the bald cypress, yet it thrives when planted in parks and cemeteries. It is the most beautiful of the junipers in cultivation. Its slender, spreading branches clothed with pendulous twigs, give unusual grace to the tree habit. The berries are silvery white and abundant. Its susceptibility to frost confines this tree's range to the Southern States.

The **Rocky Mountain Juniper** (*Juniperus scopulorum*, Sarg.) has stout twigs and limbs, usually a short trunk with several main limbs carrying the top. Its foliage is often pale grey-green —a fashionable colour on the Western plains and foothills. It climbs to elevations of over 5,000 feet, and few soils are too poor and too arid to support it. It follows the Rocky Mountains from

THE JUNIPER (*Juniperus communis*)

Branch with flowers and fruit

THE RED CEDAR (*Juniperus Virginiana*)

Blue berries take the place of cones in this conifer. Beside the scale-like leaves that are closely shingled upon the wiry twigs, needle-like, free leaves occur on the older parts. The tall narrow pyramid of short branches above a fluted trunk is familiar all over the eastern half of this country. The wood is used to make chests and wardrobes moth-proof, and in the making of pencils, pails and posts

THE WESTERN JUNIPER (*Juniperus occidentalis*)

Distinguished by its fluted trunk and twisted limbs covered with loosely scaling cinnamon red bark. It is found in the mountains of Idaho, Oregon, western Washington and California

THE LODGE-POLE PINE (*Pinus contorta*, var. *Murrayana*)

This slender pine grows in dense forests in the mountains of the West. The Indians use the saplings for lodge poles, and the nutritious inner bark is baked into bread

Alberta to Texas on the eastern slopes; on the western slopes it enters Washington, Oregon and California.

The larger fruit, requiring two years to ripen, the broader head, the stouter branches and twigs, the paler foliage, and the shreddy bark distinguish this species from the true red juniper which meets it on the hither boundaries of the Rockies, and from which it was but recently separated by botanists.

Western Juniper (*Juniperus occidentalis*, Hook.)—Low, broad-headed tree, 20 to 65 feet high, with unusually thick trunk and stout, horizontal branches. *Bark* ½ inch thick, bright crimson-red, in broad, scaly ridges, with shallow irregular interlacing furrows. *Wood* soft, light, pale reddish brown, fine grained, very durable in the soil. *Leaves* in threes, minute, closely appressed to twigs, grey-green, tapering, sharp pointed. *Flowers* cone-like, monœcious, inconspicuous. *Fruit* a blue-black berry with pale bloom, ¼ to ⅓ inch long; seeds 2 to 3. *Preferred habitat*, mountain sides and elevated plains, 6,000 to 10,000 feet. *Distribution*, western Idaho, Washington, Oregon and California, following the Sierra Nevada Mountains to the San Bernardino range. *Uses:* Wood for fencing and fuel. Bark woven into mats and cloth by Indians. Fruit an important article of food among California tribes.

Here is one of the patriarchal trees of America—one whose age ranks it with the Sequoias, dating the birth of the oldest back, assuredly, more than 2,000 years. It is impossible to find a giant with trunk sound to the core and telling the whole story in its annual rings. John Muir is probably the only man who has made serious inquiry into this matter. On the bleak ridges of the Sierras, with no soil but crumbs of disintegrating granite, these trees make scarcely any gain from year to year. Two of Muir's measurements are given below, the years being determined by the number of annual rings.

Diameter of Trunk	Age
2 feet 11 inches	1,140 years
1 foot 7½ inches	834 years

Being a poet as well as a scientist, John Muir was deterred from the killing of one of the elders, merely to appease his curiosity. Beside, dry rot and scars of ancient hurts confuse the reader of tree rings, and throw him upon estimates, after all. The difficulties of chopping down a tree 10 feet in diameter would discourage the most ardent searcher after treasures of fact hid in a tree trunk. A chip a foot deep chopped out of a medium-sized tree—6 feet in diameter—showed an average of fifty-seven years of growth required to make an inch of wood. On soil deposited in the high valleys by glacial rivers these junipers grow about as fast as oaks. They are the well-fed, commonplace members of the family, growing tall and straight under favouring skies.

I cannot forbear a quotation from John Muir's "Forests of the Yosemite Park," for he knows these mountain trees personally, and has interpreted them to the world as no other man has done:

"The sturdy storm-enduring red cedar (*Juniperus occidentalis*) delights to dwell on the tops of granite domes and ridges and glacier pavements of the upper pine belt, at an elevation of 7,000 to 10,000 feet, where it can get plenty of sunshine and snow and elbow room, without encountering quick-growing, overshadowing rivals. They never make anything like a forest, seldom come together even in groves, but stand out separate and independent in the wind, clinging by slight joints to the rock, living chiefly on snow and thin air, and maintaining tough health on this diet for 2,000 years or more, every feature and gesture expressing steadfast, dogged endurance. . . . Many are mere stumps as broad as high, broken by avalanches and lightning, picturesquely tufted with dense grey scale-like foliage, and giving no hint of dying. . . . Barring accidents, for all I can see, they would live forever. When killed, they waste out of existence about as slowly as granite. Even when overthrown by avalanches, after standing so long, they refuse to lie at rest, leaning stubbornly on their big elbows as if anxious to rise, and while a single root holds to the rocks, putting forth fresh leaves with a grim never-say-die and never-lie-down expression."

CHAPTER XV: THE TORREYAS

FAMILY TAXACEÆ

Genus TUMION, Raf.

ORNAMENTAL evergreens, with spreading, usually whorled branches and ill-smelling sap. *Leaves* 2-ranked, linear, with paler linings. *Flowers* diœcious (rarely monœcious), scaly at base. *Fruit* like a plum; seed large, solitary. *Wood* hard, durable, strong, close grained.

KEY TO SPECIES

A. Leaves linear; branches spreading, pendulous.
    B. Length of leaves $\frac{3}{4}$ to $1\frac{1}{2}$ inches, bark brown, tinged with orange; fruit dark purple, obovate, 1 to $1\frac{1}{4}$ inches long.   (*T. taxifolium*) FLORIDA TORREYA
    BB. Length of leaves $\frac{1}{3}$ to $\frac{1}{2}$ inch, bark brownish grey; fruit pale green, streaked with purple, oval, 1 to $1\frac{1}{2}$ inches long.   (*T. Californica*) CALIFORNIA TORREYA
AA. Leaves lanceolate, spiny pointed; branches spreading, compact; bark bright red; fruit ovoid, less than 1 inch long. (Exotic.)   (*T. nucifera*) JAPANESE TORREYA

The Torreyas, close relatives of the yews, are yet little known outside their native ranges, though they are coming into cultivation in the warmer parts of the country. They are objectionable only on account of the bad odour of their leaves when bruised. The tree habit is symmetrically pyramidal, the whorled limbs pendulous, and the foliage handsome. The trees furnish some fence posts. The wood is very durable in wet soil, which is their chosen habitat.

Torreyas are propagated from seeds and by cuttings. The latter grow slowly, producing plants that remain low and bushy for years. The Florida species has proved hardy in sheltered situations as far north as Boston, but the Californian cannot survive the cold of this high latitude.

The Japanese Torreya promises more hardiness than our native species, and more beauty in cultivation. In habit it is compact with erect limbs, quite different from the pendulous-limbed natives. The bright red bark adds to its beauty, as also does the breadth and fine shape of the lanceolate leaves. In Japan this tree is highly prized for its wood, which is used in cabinet work and building. A Chinese species, *T. grandis*, resembling the Japanese, is said to lack the disagreeable odour of the other species.

The **Florida Torreya** (*T. taxifolium*, Greene) is very local in the northwestern part of that state, growing on bluffs along the Appalachicola River. It is rarely 40 feet high, and is called the "stinking cedar."

The **California Nutmeg** (*T. Californicum*, Greene) is a larger tree, handsome in its youthful vigour, in age losing its pyramidal form and becoming round-topped. It is a striking evergreen at any age, with its pale grey bark and its fruits hanging like half-ripe plums among the sprays of prickly, sickle-shaped, linear leaves. The pit of the fruit resembles a nutmeg. A fine grove of these trees is within the borders of the Yosemite Park. Nowhere common, they occur on slopes of the Sierras and Santa Cruz Mountains between 3,000 and 5,000 feet above sea level.

CHAPTER XVI: THE YEWS

Family Taxaceæ

Genus TAXUS, Linn.

Evergreen trees and shrubs, with spreading, horizontal branches, and purple, scaly bark. *Leaves* linear, spiny, 2-ranked, pale beneath. *Flowers* minute, diœcious, in axillary heads. *Fruit* berry-like, fleshy, sweet, scarlet.

KEY TO SPECIES

A. Foliage yellow-green, short.   (*T. brevifolia*) PACIFIC YEW
AA. Foliage dark green, long.   (*T. Floridana*) FLORIDA YEW

There are six known species of yew, all confined to the Northern Hemisphere. The fruit is farther away from the coniferous type than that of any true member of the Family Coniferæ. Yet careful analysis of flowers and fruit show that the parts are there—the scales and the naked ovules—though development obliterates the signs of relationship to the pines and hemlocks.

The **Old-World Yew** (*T. baccata*, Linn.) is native to Europe, Asia and Africa. Its history is interwoven with the growth of civilisation. In the folk lore of the English cottagers the yew was saddest of all trees except the cypress. Branches of yew were gathered to deck the house where a body lay awaiting burial. The heads of mourners were bound with chaplets of yew. The sombre yew tree drooping over a grave was a favourite symbol in our great-grandmother's samplers, even so late as a century ago.

> "Pluck, pluck cypress, O pale maidens,
> Dusk, O dusk the hall with yew!
> Weep, and wring
> Every hand; and every head
> Bind with cypress and sad yew
> For him that was of men most true."

115

Yews were planted in churchyards, especially in the south of England. Could any dirge be sadder than the lines above quoted, or any tree a better symbol of inarticulate grief? There was another idea that probably was considered to lighten the gloom of funereal thoughts. The yew is one of the long-lived trees. It was regarded in some quarters as the emblem of immortality. The name, yew, is believed to come from the same root as *ewig*, the German word meaning "everlasting."

In the early wars the yeoman drew a long bow made of the tough wood of his native yew. Spenser called the tree "the shooter eugh." The English soldier *bent* his bow; the Frenchman *drew* his. The former was too heavy to lift. Bishop Latimer describes its use by the soldier on the battlefield:

"Keeping his right hand at rest upon the nerve, he pressed the whole weight of his body into the horns of his bow."

Beside its toughness and elasticity, the wood has other admirable qualities. It lasts indefinitely in soil and exposed to the weather. Its grain is often as handsome as mahogany. The roots often show wavy areas, which when polished and made into tables vied in beauty with the ancient and precious citron wood. Burs of yew were a favourite veneer for tea caddies.

The best soil for yew trees is chalk, hence the tree grows its best in the Channel counties of England. Yet even in Scotland famous trees of remarkable age are recorded. The Fotheringal (Fortingall) Yew, 57 feet in circumference, proved by the rings of its stump that it had lived almost 3,000 years—"a world-old yew tree." "Addison's Walk," at Glasnevin, Ireland, lies between two rows of ancient yews. A close-bodied, compact tree, and tonsile beyond any other, the yew has always been a tree to cut into grotesque and geometrical forms for the adornment of gardens in England and on the Continent. In the United States it is similarly employed where formal effects are desired. The tree is also grown and allowed to take its normal shape and reach what size it will. It is offered by nurserymen in many varieties.

The **Pacific Yew** (*Taxus brevifolia*, Nutt.)—A tree with broad head, of long, horizontal, pendulous limbs, and trunk irregularly lobed and flattened. *Bark* thin, covered with purplish scales. *Wood* heavy, hard, strong, red. *Leaves* short, linear, 2-ranked, pale beneath, yellowish. *Flowers* diœcious, minute, in leaf axils. *Fruit* a translucent, scarlet berry. *Preferred*

116

habitat, ravines and stream banks. *Distribution,* mountains of coast, from Alaska to southern California, east to Montana. *Uses:* Wood for posts, paddles and bows.

The cheerful green of its foliage relieves this yew of any funereal suggestion. It is a beautiful, if rarely a symmetrical evergreen tree, surprising tourists and delighting the birds with its brilliant berries in autumn. The Indian of Alaska cuts spear shafts, bows, paddles and other articles out of its wood. The settler uses it for fencing.

The **Florida Yew** (*T. Floridana,* Chapm.) is a small tree of bushy habit, often of many stems not 20 feet high. It has the dark green of its European relative, and the same mournful expression. It is found only along the east bank of the Appalachicola River in the northwestern corner of the state.

Our Eastern yew (*Taxus minor,* Britt.), commonly, but incorrectly, called ground hemlock, never assumes tree form, but is a sprawling shrub, its dense foliage forming in autumn a rich background for the bright scarlet berries. In cultivation this species becomes less straggling in growth. It is oftenest planted where an undercover is desired on irregular wooded ground. Its foliage takes on a warm tinge of red in winter. The berries are the delight of birds and boys. This is the hardiest yew.

CHAPTER XVII: THE PALMS AND THE PALMETTOS

FAMILY PALMÆ

THE Palm family is a large group of tropical flowering plants, related to lilies on one side and grasses on the other. Like both of these, palms have but one cotyledon (seed leaf) in the embryo, and the stem is composed of a hardened outer layer within which is a mass of felt-like tissue in which longitudinal bundles of tough wood cells are irregularly distributed. Growth is internal, about these bundles as centres—not external, from a cambium. The parts of the flowers are regularly in threes, as in the lilies. The leaves are parallel veined, and they sheathe the stem, as in the grasses. They are fan shaped or feather shaped.

Palms are allied closely to the Arums, of which our jack-in-the-pulpit is a familiar representative. Both families have monœcious flowers borne separately on different parts of a central spadix, surrounded by a conspicuous spathe, or sheath. Both families have berry-like fruit, sometimes hardened outside.

Of palms there are now recognised over one hundred genera and about one thousand species. Botanically, the family is an old one, and on the decline. Fossils of Tertiary rocks show what it was in its prime. Three hundred and sixty distinct and important uses are credited to palms by Evelyn. No human need but they supply in the primitive life of tropical people. In the commerce of the world they play no mean part. In the tropics, houses are built and furnished throughout from the native palms. Their leaves thatch the walls and roofs. They supply thread for weaving cloth, ropes, fish nets and lines, mats, fans, shields and hats. Spines furnish needles and barbed fishhooks. Sap gives wine, sugar and wax. Stems give fresh salads and sago for food, and wands for basketwork and furniture. Fruits of palms include cocoanuts, dates, and some of these yield chocolate and valuable oils.

KEY TO GENERA

A. Leaves long, feather shaped.
　　B. Fruit blue, below leaf cluster.
　　　　　　　　　　　　1. Genus ROYSTONEA, Cook
　　BB. Fruit orange-scarlet, among leaves.
　　　　　　　　　　　2. Genus PSEUDOPHŒNIX, H. Wendl.
AA. Leaves round, fan shaped.
　　B. Leaf stalks spiny.
　　　　C. Leaves 5 to 6 feet long; petioles 4 to 6 feet long.
　　　　　　　　　　　3. Genus WASHINGTONIA, H. Wendl.
　　　　CC. Leaves 2 feet long; petioles 1½ to 2 feet long.
　　　　　　　　　　　　4. Genus SERENOA, Hook.
　　BB. Leaf stalks not spiny.
　　　　C. Fruit white.
　　　　　　　　　　　5. Genus THRINAX, Sw.
　　　　CC. Fruit black.
　　　　　　D. Calyx and corolla united into a cup.
　　　　　　　　　　　6. Genus COCCOTHRINAX, Sarg.
　　　　　　DD. Calyx and corolla separate.
　　　　　　　　　　　7. Genus SABAL, Adans.

1. Genus ROYSTONEA, Cook

The **Royal Palm** (*Roystonea regia*, Cook) is one of the
noblest of tropical trees, bearing its abundant crown of foliage,
each leaf 10 to 12 feet long, and bending gradually outward and
downward, with a grace peculiarly its own. The tall trunks,
80 to 100 feet in height, rise from abruptly flaring bases, and are
enlarged in the middle. The rind is pale grey tinged with orange,
except for the upper 10 feet or more, which is always green.
The flowers of this tree are borne in branched spikes, about 2
feet long, and clustered at the base of the leafy crown. They
bloom in January and February, and are succeeded by oblong
berries, violet in colour and ½ inch long.

The trees grow from Bay Biscayne around the southern
point of Florida and on Long's Key, the vanguard of a host that
inhabits Central America and the West Indies. They are also
found on hummock lands up the Rogers River, east of Collier's
Bay. A famous avenue tree in tropical cities, the trunks are
used for piles of wharves, and walking sticks are made from the
dense outer rind.

2. Genus PSEUDOPHŒNIX, H. Wendl.

The **Sargent Palm** (*Pseudophœnix Sargenti*, H. Wendl.) is found only on Key Largo and Elliott Key. A slender tree with white rind tapering from the middle to the leafy top and the flaring base, it is distinguished from the royal palm by the shorter leaves which stand erect, and the orange-coloured fruits that hang ripe among the leaves in May and June. The tree is found in a considerable grove on Key Largo. The flowers have not been described. Young trees are sometimes met with now in Florida gardens.

3. Genus WASHINGTONIA, H. Wendl.

The **Desert Palm** of California (*Washingtonia filamentosa*, O. Kuntze) is a striking feature of the Colorado desert and of cañon sides in the neighbouring mountains. It is found in groves or in isolated clumps in wet alkali soil, where it rises to the height of 50 to 75 feet, a crown of spreading, fan-like leaves above a stout trunk clothed almost to the ground with a dense thatch of the dead leaves, which, bending back upon each other in succession, form a broad basal cone. The black berries are profusely borne on the branching spikes in September. They are dry and thin fleshed, but Indians use them for food. The Washington palm has come into extensive cultivation in California and southern Europe.

4. Genus SERENOA, Hook.

Serenoa arborescens, Sarg., grows on hummocks in swampy lands along the southwestern coast of Florida. It is a slender tree 30 to 40 feet high, often with more than one arching or prostrate stem. The fan-like leaves are pale yellow-green above, blue-green below, and about 2 feet across. The flower stems are branched and about a yard long, thickly set with minute yellowish flowers, which are followed by resinous black drupes.

5. Genus THRINAX, Sw.

The **Thatch,** or **Silk-top Palmetto** (*Thrinax Floridana*, Sarg.) has a silver lining in its glossy green fan leaves, making

THE DESERT PALM (*Washingtonia filamentosa*)

Seventy-five feet above the ground is the fountain of fan-shaped leaves. Dead leaves turn back and hang in an overlapping thatch upon the upper part of the trunk. This clothes short trees to the ground. Indians use as food the dry, black berries that ripen in September. Native to the Colorado desert, this palm has come into extensive cultivation in California and southern Europe

THE CABBAGE PALMETTO (*Sabal Palmetto*)

A globular crown of fan-like leaves surmounts a columnar stem, which is bare and smooth only when old. The average tree fifteen feet high has its trunk covered with a basket work, which is the natural interlacing of leaf bases whose fans have fallen away. The "cabbage" is the crown bud which is chopped out of the end of the stem. The trunks are used as piles for wharves

it a beautiful and showy tree. It mounts its leaf crown 20 or 30 feet high on a slender white stem which is clothed half way down in the sheaths of dead leaf stalks. The branched flower stems are pendant from among the leaves; the fruit is a white berry with bitter juice. The tree inhabits coral reefs and the mainland coast between Cape Romano and Cape Sable.

Another silver-leaved **Thatch** (*T. Keyensis*, Sarg.) rises on a supporting framework of its own roots 2 or 3 feet above the beach sand of the Marquesas Keys, Crab Key and the Bahamas.

The **Silver-top Palmetto** (*T. microcarpa*, Sarg.) has its leaves coated when they unfold with dense white down. Flowers and fruit are abundant but minute. The tree rarely exceeds 25 feet in height. It inhabits No Name and Bahia Hondo Keys, south of Florida. The leaves of the three species are used for weaving hats, baskets and ropes. The trunks are used as piles for wharves.

6. Genus COCCOTHRINAX, Sarg.

The **Brittle Thatch** (*Coccothrinax jucunda*, Sarg.) is a slender tree, 20 to 30 feet high, with a gradually tapering blue trunk. It inhabits the shores of Bay Biscayne, and follows the Keys to the Marquesas group. The round leaves furnish fibre for baskets and hats. The stems are used in construction, chiefly for wharves.

7. Genus SABAL, Adans.

The **Cabbage Palmetto** (*Sabal Palmetto*, R. & S.) is one of the characteristic features of the southeastern coast. It attains its largest size on the west coast of Florida. Its western limit on the Gulf is the mouth of the Appalachicola River. It extends north to the Cape Fear River in North Carolina.

A crown of spreading, fan-like leaves surmounts a stout stem which is covered for a considerable distance from the top with the broad concave petioles of the leaves. These are finally split by the enlargement of the growing stem, giving the trunk the appearance of being encased in a kind of regular basketwork. Trees 20 feet high are common along sandy shores. Less frequently North, but often in Florida, one sees these trees 30 to 40 feet tall, with bare, slender stems crowned with round, leafy heads, looking almost like the royal palms. The great clusters of small yellow flowers followed by black berries hang from among the leaves, ripe in autumn but persisting into the following summer.

The cabbage palmetto grows, as do all palms, from a central terminal bud. This bud is the "cabbage" in this genus, a tender, succulent vegetable which is cut out of the middle of the stem, cooked and eaten. It is said to be "the very quintescence of cabbage." It is, of course, the death of the tree to lose this growing point.

The fibrous roots are matted in an intricate fashion under these trees, and long, tough rootlets go out on all sides for twenty feet or more. The wood is soft and spongy, with many hard fibro-vascular bundles running lengthwise of the stem. The outer rind is thick and much lighter than the centre. The trunks are used as piles and manufactured. into canes and other small articles. The fibrous bark in cross section is made into cheap scrubbing brushes, and fibres of leaf sheaths make the bristles of more permanent ones. Houses are thatched with the adult leaves. Baskets, hats and mats are made from strips of the white, immature leaves. In Southeastern cities palmettos are used as a street and ornamental tree to a considerable extent. "Palmetto scrub" is the bane of hunters, surveyors and others who are obliged to go on foot through regions covered with the tough young growth of these trees.

The **Mexican Palmetto** (*Sabal Mexicana*, Mart.) grows in the valley of the Rio Grande in Texas and down the coast to Mexico. Its height somewhat exceeds that of the cabbage palmetto, which it strongly resembles. The trunks are used for wharf piles, and leaves for the thatching of houses. It is a favourite street tree in many Texas towns.

CHAPTER XVIII: THE YUCCAS

FAMILY LILIACEÆ

THE traveller who is a close observer of trees will be astonished to find the lily family well represented in our Southern silva. Now, a lily is formed by the rule of three, as shown in the flower and in the seed pod. It has parallel-veined leaves and a stem with bundles of fibres distributed through its softer substance, much like the stems of corn or bamboo.

The yuccas are our arborescent lilies. There are nine species that attain the form and stature of trees. They are beautiful flowering trees, especially prized in countries of scant rainfall. They are planted for hedges. The fibrous leaves furnish material for ropes, mattings and baskets. The fleshy roots are used as a substitute for soap.

The **Spanish Bayonet** (*Yucca aloifolia*, Linn.) grows along the coast from North Carolina to Louisiana, preferring the borders of swamps or sand dunes, and moving inland on sandy soil. It is a low tree, rarely 25 feet high, with three or four main branches above the short, thick trunk. The leaves clothe the trunk until it is quite well grown, when they are found only on the branches, the newest ones clustered in rosettes at the ends. These bayonet-shaped leaves are smooth, dark green, about 2 feet long, stiff pointed, and saw toothed on each edge. The base of each widens into a crescent. Large panicles of flowers, leathery, white, purple tinged, are followed in autumn by green, soft, cucumber-like fruits, 3 to 4 inches long, which turn black and dry up on the stem. They are eaten by birds and occasionally by people. This yucca is very common in gardens. It is a fairly hardy species.

The **Spanish Bayonet**, or **Spanish Dagger** (*Yucca Treculeana*, Carr.), of Texas, has blue-green leaves, which are lanceolate and rough on the under side. The flowers of this species are brightly flushed with purple. It grows wild in considerable areas, a striking feature of the landscape, and is common in Texas gardens.

By these two species the characters of the genus are exemplified, and the remaining seven species will readily be referred to the genus. There are no other trees likely to be confused with yuccas.

THE CACTI

Allied to the mangroves and the myrtles, but like the yuccas in some particulars, and in choosing desert regions to live in, are the cacti, two genera of which have tree-like species in the United States. The soft stems of these trees are storehouses of moisture, as are also the fleshy branches. All green surfaces perform the functions of leaves. The spiny processes are the character by which most people recognise a cactus. The flowers are large and showy, formed into a tube by many overlapping sepals and petals. The fruit is a fleshy, many-seeded berry. The tree cacti are found in desert regions near the boundary between the United States and Mexico.

DOGWOOD TREE IN FULL BLOOM (*Cornus florida*)

CHAPTER XIX: THE WALNUTS AND THE HICKORIES

FAMILY JUGLANDACEÆ

Genera, JUGLANS and HICORIA

RESINOUS, aromatic trees with hard wood. *Leaves* deciduous, alternate, pinnately compound. *Flowers* monœcious: staminate lateral, in catkins; pistillate terminal, in spikes, or solitary. *Fruit*, a bony nut enclosed in a spongy husk.

KEY TO GENERA AND SPECIES

A. Pith of twigs chambered; husk not opening at maturity; nuts not smooth.
    1. Genus JUGLANS, Linn.
  B. Fruit elongated, clammy, in racemes; heart wood light brown.   (*J. cinerea*) BUTTERNUT
 BB. Fruit globular, not clammy; solitary or paired; heart wood dark brown.
    C. Nuts deeply and irregularly ridged, large.
        (*J. nigra*) BLACK WALNUT
   CC. Nuts deeply furrowed, small, thick shelled.
        (*J. rupestris*) MEXICAN WALNUT
  CCC. Nuts faintly furrowed, small, thin shelled.
        (*J. Californica*) CALIFORNIA WALNUT
AA. Pith of twigs solid; husk opening by 4 valves; nuts smooth.
    2. Genus HICORIA, Raf.
  B. Bud scales many, overlapping, leaflets 3 to 9.
    C. Buds small, $\frac{1}{4}$ to $\frac{1}{2}$ inch long; husk of nut thin.
      D. Twigs and leaf stalks smooth. (*H. glabra*) PIGNUT
     DD. Twigs and leaf stalks silvery pubescent.
        (*H. villosa*) PALE-LEAF HICKORY
   CC. Buds large, $\frac{1}{2}$ to 1 inch long, husk of nut thick.
      D. Bark shaggy; twigs smooth.
        E. Branchlets stout, orange red; nuts large, thick shelled. (*H. laciniosa*) BIG SHELLBARK
       EE. Branchlets stout, grey; nuts small, usually thick shelled. (*H. ovata*) LITTLE SHELLBARK

EEE. Branchlets slender, reddish; nuts 4-angled, thin shelled.
(*H. Carolinae-septentrionalis*) SHAGBARK HICKORY
DD. Bark not shaggy; twigs downy.
(*H. alba*) MOCKERNUT
BB. Bud scales few, not overlapping; leaflets 7 to 13.
C. Nuts elongated.
D. Kernel sweet.
E. Leaves silvery and lustrous beneath; nuts solitary, or few in a cluster; leaflets 7 to 11.
(*H. myristicæformis*) NUTMEG HICKORY
EE. Leaves not silvery beneath; nuts 3 to 10 in cluster; leaflets 13 to 15. (*H. Pecan*) PECAN
DD. Kernel bitter; leaflets 7 to 11, twigs and husks hairy. (*H. Texana*) BITTER PECAN
CC. Nuts not elongated; bitter.
D. Buds yellow; nuts smooth; leaflets 7 to 9.
(*H. mimina*) BITTERNUT
DD. Buds red; nut angled; leaflets 9 to 13.
(*H. aquatica*) WATER HICKORY

THE WALNUTS

The walnuts (genus *Juglans*) form a noble family of ten species, in which there are no "black sheep"—and this is remarkable in any family. Each species yields valuable wood, and sweet, edible nuts. Each one deserves planting as an ornamental and shade tree.

Our American forests show four species—two spread over the eastern half of the continent, one grows in the Southwest, and one in California. To these have been added valuable exotic species. The English or Persian walnut (*Juglans regia*) is grown in the Southern States and in California; and two Japanese species, *J. Sieboldiana* and *J. cordiformis*, both of the butternut type but vastly superior to it, thrive in the regions where the English walnut is not hardy. There is also a Manchurian species in cultivation here. One or more walnuts belong in the West Indies and South America.

Butternut, Oil Nut, White Walnut (*J. cinerea*, Linn.)— A short-trunked, spreading tree, 50 to 75 feet high, with broad, rounded dome. *Bark* grey, rough, with broad furrows and narrow ridges, showing paler under bark. Shoots covered with clammy down. *Wood* light brown, light, soft, coarse grained, with satiny lustre. *Buds* often one above another in axils, hairy, flattened, terminal largest; inner scales later becoming leaf-like; flower buds naked. *Leaves* alternate, compound, of 11 to 19 leaflets, hairy, taper pointed, serrate, sessile, except terminal leaflet, 15 to 30 inches long, yellow-green, turning yellow in autumn; leaflets 3 to 5 inches long; petioles and veins pubescent and clammy. *Flowers*, May, with leaves, staminate in catkins, 3 to 5 inches long, yellow-green with copious pollen; pistillate in 6 to 8-flowered racemes, covered with glandular hairs; stigmas 2, bright red, spreading; ovule solitary at base of pistil. *Fruit*, October, an oblong nut in spongy, clammy, sticky, indehiscent husk, with pungent odour; shell thick, deeply sculptured; nut oily, sweet, edible. *Preferred habitat*, deep, rich loam of river valleys, or well-drained hillsides. *Distribution*, New Brunswick to Delaware, and along mountains to Georgia and Alabama; westward through Ontario to Dakota, south to Arkansas. *Uses:* Planted for shade and for nuts. Wood used for interior finish of houses and for cabinet work. Inner bark and husks yield yellow dye and medicinal substances. Sap sweet, sometimes added to maple sap in making sugar. Nuts pickled when green; locally sold when ripe.

The butternut is a short-trunked, low-headed tree, with far-reaching arms that make a crown wider than it is high. There is a tendency to develop the under buds on each twig. This gives a horizontal rather than an upward trend to the limbs. The foliage, trunk and wood are lighter in colour than those of the black walnut. It is a cheerful tree, but unfortunately short lived, and it is rare to see a tree of considerable size that is not diseased by fungi and blemished by insects. The wind breaks the long limbs, whereupon enemies enter and take possession. The winter buds of the butternut are full of character. The leaf scars are prominent, and two or three buds stand in a vertical row above each one. The first bud, just above the hairy "beetling brow" of the leaf scar, is to produce the leafy shoot next spring. Those higher up at the same joint are bare little green pineapples— the staminate catkins in an immature state. The grey-green downy twigs are clammy to the touch, and inside is the wonderful chambered pith that distinguishes all the walnuts.

One need only crush a twig or leaf of a walnut tree to have revived the memory of long-forgotten experiences in brown

October's woods. O the smell of those juicy brown husks as we cracked the green nuts on a convenient stone, and wiped our damp fingers ineffectually on the grass! The stains wore off at length, but the memories are indelible. The Shakers of Lebanon, Massachusetts, got a rich purple dye by adding something to the brown extract of those husks.

The wood of butternut is not so hard nor so strong as black walnut, but for the interior finish of houses it has a distinct advantage. Black walnut is sombre compared with the cheerful browns and fawn colours which this wood shows. The "natural wood finish" brings out these quiet tones and imparts a soft lustre to the grain. It is a pity that this wood is not more common and more widely employed for this particular purpose. It is made into wooden bowls, and used for veneering bureaus, for carriage panels, and for coffins, posts, rails and fuel.

The frugal housewife in the country looks with interest upon the butternut when it is half grown—when the pale green, clammy, fuzzy fruit hangs in clusters, surrounded by its umbrella of leaves. If a knitting needle goes through husk and nut without hindrance, it is not too late to make "pickled oil nuts," which are a delectable relish with meats in winter. The husk and all are put down in vinegar, sugar and spices. The unpleasant part of this process is the rubbing off of the "fur," after scalding the nuts. This task usually falls to the children.

Butternut husks and bark have long been used in home remedies, and in dyeing woollen cloth. The backwoods regiments in the Civil War were clad in "butternut" jeans, a home-made, home-dyed uniform that worthily stood the hardest service.

Black Walnut (*Juglans nigra*, Linn.)—A majestic, spreading tree, 80 to 150 feet high, with tall trunk, 4 to 6 feet through. *Bark* dark brown, furrowed, scaly. *Wood* dark purplish brown, with silvery lustre; hard, fine grained, heavy, strong, durable in contact with soil. *Buds:* terminal, flattened, silky, tomentose; axillary, small, globose, silky; flower buds naked. *Leaves* alternate, 12 to 24 inches long, odd pinnate of 13 to 25 leaflets, ovate-lanceolate, serrate, pubescent beneath, 3 to 3½ inches long, sessile on leaf stem; yellow-green, becoming yellow in autumn; petioles downy. *Flowers*, May, with leaves, greenish, monœcious, staminate in catkins 3 to 6 inches long on wood of preceding year; pistillate on new shoots, in axillary few-flowered clusters, or

A. Pistillate flowers   B. Pith chambers   C. Winter buds   Staminate flower

THE BUTTERNUT (*Juglans cinerea*)

A clammy down covers new shoots and leaf stalks. Aromatic sap and chambered pith characterise all walnuts. The winter buds and leaf scars are peculiar. The flowers appear in May with the leaves. The staminate are in pendulous catkins; the pistillate in terminal racemes. The wood is brown with a satiny lustre

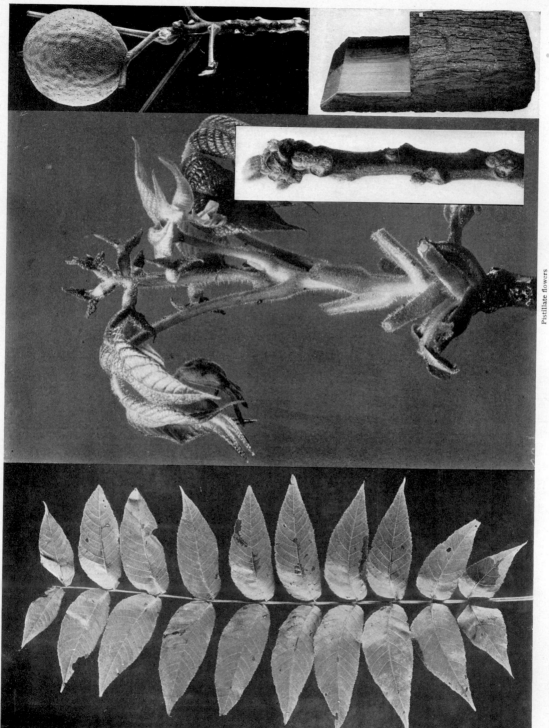

Pistillate flowers

THE BLACK WALNUT (*Juglans nigra*)

Young shoots are velvety and aromatic but not clammy. The leaves are velvety beneath. The pistillate flowers are in terminal spikes of 3 to 5 flowers. The spreading, forked stigmas are tinged with red. The globular nuts are solitary or paired on short stalks. The spongy husk is yellowish brown and pitted, but not hairy or sticky. The wood is purplish brown; the bark reddish and dark

solitary; stigmas red, prominent. *Fruit* 1 to 2 in almost sessile clusters, globose 1½ to 2 inches in diameter; husk yellow-green, pitted, strongly aromatic, spongy, indehiscent; shell hard, deeply sculptured, kernel convoluted, oily, sweet, edible. *Preferred habitat,* rich woods. *Distribution,* southern Ontario to Florida, west to Nebraska and Texas. *Uses:* Fine shade and park tree; lumber valuable for veneering furniture, interior finish of houses, gun stocks and coffins, and for boat and shipbuilding. Nuts locally commercial. Husks occasionally used for dyeing and tanning.

The early settlers did not realise the folly they committed by chopping down black walnut trees, rolling them together and burning them. They were clearing the land to make farms, and trees were weeds they had to conquer. They did not discriminate between species in the general holocaust. They knew that black walnut was durable, so made fence posts and rails of it. Besides, this wood split easily.

The peculiar fitness of black walnut wood for gun stocks and for furniture was realised later. Trees were sacrificed by thousands to supply the home and foreign markets, and only Nature planted for the generations to come. The result is the present shortage of walnut lumber, and its excessive price. Enterprising individuals go into cleared ground and pull the stumps of trees long dead. They are still sound, and there is valuable veneering stuff in the most of them. Old and worn furniture of solid black walnut is bought and sawed thin for the same purpose. Do we realise yet the usefulness and the beauty of black walnut wood? The silvery grain, the rich, violet-purple tones in the brown heart wood, the exquisite shading of its curly veinings, and the lasting qualities of the wood? If we did, we would plant groves of it.

As a fruit tree the black walnut has limitations. The oil in the kernel soon becomes rancid, so that there can be but a local market for the nuts, though they are very good for a time, when carefully dried.

The black walnut is majestic as a shade tree—a noble ornament to parks and pleasure grounds. It needs room and distance to show its luxuriant crown and stately trunk to advantage. Then no tree excels it. "It unites almost all the qualities desirable in a tree: beauty, gracefulness and richness of foliage in every period of its growth." The bark and husks may be employed in the important arts of dyeing and tanning. The fruit is a food, and yields a valuable oil. The wood is one of the most useful and most elegant.

The growth of the black walnut is rapid and sure from the seed. Nuts gathered in the autumn should be stratified in gravel over winter, and planted next spring. The way to restore what we have lost is to plant walnuts wherever there is a place suitable for such a tree.

The **Walnut** (*J. rupestris*, Engelm.) of the far Southwest grows on cañon sides and stream borders, climbing the mountains to an elevation of 6,000 feet—a shrub in the high semi-arid regions, a spreading tree where its thirsty roots can find water in unfailing supply. The limbs are covered with white bark, and the twigs are cottony. This makes the leafless tree a striking and beautiful feature of winter landscapes, especially where there is a dark background.

.The little nuts have deeply grooved and very thick shells, but the Indians and Mexicans are glad to take trouble to get at the sweet kernels within. The hard shell is, however, a commercial impediment. The wood is rich dark brown in colour and takes a satiny polish; but it is weak and coarse grained, and is not important in the lumber trade.

The **California Walnut** (*J. Californica*, Wats.) has small, sweet, thin-shelled nuts, faintly creased and somewhat flattened at each end. The tree is graceful and symmetrical, with luxuriant foliage, of cheerful light green. It grows to medium height on the bottom lands of the coast region from the lower course of the Sacramento River to the foothills of the San Bernardino Mountains, where it climbs to an elevation of 3,000 feet and becomes a stunted shrub.

The chief value of this tree is that it serves as a hardy stock for the cultivated *J. regia*, and as such has extended nut culture north to central California. Seedlings of the native tree are root grafted with cions of French varieties, and old trees are successfully top grafted. Independent of this signal service to horticulture, the California walnut is a fine ornamental and nut tree.

The **English** or **Persian Walnut** (*Juglans regia*, Linn.)—a royal tree and nut indeed!—is the walnut of classical literature, beloved of gods and men. From the hillsides of Persia and the regions far East this species was carried into southern Europe, whence it spread to England and finally to America. The tree is grown for lumber, for ornament, and for its fruit in the countries that feel the warm breath of the Japan Current and the Gulf Stream. The best nuts come from France and Italy. In England the nuts are generally pickled green, as the season is too short to insure their ripening. The English walnut, like the English elm, came to us via England, and got its name en route. Neither species is a native of that island. Importations of the nuts came to us also through England until recent years.

The wealth of Europe has been increased by the enforced planting of walnut trees. In the seventeenth century in certain countries there was a law requiring a young man to produce a certificate of his having planted a certain number of walnut trees before he could obtain permission to marry! The names of this tree are full of tradition and poetry. The English had the nuts before they introduced the trees. *"Walnut"* means "a nut brought from a foreign country." *"Juglans"* is a contraction of *Jovis glans*, "the acorn of Jove"—for so the Greeks and Romans esteemed it. To extend its culture through allied countries was a work that rulers busied themselves about. *Nux regia* was the growers' name for the new tree, "because these nuts were brought to them by kings."

Through centuries of cultivation, many improved varieties of these Persian walnuts have arisen. Parkinson describes in 1640 a kind of "French wallnuts, which are the greatest of any, within whose shell are often put a paire of fine gloves neatly foulded up together." Another variety he knew "whose shell is so tender that it may easily be broken between one's fingers, and the nut itself is very sweete."

The culture of *J. regia* in southern California is highly special-ised and very profitable. Irrigation and tillage are practised in these orchards. Frost and walnut blight are the nut-growers' chief enemies—unless the brokers who control prices may be listed as a third. The nut crop of 1901 in four counties was about 6,000 tons, worth more than a million dollars. The tree grows in the Southern States, and has proved hardy even in Massachu-setts, but it is not cultivated commercially outside of California.

Walnut lumber (of *J. regia*) has had a variable and interesting history in Europe. The brown heart wood, always beautiful, often waved and watered in lovely patterns and shadings, yet

131

suffered long in comparison with oak, as it had not the strength and durability of the latter, and its greyish sap wood was commonly "subject to the worm"—liable to become worm eaten. The best lumber came from Italy, the next best from the Black Sea regions, next from France, and the poorest grew in England.

In the early part of the eighteenth century a craving for walnut furniture struck the fashionable world. Oak became second in popularity. Then came a cold winter which killed the walnut trees. The Dutch Government bought the dead trees and cornered the market for a time. France prohibited the exportation of walnut; then mahogany began to be imported from tropical America and became the popular wood for fine furniture.

In the turmoil of international wars, each country wanted walnut for gun stocks. In 1806 France·used 12,000 trees. The English Government is said to have paid before the battle of Waterloo £600 for a single walnut tree! In the height of the walnut vogue, cabinetmakers paid as high as £60 per ton for roots and burs, which were sawed very thin and used for veneering pianos and other elegant furniture. No wood excels this curly walnut in beauty.

In later years the importation of black walnut from America · relieved the stress in the lumber trade. This tree grows well in Europe, and is an important species in the government forests of various countries. It has doubled in price in the past fifty years, and American walnut is now in greater demand abroad than the native species.

THE HICKORIES

Hickories are North American trees—none now inhabit any other part of the world. There are twelve known species, one of which is Mexican; the remaining eleven are restricted to the states east of the Rocky Mountains. Arkansas assembles the whole group within her borders and offers a great opportunity to the student of the genus Hicoria.

Once Europe had numerous species of this genus, and there were others in Greenland and in the west of North America. The ice cap wiped them all off the face of the earth; the only record of them is in the Tertiary rocks. After a century of effort, only a few good specimen trees are to be found growing in Europe. The species thrive only in their natural range. There are reasons for believing that these trees will grow well in Japan and eastern China.

No group of trees has higher qualities than the hickories. The wood of most species is tough, strong and flexible—especially valuable for farm implements, tool handles and the like. There is no other fuel that excels dry hickory for heat and brilliancy of flame. No other of our trees bear such valuable nuts. No finer tribe of shade and ornamental trees is to be found. With all their positive good qualities, the hickories have scarcely a bad one. The worst thing you can say of any hickory is that it is not quite up to the family standard.

The Indians knew the value of these trees before the white man came. "Hickory" is an Indian name. The Creeks and Algonquins gathered the nuts into their storehouses in the autumn. The squaws pounded shells and all in water, until the latter became a milky emulsion. This became the Indian drink, "powcohickora," after it had fermented. Added fresh to venison broth it made a rich food, very agreeable to European palates. (Of course the shells went to the bottom of the pot.) The "hickory milk," strained of its shell fragments and thickened with meal, made corncakes fit for a king! It was used also in cooking hominy. An oil pressed from these nuts was staple in early cookery in the colonies. The Virginians learned its use from their Indian neighbours. It was considered equal to olive oil in flavour, though no attempt was made to refine it.

Many insects prey on hickory trees. None of these unfit them for dooryard planting, if one keeps close watch to poke out early the nests of fall web-worm and kindred pests. Many of its enemies are borers which work in the wood. The twig pruners are an interesting tribe; and some of our most beautiful silk spinners and underwing moths live their youthful days out on the foliage of hickory.

What can that sound be that comes out of the backlog, like the creaking of the old rocking chair in the chimney corner? It has been heard every night when the family gather around the fire, and it has a weird, ghostly sound. A plump young hickory borer, deep in the wood, is whetting his teeth on the walls of his

133

burrow. He is safe, for hickory burns very slowy, and the back-log is good for many a day yet. Probably before the stronghold of the youngster is reached he will have ceased his gnawing, and fallen asleep in a chrysalis. Then of a sudden, some March night in the midst of a thrilling tale told by the firelight, a strange visitant will appear, startling the whole company, and interrupt the story. It is an elegant grey beetle, with horns of surprising length, made of jointed rods. After a long and arduous youth spent in the dark channel of his own making, he has come forth into the light equipped with wings, and ready to mingle with his kind in a life of which he has probably not dreamed before. Who would be so inconsiderate, so inhuman, as to cast this handsome creature into the fire! Certainly nobody who knows anything about the old life he has left behind him, and the new life that lies before. Take him, rather, to the window, and as he flies forth into the night take up the story where it was broken off.

Pignut, White Hickory (*Hicoria glabra*, Britt.)—A stately, round-headed tree, 50 to 100 feet high, with narrow head of pendulous contorted branches. *Bark* grey, coarse, rough, not scaling off in plates. *Wood* brown, tough, elastic, hard, heavy. *Buds* terminal ones, globular, blunt, shedding outer scales early in winter; inner scales expand, and recurve as leaves unfold; lateral buds small, pointed. *Leaves* alternate, 8 to 12 inches long, odd-pinnate, of 5 to 7 leaflets, oblong or obovate-lanceolate, smooth, dark yellow-green; lighter and sometimes tufted with hairs in axils of veins beneath; upper leaflets much larger than lower ones. *Flowers:* staminate catkins, axillary, 4 to 7 inches long, in threes; pistillate spikes, 3 to 5-flowered, terminal, greenish. *Fruit* pear shaped, or globose; variable, thick or thin shelled, reddish brown, somewhat hairy, cleft into 4 valves, partially or wholly opening; nut obscurely 4-angled, smooth; kernel sweet or slightly bitter, small. *Preferred habitat*, dry ridges and hillsides. *Distribution*, Maine to Florida; west through Ontario and Michigan to Nebraska, south to eastern Texas. *Uses:* Wood used as that of shagbark is. A valuable ornamental and shade tree.

The pignut is unfortunate in its common name. A fine park and shade tree is under a severe handicap. For who would wish a "pignut" planted in his front yard? A "smooth hickory" will rather be chosen, every time—though it is the very same tree, *H. glabra.* In the early days pigs turned into the autumn woods

A. Sterile flowers   B. Fertile flower

THE PIGNUT (*Hicoria glabra*)

The tree is draped with green fringe—the staminate catkins—in May. The first leaves usually have but five leaflets. Later ones have seven, rarely nine. They are smooth and turn yellow in autumn. The buds are plump, and small for a hickory; the outer scales are shed early in winter. The bark is furrowed and gray. This twig has no pistillate flowers

THE PIGNUT (*Hicoria glabra*)

The nuts are variable in form and size. They are often obovate or pear-shaped—the thin husk opens but part way down. The nut is smooth and round or angled. The yellowish kernel is insipid. The leaves and shoots are smooth from the first

THE BITTERNUT HICKORY (*Hicoria minima*)

The bright, yellow, angled buds are the best identification sign. The bark is greyish brown. The leaves are thin and have an apple-like fragrance when crushed. The leaflets are often narrow and small

crunched these hickory nuts which nutters, looking for shellbarks, scornfully left under the trees. The insipid meats were distasteful to human palates—fit only for pigs.

Yet here is one of the finest of the hickories. Its bark is close textured like that of a white ash. Its leaves and shoots soon lose their down and become smooth and lustrous. The small winter buds are ovate, and during autumn their outer scales drop. The nuts are roundish and smooth shelled. The thin husks split but half way down, and are there grown fast to the shell. These characters mark the typical Eastern pignut. West of the Alleghanies is a form that sheds its husks, and has angled, ovoid nuts. The bark of this variety—*odorata*—is rough, like an American elm, but not shaggy.

Variety *microcarpa* is a pignut with bark of the *H. ovata* type, stripping into narrow, thin, springy sheets. The roundish nut is white or grey, and thin shelled. The kernel is sweet. There are reasons for believing this to be a natural hybrid between *H. ovata* and *H. glabra*. Its branches are likely to be pendulous, and the head more oblong than the ordinary pignut. It is commonly called "false shagbark."

The extreme variability of the species *glabra*, and the good quality of fruit in var. *microcarpa* make horticulturists believe that the pignut is worthy of cultivation. Experiments are now in progress looking toward the improvement of the fruit for commercial purposes. The signs are hopeful.

With wood equal to the best in its genus, exceptional merits as a shade and ornamental tree, and promise of developing orchard varieties that will rival the shagbarks as nut trees, the pignuts seem to be one of the "coming trees" in the Eastern States. It is to be hoped that the popular name will be abandoned and the more suitable one, "smooth hickory," substituted. This is a literal translation of its scientific name.

The **Pale-leaf Hickory** (*H. villosa*, Ashe) has tomentose slender twigs, with silvery scales, and very pale leaf linings. The nuts are thick shelled and faintly angled like the mockernut, and the bark is very deeply furrowed and rough, but not shaggy. It grows, a small, narrow-headed tree, in barren soil from New Jersey to Florida, west to Missouri and Texas.

Big Shellbark (*H. laciniosa*, Sarg.)—A tall tree 100 to 120 feet high, with narrow, oblong head. Branches small, spreading.

135

Bark thick, grey, shedding in long thick plates that hang on for years. Twigs orange yellow. *Wood* heavy, hard, strong, tough, very flexible, dark brown, close grained. *Buds* terminal, very large, ovate, obtuse; scales silky, outer ones, brown, keeled and pointed; inner ones grow to 3 inches long and 1 inch wide and recurve as leaves appear, turning rosy or yellow on inner, lustrous face; lateral buds small. *Leaves* 15 to 22 inches long, of 5 to 9 obovate or oblong-lanceolate leaflets, dark green and lustrous above, pale yellow-green or bronzy pubescent below; petioles stout, enlarged at base, recurved and persistent during winter. *Flowers:* staminate in catkins 5 to 8 inches long, smooth, or rufous pubescent ; pistillate in spikes, terminal, 2 to 5-flowered, pale tomentose, angled, green. *Fruit* solitary or paired, in woody, 4-valved husk, sutures opening half way at maturity, downy, orange brown, $1\frac{3}{4}$ to $2\frac{1}{2}$ inches long; nut compressed, with 4 to 6 ridges, $1\frac{1}{4}$ to $2\frac{1}{4}$ inches long; hard, bony, thick, enclosing sweet, fine-flavoured kernel. *Preferred habitat,* rich, deep bottom lands. *Distribution,* Iowa, Missouri and Arkansas, eastern Kansas and Oklahoma; Illinois and Indiana to Tennessee, New York and Pennsylvania. *Uses:* Nuts commercially valuable. Wood not distinguished from that of *H. ovata.* A worthy ornamental tree.

In the markets we often see nuts of large size—more flattened than English walnuts and fully as large—which the dealer calls "shellbarks." They look like a larger form of the little shellbarks; but we hesitate. They are strangers, and their flavour is an unknown quantity. These are the "king nuts"—not equal to the little shellbarks in quality, yet sweet, edible nuts, though in thick shells. They are distributed from the cities along the Mississippi, and are appearing in increasing quantities in Eastern markets.

In winter the tree may be recognised by its dead petioles, curving back on the twigs which bore leaves the past summer. The very large terminal buds are another winter trait. At any season the orange-coloured twigs are the best distinguishing feature of the species. This tree has shaggy bark, though this character is less pronounced than in *H. ovata.* It is hardy in the Arnold Arboretum, near Boston, and seems to grow more rapidly than other hickories in cultivation. In the wild it grows in bottom lands, but does well on dryer, sloping ground.

A hybrid between the pecan and *laciniosa* is reported by Dr.

Trelease, and named for its discoverer the "Nussbaumer Hybrid." It is not especially promising.

Shagbark Hickory, Little Shellbark Hickory (*Hicoria ovata*, Britt.)—A ruggedly picturesque, stately tree, 75 to 120 feet high, with long tap root, straight trunk and angular, short branches, forming an irregular, oblong head. *Bark* light grey, shedding in thin, vertical strips, or plates. Branches smooth, twigs shining, grey. *Wood* brown, close grained, tough, hard, elastic, heavy. *Buds* terminal ones, large, broadly ovate, with dark, narrow-pointed pair of outer scales persisting through the winter; inner scales silky, elongating to 5 to 6 inches and curving back in spring; lateral buds small, globular. *Leaves* alternate, deciduous, 12 to 20 inches long, compound, of 5 (rarely 7) leaflets, all sessile but terminal one, smooth, leathery; smallest leaflets at base; all serrate, broadly obovate, abruptly acuminate, dark yellow-green above, paler beneath, becoming brownish yellow in autumn; petioles stout, smooth, swollen at base, and grooved. *Flowers*, May, with leaves; monœcious, greenish; staminate in slender, hairy, flexible catkins 4 to 6 inches long, in threes from common stem, at base of new shoots; pistillate single or few in terminal cluster, hairy, greenish with spreading, divided stigmas. *Fruits* solitary or paired; husk smooth, leathery, dividing to base into 4 valves, $\frac{1}{2}$ inch thick, and separating from nut at maturity; shell hard, 4-angled, flattened, pale, smooth; kernel large, sweet, edible. *Preferred habitat*, deep, rich, moist soil. *Distribution*, Maine and Quebec to Delaware and along mountains to Florida, northern Alabama and Mississippi; west to Minnesota and Nebraska; south to Texas. *Uses:* Lumber used extensively in the manufacture of vehicles, agricultural implements, wheels, sled runners, axe handles, baskets, chairs and for fuel. Nuts valuable in commerce. Tree planted for ornament and shade.

The vertical sheets of shaggy bark give this tree its name. The springiness and toughness of the wood is prophesied in these thin, narrow flakes, so obstinately clinging to the trunks for years. From the close-knit covering of the utmost twig down to the ground the gradual evolution of this bark is a fascinating study. The character of the shagbark is also expressed in the angular twigs and the lithe arms of the tree, etched with perfect distinctness against the sky of winter. Strength, symmetry and grace are there, but never a look of heaviness.

137

As a fruit tree the shagbark deserves our best attention, No other hardy nut tree compares with it in commercial importance. The value of its lumber has led to the sacrifice of the large trees in the woods. The nuts are diminishing as a wild crop, but the demand is ever increasing. Hickory-nut orchards are being planted. Nurserymen are studying how best to propagate the trees, and to improve the varieties. "Hales' paper-shell hickory nut" was discovered on a single tree in New Jersey. The nuts are unusually large and plump, with thin shells. The kernels have superior delicacy and richness of flavour, and remarkable keeping qualities. A shrewd man began to propagate this exceptional strain. Grafted trees of this variety are beginning to be sold by nurserymen. Several other choice kinds from selected seed are offered. As transplanting is attended by considerable loss, it is best to plant the nuts where the orchard is to stand.

Hickory flowers are not conspicuous in colour or size, but the tree is a wonderful spectacle throughout the spring. First, the buds drop their two black outer scales, and the silky inner ones glisten like lighted tapers on every upturned twig. They grow in breadth and length as they loosen, and a cluster of leaves, small but perfect, and clothed in the softest velvet stand revealed. Then the great scales turn back like sepals of an iris, displaying rich yellows and orange tones, softened and blended by their silky coverings. The opening leaves, delicate in texture and colouring, may easily be mistaken for parts of a great flower.

But the leaves soon declare themselves, and the scales fall. The tree is then draped in long chenille fringes of green. The wind shakes the pollen out of these staminate catkins, and the inconspicuous green nut flowers, clustered in the tips of leafy shoots, spread their stigmas wide to catch the vitalising golden dust. The fringes now strew the grass under the tree; the bloom is past. Summer matures the crop of nuts.

The first frost hastens the opening of the thick husks. The nuts fall, and schoolboys, who have marked the tree for their own weeks before, are on hand to bag the crop to the last sweet nut, if squirrels do not thwart them. In the open space in the barn loft alongside of the bin where pears are spread out to mellow, the nuts dry and sweeten. In the dead cold of winter evenings the story of "Snow Bound," in modern settings, perhaps, but still the same

A. Pistillate flower   B. Staminate flowers

THE BIG SHELLBARK (*Hicoria laciniosa*)

This lusty tree has the biggest buds and nuts in the hickory family. The leaves are 15 to 22 inches long. The orange-coloured twigs are the distinguishing features the year around The inner bud scales grow and curl back from the cluster of new leaves. The staminate flowers are like greenish chenille fringe. The bark is grey and somewhat shaggy

1 Fertile flowers (leaves cut off)   2 Leaf   3 Fruit

THE SHAGBARK HICKORY (*Hicoria ovata*)

The bark springs away from the trunk in thin, narrow strips. The thick husk parts and falls away from the angled nut in October. In June the nuts and next spring's buds may be seen. This hickory leaf has five leaflets, the basal pair small

in spirit, will be re-enacted in farm homes in widely distant parts of the country. Nuts and apples and cider in the firelight!

We have been setting fuel down as the last of a tree's uses. Naturally, burning is the end of things, and it is often an ignoble end. But fire is one of the great elemental forces in nature. A great conflagration is magnificent; a smouldering rubbish heap is not. Some kinds of wood sputter peevishly in burning. The most splendid wood fire is made of seasoned hickory. Wake up the old backlog, charred by half a hundred fires. Lay in the kindling and feed the growing flames at last with shagbark cordwood. There is no flame so brilliant as this; no wood burns with a more fervent heat. No wonder "the great throat of the chimney laughs." The passing of hickory wood in flames back to its primal elements is the fitting end of a noble tree.

The **North Carolina Shagbark** (*H. Carolinæ-septentrionalis*, Ashe) differs from the preceding species in its smaller size and slenderer habit throughout. The twigs are dark red and slender and the leaflets are small, lanceolate, with long, tapering points. The buds are scarcely $\frac{1}{4}$ inch long, thin inner scales lengthening to 1 to 2 inches and becoming bright yellow as they unfold. The little nuts have thin shells and the kernels are sweet. The bark of this tree is much like its more burly cousins. The strips are equally tough and persistent, but not quite so large.

The range of this shagbark covers the limestone uplands of eastern Tennessee and western North Carolina, and extends south along river bottoms into Georgia and central Alabama.

Mockernut, Big Bud Hickory (*Hicoria alba*, Britt.)—A slender, tall, pyramidal tree, 50 to 80 feet high. *Bark* grey, thick, hard, close, rough, scaly; twigs pubescent, resinous, dotted. *Wood* dark brown (sap wood white), heavy, hard, strong, elastic, close. *Buds:* terminal ones large, ovate; outer scales ovate, acute, often keeled, falling in autumn; lateral buds small, yellowish brown. *Leaves* alternate, 15 to 20 inches long, of 7 to 9 leaflets, sessile, except end one, serrate, oblong-lanceolate, downy, yellowgreen, russet or yellow in fall; petiole downy, swollen, large. *Flowers:* staminate in catkins 4 to 8 inches long, hairy; pistillate 2 to 3 on terminal spike, May. *Fruit*, October, 1 to 3 nuts, globose or oblong, often long-pointed; $1\frac{1}{2}$ to 2 inches long, red-brown, strong scented; sutures opening to middle or nearly to base; nut globular, 4-ridged near top, thick shelled; kernel small, sweet, edible; often replaced by spongy mass. *Preferred habitat*, rich soil, on hillsides, North; near bogs and swamps South. *Distribution*, Ontario to Florida; west to Kansas and Texas. *Uses:* Lumber confused with shellbark hickory; nuts edible, but small, and very thick shelled. Tree planted for ornament and shade.

. The mockernut has downy buds in winter—this alone will distinguish it from the two smooth-budded shellbarks, which have buds even larger than this species. The outer scales are almost black on the buds of *H. ovata* and *H. laciniosa;* on *H. alba* they are yellowish, for the darker outer scales fall early in autumn. The bark of the mockernut looks more like that of an ash than a hickory. It is broken by shallow fissures into intersecting ridges, and is coated with silvery scales. The branches are stout and curved, giving the tree in winter an expression of strength and grace.

The heart wood is dark brown, but the white sap wood largely predominates, to the advantage of the lumber. The elasticity of hickory wood is somewhat lost in the mature heart wood, so sap wood is best. For this reason second-growth hickory, which is almost all sap wood, is especially valuable. The names *alba* and *white heart* both refer to the colour of the sap wood.

The nut is truly a mockery to anyone who considers his thumbs. The husk is thick and stubbornly adherent at the base. The shell is almost invulnerable. When at last it is shattered by a blow, the kernel, though sweet, is small, and poorly repays the trouble. Oftentimes there is no kernel at all.

The mockernut is the commonest hickory tree in the South. It is believed to hybridise with the pecan, possibly with *H. ovata* and some varieties of *H. glabra*. The parentage of trees intermediate between one species and another can only be surmised; never proved. If artificial crossing produces duplicates of the questionable trees, then surmises may be considered well founded.

Nutmeg Hickory (*H. myristicæformis*, Britt.) — A tall, straight tree, with narrow, open head, 80 to 100 feet high; branches stout, spreading. *Bark* reddish brown, broken into small, scaly plates; branchlets with golden scales. *Wood* heavy, hard, tough, light brown. *Buds* brownish, silky, hairy, small. *Leaves* 7 to 11 inches long, odd pinnate, of 5 to 11 leaflets, ovate-lanceolate to oblong-obovate, thin, firm, dark green, lustrous, silvery white beneath, sometimes pubescent; change to bronze in autumn.

Flowers: staminate in catkins, 3 to 4 inches long, brownish pubescent, densely flowered, in threes; pistillate terminal, greenish, solitary or few, scurfy pubescent. *Fruit* small, with sweet kernel, in very thick shell, smooth, rounded, pointed at both ends, in thin, scurfy, hairy, 4-valved husk, with winged sutures that open almost to base at maturity. *Preferred habitat,* rich, moist soil of swamps, or river banks; sometimes dryer hillsides. *Distribution,* coast regions of South Carolina, central Carolina, central Alabama and Mississippi, southern Arkansas. *Uses:* Cultivated sparingly in Eastern States. Beautiful ornamental tree. Locally used as fuel and lumber.

It is the lustrous foliage that makes this tree the most beautiful of all the hickories. The deep, perpendicular roots that make transplanting a difficult matter among all the hickories have probably kept this one from the full recognition it deserves at the hands of nurserymen and planters. Its narrow range in sections that do not lack beautiful trees is another cause. In fact, the tree itself was not really discovered by a competent observer until 1890, although the nuts were seen by Michaux as early as 1802. The tree is rare in the Southeast, but is common in southern Arkansas. The fine specimen in the garden of the Department of Agriculture at Washington proves its hardiness in that latitude, and brings its good qualities to the attention of the public.

Since we have all the hickories here in our Eastern States, it certainly behooves us to foster them, and share them with the rest of the world. The first step is to learn how best to propagate and transplant the various species. The next is to plant them freely, and so set forth their superior merits to all who see these plantations. There are few species which do not repay the cost in returns substantial as well as æsthetic. Hickory nuts and lumber are in constant demand, so each year adds to the value of the trees.

Pecan (*Hicoria Pecan,* Britt.)—Large, thick-trunked tree with broad top; 100 to 170 feet high, 4 to 6 feet in diameter at base. *Bark* light reddish brown, broken into small, scaly plates; branches smooth, twigs pubescent, with orange-coloured lenticels. *Wood* light brown, compact, heavy, hard, not strong. *Buds* small, yellow, pointed, pubescent, with narrow scales that elongate slightly in spring. *Leaves* 12 to 20 inches long, of 9 to 17 leaflets, short petioled, often falcate, lanceolate, serrate, bright yellow-

141

green above, paler below; petioles yellow. *Flowers:* staminate in catkins, profuse; pistillate terminal, in spikes; each flower greenish, scurfy, 4-angled, tapering. *Fruit* 3 to 11 in cluster, pointed at both ends, elongated, husk thin, 4-angled, winged at sutures which open at maturity; nut smooth, reddish, cylindrical, thin shelled; kernel sweet, with red, astringent, granular coat. *Preferred habitat*, low, rich ground near streams. *Distribution*, southern Iowa, Illinois and Indiana, and Southern States bordering the Mississippi River to central Alabama. Range extended by cultivation into all Southern States. *Uses:* Most valuable native nut tree. Wood not much used in construction; excellent for fuel. Fine shade and ornamental tree.

One of the things that solaced Evangeline's people, homesick for their lost Acadia, and wandering in a new and unknown region, was the wealth of sweet, nutritious nuts that grew on trees the Indians called *pecans*. The "Cajons" called the trees, *Pecanier*, translating the name into their own language. Twice it stood between them and famine before they became established along the lower courses of the Great River.

The salvation of the pecan tree is the inferiority of its wood. Being brittle, it does not commend itself to the makers of wagon tongues and axe handles. Many a superb specimen adorns the roadside and more than pays its way at nut harvest, while other hickories have all been felled and dragged off to the factory. No finer tree adorns the avenues of Southern cities than the pecan. Furthermore, the value and importance of the nut crop is an ever-increasing quantity. Orchards of pecans are being planted, large thin-shelled nuts being chosen for seed. Grafting and budding have been attempted, but usually failed. Success in this is coming and will quickly improve the character of the nuts, only the trees with the best nuts being used for propagation by enterprising growers. Good seed cannot be depended upon to reproduce itself in the fruit of the seedling trees. Cions and buds produce the same sort of nuts, when they come to bear, as the parent tree.

Pecans are, 95 per cent. of them, still gathered in the woods. Buyers pay nut gatherers from 3 cents to 5 cents per pound for them at the railroad. The retailer gets 15 cents to 75 cents per pound. The yield varies with the years, and quantities are kept over in cold storage against a nut famine. The prices fluctuate surprisingly, and offer great opportunities for speculation.

THE SHAGBARK HICKORY (*Hicoria ovata*)

The buds have dark, pointed outer scales which persist all winter. The inner scales elongate and curl back in May. A fountain of velvety young leaves and pendant, 3-branched staminate catkins surround the new shoot, whose tip often bears two or three pistillate flowers

WATER HICKORY (*Hicoria aquatica*)

THE PECAN (*Hicoria Pecan*)

The crown spreads into a broad dome in open situations. The foliage mass is of graceful, lustrous, sickle-shaped leaflets of variable numbers. The wood is of little value, compared with other hickories. The bark is furrowed but not shaggy

The shiny red pecans in the grocer's box owe their polish and fresh colour to rapid friction with other nuts in revolving barrels. Unfortunately this process restores the bloom of youth to the shells of stale nuts which are commonly mingled with the fresh ones. In many places the nuts are cracked and shelled, the meats sold at 50 cents to 60 cents per pound. There is economy of time, at least, in this for the confectioner and the cook.

The "get-rich-quick" man is sure to be interested in pecans and pecan culture. Large, thin-shelled nuts, for seed, bring from 50 cents to $2.50 per pound. Budded and grafted trees, one or two years old, cost from 50 cents to $1.50 each at the nursery. An orchard of thrifty, prolific trees, whose nuts have thin-shelled, plump kernels, with delicate flavour and the minimum of the astringent red shell lining, is certainly as good as a gold mine on any farm.

Of the seventy and more varieties that have been described, not twenty are worth considering. Anyone interested in the subject should get the Report on Nut Culture, Division of Pomology, Department of Agriculture, Washington, D. C.

Bitternut, Swamp Hickory (*Hicoria minima*, Britt.)— A tall, handsome tree, 60 to 100 feet high, with straight trunk, stout branches and slender twigs, forming a broad, symmetrical head. *Bark* greyish brown, smooth, close; branches smooth; twigs yellowish brown, pale, dotted. *Wood* brown, heavy, hard, close grained, tough. *Buds* slender, pointed, yellow, granular. *Leaves* alternate, compound, 6 to 10 inches long, of 7 to 11 narrow, almost willow-like leaflets, bright green, paler beneath, leathery; yellow in autumn; petioles downy, slender. *Flowers* in May, with leaves; monœcious, staminate catkins, 3 to 4 inches long, in threes, stalked; pistillate on terminal peduncles, 1 to 3 flowers, $\frac{3}{4}$ inch long, with spreading stigmas, green. *Fruit* globular, or pear shaped, $\frac{3}{4}$ to 1 inch long, wider; husk thin, with 4 prominent winged sutures, reaching half way to base; sometimes 2 go to base, never 4. Golden scurf on husk. Nut thin shelled, compressed, marked with dark lines; kernel bitter, white. *Preferred habitat*, low wet woods; swamps. *Distribution*, Maine and Ontario to Florida; west to Minnesota, Nebraska and Texas. *Uses:* Valuable ornamental and shade tree, not yet appreciated. Wood used for ox yokes, hoops and for fuel.

The bitternut is known among the hickories by its flattened, tapering, yellow buds, which it always carries, no matter what the season. There are always dormant buds in spring, even when growth is at its height. One needs only to follow along any twig to discover several of such lateral ones of the previous year. Very soon the new buds thrust their little yellow noses up from the axils of the leaves, and you have there the sign which remains until growth begins next spring.

The bark of *H. minima* is close and thin; the habit of the tree is like a hard maple's; its leaflets are the smallest among hickories, and the twigs are the slenderest.

One need not depend on the fruit as an identification sign. The smooth, round nut comes easily out of the thin shell. But the kernel, white and plump, is bitter as gall. No woodland creatures eat it. This is one of the reasons why the trees are so numerous. Nuts roll away from the parent tree, and are privileged to grow, while edible nuts are devoured.

The bitternut has all the good qualities of an ideal park tree, and excels the other hickories in rapidity of growth. The landscape gardener of the coming generation will know and appreciate it, for the native trees are receiving more and more consideration, and their names are appearing, in increasing numbers, in nurserymen's catalogues.

The **Bitter Pecan, or Water Hickory** (*H. aquatica*, Britt.), is least in size and value among the hickories, though it shoots up occasionally to the height of 100 feet. It grows in inundated districts—in swamps of the coast region from Virginia to Texas, and along the Mississippi River to southern Illinois. There is little to regret in its comparative uselessness, for the trees are practically inaccessible. The bitter little nut is roughly sculptured and ridged, reminding one of the butternut shell. This probably led Michaux to call it a walnut. The kernel is thickly coated with a bitter red powder, like that of the pecan.

CHAPTER XX: THE POPLARS

FAMILY SALICACEÆ

Genus POPULUS

QUICK-GROWING trees with angled or round twigs, set with scaly buds, soft, light wood, and bitter bark. *Leaves* deciduous, simple, alternate, usually broad, on long petioles. *Flowers* diœcious, both kinds in crowded, pendulous catkins; each flower subtended by a bract with deeply cut, hairy margin. *Fruit* pendulous racemes of 2 to 4-valved pods; seeds minute, with dense, silky float attached.

KEY TO SPECIES

A. Leaf stalks flattened.
  B. Buds smooth, resinous.
    C. Leaves triangular, coarsely serrate.
      D. Blades of leaves 3 to 5 inches long.
          (*P. deltoidea*) COTTONWOOD
      DD. Blades of leaves 2 to 2½ inches long.
        E. Twigs slender, pubescent, yellow.
            (*P. Fremontii*) COTTONWOOD
        EE. Twigs stout, smooth, orange.
            (*P. Wislizeni*) COTTONWOOD
    CC. Leaves roundish, finely serrate.
            (*P. tremuloides*) QUAKING ASP
  BB. Buds downy; leaves ovate, coarsely toothed.
          (*P. grandidentata*) GREAT-TOOTHED ASPEN
AA. Leaf stalks round; buds resinous.
  B. Foliage green on both sides.
    C. Shape of leaves lanceolate.
          (*P. angustifolia*) NARROW-LEAVED COTTONWOOD
    CC. Shape of leaves rhombic or deltoid, with long-
        pointed apex.
      D. Margins finely serrate.
          (*P. acuminata*) LANCE-LEAVED COTTONWOOD
      DD. Margins coarsely and crenately toothed.
          (*P. Mexicana*) MEXICAN COTTONWOOD

145

    BB. Foliage pale, silvery or rusty below; margins finely
        serrate.
      C. Buds thickly covered with yellow resin.
                    (*P. balsamifera*) BALM OF GILEAD
      CC. Buds somewhat resinous.
        D. Bark pale grey.
               (*P. trichocarpa*) BLACK COTTONWOOD
      DD. Bark reddish brown.
              (*P. heterophylla*) SWAMP COTTONWOOD

Trees of the genus Populus form extensive forests in low, rich land and on high slopes of mountains. They attain large size, are quick of growth, and have exceeding tenacity of life, striking roots from twigs and sending up suckers from underground. Seeds are also a reliable means of reproduction, as they are produced in great numbers, and are widely scattered by the wind. The wood is one of the best materials for pulp making, and for a multitude of cheap wares for which a wood easy to work is demanded. The trees are largely planted for shade and ornament, for windbreaks, and to hold the banks of streams.

There are twenty-five species of Populus known, eleven of which are native to America. European species are often planted in this country, where they usually thrive as if at home. Some Russian varieties are successful on the Western prairies. China and Japan each have representative poplars here.

Cottonwood (*Populus deltoidea*, Marsh.)—Much-branched tree, 60 to 150 feet in height; diameter 5 to 7½ feet. *Bark* deeply furrowed, grey-brown, becoming greenish; often ashen grey on old trees. *Wood* dark brown; sap wood white; weak, compact, light. *Buds* large, pointed, resinous. *Leaves* broadly ovate, taper pointed, 3 to 5 inches long, margin wavy and coarsely toothed, thick, shining, paler beneath, yellow in fall; petiole long, slender, flat, red or yellow. *Flowers*, March, in pendant catkins, 3 to 5 inches long, loosely flowered; staminate red, numerous; pistillate green, sparse on trees. *Fruits*, May, aments 6 to 12 inches long; capsules ovate, often curved, 2-valved; seeds in white, cottony mass. *Preferred habitat*, moist soil along streams. *Distribution*, Quebec to Northwest Territory; south to Florida; west to Colorado and New Mexico. *Uses:* Much planted for shade and windbreaks in the prairie states. Wood has recently come into use in making packing cases.

THE COTTONWOOD (*Populus deltoidea*)

The quick-growing tree assumes dignity with age, though wind breaks its limbs. The leaves keep fresh despite the smoke and dust. The catkins appear before the leaves in March. On pistillate trees the seeds ripen in green balls, which open to discharge their fluffy contents in May. The buds are sealed with wax. The wood is now being used for boxes

SILVER POPLAR (*Populus alba*) GREAT-TOOTHED ASPEN NARROW-LEAVED
(*Populus grandidentata*) COTTONWOOD
(*Populus angustifolia*)

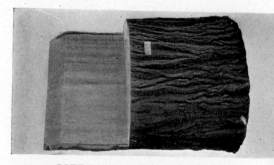

COTTONWOOD (*Populus Fremontii*) SWAMP COTTONWOOD (*Populus heterophylla*)

BALM OF GILEAD (*Populus balsamifera*)

We all concede that the cottonwood has faults. The brittle wood cannot withstand the winds, the leaves drop untidily through the summer, the cast-off staminate catkins are a nuisance in spring, and the fluffy cottony seeds shed so deliberately in early summer by the fertile trees fill the air and the meshes of door and window screens to the exasperation of the whole neighbourhood.

But go out into one of the little breathing spaces called parks in a great city like New York in the early spring days when the children of the tenements and the stuffy flats are brought out for a first breath of the spring air. The old cottonwood has its buds all a-glisten with promise, and in a few days longer the dainty little leaves twinkle all over the treetop with the most cheerful green. In the late summer, in spite of its losses, the tree still carries a bright green crown of shade which turns yellow before it falls. With all its faults, it endures the heat of cities, and the dust and soot with commendable patience. In the protection of great buildings it does not suffer by winds as it does in exposed situations.

There are better, longer-lived trees for the open country, but in cities the cottonwood has a use and a message of cheer for rich and poor who look up and learn to know the tree. Unlike the variety next described, the cottonwood takes on dignity with added years.

The **Carolina Poplar**, considered a variety (*Carolinensis*) of the cottonwood above, is a strict pyramidal tree of vigorous and surprisingly rapid growth. In cities the varnish on the leaves evidently protects them from dust and smoke. Nurserymen have exploited this tree in America and Europe far beyond its merits, for though useful as a temporary tree, giving shade very soon, poplars should give way gradually to more permanent species planted with them. This poplar soon outgrows the beauty and luxuriance of its youth, and becomes broken and ugly. The immoderate planting of these trees gives a cheap character to many an otherwise handsome town or country place. New summer resorts and city "additions" show poplars in great numbers about their premises. The "poplar habit" is a very short-sighted one and expensive in the long run. J. Wilkinson Elliott, of Pittsburg, persuades his clients to plant Balm of Gilead, a much more satisfactory species.

147

The **Cottonwood** (*P. Fremontii*, Wats.) grows in western California, from Sacramento south, and eastward to Colorado and Texas. It is a favourite shade tree, and an important source of fuel. Cut back systematically, the trees produce abundant crowns of suckers in a very short time.

Frémont's cottonwood is distinguishable from the preceding species by the smaller size of its leaves and the pubescence of its buds. Its leaves are sometimes kidney shaped. The bark of old trees is reddish brown. The trees reach 100 feet in height.

The **Cottonwood** (*P. Wislizeni*, Sarg.) of the Rio Grande Valley in Texas and New Mexico, is a large, wide-crowned tree, with stout, smooth, orange-coloured twigs and leathery, yellow-green leaves. Without these distinguishing characters it might easily be confused with the two species last described. The tree is not met with outside its natural range.

Aspen, or **Quaking Asp** (*Populus tremuloides*, Michx.)—Slender tree, 40 to 80 feet high, with angular, scarred twigs, and large, vigorous roots. *Bark* rough, dark on base of trunk, becoming pale greenish brown or nearly white, and marked with broad, dark bands below the limbs. *Wood* light brown, sap wood white, soft, close grained, light, weak, not durable. *Buds* waxy, conical, scaly, brown. *Leaves* alternate, simple, $1\frac{1}{2}$ to $2\frac{1}{2}$ inches long, ovate or almost round, with straight base and apex acute; margin faintly toothed; thin, shining green above, dull yellow-green beneath; autumn colour yellow; petiole flattened, flexible, slender. *Flowers* in April, diœcious; catkins pendulous, $1\frac{1}{2}$ to $2\frac{1}{2}$ inches long, each flower on notched bract, fringed with hairs; stamens 6 to 12 on disc; ovary conical; stigmas 2-lobed; disc broad, persistent. *Fruits*, May, borne in drooping aments, 4 inches long; capsules oblong-conical, 2-valved, pale green; seeds oblong, covered with brush of long white hairs. *Preferred habitat*, sandy or gravelly soil, dry or moist. *Distribution*, Newfoundland to Hudson Bay and Alaska; south to New Jersey, Pennsylvania, Kentucky, Nebraska; also high altitudes throughout the Rocky Mountains and coast ranges. *Uses:* Most valuable cover for forest land devastated by fire. Comes up from seed scattered broadcast by wind, and acts as nurse to hardwoods and conifers that later succeed them. A pretty shade and ornamental tree, though short lived.

Aspen is a general term applied to trees of this genus whose leaves have flattened stems. The round-stemmed ones are poplars, proper. The Russian adage: "There is a tree that trembles without even a breath of wind," might well fit this most apprehensive of all the aspen trees. Its dainty round leaf blades twinkle in the sun, a grove of the trees together producing at a little distance the appearance as well as the sound of rippling water. It is the gayest of trees. That was a lugubrious wight who imagined it accursed by being the tree on which Judas Iscariot hanged himself, and doomed "ever afterward to shudder and tremble on account of its connection with the tragedy of Calvary." The same legend attaches to the pretty little redbud, the Judas tree.

"The green wood moved, and the light poplar shook
    Its silver pyramid of leaves."

We might easily adapt these graceful lines to our quaking asp, but that the word "silver" will not apply accurately. The English poet, Barry Cornwall, was describing the white poplar with white leaf linings.

There is no mystery in the trembling of these aspen leaves. Examine one. The stem is long and flexible. It is flattened in a plane at right angles with the blade of the leaf. Now, given a leaf that is dangling from its twig, and has four flat surfaces exposed, it is a cautious breeze indeed that is able to get by without disturbing the leaf's unstable equilibrium. Given, a treetop of leaves similarly made and hung, and you have a quaking asp. It waves you an invitation to examine, and see if the explanation above is not correct.

Homer's famous simile based on the leaves of poplar trees is not ungallant as that of Gerarde, who compares them to "women's tongues which seldom cease wagging."

The most delicate colouring is found in this aspen tree. The pale bark takes on a cool, greenish tinge in earliest spring. The furry catkins flush pink with their silvery grey silk. The opening leaves unroll, soft and white, like flannel—"ju' luk a kitten's ear," each one of them, to quote Uncle Eb. They pass through various tones of rose and olive on the way to their lustrous adult stage. Every day from early March till May it is worth while to go by a copse of trembling aspen and look up to see what new phase of the trees' life history has opened since last we passed that way.

149

Large-toothed Aspen (*Populus grandidentata*, Michx.)— Narrow, round-headed tree, 50 to 75 feet high, with stout, angular branchlets, roughened by leaf scars. *Bark* dark brown and deeply fissured between broad ridges on old trunks; grey-green on limbs. *Twigs* smooth, pubescent at first. *Wood* soft, weak, pale brown; sap wood white. *Buds* ovate, pointed, scaly, waxed. *Leaves* ovate to roundish, heart shaped at base, acute, with sparse, irregular-rounded teeth; 3 to 4 inches long, 2 to 3 inches wide, thick, green, with pale somewhat tomentose linings; petioles slender, laterally flattened, 2 to 3 inches long. *Flowers*, April, diœcious, in pendulous catkins, 2 to 3 inches long; staminate red from anthers; pistillate green from spreading stigmas; bracts deeply cleft. *Fruits*, hairy capsules, 2-valved, thin walled, slender, crooked, filled with minute seeds, each with white, hairy float; May. *Preferred habitat*, rich, sandy loam, on borders of streams. *Distribution*, Nova Scotia to Minnesota; south to New Jersey, and on Alleghanies to North Carolina, Tennessee and Kentucky.

The coarse, thick leaves with large, rounded teeth on the margins, distinguished this great-toothed aspen from its dainty cousin, the quaking asp, with which it is often associated in the woods. In fact, the tree is coarser throughout, the branchlets stout and the buds downy, so no one who is interested and observant will have any trouble to tell them apart.

The **Narrow-leaved Cottonwood** (*P. angustifolia*, James) has lanceolate leaves, more like a willow's than a poplar's. The margins are finely saw toothed, the petioles short, and the texture thin and firm. It is easy to see that the tree is a poplar, the flattened petiole alone being a sufficient clue. The tree lines the banks of mountain streams of the Rockies, 5,000 to 10,000 feet in elevation. It grows from 40 to 60 feet high, a narrow pyramid of slender limbs.

The **Lance-leaved Cottonwood** (*P. acuminata*, Rydb.), with scarcely wider leaves than the preceding species, is a compact, round-headed little tree that grows on stream borders and arid foothills of the Rocky Mountains from British Columbia to southern Nebraska and Colorado. Its distribution is not fully ascertained. It is used for fuel and planted for shade in communities within its natural range.

The **Mexican Cottonwood** (*P. Mexicana*, Wesm.) grows, a graceful, wide-spreading tree of medium size, along mountain

1 Leaves: A, **Under side**; B, **Upper side**   2 Young leaves unfolding   3 Bark and wood

THE QUAKING ASP (*Populus tremuloides*)

The leaves look like white flannel when they open in early April. In summer they are ovate, sometimes almost round, with fine teeth, and hung on flexible, flattened petioles, on which they flutter on the stillest days. The bark is pale and smooth, breaking into furrows and excrescences which show the darker under bark

Staminate flowers

Winter buds

Pistillate flowers

THE QUAKING ASP (*Populus tremuloides*)

The scale under each little flower is cut into a fringe. This gives the furry appearance to the pink and silvery staminate catkins. On other trees the greenish pistillate catkins soon show the conical seed capsules. This tree shows its "pussies" in early March, and its fluffy seeds are flying in May

streams near the Mexican border of Arizona and New Mexico. Its rhombic, long-pointed leaves are very coarsely toothed, and when they first unfold are dark red, soon becoming yellow-green and leathery. The bark is grey or almost white.

Balm of Gilead (*Populus balsamifera*, Linn.)—Large tree with stout trunk, 75 to 100 feet high. *Bark* grey, broken into broad ridges; branches greenish, smooth or with warty outgrowths. *Wood* pale, soft, compact, weak, light brown. *Buds* long, slender, shining with yellow wax. *Leaves* broadly ovate, acute, finely and bluntly toothed, thick, shining, dark green, pale, often rusty beneath, 3 to 5 inches long; petioles slender; autumn colour yellow. *Flowers*, March, before leaves; aments drooping, hairy; stamens 18 to 30, crowded on disc; anthers pale red; pistils green with spreading stigmas; flowers scattered. *Fruits*, May, capsules scattered on stems 4 to 6 inches long; seed brown, buried in cottony float. *Preferred habitat*, moist or dry soil near water. *Distribution*, Newfoundland to Hudson Bay and Alaska; south to Maine, New York, Michigan, Nebraska, Idaho and British Columbia. *Uses:* Well worthy of planting for shade, ornament and shelter.

The fragrant wax that saturates the winter buds and coats the young leaves in spring gives this tree its name. The bees find it as soon as the sap stirs and the wax softens. Quantities of it are collected and stored in hives "against a rainy day"; for this is what bees use to seal up weather cracks in their hives. It is known to bee keepers as "propolis." The service this wax renders the tree is to prevent the loss of water from the buds, and the absorption of more, after they are ready for winter. It is not "to keep the buds from freezing," as some people fondly imagine. The buds freeze solid, but it does them no harm. They are adjusted to it. In the far North the Indian uses the balsam of Balm of Gilead trees to seal up the seams of his birch-bark canoe, and of dishes and other utensils made of the same material.

The forests of Balm of Gilead stretch away over the lake margins and bottom lands of upper Canada, the largest and most prominent feature of vegetation in the vast regions that approach the Arctic circle, and extend down into the northern tier of states, from ocean to ocean.

The chief interest that centres about the tree is its good record when planted as a shade and ornamental tree, and in shelter belts. It is a hardy tree of excellent habit, compact and erect, but not too narrow for shade. It is easily propagated and transplanted, and grows rapidly. The tree is handsome, winter and summer. It has all the good points of the Carolina poplar, and lacks its fault of becoming so soon an unsightly cripple.

The **Black Cottonwood** (*P. trichocarpa*, Hook.) is the giant of the genus, reaching 200 feet in height and 7 to 8 feet in trunk diameter. It is tall and stately, with a broad, rounded crown supported upon heavy upright limbs. One of the beautiful sights of the Yosemite Park is the autumnal gold of black cotton-wood groves whose abundant foliage embowers the stream borders at the altitude of about 4,000 to 5,000 feet. The tree's range covers the coast plain and western slopes of mountains from Alaska to southern California. The largest trees are on the lowest levels. The dark rich green of the leaves gives this tree its name. They are ovoid, 3 to 4 inches long, with the finest of saw-toothed margins. The wood has come into extensive use for the manufacture of various woodenwares and for staves of sugar barrels.

Swamp Cottonwood (*Populus heterophylla*, Linn.)—Round-topped tree, 50 to 90 feet high. *Bark* red-brown, in narrow, loose plates; twigs red or grey, containing orange pith. *Wood* brown, light, compact. *Buds* resinous, ovate, with red scales. *Leaves* broadly ovate, 4 to 7 inches long, serrate, dark green with pale lining, when mature, covered with white tomentum as they unfold; petioles round, slender; yellow or brown in autumn. *Flowers*, March or April; staminate aments crowded, erect until blossoms open; anthers deep red; pistillate aments few-flowered, drooping. *Fruit*, May, aments 4 to 6 inches long; capsules few, 2 to 3-valved, $\frac{1}{2}$ inch long, bell shaped. *Preferred habitat*, wet soil. *Distribution*, swamps from southern Connecticut to Georgia and Louisiana; north along Mississippi to Arkansas and Indiana.

The swamp cottonwood is variable in the base, apex and margin of its leaf. It may exhibit coarse or fine saw teeth, a blunt or sharp-pointed apex, a square or heart-shaped base. The conspicuous netted veins are always present, and the leaves are always large and broadly ovate, with slim, round petioles. The orange-coloured pith of the branchlets best distinguishes the tree from other poplars. The new shoots and the unfolding leaves are coated with white down. It often takes a whole summer to get rid of it.

The Acadians (probably) are responsible for the name *langues de femmes*, by which the tree is known in Louisiana. The mild calumny of Gerarde is thus perpetuated and extended to a species whose leaf stems are merely flexible, not flat at all! In the lumber trade the wood is known as "black poplar." It is dark brown in colour.

THREE EUROPEAN POPLARS IN CULTIVATION IN AMERICA

A. Leaves bright green, lined with white down, irregularly
   lobed and toothed.
   (*Populus alba*) ABELE or SILVER-LEAVED POPLAR
AA. Leaves dark green on both sides, smooth, broad as long,
   finely and regularly toothed; apex tapering.
   B. Shape broadly pyramidal. (*Populus nigra*) BLACK POPLAR
   BB. Shape narrowly pyramidal.
   (*P. nigra*, var. *Italica*) LOMBARDY POPLAR

The **Abele** or **White Poplar** (*Populus alba*, Linn.) is much planted about American homes, its downy-leaved and "maple-leaved" varieties having the preference. The silvery velvet of the leaf linings is in sharp contrast to the dark, shining upper surfaces of the leaves. The flexible stems give the wind much freedom in the treetops, and the sunlight is reflected from the leaves much as it is on rippling water. The pale outer bark breaks in streaks and spots, showing the dark under layers, much as the palest trunks of cottonwoods do. The tree is distinctly a poplar in flowers and fruits.

Two bad habits have these silvery poplars: (1) their roots send up suckers, to the distress of owners and neighbours; (2) their leaves accumulate and hold dust and coal soot until they are filthy before the summer is half done. Moral: Plant your silver poplar in the background, where its sprouting can be controlled without damage to the lawn and where distance lends enchantment to the view of its foliage.

The **Black Poplar** (*P. nigra*, Linn.), of Europe and Asia, has become established in certain parts of the Eastern States, but it is now chiefly met with in its cultivated forms. Variety *elegans* is a dainty tree with small, bright, twinkling leaves and ruddy twigs and petioles. The following variety is much more extensively known, though it has less horticultural merit.

The **Lombardy Poplar** (*Populus nigra*, var. *Italica*) is the exclamation point that marks by its soldierly rows so many familiar boundary lines of farms and village properties. It has the merit of infringing but slightly even by its shade on the rights and premises of others. Indeed, that such a tree should be planted for the shade it gives is scarcely probable. The pencil-like form and the twinkling of the green leaves are attractive. Italian villas were punctuated with them, and any piece of planting may well be diversified and accented by a group of these trees. But they need to be flanked by trees of diffuse habit—never set alone or in rows! The great fault of these poplars is the early dying of their limbs, because of much crowding. The tree retains these dead limbs, and so loses its youthful beauty and becomes scraggy topped. As the scientific name points out, these trees are an Italian variety of the black poplar.

CHAPTER XXI: THE WILLOWS

FAMILY SALICACEÆ

Genus SALIX

CHIEFLY quick-growing, water-loving trees and shrubs, with slender, supple twigs, and buds with a single protective cap or scale of two coats. *Wood* light, soft. *Leaves* simple, alternate, narrow and pointed, deciduous. *Flowers* diœcious, in loose catkins, each flower subtended by a bract having an entire hairy margin. *Fruit* a 2-valved pod with papery walls; seeds minute, in copious hairy floats.

KEY TO SPECIES

A. Shape of leaves linear-lanceolate, taper pointed.
  B. Leaves green on both sides.
    C. Stipules persistent.   (*S. nigra*) BLACK WILLOW
    CC. Stipules deciduous. (*S. fluviatilis*) SANDBAR WILLOW
  BB. Leaves pale and silky, hairy below.
                  (*S. sessilifolia*) WILLOW
AA. Shape of leaves lanceolate, sharp pointed.
  B. Stamens more than 2 on each scale of catkin.
    C. Petioles without glands.
      D. Leaves silvery beneath.
             (*S. longipes*) BLACK WILLOW
      DD. Leaves glaucous beneath.
        E. Petioles slender; leaves thin, pale green.
            (*S. amygdaloides*) PEACH WILLOW
        EE. Petioles stout; leaves leathery, dark green.
            (*S. lævigata*) BLACK WILLOW
    CC. Petioles with glands at apex; leaves dark green,
      lustrous, pale beneath.
      D. Leaves leathery.   (*S. lucida*) SHINING WILLOW
      DD. Leaves not leathery. (*S. lasiandra*) BLACK WILLOW
  BB. Stamens 2 on each scale of catkin.
    C. Leaves pubescent and silvery beneath.
       (*S. Missouriensis*) MISSOURI WILLOW
    CC. Leaves smooth, with pale linings.

155

      D. Leaf linings silvery; blades broad.
                      (*S. discolor*) PUSSY WILLOW
     DD. Leaf linings pale; blades narrow.
            (*S. cordata*, var. *Mackenzieana*) HEART WILLOW
AAA. Shape of leaves oblong or ovate.
  B. Leaf linings pubescent, white.
    C. Apex blunt.   (*S. Hookeriana*) WILLOW
    CC. Apex short pointed.   (*S. Bebbiana*) WILLOW
 BB. Leaf linings smooth, pale; apex blunt.
                 (*S. balsamifera*) WILLOW

The genus Salix is distributed from the equator to the Arctic circle. It embraces 170 species, beside numbers of natural hybrids between closely related species. Most of them prefer moist soil; a few prefer dry. They ascend from sea level to the tops of mountain chains. They vary from great trees to prostrate shrubs. No climate or soil but can show its native willows. Among woody plants they are comparable to grass among the herbs.

The wood of willow is uniformly light and weak. The trees are likely to get less than their due of credit, when compared with the average large genus of hardwoods or conifers. But uses have been found for them from time immemorial. Their soft, light wood makes superior charcoal for gunpowder and other uses, and is largely used for summer fuel where a quick, hot fire is desirable. The tough, flexible twigs of several species form the basis of the wickerware industry. Tannin is obtained from the bitter bark. In Holland and other countries willows are planted to hold the banks of streams and ditches. Willow branches formed the original jetties that opened and kept open to navigation the channel of the Mississippi. Willows are among our best trees for quick-growing shelter belts, in the newer parts of the country. They furnish ornamental and shade trees of value—pretty when young, dignified in age.

The cultivation of willows is very easy. A twig stuck into moist soil grows into a tree. Willow posts set out green soon grow into roadside trees, thus serving a double purpose. In damp situations their roots drain and greatly improve the land. Many species have twigs that snap off at the base. These twigs strike root if they fall on damp ground; many waterside willows cast their twigs in this way, and the stream carries them down, lodging them on shoals and bars, which soon become clothed with

THE GOLDEN OSIER WILLOW (*Salix alba,* var. *vitellina*)

This is the common yellow-twigged willow, familiar in rows along country roads. The leaves are pale beneath, so they look very cheerful and cool in mid-summer. The tree is much more vigorous than the parent species in this country. It takes on dignity with years and gets a mighty trunk in its venerable age. It always branches very near the ground

1 Leaves

2 Winter bud

THE GOLDEN OSIER (*Salix alba*, var. *vitellina*)

This tree is known by its yellow twigs. The leaves are narrow and white-lined.
The bud in all willows is capped with a single conical protective scale

3 Winter bud

4 Leaves

THE SILKY WILLOW (*Salix sericea*)

This red-stemmed shrubbery willow has large red buds, and in summer is beautiful in
its lustrous silky foliage

trees. It is an unmeasured advantage to a region to have its shifting sands and mud banks established thus, and covered with green.

There are comparatively few willows that grow into large trees. The rank and file of trees even in these species are small. From Europe we have naturalised two large species, *S. alba* and *S. fragilis*. The golden osier, whose yellow limbs are bright in early spring in many a fence row, is called var. *vitellina* of *S. alba*, the white willow of Europe. The Babylonian willow, *Salix Babylonica*, is the much-planted weeping willow of the Eastern States. Var. *dolorosa* is the popular "Wisconsin Weeping Willow." One of the best ornamental willows is *S. pentandra*, the laurel willow, whose crown of glossy, broad, green leaves adorns many parks. This species is coming into well-deserved popular favour. The Kilmarnock Willow is a weeping horticultural variety, *pendula*, of *S. Caprea*, Linn., the European goat willow. The staminate tree is loaded in spring with catkins which are coarse and ugly compared with those of our own pussy willow, *S. discolor*.

Black Willow (*Salix nigra*, Marsh.)—Medium-sized tree, 50 to 100 feet high, but usually smaller. Twigs slender, brittle at base. *Bark* dark brown, flaky, deeply furrowed, often shaggy. *Wood* light reddish brown, weak, soft, fine grained. *Buds* small, acute, red-brown. *Leaves* narrowly lanceolate, acuminate at apex, finely and evenly serrate, green on both sides; petioles short, 2½ to 5 inches long; stipules leaf-like, semi heart shaped or crescent shaped, deciduous or persistent. *Flowers* with leaves, on short lateral twigs, diœcious; catkins 1 to 3 inches long, pencil-like, erect; ovaries short, distinct, smooth; stamens 3 to 7; scales oval, hairy, deciduous. *Fruit* loose racemed capsules, ovoid, tapering; seeds minute. *Preferred habitat*, borders of lakes and streams. *Distribution*, Newfoundland to Florida, west to Rocky Mountains, reappearing in California.

The black willow earns its name by the black bark of old trees. An interesting feature of the foliage is the pair of leaf-like, heart-shaped stipules that persist throughout the summer, as a rule, at the base of each leaf. Among narrow-leaved willows this is the only one with foliage uniformly green on both sides. The leaves are often curved like a sickle. No willow has a wider distribution than this intrepid species, which takes possession of stream borders, climbs mountains and crosses arid plains to plant itself in new territory. It is one of the largest of our native species when it comes to maturity.

The **Black Willow** (*S. longipes*, Anders.) differs from *S. nigra* in the wider, more typically lanceolate leaf and the silvery lining which lightens the foliage mass wonderfully as the wind plays among the leaves. The two heart-shaped stipules are usually persistent; they can always be found near the tips of growing shoots, even in midsummer.

The centre of this tree's distribution is in the Ozark Mountains. Rocky banks of streams are its preferred habitat. It grows, a small tree, from Washington, D. C., to Florida, and west to Missouri and New Mexico.

Sandbar Willow (*Salix fluviatilis*, Nutt.)—Slender tree, 20 to 30 feet high, or much-branched shrub. *Leaves* silky, becoming smooth, linear-lanceolate, coarsely toothed, tapering at both ends, often falcate, 2 to 4 inches long, thin yellow-green, paler beneath; petioles short; midrib raised, prominent; stipules minute, leafy, deciduous. *Flowers* in slender, silky aments on leafy side twigs. *Fruits* ovoid-conic, sessile, scales smooth. *Preferred habitat*, moist soil along streams. *Distribution*, Quebec to Northwest Territory; south to Virginia, Kentucky and New Mexico.

The sandbar willow, like *S. nigra*, does a good work in holding in place a body of drift which without them would be moved by floods. The beautifying of rivers by embowering the mud flats and sandy shoals in billowy green is a distinct claim this tree has to the gratitude of communities. A little tree, indeed, but widely distributed, it is one of the most useful. A variety, *argyrophylla*, with silky, downy leaf, is found from Texas west to California and north to British Columbia.

The **Silver-leaved Willow** (*Salix sessilifolia*, Nutt.), with scarcely any stem for its narrow silky-lined leaves, is a little tree that follows stream borders from Puget Sound south to the western slopes of the Sierra Nevada. It is one of the commonest willows of the coast region of southern California. The hoary tomentum that clothes the opening leaves is never quite lost from the under sides of the leaves. They are pale yellow-green on the upper sides at maturity.

Peach-leaf Willow (*Salix amygdaloides*, Anders.)—Erect, straight-branched tree, 30 to 40 feet high, rarely 70 feet high. *Bark* brown, scaly, on thick plates. *Wood* soft, weak, pale brown.

Buds ovate, lustrous, brown. *Leaves* broadly lanceolate or ovate, serrate, taper pointed, 3 to 5 inches long, 1 inch wide, glabrous, paler, and glaucous beneath; petioles slender, compressed; stipules kidney shaped, broad, serrate, soon dropping. *Flowers* with the leaves; catkins loosely flowered, 1 to 2 inches long. *Fruits* narrowly ovoid capsules, taper pointed, smooth on stem of equal length. *Preferred habitat*, borders of streams and lakes. *Distribution*, Quebec to British Columbia, south through New York, Missouri and New Mexico.

The resemblance of the foliage of this tree to that of peach trees is striking. The leaves curl slightly, and hang pendant on their slender, flexible stems. It is one of our few willow trees that rise above medium height. Rare in the East, it is common in the valley of the Ohio, and along streams that flow down the eastern slopes of the Rocky Mountains. It is often met in cultivation in the Middle West.

The **Black Willow** (*S. lævigata*, Bebb.) is recognisable by its pale blue-green, leathery leaves, which are pale and glaucous beneath and finely serrate or almost entire on the margins. It is a native of California, following streams on the western slopes of the Sierras. It is rarely more than 40 feet high, averaging a little over half that height.

The **Shining Willow** (*S. lucida*, Muehl.) is an inhabitant of the North. From Newfoundland it ranges westward to Hudson Bay and the Rockies, and southward only as far as Pennsylvania and Nebraska. A small, round-headed tree, its distinction is the lustre of its ruddy twigs and the beautiful sheen of its dark green, leathery leaves. It is coming to be recognised by landscape gardeners and nurserymen as a species of considerable horticultural value.

The **Western Black Willow** (*S. lasiandra*, Benth.) grows to be a tree 60 feet high on river banks and lake shores from British Columbia to California and east into Montana, Colorado and New Mexico. The type becomes modified in the remote limits of its range. The leaves are 4 or 5 inches long, lanceolate and finely cut-toothed; they are a dark, lustrous green above, paler or glaucous below.

Missouri Willow (*Salix Missouriensis*, Bebb.)—Tree, to 50 feet high, with trunk to $1\frac{1}{2}$ feet thick. Twigs pubescent. *Bark* grey, thin, with small scales. *Wood* dark brown. *Leaves*

159

lanceolate, acuminate, finely serrate, with rounded bases, 3 to 6 inches long, ½ to 1½ inches wide; pubescent at first, becoming smooth, green above, pale and glaucous below; stipules leaf-like in pairs, often persistent; petioles about ½ inch long. *Flowers* before leaves; aments slender, long; scales persistent, hairy; stamens 2; style short. *Fruit* capsules, stalked, narrowly ovoid, smooth, above hairy oval scale. *Preferred habitat*, river banks. *Distribution*, northern Missouri, northeastern Kansas, Nebraska and western Iowa.

Pussy Willow (*Salix discolor*, Muehl.)—Shrub, or small tree, to 25 feet high, with stout branchlets, purplish red with pubescent coating. *Buds* reddish, flattened, pointed. *Leaves* oblong-lanceolate, acute at both ends, irregularly serrate, often crenate, thick, 3 to 5 inches long, bright green, with pale or silvery lining; midribs broad, yellow; stipules leaf-like, half-moon shaped; petioles slender. *Flowers*, March, often showing earlier, before the leaves; aments silky, oval, grey, turning yellow as flowers open. *Fruits* aments of beaked capsules, each long pointed, on long stem, with broad, hairy scale. *Preferred habitat*, swamps and moist hillsides. *Distribution*, Nova Scotia to Manitoba; south to Delaware and Missouri.

This is the familiar bog willow which we rarely recognise in leaf. The twigs are usually cut when the little furry catkins peep out in late winter. Florists in Eastern cities buy large quantities of these twigs in winter, and force them out for the early spring trade.

The **Heart Willow** (*S. cordata*), a shrub in the East, has a Western variety, *Mackenzieana*, Hook., that assumes the tree habit and size. It extends from the far North to the Rocky Mountains in Idaho and west into California. The narrow leaves are acute at the apex and bear minute kidney-shaped stipules throughout the summer. It is an extremely variable willow.

The **Hooker Willow** (*S. Hookeriana*, Hook.) has broad, oblong leaves, blunt at apex, and white below, with hoary tomentum. It is the little willow of sand dunes and salt marshes from Vancouver Island to southern Oregon. Its hoary twigs further identify it. It rarely grows above 30 feet in height.

Bebb's Willow (*Salix Bebbiana*, Sarg.)—Small tree, with short trunk, 10 to 20 feet high, with downy twigs and smooth,

THE PUSSY WILLOW (*Salix discolor*)

This is the familiar bog willow whose grey, silky catkins appear in earliest spring. People rarely see this tree in summer

1 Mature staminate flower   2 Immature staminate flower   3 Mature pistillate flower   4 Fruit unripe   5 Fruit ripe

THE PUSSY WILLOW (*Salix discolor*)

On staminate trees the catkins turn yellow by the ripening of the pollen in the anthers. On pistillate trees the catkins are made up of pistils, each on a silky, entire scale. In late spring these matured pistils form beaked, 2-valved pods. The seeds are minute, and each has a silky float

reddish bark. *Leaves* 1 to 3 inches long, oblong-obovate, acute or blunt at apex, sparingly toothed or entire, dull green and downy above, distinctly veined and pale blue or silvery, hairy beneath; petioles short; stipules semi-cordate, acute, deciduous. *Flowers* with leaves, sessile, erect, terminal; staminate silky white, becoming golden; pistillate silky, with yellow stigmas which spread in pairs. *Fruits* pubescent, beaked capsules; stalk much longer than scale. *Preferred habitat*, dry soil or stream borders. *Distribution*, throughout British America and south to New Jersey, Nebraska and Utah.

The **Balsam Willow** (*S. balsamifera*, Barr.) is dressed in spring, like the Balm of Gilead, in young shoots that glisten in a coating of balsam. The broad, ovate leaves are blunt at the apex, and look scarcely willow-like, but the flowers and seed pods maintain the family traditions and leave us no doubts. The tree is found in the northern tier of states and ranges far north, becoming a prostrate shrub. In its best estate it grows into a long stem crowned with a small clump of branches bearing the foliage. It is an inhabitant of cold bogs, and extends no farther west than Minnesota.

Golden Osier (*Salix alba*, Linn., var. *vitellina*)—Venerable-looking tree, with short trunk and regular, spreading top, 40 to 60 feet high. *Twigs* golden yellow. *Bark* grey, rough. *Leaves* elliptical, sparingly serrate, tapering at both ends, 2 to 4 inches long, silky hairy, becoming smooth; lining white and somewhat hairy; stipules ovate-lanceolate, deciduous; petioles short. *Flowers* with leaves; scales deciduous; stamens 2; stigmas sessile. *Fruits* flask shaped, sessile, smooth capsules. *Preferred habitat*, moist, rich soil. *Distribution*, eastern North America.

This American derivative of the white willow of Europe deserves mention among native trees. It is truly naturalised. Its yellow twigs are its best identification. It is far more common in cultivation than its parent, although the latter is occasionally seen. This variety is one of the most vigorous and useful of all the willows grown in this country.

CHAPTER XXII: THE HORNBEAMS

FAMILY BETULACEÆ

1. Genus OSTRYA Scop.

SMALL trees with very hard wood and scaly bark. *Leaves* simple, alternate, ovate, deciduous. *Flowers* small, monœcious, both in catkins. *Fruits* conical, hop-like, of many nuts, each one in an inflated sac.

KEY TO SPECIES

A. Leaves 3 to 5 inches long, tapering to point.
(*O. Virginiana*) HOP HORNBEAM
AA. Leaves 1 to 2 inches long, rounded at point.
(*O. Knowltoni*) IRONWOOD

2. Genus CARPINUS, Linn.

Small tree, with smooth, grey bark, showing swellings like veins. *Leaves* simple, alternate, oblong-lanceolate. *Flowers*, both sorts in aments, monœcious. *Fruit*, paired nutlets, each with a 3-lobed wing. (*C. Caroliniana*) HORNBEAM

The hornbeams, or ironwoods, are little trees hiding in the shadows of the forest. They are of slow growth; their wood is very hard. They bear their flowers in catkins, the two sorts upon the same tree: the staminate axillary, the pistillate terminal. The seeds are formed for wind distribution. Birches, alders, and that shrubby genus Corylus, the hazels, are associated by family characters. America has five of the six genera that compose the family.

As a rule the hardest woods come from tropical forests. Witness the lignum vitæ, hardest of woods, which grows in Florida, the West Indies, and northern South America; the mahogany of Central America; the rosewood from Brazil; and the ebony from Ceylon, tropical Africa and Cuba. Northern forests, too, furnish some species with exceptionally hard wood. The hornbeams are the best proof of this statement; the strength, hardness and flexibility of their wood rival steel. In durability they excel the best oak.

The name, ironwood, is locally given to any tree whose wood is hard.

1. GENUS OSTRYA, SCOP.

Hop Hornbeam, Ironwood (*Ostrya Virginiana*, Willd.)— Small, slender tree, with round head of stiff, wiry branches. *Bark* greyish brown, furrowed into narrow, scaly ridges, which break into small, oblong plates. *Wood* reddish brown, heavy, cross grained, tough, strong and hard to work. *Buds* lateral, ovate, acute, small, brown. *Leaves* ovate, acuminate, sharply and doubly serrate, 3 to 5 inches, thin, tough, dull yellow-green above, paler beneath; yellow in autumn; petioles short, hairy. *Flowers* with leaves, April and May, monœcious; staminate in catkins formed previous season; pistillate erect, loose catkins, each flower surrounded by three united bracts. *Fruit* a hop-like cluster of inflated bags, formed of bracts, each containing a hard little seed. *Preferred habitat*, shady forest ground. *Distribution*, Nova Scotia to Black Hills; south to Florida and Texas. *Uses:* Wood used for mallets, levers and tool handles. Desirable for ornamental planting, but rarely used.

The hop hornbeam looks like a relative of the birches. Its leaves convey this impression, and slender limbs in winter bear green catkins that cluster in threes on the ends of twigs and wait for spring, just as the birch catkins do.

The bark of this hornbeam is thin and scales off in narrow strips whose surfaces are covered with squarish scales. The pale colour and the stripping of the bark reminds us of the shellbark—its shaggy strips reduced to a small scale. Among the branches the bark is smooth and close, and the twigs look like fine wires, springing out at right angles from the stem.

In spring the staminate catkins swing out, even as the birch flowers do, but the pistillate clusters have to be looked for. The red, forked tongues thrust out for pollen may be seen at the ends of leafy side shoots. Here the midsummer shows a hop-like cluster of little pale green sacs, each with a shining seed inside.

The hop hornbeam is of a retiring disposition, preferring to hide in the shadows of taller trees. But there is nothing dark or funereal about it. The leaves, bright and green, are held out in level platforms where they can get the sunbeams that trickle down to them. Then comes summer, and the pale green "hops" make the tree a centre that seems to shed light into dark places. The little hop tree, *Ptelea trifoliata,* is shining in its corner, and at a short distance the two trees might be confused. Each one is a blessed sight on a hot day, for pale green against dark green is always a cool colour scheme.

In the late autumn, after the leaves turn yellow and fall, the hops still hang, grudgingly giving up one little seed balloon after another to the insistent wind. There is likely to be a long sail for each one, and perhaps more than one, for until the bag is punctured and the seed covered, the wind gives it no rest.

The wood of the hop hornbeam is vexatious stuff for the turner, and whoever else tries tool upon it. But once it takes shape it lasts indefinitely. Sled stakes, levers, rake teeth, tool handles; wedges, do not soon need replacing if made of this material. It is equally satisfactory when used for fence posts.

The parks about Boston have beautiful specimens of the hop hornbeam, showing that its merits as an ornamental tree are being recognised by the best judges. The next step will be its increasing popularity for private grounds.

The **Western Ironwood** (*O. Knowltoni*), which was discovered in Arizona but a few years ago, is smaller in every way than the Eastern species, but every trait proclaims it a hop hornbeam. The leaves, catkins and hops are short and blunt pointed. The protective pubescence which belongs to desert plants is on the young shoots and the leaves and fruits of this tree. Its limbs are often gnarled, but it forms a rounded symmetrical top, and is sometimes 30 feet high.

The tree is probably one of the rarest in the country, for as far as known it has not been found except in one locality, where it has formed a considerable grove. How this species has been cut off from its near relative in the East is a problem worthy of investigation.

1 Winter twigs   2 Pistillate flowers   3 Staminate flowers   4 Fruit branch

THE HOP HORNBEAM (*Ostrya Virginiana*)

The bark peels off in narrow, thin strips from wood as hard as iron. The wiry twigs put out their leaves with the greenish racemes of pistillate flowers and the long yellow staminate catkins. The winter twigs show these already half grown. The pistillate are concealed in buds. The fruit is a pale-green, hop-like cluster of bags, each one of which is a little balloon carrying a single seed

THE AMERICAN HORNBEAM (*Carpinus Caroliniana*)

The treetop is often broad and flat, a maze of wiry twigs infinitely divided, bearing the pale-green fruits and the thin, silky leaves. The peculiar swellings on trunk and limbs look like veins on a blacksmith's arm. The winter reveals the beech-like bark and the wiry twigs

2. GENUS CARPINUS, LINN.

American Hornbeam, Blue Beech (*Carpinus Carolini-ana*, Walt.)—Small, shapeless tree with irregular limbs, often pendulous, and slender, wiry twigs. *Bark* furrowed at base of trunk on old trees; smooth, bluish grey above, swollen as by veins underneath the bark; twigs brown. *Wood* light brown, heavy, hard, strong, fine, hard to work. *Buds* all lateral, ovate, small, brown. *Leaves* ovate-oblong, long pointed, irregularly doubly serrate, often unequal at base, dull green, pale beneath, orange or scarlet in autumn; hairy petiole and veins. *Flowers* monœcious, with leaves, in April; staminate catkins, 1½ inches long, pendulous, lateral; pistillate flowers in racemes, terminal, loose flowered, with forked red stigmas under green scales. *Fruit* racemed, hard nutlets in pairs, each supported by a large, leaf-like, 3-lobed bract. *Preferred habitat*, swampy rich soil near streams, in shade of taller trees. *Distribution*, Georgian Bay (southern Canada) to Florida; west to Minnesota and Texas; also in Mexico and Central America. *Uses:* Curious and interesting tree for planting along watercourses, but rarely seen in landscape gardening. Wood used for tool handles, levers and ox yokes.

The American hornbeam has no "hop" in its name because its fruit has none. Each little seed in the terminal cluster has a mate on the other side of the stem, and all summer they have grown close together, back to back, generally crowding for more room. Each seed sits in the prow of a little boat, shaped like a red maple leaf, but hollowed like a scallop shell. The wind finally loosens the hold of each, and for a time seed and boat hang by a thread. This breaks at last, and the little nut sails off at the will of the wind, to grow, if it falls in wet ground.

This hornbeam resembles Ostrya in many particulars—its leaves, its flowers, its delicate wiry twigs, its foliage, and the hardness of its wood. It grows, too, in the shadows of other trees. The bark it is that sets the trees apart. This tree has bark like a young beech, a thin, smooth, blue-grey rind, that has strange flutings or vein-like swellings coursing up the trunk and out on the larger limbs. They remind one of the veins of a blacksmith's sinewy arm, or an athlete's. A trunk a foot in diameter at the

165

base generally shows a few furrows, and some minor roughness near the ground, but above, the smoothness is unbroken.

The hornbeam grows often in thickets, sometimes as scattered, single trees, in marshy ground and along streams. It is a pretty tree, with blue-green leaves that turn to orange and scarlet in the autumn. It is coming into notice as an ornamental tree, now that people are learning that the best way to make a park is to do less levelling and filling, and plant in the lower ground trees and plants that choose such situations naturally.

The anguish of working in this wood was experienced by the early colonists, who appreciated its value. "The New England Prospect" says: "The Horne bound tree is a tough kind of wood that requires so much paines in riving as is almost incredible, being the best for to make bolles and dishes, not being subject to cracke or leake." Heads of beetles, stocks, mill cogs, yoke timbers, levers—for such uses it is ideal wood.

The **European Hornbeam** (*Carpinus Betulus*, Linn.) ranges from Scandinavia and England to the Caucasus, and is a beautiful tree of no small note. The "hornbeams" of ancient ox yokes wore indefinitely, becoming as hard and smooth as horn. The trees grow in cold, forbidding situations, where most trees fail, and so serve as windbreaks and as covers of barren clay soil. The wood makes excellent fuel and charcoal, beside its special uses to the turner. In the old days of formal gardens, the hornbeam was popular, for it suffered itself to be clipped with as much patience as the linden, the beech or the yew. It was a famous hedge tree. The Germans made fences by planting rows of the saplings leaning so that each two plants formed a cross. The bark was scraped at the point of intersection, and then the two were bound together with straw, until they grew fast to each other. Careful pruning made of this in a short time a beautiful and impenetrable wall. Miles of this fencing were seen in Evelyn's day. The Germans also planted the trees near the gates of the great cities, training their branches to cover arbours "for convenience of the people to sit and solace in." Travellers in Europe will find the hornbeam still much used as in earlier centuries.

China, Japan and India have native hornbeams; there are nine or ten species in all. The race is old—the rocks show fossils of extinct species that once inhabited western America.

1 Fruiting Branch

2 Staminate Flowers

3 Pistillate Flowers

THE AMERICAN HORNBEAM (*Carpinus Caroliniana*)

The pistillate catkins are borne at the ends of the twigs, the staminate from side buds close by. In autumn the thin, beech-like blue-green leaves turn to scarlet and orange. The trunks are gnarled and swollen in ridges under the close gray-blue bark. The seeds are borne on leafy triangular bracts.

THE AMERICAN WHITE BIRCH (*Betula populifolia*)

In winter this little tree exhibits the peculiar triangular or V-shaped marks of black that diverge below each branch. The delicacy of the twig system is scarcely concealed in summertime, so light is the spray of fluttering, poplar-like leaves. If started by a cut lengthwise the bark may be peeled off around the smooth limbs. But it is very hard work, and then the bark does not part into papery sheets. The dark bands the peeling makes often deceive people into calling this the canoe birch

CHAPTER XXIII: THE BIRCHES

FAMILY BETULACEÆ

Genus BETULA, Linn.

TREES with smooth bark marked with conspicuous horizontal slits (*lenticels*), usually curling back in thin horizontal layers. *Leaves* simple, alternate, deciduous, serrate, stalked. *Flowers* monœcious, in catkins. *Fruit* cone-like, scaly; seed flat, winged.

KEY TO SPECIES

A. Bark chalky white, yellow beneath.
  B. Leaves triangular, bark close.
              (*B. populifolia*) WHITE BIRCH
  BB. Leaves ovate; bark separating freely into layers.
              (*B. papyrifera*) CANOE BIRCH
AA. Bark grey, curling back, yellow beneath.
              (*B. lutea*) YELLOW BIRCH
AAA. Bark red, curling in thin ribbons; cones ripe in June.
              (*B. nigra*) RED BIRCH
AAAA. Bark dark brown, lustrous.
  B. Twigs aromatic; bark separating into thick plates.
              (*B. lenta*) SWEET BIRCH
  BB. Twigs not aromatic; bark separating into thin, papery layers. (*B. occidentalis*) WESTERN BLACK BIRCH

There is no denying the inferiority of the wood in most species of birch. The toughness and durability of the bark prevent the prompt evaporation of the abundant sap, which ferments and breaks down the wood cells. It is not uncommon to find in the woods a birch trunk with the bark intact, but the wood crumbling like chalk when touched. When the trees are stripped of their bark immediately after being cut down, the wood seasons properly and lasts fairly well as lumber.

There are twenty-eight known species of the genus Betula distributed over the Northern Hemisphere, and a fugitive species grows in Terra del Fuego! Ten of these are North American, seven or eight Asiatic, and six European. The white birch of Europe extends through Asia to Japan, and is cultivated in many varieties in America.

American White Birch, Aspen-leaved Birch (*Betula populifolia*, Marsh.)—Small, short-lived tree, 25 to 40 feet high, with slender horizontal branches and tremulous foliage. *Bark* chalky white or greyish, with triangular dark patches where branches are or have been; not easily separated into layers; white does not rub off on clothing; branches dark brown. *Wood* light, soft, weak, close grained, not durable in contact with soil; light brown; takes good polish. *Buds* slender, brown, ¼ inch long. *Leaves* alternate, simple, triangular, 2 to 3 inches long, long pointed, double saw toothed; dark green above, paler beneath, yellow in autumn; teeth of margin glandular; petioles long, slim, twisted. *Flowers* before leaves, April, monœcious; staminate in terminal catkins, single, or paired, formed in previous summer; pistillate catkins, ½ inch long, pale green, scales ovate. *Fruits* cylindrical cones, 1 inch long, blunt at both ends, drooping; scales downy, 3-lobed, side lobes large, spreading; nut oval, pointed, with broad wing. *Preferred habitat*, dry, gravelly soils, or borders of swamps. *Distribution*, Nova Scotia along coast to Delaware; northwest to Lake Ontario. *Uses:* Graceful and hardy ornamental tree; thrives in any soil, but rarely planted. Wood used for spools, shoe pegs, wood pulp and fuel. Valuable nurse trees to hardwoods and conifers on land Nature is reforesting.

The only native species with which this white birch might be confused is the canoe birch. Look first at the bark. It is chalky white and yellowish beneath, but the chalk does not rub off. It is hard, close bark, which does not part into thin layers. It is cracked in growth, and the short crevices are dark, making the trunk look grey at a distance. Wherever a bud or branch has been, a large, ever-widening black V brands the trunk and limbs. Near the base of the trunk, the white bark is about all gone, leaving a black, furrowed area that grows gradually higher.

The foliage mass of the American white birch is much thinner and lighter than that of the canoe birch. The leaves are small and dainty, triangular, taper pointed, suggesting in shape and tremulous poise the aspens or poplars.

This is the one of our birches that most nearly resembles

Fruiting branch   A. Pistillate flowers   B. Staminate flowers   C. Fruit   D. Detail of fruit

THE AMERICAN WHITE BIRCH (*Betula populifolia*)

The narrow, táper-pointed, triangular leaves are very glutinous when they unfold. They tremble like aspen leaves, and form a thin foliage mass. The long, pendulous staminate catkin shown has a slim green pistillate one above it. The flowers appear in April before the leaves are half-grown. The narrow, oblong cone has scales with two spreading side lobes. Its wings are broader than the seed. The bark is dirty white and marked with a conspicuous black triangle or an inverted V under each branch. The bark can with difficulty be stripped horizontally. It is not easily separable into thin sheets. The bases of old trunks become dark and furrowed

C. Fruit   D. Details of fruit and fruit scales   A. Pistillate flowers   B. Staminate flowers

THE CANOE BIRCH (*Betula papyrifera*)

The bark of this tree is a dull, chalky white, and curls away from its few furrows in horizontal plates. On old trees the bases of the trunks are dark-coloured. The winter twigs often end in three stiff catkins, the staminate flowers sealed tight to pass the winter. In April the ovate leaves come out with the flowers, the green pistillate catkins erect to catch pollen. In autumn the seeds fall away from the 3-lobed scales in the pencil-like cones. Each seed has a pair of broad wings

the European white birch. It is not a large tree, and the woodsman scorned it, until the manufacturer of wood pulp, shoe pegs and spools sent forth a demand for it. Now the owner looks with satisfaction upon the graceful, bending birches that bow to each other in the swamps along the streams, over abandoned fields and deforested mountain sides. The harvest is his in due season. This threatened doom of the white birch casts no warning shadow across these sunny, thick-set acres. The trees are all young together, and no matter how scant a living the sterile soil yields, these gypsy trees never seem to languish. Their silken ribbons of dirty white bark are flaunted gaily against the sombre background of evergreens, and they "lean out over the stream," as Doctor Van Dyke puts it, "Narcissus-like, as if to see their own beauty in the moving mirror." Life is short—but it is care free and joyous.

There is a philosophy in the lives of these vagabond birches we may well ponder upon. Do they not clothe with beauty the most uninviting places? Do they not come again, after a general slaughter, promptly and abundantly, from stump and from scattered seed? A noble persistence and patience under adverse conditions is revealed for our contemplation in the parable of the white birch.

Canoe Birch, Paper Birch (*Betula papyrifera*, Marsh.)— Large tree, 60 to 80 feet high, with few erect, large limbs and numerous horizontal branches with flexible twigs, forming a broad, open head. *Bark* dull, chalky white, when exposed to the sun, stripping horizontally into thin sheets, with frayed edges; chalk rubs off. *Wood* light brown, reddish, light, hard, tough, close grained. *Buds* resinous, dark brown, sharp pointed. *Leaves* 2 to 3 inches long, ovate, abruptly pointed, finely and irregularly serrate, thick, dull, dark green, with paler lining, yellow in autumn; midrib raised and marked with black dots; petioles grooved, downy, slender. *Flowers* monœcious, April, before leaves; staminate catkins, 3 to 4 inches long, pendulous, clustered or paired; pistillate catkins, 1 to $1\frac{1}{2}$ inches long, on stalks 1 inch long; scales tapering; pistils red. *Fruit* slender cones $1\frac{1}{2}$ inches long, cylindrical, stalked; scales smooth, 3-lobed, two outer points smaller than middle one; seed oval, with broad wings. *Preferred habitat*, river banks and rich slopes of mountains. *Distribution*, Labrador to Alaskan coast; south to Long Island,

169

northern Pennsylvania, central Michigan and Minnesota, northern Nebraska, Black Hills, northern Montana and northwestern Washington. *Uses:* Picturesque, graceful ornamental tree; hardy, rapid grower, vigorous, easily transplanted; wood used for spools, shoe lasts, wood pulp and fuel. Starchy cambium furnishes food to Indians and trappers. Bark used for canoes, letter paper and a great variety of articles, useful and decorative.

The Indians easily proved their ingenuity in the uses of the paper birch. They framed their tents of it, and built canoes, ribbing them with cedar, and covering them with large sheets of birch bark. They sewed the seams with threads made of spruce or cedar roots, and closed the chinks with pitch or gum of the Balm of Gilead. These small craft were graceful and durable, and the Indian managed them with consummate skill. An early letter writer from the colonies described these "delicate canowes so light that two men will transport one of them overland whither they list, and one of them will transporte tenne or twelve Salvages by water at a time." Hunters and trappers, following clumsily the Indian's example, are able to supply their camps with all necessary utensils, such as baskets, buckets, dippers, dishes—all made of this material. The weather is never so wet but that fragments of birch burn merrily to start a campfire.

The range of the canoe birch is remarkable. It reaches a higher latitude than any other deciduous tree, and covers a wider territory. It is a noticeable feature of the almost continuous forest that once stretched from Newfoundland to Washington state, south to Nebraska and Pennsylvania and north to within the Arctic circle.

The bark, which gives name and character to this tree, is distinguishable from the white bark of other species by its pearly surface and chalky whiteness which rubs off on clothing. It strips readily into thin horizontal sheets, marked with elongated lenticels, or breathing holes. The feminine tourist in Northern woods loses no time in supplying herself with birch-bark note paper. The bark is usually removed in thick plates, from which the thin sheets may be stripped at leisure. These sheets are orange coloured, with a faint purplish bloom upon them, and darker, purplish lines. Alas! for the zeal of these tourists. They usually cut too deep, and the strip that tears off so evenly, girdles and kills the tree, because nothing is left to protect the living

THE YELLOW BIRCH (*Betula lutea*)

Very different is this tree's habit in woodlands and on a rocky declivity. The bark is rougher and darker on the gnarled tree. Thin plates of bark cover old trunks

1 Fruit and leaf   2 Fruit   3 Section of fruit   4 Seeds   5 Seed on scale   6 Upper side of scale   7 Under side of scale   8 Flower buds
9 Flowering branch: A, Sterile or staminate flower;   B, Fertile or pistillate flower   10 Bark and wood

THE YELLOW BIRCH (*Betula lutea*)

(Upper.) A flowering twig in early April. Staminate catkins pendulous at tip. Pistillate catkins smaller, solitary, erect, lateral.
(Lower.) Leaf, cones, 3-lobed cone-scales and heart-shaped, winged seeds, ripe in autumn. Twig with staminate catkins half grown and sealed up for winter

cambium. A black band (of mourning) soon marks the doomed tree, and it eventually snaps off in the wind.

The strain of the growing wood breaks the bark here and there and it curls back at the broken edges. Strips gradually come off, on trunk and branches, leaving black bands. But this is not a very shaggy birch. The pearly lustre of its clean white bark and the density of its lustrous foliage make *B. papyrifera* one of the most beautiful, as it is one of the largest, of our native birches.

Yellow Birch, Grey Birch (*Betula lutea*, Michx.)—Medium-sized tree, 50 to 75 feet, rarely 100 feet high, with broad, round top with slender, drooping branchlets ending in fine, leafy spray. *Bark* aromatic, bitter, dark grey, rough, with deep, irregular furrows, and thick plates; younger stems silvery yellow, peeling horizontally in ribbons; remnants of this lustrous bark seen on plates of old trunks; twigs pubescent the first season. *Wood* reddish brown, pale, heavy, hard, strong, close grained, satiny. *Buds* pointed, ¼ inch long, brown, shiny. *Leaves* ovate, 3 to 4 inches long, sharply and doubly serrate, pointed, oblique at base; veins conspicuous, hairy beneath, midrib stout; petiole short, hairy; colour dull dark green, with yellow-green lining; autumn, pale yellow. *Flowers* before leaves in April; staminate catkins, 3 to 4 inches long, brown above, yellow below the middle; pistillate catkins ⅔ inch long, reddish green, hairy. *Fruits:* cones oblong or ovoid, stout, 1 inch long, erect, scales 3-lobed, narrow, tapering, hairy; nut oval, with narrow wings. *Preferred habitat,* rich, moist uplands. *Distribution,* Newfoundland south to Delaware, North Carolina and Tennessee; west to Minnesota. *Uses:* A desirable ornamental tree, but rarely planted. Wood valuable for implements, furniture, wheel hubs, button moulds, boxes, and for fuel.

The bark again gives the name to a large birch that grows here and there in the forests of the Northern States. The fringed and tattered outer bark, dingy grey with pearly lustre, and showing gleams of gold at every rent, is unlike the other birches. The twigs are aromatic, but not to compare with the black birch. In grace and lustiness the two trees are well matched. The yellow birch leads in size, of its catkins, fruiting cones, and the tree itself. The leaves are not larger, but they are more distinctly toothed, the double serrations being regular and clear cut.

The yellow birch is one of the best of timber trees. The

171

frames of sledges are made of it in the North. An infinite number of small articles employ it. The burs make good mallets; the fantastic arching roots sometimes show curly grain. Often a great yellow birch, shaggy with age, stands long in the woods after it is dead. Such a specimen was lighted on a dark night by a camping party. The flames swept the trunk in a flash, turning the whole tree into a magnificent pillar of fire which consumed it utterly before it had time to fall! So a veracious camper declared. The safety and morals of such a bonfire were evidently not considered by the party. Doubtless this is a common temptation to camping parties in the north woods. It might be quite justifiable if the fire could always be controlled. But here, as elsewhere, playing with fire is dangerous business, and responsible and law-abiding citizens will abstain from it.

Red Birch, River Birch (*Betula nigra*, Linn.)—Tree 60 to 90 feet high, numerous pendulous branches forming round head; trunk usually dividing into a few main limbs which spread slightly. *Bark* dark reddish brown, furrowed, with scaly surface; on branches cinnamon red to silvery, curling back in sheets, fringed with tatters throughout. Lenticels prominent. *Wood* light brown, strong, close grained. *Buds* chestnut brown, shining, $\frac{1}{4}$ inch long, ovate. *Leaves* alternate, 1 to 3 inches long, oval, pointed, twice saw toothed, thin, tough, shining dark green above, pale yellow-green beneath; dull yellow in autumn; petioles short, flattened, fuzzy, slim. *Flowers* before leaves, March or April; staminate catkins in threes, 2 to 3 inches long, yellow and brown mottled, pendulous; pistillate catkins $\frac{1}{3}$ inch long, erect, green, fuzzy, stalked. *Fruit* ripe in June, erect, cylindrical cones, 1 to 2 inches long, bracts 3-lobed, hairy, divisions narrow, spreading, central one longest; nut oval, with broad wings, hairy. *Preferred habitat*, along rivers, ponds and swamps inundated part of the year. *Distribution*, Massachusetts to Florida, west to Texas, north along Mississippi to Minnesota, southern Wisconsin, eastern Nebraska, and in Ohio. *Uses:* Desirable ornamental tree; planted in copses to hold stream banks from washing. Wood used for fuel, furniture, ox yokes, shoe lasts, shoes and small woodenwares. Branches make hoops for rice casks.

The red birch earns its name by its bark, which is reddish or chocolate coloured from root to twig. The tree is a tall, graceful fountain of leafy spray; the central stem breaks into two or three divergent limbs that support the pendulous horizontal branchlets. No birch loves the stream borders more ardently than this Southern member of the family. The lustrous leaves do not conceal the flying silken tatters of bark which cover the tree to its leafy twigs the year round. It is foolish to call this tree *nigra*, for it is not black but red, from top to bottom. It is at its best along the bayous of the lower Mississippi, where its roots and base of trunk are inundated for half the year.

The fruits of the red birch are ripe in June, and the wind, shaking the erect cones, scatters the seeds on the rich land from which the water has subsided. Here they germinate at once, and are rooted, vigorous little seedlings by the time the floods return, able to keep their heads above water, and to thrive like their parents, adding colour and grace of line and motion to the landscapes of many different regions.

It is a surprise to find this, our semi-aquatic and southernmost birch, growing in apparent complacency and comfort in dry, upland soil in the New England States and Minnesota. But so it behaves in cultivation. It well exemplifies the versatility of the family.

Cherry Birch, Sweet Birch, Black Birch (*Betula lenta*, Linn.)—Handsome, round-headed tree, 50 to 80 feet high, symmetrical, with slender, often tortuous but graceful limbs, lower ones drooping; twigs delicate, polished. *Bark* dark brown, broken by furrows into thick irregular plates which show fragments of the smooth, silky bark that covers young limbs. Lenticels prominent as horizontal lines; inner bark aromatic, spicy. *Wood* dark brown, reddish, heavy, strong, hard, close grained. *Buds* slender, acute, brown, $\frac{1}{4}$ inch long. *Leaves* ovate, 2 to 6 inches long, pointed, doubly serrate, dull, dark green above, yellow-green below; midrib yellow; veins prominent, straight, downy; petioles short. *Flowers* before leaves, April; staminate catkins, 3 to 4 inches long, purplish yellow, pendulous; pistillate, erect, sessile, $\frac{1}{2}$ to 1 inch long; bracts hairy, ovate. *Fruit*, June, erect cones, sessile, scales broad, of three equal, rounded lobes; nuts with narrow wings, tapering at base. *Preferred habitat*, fertile soil, moist and well drained. *Distribution*, Newfoundland to western Ontario; south to Florida, Kentucky, Tennessee and Kansas. *Uses:* Occasionally cultivated for shade and ornament; wood used for wheel hubs, furniture and fuel; inner bark yields

173

salicylic acid and wintergreen oil, used in medicine; sap made into birch beer.

The cherry birch has several common names, and each one has a good reason for being. The bark is very dark, and it breaks into rough, square plates with edges curling stiffly back but not fraying into ribbons at all. The smooth outer layer, with its prominent horizontal lenticels, reminds one of the bark of cherry trees. This epidermis finally disappears from the large trunks, but it may always be found covering the limbs.

This birch is one of the handsomest trees of the woods. In winter the grace of the pendulous branches and the symmetry of the round head are best revealed. On the bark, from dark brown trunk to golden-brown twig, a satiny sheen gives brilliancy and depth to the colours. The tree seems aglow with life even in its winter sleep, and the plump buds and the impatient catkins, already nearly an inch long, promise what the spring fulfils. The abundant sap which mounts upward in early April forces out the catkins into tassels that hang, all purplish yellow, and very large, from near the ends of the branches. Erect among them are the green pistillate ones, rising on the ends of short side shoots. The abundance of its leaves and their glossy sheen and brightness set this birch apart from others in midsummer. In autumn they turn to gold.

The small boy pulls a twig off the sweet birch sapling, and chews it sedulously as he fares through the woods. The stimulating flavour of wintergreen, which is in the bark the year round, is especially strong in spring. Wintergreen oil, used in flavouring medicines, and esteemed in the treatment of rheumatism for the salicylic acid it contains, is extracted from the bark of this species. Birch beer is brewed from the sweet sap. The spicy fragrance extends to the leaves also, and a twig enables one to identify the tree at any time of year. In Kamchatka the natives strip the inner bark of *B. lenta* into long shreds like vermicelli. This is done in spring, when it is richest in starch and sugar. These strips are dried for winter use as food. They are boiled with caviar and with fish.

The wood of cherry birch is stained to imitate mahogany and cherry. This is a pity, for it has character of its own and beauty that deserve recognition. It has its own good colour, reddish brown, and this in "natural finish," well rubbed, is lustrous and

174

Fruit and details of fruit   A. Pistillate flowers   B. Staminate flowers

THE CHERRY BIRCH (*Betula lenta*)

The brown bark has a silky outside layer marked with horizontal slits, just as cherry trees have. On old trunks this smooth layer is replaced by rough, broken plates. The wood is like black cherry. The twigs have a pleasant, aromatic taste, quite unlike the rank, bitter taste of cherry bark. The leaves come out in pairs from side buds in late April. The staminate catkins are in evidence in winter, sealed up tight at the ends of twigs. In early April they shake out their golden pollen on every breeze, and the erect green catkins of pistillate flowers show themselves close at hand. In early summer the oval, erect cones shed their seeds. One figure shows the 3-lobed bracts still hanging by threads from the central cone stem

Frui   A. Pistillate flower   B. Staminate flower

THE RED BIRCH (*Betula nigra*)

    This tree blossoms in March, before the leaves, and its winged seeds are falling in June from the erect, oblong cones.   The trees are pyramidal, with many drooping, horizontal branches.   The bark of limbs and old twigs frays into ribbons.   Throughout, its colour is red.   The glossy foliage turns to yellow before falling

satiny, often showing what the cabinetmaker calls "landscape" or clouded areas of unusual beauty.

The **Western Black Birch** (*B. occidentalis*, Hook.) grows from the Black Hills westward, widening its range to south and north, into Alaska and California along the coast, and following the Rocky Mountains to New Mexico. It is widespread, but nowhere common. This graceful little tree is a true birch in habit and in the lustrous, horizontal lenticelled bark, the bronze colour of which is quite sufficient to justify its name and to identify the tree. Unlike the cherry birch, this tree sheds its bark in thin, papery layers.

The brown wood is locally used for fencing and fuel. It is too small a tree to be important for its lumber. It commends itself to planters in the Western States, especially where its roots can get water, for it is as thirsty as an alder, following streams always, or the borders of lakes.

The **White Birch** of Europe (*Betula alba*, Linn.) we rarely see. The weeping and cut-leaved varieties of this species adorn American parks and gardens—their only fault, that they are short lived. "Like a fair lady in a far country" is the white birch here, and we cherish our specimen trees with profound solicitude.

In its own country the peasants depend upon the birch forests in a great many ways. In the north of Europe birch is the principal fuel in houses and smelting works. It makes good charcoal. The Russians eat with wooden spoons, and wear wooden shoes, both made of birch. They live in houses furnished with birch furniture, and shingled with slabs of birch bark. They strip and grind the soft inner bark, and mix it with meal in their bread. Even the tiny winged seeds serve a useful purpose. Birds, especially the white ptarmigan in Lapland, feed upon them through the long, cold winters, when deep snows cover all other foods. Lopped trees send up suckers which are cut and bound into birch brooms. The inner bark is stripped into sheets and serves for paper. The famous books of Numa Pompilius were written on birch bark, if Plutarch is to be believed. Birch wood contains abundance of sap. In spring a tree will often yield its weight in sap in a fortnight. Birch mead and wine are most refreshing beverages. Birch bark yields tannin, a yellow dye, and an oil which gives Russia leather its characteristic

colour and odour. Swedish farmers look for the opening leaves
of the birch as a sign to sow their barley. In England the elm
is watched for the same reason.

In Parkinson's day the "physicall uses" of birch were few.
But he adds:

"Many other civill uses the Birch is put unto, as first to
decke up Houses and arbours, both for the fresh greennesse and
good sent it casteth; it serveth to make hoopes to binde caskes
withall; the young branches being fresh are writhed, and serve
for bands unto faggots: of the young twiggs are made broomes to
sweepe our houses, as also rods to correct children at schoole,
or at home, and was an ensigne borne in bundles by the Lictors
or Sargeants before the Consulls in the old *Romans* times, with
which, and with axes borne in the like manner, they declared
the punishment for lesser, and greater offences, to their people."

In the very end of their swift decay birch trees served the
fashionable world in the heydey of the powdered wig. "The
whitest part of the old wood of *doating* birches is made the grounds
of our effeminate farined Gallants' sweet powder."

American birches are more valuable lumber trees and more
graceful for ornamental uses than the forest birches of Europe.
Let us cease to compare them with oaks and hickories, and set
ourselves to appreciate those peculiar virtues and charms that the
birches alone possess.

CHAPTER XXIV: THE ALDERS

Family Betulaceæ

Genus ALNUS, Linn.

Small water-loving trees of rapid growth. *Leaves* simple, deciduous, alternate, short stemmed. *Flowers* apetalous, monœcious, in catkins. *Fruit* woody, cone-like, oval, with 2 seeds on each scale.

KEY TO SPECIES

A. Flowers in autumn. (*A. maritima*) SEASIDE ALDER
AA. Flowers before leaves in winter or early spring.
 B. Staminate catkins becoming 4 to 6 inches long.
  C. Bark smooth, pale grey or white; tree with narrowly pyramidal head. (*A. Oregona*) RED ALDER
  CC. Bark ridged, dark brown; tree with wide, open head. (*A. rhombifolia*) WHITE ALDER
 BB. Staminate catkins becoming 2 to 3 inches long.
  C. Leaves narrow, tapering to base and apex.
    (*A. oblongifolia*) LANCELEAF ALDER
  CC. Leaves broad, oval, papery.
    (*A. tenuifolia*) PAPERLEAF ALDER
AAA. Flowers after the leaves in spring or summer.
    (*A. Sitchensis*) ALASKA ALDER

The genus Alnus includes twenty species of shrubs and trees, nine in North America, six of which are trees in habit and size. The largest and most important timber tree is the black alder of the Old World. Widely distributed by Nature and by man, this genus is the source of many hardy ornamentals adapted to damp soils.

"Alder, the owner of all waterish ground."

Seaside Alder (*Alnus maritima*, Nutt.)—A round-topped tree 15 to 30 feet, with slender branches. *Bark* thin, smooth, light brown; twigs greyish. *Wood* soft, light brown, close grained.

177

Buds acute, dark red, ¼ inch long, with silky pubescence. *Leaves* 3 to 4 inches long, oblong, ovate or obovate, acute at both ends, shining dark green above, pale green and dull beneath, edges set with fine incurving teeth; petioles short. *Flowers* autumnal, from buds of previous spring; monœcious; staminate catkins, golden, 1 to 2 inches long; pistillate, oblong, ⅛ inch long, with red tips of stigmas protruding from scales. *Fruit*, a woody, oval strobile, ripe a year after blooming; scales thick, shiny, each bears two flat, obovate, pointed nuts or seeds. *Preferred habitat*, borders of streams and ponds, near, but not actually on, seacoast. *Distribution*, eastern Delaware and Maryland, Indian Territory. *Uses:* Rarely planted, but deserving of cultivation for its glossy foliage and the beauty and unusualness of its golden catkins, appearing in September.

The seaside alder divides with the witch hazel the distinction of bearing flowers and ripening fruit simultaneously in the fall of the year. They do not compete for popular favour, because the alder comes first, hanging out its golden catkins in clusters on the ends of the season's shoots in August and September. Nothing is left of them when the witch hazel scatters its dainty stars along the twigs in October and November. The tiny pistillate cones of the alder are scarcely larger than the buds that keep them company.

The seaside alder grows well in the Arnold Arboretum, at Boston, flowering profusely, thus proving itself hardy in New England, and comfortable in dryer soil than it naturally chooses. It is quite worthy of the attention of those who seek for beauty and novelty of habit among little native trees.

The **Oregon,** or **Red Alder** (*A. Oregona*, Nutt.), is a large tree for an alder, sometimes 80 feet in height, with a narrow pyramid of drooping branches about a trunk that may exceed 3 feet in diameter. The smooth, pale grey bark of this tree sets it apart from other alders. The flowers and strobiles are large to match the tree; the ovate leaves are crenately lobed and finely cut toothed. They are lined with rusty pubescence, and are usually smooth and dark green above.

This is the alder of the Western coast that climbs mountains until it leaves the spruces behind, but reaches its greatest size about Puget Sound. From Sitka south through Washington and Oregon it lines the stream borders, and along the mountains it reaches as far as Santa Barbara in California. It loves also the cañon sides in the coast range.

The reddish-brown wood is beautifully satiny when polished. It is light and easily worked, and though weak and brittle is made into furniture. The Indians make "dug-outs" of the butts of large trees.

The **White Alder** (*A. rhombifolia*, Nutt.), equal in size to the preceding species, grows along the mountain streams from northern Idaho to southern California. It has a white scurf on its new shoots and the opening leaves are clothed with white hairs. Its wide sap wood is also white. The tree's spring appearance probably justifies its name. The irregularly diamond-shaped leaves are sharply and finely cut on thin wavy margins.

The wonderful thing about this tree is its blooming in January or February, hanging its conspicuous yellow catkins out while yet all other trees are asleep. Even in California this is a striking phenomenon along the mountain streams fringed with these trees.

The bark of the trunks of white alder is furrowed and dark brown. The trees need not be confused with the Oregon alder, if the trunk be examined.

The **Lanceleaf Alder** (*A. oblongifolia*, Torr.), whose name describes it well, comes up from the Peruvian Andes, through Mexico, and is found at high altitudes along cañon sides in New Mexico and Arizona.

The **Paperleaf Alder** (*A. tenuifolia*, Nutt.)—A small tree with thin, firm-textured leaves, ovate in shape with laciniate lobes, twice saw toothed, one of the prettiest of the alders, is abundant in thickets along the headwaters of streams that rise in the Western mountains. It follows the various ranges from British Columbia to Lower California, Colorado and northern New Mexico.

Poets do not always realise their responsibility. The one who characterised the trees that fringed the sluggish streams and cover the "water galls" in England as "the water spungie alder, good for naught," put into rhythmic form, too easy to remember, a stigma that brands a really picturesque and useful tree. The alder's primary virtue is that it will thrive in places so boggy that even willows and poplars cannot grow there. Can any lover of English landscapes spare the alders from unsightly places whose lines they soften and whose baldness they conceal with billows of living green? "He who would see the alder in perfection must follow the banks of the Mole, in Surrey, through the sweet vales of Dorking and Wickleham, into the groves of Esher."

The English people cherish an affectionate regard for their native black alder, a description of which follows. The hawthorns of their hedgerows are not more a part of the life of the people. John Evelyn expresses the sentiment when, after recounting the many practical uses of the tree and its wood, he adds two more: "The fresh leaves alone applied to the naked sole of the foot, infinitely refresh the surbated traveller"; and "The very shadow of this tree doth feed and nourish the grass that grows under it."

The **Black Alder** (*Alnus glutinosa*, Gærtn.), native of Europe, Asia and North Africa, is the most picturesque of water-loving trees, with its dark green, round or oblong leaves glutinous when they unfold in the spring. The trees are tall and erect, with dark trunks. The tallest sometimes reach 70 feet and have a trunk diameter of 3 feet. These giant alders are dignified, indeed, but the rank and file of the species are smaller trees. They hang out their long yellow catkin fringe on the bare twigs in earliest spring, a sight to repay a visit, even if it involved the wearing of rubber boots; and the little green knobs on the branching side stems grow by autumn into ripe cones, out of whose slits fall the little flat seeds.

Compared with oak and ash timber, alder is indifferent in quality and does not interest the lumberman, but there are special uses to which alder is always put. Growing in water, it seems to recognise its element; alder piles, water pipes, pumps and watering troughs kept always saturated last indefinitely. The piles of the Rialto in Venice and those of Amsterdam, according to ancient authorities, are of alder. Exposed to conditions of alternate wet and dry, the wood soon rots. It was a canny Scot who buried alder boards in a peat bog, in which lime was also thrown. This prevented the invasion of destructive insects, and turned the pinkish brown wood to the colour and hardness of mahogany. The grain of alder is smooth, fine and lustrous. It does not warp nor splinter. In the old days it was a wood for the boatbuilder. "Excepting Noah's Ark, the first vessels we read of were made of alder." Virgil gives a pretty glimpse of northern Italy in one of his Georgics:

"And down the rapid Po light alders glide."

Alder wood serves many cheap and common uses: for sabots and clogs, and wooden heels; truncheons, kneading troughs, barrel staves, bobbins, trays, hop poles, and the like. The bark and cones yield tannin used in tanning leather and in medicine, and a yellow dye which is also used in the making of ink. The best charcoal for gunpowder is made from willow and alder. Warty excrescences on old trees and twisted roots furnish the inlayer with small but beautifully veined and very hard pieces. Articles made of this once brought high prices.

One of the best uses to which alder is put is planting in hedges along borders of streams where their roots, closely interlacing, hold the banks against crumbling.

The black alder is most often met in horticultural forms in America. There is a variety with large, shining leaves and red veins and petioles. The daintiest varieties are those with finely cut leaves, of which *imperialis*, with fingered leaves like the white oak, is a good example.

The **Hoary** or **Speckled Alder** (*Alnus incana*, Willd.), native of both hemispheres, is a handsome tree of medium size in Europe and Asia, but it rarely rises above a shrub in America. It is second only to the black alder, from which it is easily distinguished, for its branches are speckled with white spots. Its leaves are pointed and lined with a hoary bloom; and there is nothing glutinous about the opening leaves and shoots. The wood is very similar to that of the other species.

Two Japanese species of alder have come into American gardens, both vigorous, large-leaved trees, of good size and excellent habit. *Alnus Japonica* has a pyramidal head of shining dark green foliage; *Alnus tinctoria* is round headed, with handsome foliage, and is proving hardy and rapid of growth in New England. A cardinal merit of these cultivated alders is that they thrive in ordinary garden soil.

CHAPTER XXV: THE BEECHES

FAMILY FAGACEÆ

Genus FAGUS, Linn.

TREES valuable for their timber and nuts, and also for shade and ornamental planting. *Leaves* simple, alternate, feather veined, deciduous. *Flowers* monœcious, small, crowded into spikes or heads. *Fruit* a pair of triangular nuts in a 4-valved bur.

The great family of the cup bearers includes the beeches, chestnuts and oaks—trees of profound importance to the human race. They are the mast trees, whose fruit has fed man and beast from the days when they both depended upon Nature's bounty. Times have changed, and men have less primitive appetites, but their need of these trees is not diminished, but rather broadened with the advance of civilisation. Mast of oak, beech and chestnut remain the chief reliance of many wild animals.

There are in all five species of beech, three of which are Asiatic. America has one species and Europe one. Two are native to China and Japan. The so-called beeches of the Southern Hemisphere form a genus, Nothofagus, of twelve species. They differ in habit and in flowers from Fagus, and the leaves, often evergreen, are very small. Nevertheless, the two genera are closely related.

Beech (*Fagus Americana*, Sweet.)—A round-topped or conical tree, with horizontal or drooping branches, and dense foliage; 50 to 75 feet high. *Bark* close, smooth, pale grey, or darker, often blotched; branches grey, twigs brown, shining. *Wood* light red, close grained, hard, strong, not durable, tough; lustrous when polished. *Buds* alternate, tapering, $\frac{3}{4}$ to 1 inch long, brown, in silky scales. *Leaves* oblong-ovate, strongly feather veined, saw toothed, pointed, smooth, silky or leathery, green on both sides; autumn colour, pale yellow, persistent till late. *Flowers* monœcious, May, staminate in pendant balls, few at base of leafy shoot, yellow-green; pistillate, solitary or paired, in axils of upper

B. Staminate flowers   A. Pistillate flowers   C. Fruit

THE SEASIDE ALDER (*Almus maritima*)

Flowers and ripe cones occur together on this tree in August. The pistillate flower spikes are little green-stalked knobs, while the staminate catkins are yellow and brown

THE SPECKLED ALDER (*Alnus incana*)

This is known by the white dots on its branches. A tree in Europe and Asia, it is rarely more than a shrub in America. The second trunk is of the shrubby *Alnus rugosa*

THE BEECH (*Fagus Americana*)

A clump of these trees in June in the Arnold Arboretum. The undergrowth is all beech, from seeds and from root suckers. A solitary tree spreads into a broad, regular crown. Winter reveals the beauty of the bark and the tree frame

leaves, short-stemmed, in scaly involucre. *Fruit*, October, a prickly bur containing 2 triangular, pale-brown nuts, sweet, edible, in thin shells. *Preferred habitat*, rich river bottoms. *Distribution*, Nova Scotia to Lake Huron, and northern Wisconsin; south to Florida, Missouri and Texas. *Uses:* Beautiful ornamental and shade tree. Wood used for chairs, tool handles, plane stocks, shoe lasts, and for fuel. Nuts fatten hogs, and feed wild animals and birds.

We have but one native beech, and it is a clannish tree. Find me a single specimen in the woods, and I will show you a miniature forest of beeches springing up around it as soon as the tree comes into bearing. Squirrels carry the nuts, so do the bluejays, and the wind helps to scatter them. Beech nuts have much vitality, and the seedlings grow well, even in dense shade. This gives them a distinct advantage over the young of many other trees. Seeds of sun-loving species must fall in the clearings if they hope to grow. In a few years there is a dense beech thicket, with only large trees of other kinds. When these are cut out the area comes to be called "the beech woods."

In April and May we may see the germination of beech nuts. The gaping burs and three-cornered nuts lie in plain sight under the tree. A nut splits along one sharp edge and a slender root protrudes. It grows downward and burrows in the leaf mould. The stem emerges at the same time and place and extends in the opposite direction. It is topped by a crumpled green bundle, which unfolds directly into a pair of short and broad seed leaves, totally unlike the leaves of the beech tree.

In this case the triangular shell clings but a little while to the growing plantlet. Oftener, however, the opening is just wide enough to let the root out. Then the stem carries the shell up and wears it like a helmet until the leaves within spread themselves and cast it off.

Young beech trees are very weak and pale and twisted at first. They lean helplessly against dead leaves and twigs for support. But when the roots get a grip on the soil and the leaves turn a brighter green they become quite independent. A shoot bearing true beech leaves rises from the bud between the two seed leaves, which soon wither away. In the fall a long whip set with winter buds represents the first season's growth.

From now on the life of a little beech is just like that of a twig on an older tree. The opening of the long, pointed buds is a sight worth watching. If one has not time to go to the tree every day in spring he may bring in some lusty twigs, put them in a jar of water in a sunny window, and see the whole process exactly as it happens on the tree.

Each bud loosens and lengthens its many thin bud scales and a leafy shoot is disclosed which elongates rapidly. Daily measurements will show a wonderful record for the first few days.

As the scales drop off a band of scars appears on the base of the shoot, like the thread of a small screw. When the last of the scales has fallen this band may be half an inch wide. Each such band on a twig means the casting off of the bud scales—the beginning of a year's growth. Counting down from the tip of any twig, the age may be accurately read. Add one year as each scar band is passed. Often the band is quite as wide as the length of the season's growth.

It is plain to see that the leaves in the opening buds were all made and put away over winter, and that they have only to grow. As the shoot lengthens the outer scales fall, and each leaf is seen to have its pair of special attendant scales, each edged with an overhanging fringe. The leaf itself is plaited in fine folds like a fan to fit into the narrow space between the scales. Each rib that radiates from the midrib bears a row of silky hairs which overlap its neighbour's, so that each side of each leaf is amply protected by a furry cover. As the leaf spreads itself it gradually becomes accustomed to the air and the sunshine, and the protecting hairs disappear. Occasionally a leaf that is in a shaded and protected situation on the tree may keep its hairs on the ribs until midsummer.

As the leaves lift themselves into independent life the blossoms of the beech appear. Few people see them. The staminate ones are in little heads swung on slender stems. When they shed their yellow pollen they fall off. In twos the pistillate flowers hide near the ends of twigs. Those which catch pollen on their extruded tongues "set seed" and mature into the triangular nuts, two in each of the burs. Early in the autumn the burs open and the nuts fall, to the great delight of boys and girls as well as the little people of the woods. Though small, the nuts are very rich and fine in flavour.

The beech is the most elegantly groomed of all the trees of the

A. Staminate flower   B. Pistillate flower

THE BEECH (*Fagus Americana*)

The fine-textured bark varies from dark gray to almost white. The buds are long and pointed and shining golden brown. The prickly 4-valved pod remains long after the two triangular nuts have fallen out. The opening shoots are beautiful in May, the pendant staminate heads are as soft and silky as the baby leaves. The pistillate flowers, solitary or paired, stand in the angles of the uppermost leaves

THE CHESTNUT (*Castanea dentata*)

Aside from its value as a nut tree, many a fine specimen tree is saved from the sawmill because the community cannot spare it from the landscape woods. Its rind is smooth, close knit and of soft Quaker grey, sometimes mottled and in varying shades, and decorated with delicate lichens. The limbs are darker in colour, and the brown twigs, down to their bird's-claw buds, shine as if polished. Through the long summer the beech is beautifully clad; its leaves are thin and soft as silk. Few insects injure them, and they resist tearing by the wind. In the autumn the first touch of frost turns their green to gold, and they cling to the twigs until late in winter. Young trees in sheltered places hold their leaves longest.

The **European Beech** (*F. sylvatica*, Linn.) is one of the most important timber trees of Europe, and the parent of the purple and weeping beeches and other ornamental horticultural forms in cultivation in European and American parks and private grounds. It grows to noble size and form in America, distinguished chiefly by the darker colour of its bark from the native species. At home from middle Europe south and east to the Caucasus, the beech is much used as a dooryard tree; it grows famously in England, their beeches being the pride of many English estates.

Pure forests of beech are often seen in Germany and Denmark. The lumber is hard and heavy, one of the most important hard woods of the Continent. The multitude of its uses prevents a complete list. Beech bark with hieroglyphics cut in it bore messages between tribes, friendly and belligerent, in the earliest times. Beechen boards preserved the first records. These were the primitive *books* of northern Europe. From *beech* to *buch* is not a long etymological step in the Teutonic languages. *Book* is a lineal descendant of the Anglo-Saxon word *bece*, the name of this tree. There are those who derive the words *beaker* through *Becher*, a drinking cup, from the same old *tree* root. Justification is found in the fact that bowls and other household utensils were made of beech wood because they could be depended upon not to leak.

Beech nuts furnished, in ancient times, a nutritious article of human food, and an oil used for lamps, quite as sweet and good for cooking and table use as olive oil. Fagus (*Gr. phagein*, to eat) means "good to eat." Beech leaves furnished forage for cattle, and were dried and used to fill mattresses. Evelyn vows he never slept so sweetly as on a bed of beech leaves. The idea is certainly an attractive one, and worth carrying out.

CHAPTER XXVI: THE CHESTNUTS

FAMILY FAGACEÆ

TREES of ornamental and timber value. *Leaves* simple, oblong to lanceolate, strongly ribbed, alternate, leathery. *Flowers* monœcious, in spikes, showy. *Fruit*, nuts in spiny burs.

KEY TO GENERA AND SPECIES

A. Leaves deciduous; fruit annual.
> 1. Genus CASTANEA, Adans.
> B. Trees large; leaves smooth and green on both sides; nuts 2 to 3 in 4-valved, spiny bur.
>> (*C. dentata*) CHESTNUT
> BB. Trees shrubby, leaves pale and pubescent beneath; nuts solitary in 2-valved bur. (*C. pumila*) CHINQUAPIN
AA. Leaves evergreen; fruit biennial.
> 2. Genus CASTANOPSIS, Spach.
>> (*C. chrysophylla*) GOLDEN-LEAVED CHESTNUT

1. Genus CASTANEA, Adans.

There are five known species of the true chestnuts, three of which are American. One of these is a shrub, *C. alnifolia*, Nutt. The European species (*C. sativa*, Mill.) is the well-known sweet chestnut of Italy and Spain, as important in the diet of the peasantry as are potatoes in Ireland. This species extends its range to Eastern Asia. The Japanese *C. crenata*, Sieb. & Zucc., has been introduced into American gardens. The trees begin to bear when very young. The nuts are not sweet like our native chestnuts, but they are good when cooked.

Chestnut (*Castanea dentata*, Borkh.)—Oblong, thick-topped, symmetrical tree, 60 to 100 feet high, of rapid, vigorous growth. *Bark* grey-brown, cut into broad irregular ridges by shallow fissures; branchlets reddish, smooth. *Wood* brown, light, coarse, soft, weak, durable, easily worked. *Buds* dark brown, ovate,

186

FRUITING BRANCH OF CHESTNUT (*Castanea dentata*)

pointed, small, lateral. *Leaves* alternate, 6 to 8 inches long, tapering at both ends, strong ribbed, toothed, shining above, paler lining; autumn colour yellow; petioles short, stout. *Flowers* monœcious, in July; staminate catkins, slender, 4 to 6 inches long, clustered at bases of leafy shoots, spreading, pollen abundant; pistillate, solitary or few, short stalked on base of staminate catkins or in axils of leaves; involucre, prickly, green, styles thrust out, stigmas branched. *Fruit* 2 to 3 compressed nuts, thin shelled, in 4-valved spiny bur, 2 to 4 inches in diameter, globular, opening after frosts. *Preferred habitat*, strong, well-drained soil; pastures, hillsides, rocky woods. *Distribution*, southern Maine to Michigan; south to Delaware and Indiana; along mountains to Alabama and Mississippi. *Uses:* Valuable lumber tree, used for interior woodwork of houses, furniture, railroad ties, fence posts and fuel. A handsome shade and ornamental tree. Nuts commercially important.

The elegance of chestnut foliage must strike the most casual observer. Each leaf is so long and tapering, so regularly veined and toothed, so polished, and finally so admirably set among the others as to make it a beautiful and useful part of the great green dome that hides the limbs in summer time.

Buds of the chestnut are small and plump set askew on the smooth winter twigs. They open late in spring. The fresh leaves make the neighbour oaks look dingy. The other trees have all done blooming but the lindens and the catalpas when the chestnut dome on the hillside gradually brightens from green to pale gold, and each twig holds up its feathery plume, and waves it, pollen laden, in the wind. July has come, and the fields of grain have passed into stacks and stubble. The chestnut takes on its flower crown to harmonise with the golden midsummer landscape. It is the most beautiful thing in the woods at this time. A solitary tree on a lawn or in a lonesome pasture is a joy to every beholder.

A near view of the tree shows along the bases of certain scantily furnished spikes a few green scaly flowers, with pale yellow threads extended at the tips. These are the chestnuts in embryo, with stigmas reaching out for the pollen that "sets seed." Two or three, or sometimes only one, of these flowers are fertilised. They develop rapidly, and by the middle of August the tree bristles with spiny green globes.

The first frost is the signal for the splitting of the husks into four velvet-lined valves, from which the smooth brown nuts fall. The over-anxious small boy who beats the nuts off earlier wounds his fingers painfully in attempting to force open the stubborn husks. The nuts are not nearly so sweet and rich flavoured as those that wait until the frost unlocks their cells. But boys will never believe this.

The chestnut tree turns to gold again in autumn, and the naked tree stands "knee-deep" in its own leaves all winter. Then its massive trunk, with deep furrowed bark, and the multitude of horizontal branches, striking out from the short central shaft, are distinctly etched against the sky. The small limbs are numerous and contorted, the lower boughs often drooping. Few trees are more attractive in winter.

Chestnuts are among the trees of longest life and greatest trunk diameter. The famous giant at the foot of Mount Ætna, the "Chestnut of a Hundred Horsemen" (because it sheltered them all at one time), had a diameter of over 60 feet, and lived to be 2,000 years old. Though hollow, and with its shell in five parts when measured, records showed that a century before it had been a continuous cylinder. Each year these decaying stems wore a crown of green, until an eruption of the volcano destroyed the tree.

In our woods old chestnut stumps 6 feet in diameter and more stand covered with moss and lichens and crumbling to decay, while a circle of fine young trees, each tall and slender, with a diameter of a foot or less, have sprung up from the roots of the old tree. Specimens 10 feet in diameter were not unusual in the virgin forests, though the tallest ones were usually more slender.

The tannic acid in chestnut wood is what preserves it from decay in contact with the soil. Because of its durability it is largely cut for railroad ties and posts. It is well worthy of cultivation as a lumber tree. In woodwork and furniture chestnut is almost as handsome as oak. The chestnut is a valuable nut tree. Had it none of these merits it would still be saved from the saw in many instances because the landscape can ill afford to lose a fine old chestnut tree.

The **Chinquapin** (*C. pumila*, Mill.) is the chestnut in miniature—rarely a tree of medium height and spreading habit—usually a shrub that seizes the land by its suckering roots, and forms thickets on hillsides and bare ridges or on the margins of swamps. It is found from Pennsylvania to Florida, and west to Arkansas and

Flowering branch   A. Pistillate flowers   B. Staminate flowers

THE CHESTNUT (*Castanea dentata*)

Two or three flat-sided, silky nuts are exposed when the 4-valved spiny burs open in October. In July the green leaves are gilded by the profusion of staminate flower spikes that are waved like plumes of yellow chenille fringe at the ends of the twigs. Very inconspicuous green spikes, sparsely flowered, bear solitary green pistillate flowers at their bases. The yellow threads extruded from the tip of each spiny oval cone are the stigmas eager to catch pollen

B. Staminate flowers   A. Pistillate flowers

THE CHINQUAPIN (*Castanea pumila*)

This species seems like "the little brother" to the chestnut. The leaves are silvery hairy beneath, and the nuts grow (as the pistillate flowers do) along the bases of certain flower spikes. One nut sits in a 2-valved husk. In all other characters except size the resemblance to the larger species is striking. Shrubby in the East, it becomes a tree fifty feet high in Texas and lower Arkansas

Texas. It grows to be a tree west of the Mississippi River, reaching its greatest size and abundance in Arkansas and Texas. The leaves, flowers and nuts proclaim this tree's close kinship with the chestnut. A single ovoid nut with sweet kernel is contained in the globular spine husk. These are found in autumn in the markets of Southern cities.

The chinquapin grows lustily and fruits abundantly on a rocky bank in the Arnold Arboretum at Boston. This proves its hardiness far north of its natural range, and a sight of this thicket (or any other like it) must convince anyone that it is an ornamental shrub worthy of introduction into parks and private estates.

Where the chinquapin grows large it is used for railroad ties and fence posts. Its wood has the qualities of chestnut lumber, but is heavier.

2. Genus CASTANOPSIS, Spach.

The **Golden - leaved Chestnut** (*Castanopsis chrysophylla*, A. DC.), also called chinquapin, seems to be a connecting link between chestnuts and oaks. One American species represents the large genus which is widely distributed through Asia. Our tree grows from Oregon south along the mountain slopes that face toward the Pacific Ocean. In northern California it is one of the splendid trees of the coast valleys, often above 100 feet in height, with sturdy trunk supporting a broad, dense, rounded dome. The glory of the tree is its dark, lustrous foliage, lined with a yellow scurf. The leaves persist for two or three years, turning yellow before they fall. Thus the twigs are always decked with green and gold. The flowers are much like those of the chinquapin of the South; the sweet nut protrudes from a cup, or saucer, thickly set with long spines. One hardly knows whether to call it a chestnut bur or a spiny acorn cup. It is both—and neither. The coarse wood which resembles chestnut is sometimes used for ploughs and other implements. The bark is rich in tannin.

CHAPTER XXVII: THE OAKS

FAMILY FAGACEÆ

Genera PASANIA and QUERCUS

TREES of great lumber and horticultural value. *Leaves* simple, alternate, entire or lobed. *Flowers* monœcious, inconspicuous; staminate, in pendulous catkins; pistillate, solitary or few in a cluster. *Fruit*, a dry nut in a scaly cup (an acorn).

KEY TO GENERA AND GROUPS

A. Flowers of two sorts borne in the same cluster—an erect, crowded spike; leaves evergreen, chestnut-like.
        1. Genus PASANIA, Örst.
AA. Flowers of two sorts borne in separate clusters; staminate in pendant catkins; pistillate, few or solitary on short stalks.
        2. Genus QUERCUS, Linn.
    B. Fruit annual; leaves with rounded lobes, not spiny pointed; bark usually pale.   THE WHITE OAK GROUP
    BB. Fruit biennial; leaves with lobes spiny pointed; bark usually dark.   THE BLACK OAK GROUP

The oaks form one of the largest and noblest of the tree families. There are 300 species recognised by botanists, and this probably does not include them all. They are distributed widely over the continents of the Northern Hemisphere, and follow the mountains through Central America and across the equator along the Andes. All but a very few species are large trees, important features of the landscape and the commerce of the countries in which they grow. Among broad-leaved trees they hold a pre-eminent place, and have held it from ancient times, in house and naval architecture and in bridge building. In durability, strength and toughness oak has few superiors.

Fifty species of oak are native to America; half of them distributed in the Eastern and mid-Continental regions, half on the Western slopes. The backbone of the continent, the main chains of the Rocky Mountains, have no indigenous oaks. No Pacific coast species is distributed also in the Eastern States, and vice versa. No European, Asiatic or American species is found outside its own continent, except as it is introduced by man.

The acorn distinguishes oaks from all other trees. It is the characteristic fruit of the family, and is found nowhere outside of it. All oaks bear acorns when they are old enough. Few begin bearing under twenty years of age.

The leaf of an oak is also characteristic. People usually learn to know an oak leaf from those of other trees without realising exactly how or why. There is great variety in the lobing of the leaves, but they are all simple, alternate and almost always oval in outline, leathery, and cut by deep bays, called *sinuses*.

The flowers of oaks are separate, but near together on the new shoots. The staminate are in fringe-like catkins; the pistillate few-flowered clusters in the axils of leaves; except in the genus Pasania. The acorns are either one or two years in ripening. It happens that annual-fruited species have rounded lobes and sinuses in their leaves. *Quercus alba* is the type of this class, and as these trees generally have pale bark, they are known as the white oak group. Biennial-fruited species have dark-coloured bark and the lobes of their leaves end in angles tipped with bristly points. They form the black oak group. Their type is *Quercus velutina*.

1. Genus PASANIA, Örst.

The **Tan-bark** or **Chestnut Oak** of California (*Pasania densiflora*, Örst.), formerly included in the genus Quercus, is now set apart as our sole representative of an Asiatic genus of trees that stand half way between oaks and chestnuts. It is a handsome oak, decked the year round in evergreen foliage, similar in form to the chestnut. The leaves are coated, when young, with yellow pubescence, which lights up the tree as if with golden blossoms.

In summer the crown of the tree shines again with gold. The profuse staminate spikes stand erect with greenish pistillate flowers at their bases. The latter are scaly, but the nut finally rises out of a densely fringed cup, declaring itself an acorn, which takes two years to mature.

191

The wood of the tan-bark oak is used for fuel, but has little lumber value. Its bark, however, is more valuable to the tanner than any other. So the tree is threatened with extinction by the irresponsible bark peelers, and by forest fires carelessly set.

This tree grows along dry hillsides and in mountain ravines in California and Oregon, keeping along the coast range, and flourishing especially among the redwoods. Government protection of the latter would save from utter annihilation another remnant of former times, for the tan-bark oak is scarcely less interesting to the botanist than the redwood itself.

2. Genus QUERCUS, Linn.

I. THE WHITE OAK GROUP

Acorns annual; leaf lobes rounded; bark usually pale.

KEY TO SPECIES

A. *Pacific coast species.* Deciduous.
  B. Foliage blue with silvery lining. (*Q. Douglasii*) BLUE OAK
  BB. Foliage green.
    C. Acorns slenderly conical; branchlets slender, pendulous; leaves white lined.
              (*Q. lobata*) CALIFORNIA WHITE OAK
    CC. Acorns oval; branchlets stout, erect; leaves not white lined.   (*Q. Garryana*) PACIFIC POST OAK
AA. *Eastern species.*
  B. Foliage evergreen.   (*Q. Virginiana*) LIVE OAK
  BB. Foliage semi-persistent, blue. (*Q. breviloba*) DURAND OAK
  BBB. Foliage deciduous.
    C. Leaves pinnately lobed by deep sinuses.
      D. Under sides of leaves smooth. (*Q. alba*) WHITE OAK
      DD. Under sides of leaves downy.
        E. Branches corky; acorn large, in fringed cup.
                  (*Q. macrocarpa*) BUR OAK
        EE. Branches not corky; acorn medium in size.
          F. Acorn globose, enclosed by scaly cup.
                  (*Q. lyrata*) OVERCUP OAK
          FF. Acorn ovoid, half hid in scaly cup; leaf lobes and sinuses broad, squarish.
                  (*Q. minor*) POST OAK
    CC. Leaves sinuately dentate with shallow sinuses; linings pale, downy.

D. Lobes of leaves acute. (*Q. acuminata*) YELLOW OAK
DD. Lobes of leaves rounded.
   E. Bark dark brown, deeply furrowed.
       (*Q. Prinus*) CHESTNUT OAK
  EE. Bark light grey, scaly.
     F. Limbs shedding bark in large flakes; acorns on long stalks.
       (*Q. platanoides*) SWAMP WHITE OAK
    FF. Limbs not shedding bark in flakes; acorns sessile or on short stalks.
       (*Q. Michauxii*) BASKET OAK

The **Blue Oak, or Mountain White Oak** (*Quercus Douglasii*, Hook. and Arn.), is a striking and beautiful feature of the landscape of northern and central California. Silvery grey bark and pale blue foliage, deepened by greenish leaf linings, and lightened by their silvery pubescence! No wonder the blue oak attracts attention whether it stands among the scattered groves of California white oak in the broad valleys—a fine, round-headed tree—or climbs the western slopes of the Sierras till it dwindles to a shrub at an altitude of 4,000 feet. It is strangely variable in the shape of its leaves and fruit. Its leaf may have deep lobes like other white oaks, or it may have scarcely any noticeable waves; some leaves are entire, some have pointed, even spiny-tipped lobes like those of the black oaks. The blue of them, however, is a dependable characteristic; also the silky leaf linings.

The acorns are very numerous, and so vividly green in summer that they often overcome much of the blue of the foliage until they take on their rich, chestnut brown. The nut often bulges above the saucer-like cup as if too large for it; often it is elongated into a pencil shape.

The wood is too brittle and the sap wood too thick for use in building. It is an excellent fuel.

California White Oak (*Quercus lobata*, Née.)—A large, graceful tree with stout trunk dividing near the ground, with spreading top and pendulous branches, making a broad dome, 80 to 100 feet high, and 150 to 200 feet in diameter. *Bark* brownish grey, scaly, with shallow furrows, and ridges broken into plates; twigs hoary, grey or reddish brown. *Wood* hard, fine grained, brittle and hard to season. *Buds* ovate, small, pubescent. *Leaves* alternate, variable, oblong or obovate, 2 to 4 inches long, deeply 7 to 11-lobed, thin, firm, pubescent, paler beneath; petioles

193

short, broad, hairy. *Flowers* with half-grown leaves, February to April, staminate in hairy, yellowish catkins; pistillate, solitary and sessile, as a rule; stigmas broad. *Acorns* $1\frac{1}{4}$ to $2\frac{1}{4}$ inches long, annual, sessile (rarely stalked), solitary or in pairs, conical, elongated, with sharp, horny, hairy tip; cup shallow, tomentose, with thick scales that become finer toward fringed border; kernel, sweet, edible. *Preferred habitat*, rich, sandy loam. *Distribution*, valleys in California west of Sierra Nevada Mountains. Forms open groves, never forests. *Uses:* Splendid feature of natural scenery, but never successfully cultivated outside of its range. Wood useless except for fuel. Fruit used as food by Indians.

It is a happy circumstance for Californians and for all people who visit "the Land of the Setting Sun" that this valley oak is scorned by all lumbermen. The tree is practically worthless for timber, therefore gigantic individual trees stand scattered or grouped in the spacious valleys of western California, helping to make a landscape that cannot be duplicated this side of England. Indeed, Vancouver, journeying around the world in 1792, was astounded at the park-like Santa Clara Valley, set round with mountains, diversified with hills and intervals, covered with a carpet of verdure, and adorned with majestic oaks. Writing home of this landscape untouched by the hand of man, he says; "It required only to be adorned with the neat habitations of an industrious people to produce a scene not inferior to the most studied effect of taste in the disposal of grounds."

The California white oak is the largest and most graceful of the Western oaks. Its branches end in long shoots that are pendulous like those of the weeping willow. The trunk branches near the ground and rises and spreads out like a great fan. A British elm often has the same habit—our American elm, sometimes. The dome is broader even than that of our Eastern white oak. The twigs are willowy at first, but there is a surprising tortuousness acquired with added years. The limbs are gnarled in the most complex way. "Picturesqueness gone mad" well characterises the expression of the tree in its bare winter aspect.

"The Sir Joseph Hooker Oak," 100 feet high, 7 feet in diameter of trunk and 150 feet in spread of dome, on General Bidwell's farm in Butte County, California, was named after the great English botanist on the occasion of his visit with Asa Gray in 1877.

The tree is always broader than it is high, and bears a pro-

THE CALIFORNIA WHITE OAK (*Quercus lobata*)

The largest and most picturesque of the Western oaks. The dome is broader than high; the outer twigs droop like a weeping willow's, but acquire a wonderful tortuousness later. Lumbermen have spared this tree because its wood is not strong. Gigantic individuals stand in the park-like valleys, set round by mountain peaks, making a landscape which is unrivalled in any country

THE LIVE OAK (*Quercus Virginiana*)

The thick trunks of old trees break into horizontal limbs of great length and size, forming a broad dome not unlike a picturesque old apple tree. The small leaves remain on the twigs all winter

THE CALIFORNIA LIVE OAK (*Quercus agrifolia*)

This evergreen oak has holly-like leaves with bristly tips upon its lobes, but its acorns are annual. Nevertheless it belongs to the black-oak group. The staminate catkins are delicate and numerous. The red-headed woodpeckers store the acorns away for winter in holes they drill in the bark furrows

fusion of acorns of extraordinary length. These resemble the acorns of *Quercus alba* in other respects. The Digger Indians store them for winter use, and depend upon them as the source of their bread. They are roasted and hulled, then ground into a coarse meal, which is made into loaves and baked in rude ovens in the sand.

The leaves of *Quercus lobata* are of the true white oak type, with squarish lobes and pale linings. They vary in size and form, some being almost cut in two like those of the bur oak.

Attempts to introduce this tree into cultivation outside of its own range have proved unsuccessful. It is believed that the climate of Australia might be agreeable to the species, which is too exacting in its demands to thrive in Europe or in Eastern America.

Pacific Post Oak, Oregon White Oak (*Quercus Garryana*, Hook.)—Large tree (or a shrub) 60 to 100 feet high, with stout erect or spreading branches forming a compact head. *Bark* orange brown or greyish, with shallow fissures and broad ridges; twigs rufous, hairy. *Wood* light yellowish brown, hard, firm, strong, tough. *Buds* large, pointed, coated with red fuzz. *Leaves* obovate or oblong, 4 to 6 inches long, coarsely 7 to 9-lobed, with shallow sinuses and blunt lobes, leathery, dark green, shining, with pale or orange-brown hairy lining and conspicuous veins. *Flowers:* staminate in hairy catkins; pistillate, sessile, solitary. *Acorns* annual, $\frac{1}{2}$ to 1 inch long, pointed, in shallow, fuzzy cup with small, thin, loose scales. *Preferred habitat*, dry, gravelly slopes. *Distribution*, Vancouver Island and the valley of the lower Fraser River, along coast valleys to Santa Cruz Mountains. Best and most abundant in western Oregon and Washington. Shrubby on mountains. *Uses:* The most important timber oak on the west coast. Wood of young trees especially tough and valuable. Used in construction of ships, buildings, vehicles, agricultural implements, barrels and in finer cabinet work; excellent fuel.

This oak has leaves and rusty twigs that bear a striking resemblance to the post oak of our Eastern coast barrens. The bark, however, is pale grey, and often broken into squares by transverse fissures. The acorns are quite distinctive, being large, often over an inch long, nearly twice as long as wide, and set in a small cup, often shallow as that of *Quercus rubra*.

195

Upon the mountain slopes this oak is scrubby in growth, but in the rich loam of the lower valley land it is a lofty tree, which often loses its lower limbs by the crowding of young conifers about it. The crown expands, the outer branches become pendulous, and the tree assumes the shape of a tall Etruscan vase —a common form of our American elms.

The whiteness of the wood makes it popular for the interior finish of houses, as well as for the coarser staple uses to which white oak is devoted. Its fault is checking as it dries. It takes two years to season properly.

Robert Douglas, the great botanical explorer, named this tree in honour of Nicholas Garry, secretary of the Hudson Bay Company, in recognition of the courtesies and substantial aid rendered by him to scientists studying the flora of the Northwest.

Live Oak (*Quercus Virginiana*, Mill.)—Evergreen tree, 50 to 75 feet high, with thick trunk and horizontal limbs of great length forming a low, spreading dome, like an old apple tree. Often shrubby. *Bark* reddish brown, scaly, with shallow fissures; twigs rigid, slim, hoary at first. *Wood* light brown or yellow (sap wood nearly white), close grained, lustrous, compact with hardly distinguishable annual rings, heavy, tough, strong, durable, easy to split, hard to work. *Buds* globose, brownish, small. *Leaves* evergreen, leathery, elliptical or oblanceolate, entire, rarely wavy margined, and spiny tipped above the middle, 2 to 5 inches long, dark green above, paler beneath, brownish yellow in late winter, falling when new leaves appear. *Flowers* in March, April; staminate in hairy catkins; pistillate 3 to 5-flowered on long spikes with bright red stigmas. *Acorns* annual, brown, stalked, pointed, 1 inch long, in thin cup with tapering base and small, closely appressed scales; nut sweet, $\frac{1}{3}$ to $\frac{2}{3}$ of it embraced by the cup. *Preferred habitat*, dry sandy soil near the coast. *Distribution*, islands and coast from Virginia to Florida, west to Mexico, and in Lower California. *Uses:* Superb avenue and ornamental tree in the South. Grows rapidly and is easily transplanted. Lumber better in all respects than that of *Quercus alba,* even.

The evergreen live oak of the South is one of the handsomest of all our native trees in cultivation. Specimen trees in New Orleans, Charleston and other cities certainly challenge the observer to mention a more perfect example of all that is to be desired in tree form. The dome is low, but exceedingly broad, often spreading to twice its height and more. The trunk breaks near the base into horizontal limbs of incredible length and size. It seems as if the weight of these great arms must split the trunk, especially under the force of the wind. But the fibre of the wood is equal to resisting the strain put upon it.

The leaves are not as showy and beautiful in form as many Northern oaks. They are plain dull green beneath, lustrous above, and they last all winter until the new leaves appear in the spring. The acorns are dainty and dark brown, set in a hoary long-stemmed, top-shaped cup. They are a profuse crop, and very sweet and pleasant to taste. The Indians gathered them "to thicken their venison-soop" with, and also cooked them in other ways. "They likewise draw an Oil, very pleasant and whole-some, little inferior to that of almonds." So wrote Mark Catesby, a century and a half ago.

Live-oak timber ranks highest among the white oaks. Ship-building depended upon it in this country until the era of steel construction. Reservation of tracts of these trees in western Florida for the use of the navy was made in the early days. "Knees of oak" still brace the sides of vessels, if they can be obtained. The beauty of the wood when polished would make it in great demand for furniture and for decorative purposes, except that it is extremely difficult to work, and it splits easily when nailed. The short trunk prevents the getting out of timbers of large size.

As an avenue and shade tree the live oak deserves especial attention. It grows rapidly and is easily transplanted. It is not particular as to soils. The trees are becoming scarce in the wild. They should be saved for the landscape's sake and planting should go steadily on. To our Northern poet, these trees

"Stand like Druids of old, with voices sad and prophetic;
 Stand like harpers hoar, with beards that rest on their bosoms."

Live oaks without their draperies of moss would lose much of their charm. However, there is a great difference of opinion as to the beauty of the moss. It generally looks well in a picture, but some people think its grey straggling clusters give the oaks an unkempt and uncomfortable look, as if a parasite were choking its host.

The **Durand Oak** (*Quercus breviloba*, Sarg.) is a Southern, blue-leaved white oak, 80 to 90 feet high, with bark and leaf linings as silvery as its California cousin's. These leaves, which are leathery and scarcely 3 inches long, have indistinctly wavy margins, and tend to broaden at the tip, ending in three lobes. An ovate nut of moderate size sits in a thin saucer with hairy scales.

In the bayou region of the South, and on the dry prairies of Alabama it is a fine, tall tree, with lumber equal to the best white oak; but west of the middle of Texas it decreases in size and becomes an almost evergreen shrub which is worthless except for fuel. It grows in thickets on sterile bluffs, even across the Mexican border.

White Oak (*Quercus alba*, Linn.)—A large tree, 60 to 150 feet high, 3 to 8 feet in trunk diameter, tall in the forest, low and broad domed in the open fields. *Bark* pale grey, broken into small, thin plates. *Wood* tough, strong, heavy, hard, durable, light brown, with prominent medullary rays. *Buds* short, round, smooth, clustered at tip of twigs. *Leaves* alternate, 5 to 9 inches long, obovate or oblong in outline, with 7 to 9 rounded or finger-shaped lobes with deep, rounded sinuses between; petioles stout; colour red at first, with white silky lining, then bright green above, paler beneath; in autumn deep red, pale purplish beneath. *Flowers* in May, with half-grown leaves; staminate catkins, hairy, $2\frac{1}{2}$ to 3 inches long, yellow; pistillate, 1 to 2 on short stems, stamens bright red. *Acorns* annual, on short or long stems; cup shallow, thin, with closely appressed scales; nut of long, shiny, brown, $\frac{3}{4}$ to 1 inch long, sweet, edible. *Preferred habitat,* rich, well-drained soil. *Distribution,* southern Maine to Florida; west to Minnesota, Kansas and Texas. *Uses:* A lumber tree of highest rank. Its bark is used in tanneries in the making of leather. The wood is used in naval architecture, in house building and inside finishing, for furniture, agricultural implements, cooperage, railroad ties and fuel.

The white oak is the noblest tree of its race; king by common consent, in our forests of broad-leaved trees. It is the embodiment of strength, dignity and independence. The Briton has but one native oak on which to spend his loyalty and devotion. We have fifty kinds—all American—but the white oak is chief among them all. In this opinion the lumberman and the tree lover

THE WHITE OAK (*Quercus alba*)

We know this tree by its broad, round dome above a short, pale-grey trunk; by its finger-lobed leaves, its rounded buds and its large, sweet acorns. It embodies our ideals of strength, dignity and independence in tree form

THE WHITE OAK (*Quercus alba*)

The leaf lobes are finger-like, and the linings white. The twigs are slender. The flowers appear with the new leaves. The bark is pale gray. This species is the type of the annual-fruited oaks. It is one of the nobles of our native oaks

generally concur, and each, as he gazes on a fine old tree, feels the smouldering fires of ancestral tree worship flame once more in his breast. There is something in Anglo-Saxon blood that remembers.

We shall know the white oak in the winter woods by its pale grey bark, with shallow fissures and scaly ridges. It is a tall, narrow-headed tree where it is crowded among its forest neighbours. In the open it has a sturdy, low-branched trunk that flares into buttresses at the base and supports a rounded dome of great breadth and dignity. The mighty arms reach toward the horizon or the sky, breaking into tortuous limbs and these into dense thickets of twigs. Over these is the luxuriant thatch of fingered leaves, through whose narrow sinuses the light sifts so freely that even the inner framework of the dome bears leafy twigs. The characteristic arrangement of these leaves is a tuft of them on the end of a twig, spread out like the divisions of a horse-chestnut leaf.

In spring a shimmering veil of rose and silver covers the grey old tree. The edges are fringed with the yellow tassels of the staminate flowers. From the axils of the opening leaves the forked tongues of the pistillate flowers are thrust out into the pollen-laden air.

All summer the leaves are bright green with pale linings. In autumn the red comes back again with bluish tones that blend into beautiful vinous reds and violet purple. Gradually the colour fades out, but the leaves usually hang on until pushed off, even as late as the following April.

We shall find no acorns on white oak trees in winter, for they mature in a single season, and fall without delay. The crop is usually a light one, and it is hard to find acorns even under the tree. The sweet-flavoured nut is a favourite food of animals, wild and domestic. The Indians and the early colonists ate them. These shrewd and provident ancestors of ours discovered also that this "ackorne" had other good qualities. "By boyling it long, it giveth an oyle which they keep to supple their joynts." They skimmed this oil from the water before they ate the acorns in the pot.

White-oak lumber is becoming rare and correspondingly high priced. Its quality is of the first order. Clear, quarter-sawed oak exhibits a higher percentage of the "mirrors" (pith rays) than any other species. Its durability, hardness and fine colour are exceptional among oaks. So great is the demand for it in the finer decorative arts employing wood that it is going out of use in general construction where inferior woods can be substituted. Roots of white oak, sawed, planed and polished, present a wood of extraordinary beauty. It is pale yellow in colour, tinged with olive, and shows a feathered grain of intricate and graceful pattern. The lustre of it is equal to that of mahogany or rosewood. Fifty years ago Nuttall cited an instance of an English cabinetmaker paying five pounds sterling for the roots of a single tree, counting that furniture veneered with it would vie with the finest.

Bur or **Mossy-cup Oak** (*Quercus macrocarpa*, Michx.)—A large tree, 75 to 160 feet high, with spreading branches, and irregular, round head. *Bark* greyish brown, deeply furrowed, becoming scaly; branches roughened with thick, corky ridges; twigs winged or smooth, stout, and pubescent at first. *Wood* brown, with paler sap wood, close grained, heavy, hard, durable in soil; medullary rays conspicuous. *Buds* small, blunt pointed, pubescent. *Leaves* obovate, alternate, 6 to 12 inches long, 3 to 6 inches wide, 5 to 7-lobed; sinuses rounded, shallow or deep, middle ones often wider, opposite and nearly reach the midrib; petioles short, grooved; summer colour lustrous dark green, with pale, or silvery pubescent lining; autumn colour yellow or brown. *Flowers* with half-grown leaves in May; staminate in hairy yellow catkins; pistillate, with hairy red scales and bright red stigmas. *Acorns* annual, $\frac{1}{2}$ to 2 inches long, ovoid, variable in size and shape, pubescent, in deep (rarely shallow) cup, brown, hairy, with loose scales and mossy fringe. Kernel white, sweet. *Preferred habitat,* rich, well-drained soil. *Distribution,* Nova Scotia to Montana; south to Pennsylvania, Tennessee and Texas. *Uses:* Same as *Q. alba*. Picturesque park tree. Easily transplanted when young.

The bur oak is a rugged-looking tree, more picturesque than its near relative, the white oak, which is conventional and symmetrical when it has its own way in growing. The bur oak flings out its antlered arms without regard for balance and symmetry, and casts off the bark of its shaggy limbs with utter indifference to any law of neatness. Broad corky wings are seen even on young twigs, and these are stout and curiously gnarled.

THE BUR OAK (*Quercus macrocarpa*)

Stout angled and corky-winged twigs, leaves with wavy margins each almost cut in two by a broad middle pair of sinuses, and large acorns set in fringed cups—these are the signs by which this "mossy cup oak" tells us its name. The bark is pale-gray and the acorns annual, which prove the species one of the white oak group

THE CHESTNUT OAK (*Quercus Prinus*)

The dark-coloured bark and pointed buds would class this species among the black oak group, but the wavy-margined leaves and the annual acorns decide the case. This is one of the important tanbark oaks

The leaves are of unusual length and deeply cut into irregular fingers, or broader lobes. Often two opposite sinuses, wider than the rest, almost cut the leaf in two in the middle. Bright and shining above, these leaves are woolly lined and thick.

The acorns are very striking in appearance. The brown nut is often 2 inches long and set in a thick, hairy cup, covered with coarse, pointed scales that become elongated toward the rim, and form a loose, fringed border. The nut is half covered by the cup as a rule. Sometimes it is quite swallowed up in it. From this the species is sometimes, but erroneously, called the overcup oak.

This tree is one of the most widely distributed and valuable of North American oaks. It has an astonishing power of adaptation to different regions and climates. It grows from Nova Scotia to western Texas; there are forests of it in Winnipeg; it forms the "oak openings" of Minnesota and Dakota. It seems as much at home in the hot and arid stretches of the West and Southwest as in the cold, damp air of the coast of New England, or the fertile valley of the Ohio, where it reached nearly 200 feet in height in the virgin forests.

The sturdiness of the bur oak, its rapid growth in good soil, its rugged picturesqueness, winter and summer, all commend it to planters. It is one of the most ornamental of American oaks in cultivation; and the raising and transplanting of it are fairly easy. People who do not plant oaks because they take so long to become big trees miss much pleasure they have not counted on. It may be children's children who see the aged tree, beautiful in its expression of massiveness and rugged strength. But the planter enjoys the grace of the sapling, the rich foliage of the young tree which is always larger than on the old ones; and there is very early seen in any bur oak the stocky build and the shaggy bark that mark the adult tree. It grows rapidly, and soon blossoms and fruits freely. Every year shows gains, and the cycle of the year in the treetop is worthy of close attention.

The wood of white oaks is of highest quality, the English oak itself being one of this group. The bur oak is counted even better than that of *Quercus alba*, when grown in rich soil. The planting of bur oaks on the prairie is especially recommended by those who understand the conditions prevailing there. It is grown for shade and for lumber.

Overcup Oak, Swamp Post Oak (*Quercus lyrata*, Walt.)— Large tree, 70 to 100 feet high, with small pendulous branches forming a symmetrical round head. *Bark* grey or reddish, furrowed and shedding in thick plates. *Wood* dark brown, strong, heavy, hard, durable. *Buds* small, blunt pointed, hairy, brown. *Leaves* obovate, narrowed at base, 6 to 8 inches long, with 3 to 5 pairs of oblong or pointed lobes, with wide sinuses, especially the middle pair, bright green above, shining, with dense white down beneath. *Acorns* annual, short stalked; nut flattened and almost or entirely enclosed by the round, rough-scaled cup; 1 to 1½ inches across. *Preferred habitat*, coast or river swamps. *Distribution*, Maryland to Florida; west to Missouri and Texas. Rare except in the Southwest. *Uses:* Rare in cultivation. Wood confused with white oak in the trade.

The distinguishing feature of this oak is its button-like acorns. The scaly cup quite swallows up the nut, as a rule. The grey of bark and leaf lining, the narrow, deeply cut leaves, and the strong, durable wood are all characteristics that show this tree's close kinship with the bur oak on one side and the post oak on the other. It grows to majestic proportions in watery ground and wears a luxuriant crown of shining foliage.

Post Oak, Iron Oak (*Quercus minor*, Sarg.)—A dense, round-topped tree, scrubby or 40 to 50 feet high, with low, crooked branches and stubby, rough twigs. *Bark* greyish brown, deeply furrowed, scaly wide ridges; branches brown; twigs brownish with yellow fuzz. *Wood* pale brown, close grained, hard, strong, heavy, durable in contact with soil. *Buds* small, round, rusty, downy. *Leaves* 4 to 5 inches long, clustered, abundant, stiff, rough, dark, shining above, brown woolly beneath, obovate, with 5 to 7 unequal, square-tipped lobes separated by wide sinuses, hanging on all winter, turning yellow or pale brown. *Flowers* in May with half-grown leaves; staminate catkins, 3 to 4 inches long, yellow, hairy; pistillate flowers, almost sessile; stigmas bright red. *Acorns* annual, ¾ to 1 inch long, ovoid, brownish, in shallow cup of loose, blunt-pointed scales, enclosing only ⅓ to ½ of the nut. Kernel sweet. *Preferred habitat*, dry, sandy or rocky soil. *Distribution*, southern Massachusetts to northern Florida; west to Missouri and Texas. Especially common in the Southwest. *Uses:* Hardy ornamental oak; grows well in dry, rocky soil. Lumber used largely for railroad ties, fuel and

202

fencing; also for cooperage and construction. Seldom distinguished in the trade from white oak.

The post oak looks like a tree with its trunk buried in the ground. Its head is broader at the top, no matter how it is crowded in the woods, and the multitude of stubby branches are "full of elbows," i. e., the angles between limb and branch are all wide open, giving the tree a distinct character.

The foliage is another means of knowing the post oak. At a distance it looks almost black in summer. Come nearer. The leaf lining is coated with greyish pubescence. The texture of a leaf makes you cringe as you crumple it in your hands. It is thick and leathery, and roughened above by wonderfully branched hairs, that are star-like under a magnifier. Three broad, squarish lobes form the top, and the blade tapers from these to the stubby petiole. Sometimes there are five lobes altogether; sometimes only the three at the top. Each twig holds out a cluster of these leaves, like a fan. In the autumn they turn yellow or brown, but the twigs will not let them go. A characteristic post oak is densely leafy all winter, and until the opening shoots push the stubborn old leaf stalks out of the way. This habit gives the post oak much of its picturesqueness in winter, for the foliage does not entirely conceal its ruggedness and crookedness of limb.

The acorns are trim and dainty. The annual crop rarely fails. They are very sweet, and in the old days were devoured by wild turkeys. Then people knew it as the turkey oak.

The names of this species, iron oak and post oak, indicate the reputation of its wood for durability in contact with the soil and with water. Post-oak staves from Baltimore were preferred in the West Indian trade in sugar, rum and other barrelled commodities. "Knees" of post oak are always in demand, and, where trees attained sufficient size, the timbers are used in the framework and sides of ships.

Chestnut Oak, Tan-bark Oak (*Quercus Prinus*, Linn.)— A forest tree with broad, irregular head on a short trunk, 50 to 100 feet high. *Bark* dark brown, deeply furrowed, rich in tannic acid; twigs smooth. *Wood* dark, reddish brown, close grained, with conspicuous medullary rays, tough, heavy, hard, strong, durable in contact with soil. *Buds* pointed, long, smooth, greyish red. *Leaves* alternate, 5 to 9 inches long, obovate, with coarse teeth rounded at the tops, thick, yellowish green above, paler, usually pubescent beneath; autumn colour yellow and brown. *Flowers* in May, solitary or paired; staminate yellow; pistillate on short spurs; stigmas short, dark red. *Acorns* usually solitary, peduncled, annual, 1 to 1½ inches long, shining, brown; cup thin, downy lined, covered with small tubercular scales. Kernel sweet, edible. *Preferred habitat*, rocky upland soil, like the sides of ravines and stream borders. *Distribution*, southern Maine to western New York; south to Maryland, Kentucky and Tennessee; along mountains into Georgia and Alabama. *Uses:* A handsome tree for parks; grows well in dry ground; lumber used for railroad ties, fencing and fuel; bark, in tanning leather.

The chestnut oak is the type of a group of white oaks whose leaves are like those of a chestnut tree. This group has sweeter nuts than any other oaks. All but this species have pale bark. *Quercus Prinus* has bark so dark in colour and so deeply furrowed that it has often been mistaken for one of the black oak group, although its wavy leaf margins and annual fruit deny the insinuation most emphatically.

It is a vigorous tree, and grows very rapidly in dry soil. Its acorns in their fuzzy cups often sprout before they fall to the ground! The tree is handsome, and worthy a place in any plantation. It finally makes the best of fuel.

The name, "rock chestnut oak," refers to the hardness of its wood. "Tan-bark oak" calls attention to the tannin which makes this tree the prey of "peelers" throughout its range. Only the black oak yields as good bark to the tanner.

The **Yellow Oak** (*Quercus acuminata*, Sarg.) has smaller and narrower leaves than *Quercus Prinus*, and the margins are coarsely and sharply toothed. They closely resemble chestnut leaves in form, but are lined with pale pubescence. The tree reaches 160 feet in height in the lower Ohio Valley and extends from Vermont to Minnesota, and south to Alabama and Texas. It prefers dry soil, and is a worthy shade and ornamental tree. The silvery grey bark and handsome leaves, shining yellow-green above and white beneath, trembling on slender petioles, make it a beautiful object in any landscape. The yellow-green of the foliage mass gives the tree its common name.

The **Chincapin Oak** (*Quercus prinoides*, Willd.) is a shrub, which spreads by underground stems. Its opening leaves are silvery below and orange-red above. In autumn they turn

THE OVERCUP OAK (*Quercus lyrata*)

The narrow leaves broaden toward the apex; the largest of the lobes are above the middle. The leaf lining is dense white down. The wood is confused with other white oak. The bark is gray, tinged with red. The best character is the acorn, which is usually entirely enclosed by the cup

THE LIVE OAK (*Quercus Virginiana*)

These leathery leaves are individually small and characterless, as oak leaves go, but the mass of them keeps the treetop green and glossy until spring produces a new crown of foliage. The slender acorn seems too big for its thin little cup. The wood ranks higher than any other species of oak

THE WILLOW OAK (*Quercus Phellos*)

The leaves are like a willow's, but the acorns prove this southern tree an oak. Though its leaves lack spiny lobes, the tree is biennial in fruiting

THE SWAMP WHITE OAK (*Quercus platanoides*)

The leaves are obovate, with wedge-shaped bases and white, downy linings. They are green when they open. The annual acorns are sweet. The wood is not distinguished in the trade from other white oak

bright red again. The little sweet acorn probably suggested the common name. From its leaves and habit this oak is called the scrub chestnut oak. It occurs from Maine to Minnesota, and south to Alabama and Texas. In the West it seems to intergrade with the preceding species. Horticulturally it is a desirable species for covering dry, sterile areas.

Swamp White Oak (*Quercus platanoides*, Sudw.)—A shaggy picturesque tree, 70 to 100 feet high, with pendulous branches, and crooked twigs forming a narrow, round head, bushy with dead twigs that hang on. *Bark* pale greyish brown, peeling in thin flakes from branches and trunk. *Wood* pale brown, coarse grained, heavy, tough, strong. *Buds* short, blunt, brown, hairy, clustered at tips of twigs. *Leaves* alternate, obovate, 5 to 7 inches long, wedge shaped at base, wavy toothed or lobed regularly, dull, dark green above, white downy beneath. *Flowers* staminate, hairy, yellow catkins; pistillate few on long peduncles, hairy with red stigmas. *Acorns* annual, paired, on long stems; nut oval, 1 to 1½ inches long, brown, hairy at tip, in rough cup with thickened scales, sometimes fringed at border; kernel sweet, edible. *Preferred habitat*, moist or swampy soil. *Distribution*, southern Maine to southern Iowa; south to Maryland, Kentucky and Arkansas; along mountains into Georgia. Commonest about the Great Lakes. *Uses:* Picturesque tree in landscape, but rarely planted. Lumber not distinguished commercially from other white oak. Used in construction of houses, boats, agricultural implements and vehicles; also, for fencing, railroad ties and fuel.

The swamp white oak loves the waterside, and many a noble specimen has been swept away by spring floods or by the gradual undermining of the bank on which it grew. Such was the fate of the famous Wadsworth oak, a landmark in the Genesee Valley in New York State, even when the Indians were the only people there to admire it. A young tree of this species is generally pyramidal and quite symmetrical in form, its stout branches short and horizontal, the lower ones tending to droop. The strength of character, however, the ruggedness that make so strong appeal to us in this tree, comes when it has put by the comeliness of youth and the stern battle of life has left its scars on the veteran.

Look at a swamp white oak against a winter sky. I mean

that old one which has stood there with its feet in the water as long as you can remember. In fact, it seemed to be grown up when first you were told its name. The head is narrow for an oak, the limbs short and tortuous, especially on the lower half of the tree where they have a downward tendency, seeming to sprawl as widely as their grizzled and stubby length permits. Storms have cut gashes in the outline of the top. A weird grey pallor heightens the expression of age. The bark strips off of the branches somewhat after the sycamore's mode of moulting. Nothing contributes more to the picturesqueness of a tree than ragged bark.

In spring the rough coat of the tree is concealed by the opening leaves. The black oaks flush crimson when they wake in the May sunshine. The young leaves of the swamp white oak are green, with a silvery scurf that lines them the summer through. Even in its autumn colour the foliage turns yellow and never red. All through the summer the brilliant foliage, lustrous yellow-green above, turns its silvery linings out in every breeze, and fairly illuminates the duller trees that stand about. One authority calls it *Quercus bicolor*, for the two colours of its leaves.

This is one of the chestnut oak group. The leaf proves it by its shape and margin. The long, sweet nut in its fringed or plain cup is worthy the attention of any hungry man or beast.

The swamp white oak is easily transplanted and it grows rapidly, but because it is known to be a hard drinker people do not plant it, forgetting that trees sometimes are happy out of their normal habitat. This oak flourishes as a street tree, and does well in any moist, rich soil, graciously waiving, for our satisfaction, its natural preferences.

But he who would have this tree in its grandest state will wish it set at some distance from his house, and where it is made very comfortable. While we transplant small saplings into our grounds, let us exert ourselves to cherish the old ones and help the community to realise what a precious thing one of these veteran trees is—the natural heritage of all who can see it.

Basket Oak, Cow Oak (*Quercus Michauxii*, Nutt.)—A large handsome tree, 60 to 100 feet high, 3 to 7 feet in diameter at base, with stout ascending branches forming a round, dense head. *Bark* scaly, silvery or ashy grey, with reddish tinge. *Wood* hard, strong, tough, durable, close grained with large medullary rays and spring wood ducts, separating it into annual layers. Similar to other white-oak lumber. *Buds* pointed, ¼ inch long, scaly, with red hairs. *Leaves* 6 to 8 inches long, broadly obovate, regularly undulate on margins, sinuses equal to the lobes in size and shape, shining, dark green above, pubescent, often silvery white below. Crimson in autumn. *Flowers* with half-grown leaves, March to May. *Acorns* annual, solitary or paired, on short stem 1 to 1½ inches long, oval, pointed, bright brown, in shallow, scaly cup, which is flat bottomed and lined with down; kernels sweetest of Eastern acorns, eaten by children, negroes and domestic animals. *Preferred habitat,* swamps and bottom lands liable to inundation. *Distribution,* northern Delaware to Florida; west to Illinois, Missouri and Texas. *Uses:* Important timber tree, lumber ranking with white oak. A handsome ornamental tree, worthy of cultivation in wet ground.

The common names of trees are interesting, always, and often confusing. It is sometimes difficult to trace their origin and to explain their meaning. This beautiful tree, the most valuable annual-fruited oak of the Southeastern States, differs from others of the group in that its wood separates like that of the black ash into annual layers. The toughness and strength of these sheets adapt them to basket making—the most durable bushel baskets, china crates, etc., are made of strips of this oak. It is easy to see why the name "basket oak" came into use. But who shall explain the name "cow oak"? Perhaps it is enough that the acorns are sweet and cows eat them. Perhaps if I lived where the cow oak does I might give an answer that is more than simply a guess. The basket oak is one of the best mast trees in the country. The trees are very prolific, and each year hogs are fattened upon the acorns wherever the trees are common in the woods.

There would be an appearance of heaviness, perhaps, in this handsome oak, if it were not that the lustrous leaves are lined with silver that seems to catch and hold the light, reflecting it to the inner parts of the treetop. When the wind blows the contrast of light and shade is strikingly beautiful. In many particulars the basket oak resembles the swamp white oak, and some authorities hold that *Quercus Michauxii* is the Southern form of *Quercus platanoides,* for their ranges meet and do not overlap.

II. THE BLACK OAK GROUP

Acorns biennial; leaf lobes spiny tipped; bark dark.

KEY TO SPECIES

A. *Pacific coast species.*
  B. Leaves holly-like, evergreen.
    C. Young growth golden tomentose; branchlets pen-
      dulous.   *(Q. chrysolepis)* MOUNTAIN LIVE OAK
    CC. Young growth hoary; branchlets erect.
      D. Acorns elongated; leaves pubescent; fruit annual.
        (Q. agrifolia) CALIFORNIA LIVE OAK
      DD. Acorns ovate; leaves smooth.
        (Q. Wislizeni) HIGHLAND OAK
  BB. Leaves not holly-like, deciduous.
    (Q. Californica) KELLOGG'S OAK
AA. *Eastern species.* Deciduous.
  B. Leaves pinnately toothed and cleft by deep sinuses, petiole
    slender.
    C. Acorn cup shallow, broader than high.
      D. Tree pyramidal; branches with pin-like spurs.
        (Q. palustris) PIN OAK
      DD. Tree spreading; acorn large, in smooth, shallow
        saucer   *(Q. rubra)* RED OAK
      DDD. Tree of oblong head; acorn cup greyish, downy.
        (Q. Texana) TEXAN RED OAK
    CC. Acorn cup hemispherical, as high as broad.
      D. Leaves thin, glabrous beneath; acorn cup drawn
      in at top.   *(Q. coccinea)* SCARLET OAK
      DD. Leaves coarse, tufted with rusty hairs below;
      acorn cup not drawn in at top.
        (Q. velutina) BLACK OAK
      DDD. Leaves firm, pale greyish downy beneath; acorn
      cup drawn in at top.
        E. Lobes 5 to 7, lanceolate or sickle-like.
          F. Leaves thin, 6 to 7 inches long; lobes
          entire   *(Q. digitata)* SPANISH OAK
          FF. Leaves thick, 3 to 12 inches long; lobes
          toothed.   *(Q. Catesbæi)* TURKEY OAK
        EE. Lobes 3 to 5, broad, spiny tipped.
        (Q. nana) BEAR OAK
  BB. Leaves 3 to 5-lobed at apex or nearly entire, on short
    petioles, becoming glossy.
    C. Tree squat, contorted, spreading.
      (Q. Marilandica) BLACK JACK
    CC. Tree slender, tall, graceful. *(Q. nigra)* WATER OAK

THE POST OAK (*Quercus minor*)

The leaves are leathery, lined with brown wool, and they cling to their twigs all winter. Three large square lobes above the middle form the broadest part of the leaf; below the middle sinuses is a triangular basal portion and the short petiole. The wood is peculiarly adapted for use as posts, railroad ties and barrel staves

THE BLUE JACK	THE COW OAK	THE BLACK JACK	THE WATER OAK	THE YELLOW OAK
(*Quercus brevifolia*)	(*Quercus Michauxii*)	(*Quercus Marilandica*)	(*Quercus nigra*)	(*Quercus acuminata*)

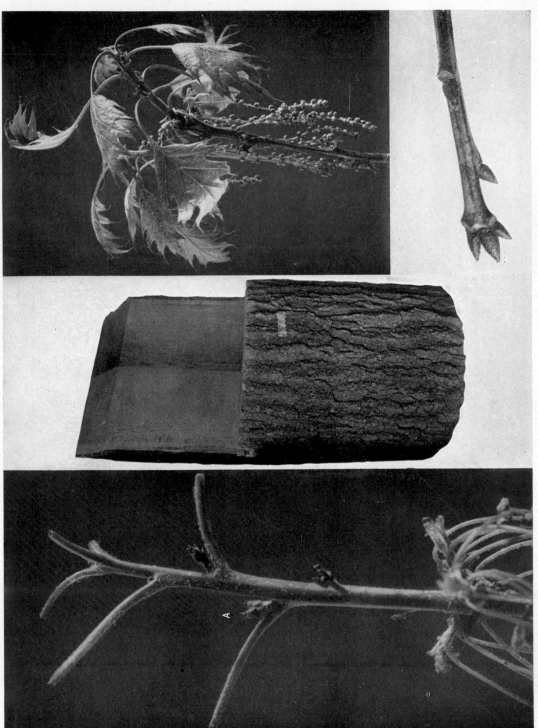

A. Pistillate flower (leaves cut away to show flowers)

THE RED OAK (*Quercus rubra*)

The bloom of this species is abundant. The tree is draped in May with its yellow catkins, and the red stigmas of the acorn flowers shine out against the silvery pink of the unfolding leaves. Wood and bark have reddish tones

BBB. Leaves entire, elongated, rarely toothed.
    C. Foliage willow-like, shining. (*Q. Phellos*) WILLOW OAK
    CC. Foliage laurel-like, shining.
        D. Tree pyramidal, pendulous.
            (*Q. imbricaria*) SHINGLE OAK
      DD. Tree round, thick topped.
           (*Q. laurifolia*) LAUREL OAK

Mountain Live Oak, Maul Oak, Gold-cup Oak (*Quercus chrysolepis*, Liebm.)—A low, broad tree, with drooping limbs, scrubby in high altitudes, 40 to 50 feet high, rarely 100 feet, and 100 to 150 feet across; trunk 2 to 6 feet through. *Bark* pale grey or reddish brown, flaky. *Wood* pale brown, close grained, tough, strong, hard to work. *Buds* broadly ovate, small, scaly. *Leaves* evergreen, oblong, entire, acute, 1 to 2 inches long, bright green, shining above, yellowish pubescent below. *Flowers*, June; staminate catkins profuse; pistillate, sessile, solitary or few in a cluster; scales golden tomentose. *Fruits* solitary, $\frac{1}{2}$ to $1\frac{1}{2}$ inches long; cups shallow, thick, of triangular scales, concealed by yellow tomentum. *Preferred habitat*, cañon sides and rocky gulches. *Distribution*, southern Oregon to Lower California, on western slopes of Sierra Nevada and coast mountains, mountains in southern Arizona and New Mexico. *Uses:* Most valuable timber oak of the Pacific coast. Used for wagons and farm implements.

The mountain live oak is not a horticultural tree, beautiful as it would be in the broad, rolling valleys of California. It is a wild thing, untamable as the mountain goat, loving the rocky cañon sides and the high terraces on which earthquake and avalanche have left mighty indelible scars. Two thousand feet above sea level these trees begin to appear. On these heights they rear their sturdy, buttressed trunks which soon break into limbs that spread into broad, low domes. The width of these trees is often twice their height, and their resemblance to the live oak of the Southeastern States is striking. Instead of the Spanish moss that decks these Southern trees and gives them such a funereal look, here is nothing to droop but the tree's own long, flexible twigs clad in leaves all yellow-green and shining, which brighten the sunshine that sifts through them. They are lined all summer with yellow down, and the spring catkins and autumn acorn cups give an extra Midas touch to the tree at both ends of the growing season.

There is a wonderful story of struggle and victory mutely but eloquently told by this tree, as it contends with the adverse conditions of soil and weather, grappling the rocky ground with its spreading roots and losing nothing in dignity and character as its size dwindles and it reaches its limit—5,000 feet. This low, knotty oak chaparral that the mountain climber grasps so thankfully as he faces toward the summit is fringed with yellow tassels in the spring and set in autumn with golden acorn cups, even as are its brethren, the gnarled giants he passed on the terraces 3,000 feet lower down. In the highest elevations, 8,000 to 9,000 feet above the sea, this oak is reduced to a foot in height. This is the "huckleberry oak" of the Sierra Nevada range, variety *vaccinifolia*, of the parent species. Another dwarf variety, *Palmeri*, called the Palmer oak, grows on the boundary between California and the lower peninsula.

The **California Live Oak** (*Quercus agrifolia*, Née.), with holly-like leaves, is a ponderous tree with a low, wide dome, very common in California, extending to the coast and farther to the islands of the southern half of the state.

The wood of this species is of a hard, durable sort, but can be got out only in short boards, as the trunk is not tall. It is excellent for fuel.

The **Highland Oak** (*Quercus Wislizeni*, A. DC.) is a large tree on the elevated foothills back from the coast in California. Its dark green, shining evergreen leaves resemble those of holly, *Ilex opaca*, except that they are more finely toothed, and sometimes entire. The acorn is long and slender. The wood is of especial value in mechanical construction, being hard, tough, strong and durable. It is also valuable as fuel.

The **Kellogg Oak,** or **California Black Oak** (*Quercus Californica*, Coop.), is large and beautiful, spreading wide its picturesquely gnarled branches covered with smooth, bright green leaves, much like those of the Eastern red oak. It has also stout twigs and rough dark-coloured bark, and the reddish coarse-grained wood strengthens still farther the resemblance of the two trees. The acorns of the Western tree, however, sit in deep cups that half conceal them; the red oak holds its nuts in shallow saucers.

The uplands only satisfy this Western black oak. It holds aloof from the plains and keeps back from the sea. Sunny open

THE PIN OAK (*Quercus palustris*)

Notice the half-grown acorns in pairs on the short stubs. The pistillate flowers appear in the axis of the leaves; the staminate catkins cluster at the base of the new shoot. The pyramidal habit of the tree and the bristling pin-like twigs that arm the branches easily distinguish this species

THE PIN OAK (*Quercus palustris*)

The thin, deeply cut leaves vary from the delicacy of the scarlet oak to the lustiness of the red oak. The squat little acorns resemble neither of these. When ripe the nuts are brown, daintily striped with black. The kernels are white and bitter

groves of it, mingled with white oaks, are common among conifers on mountain slopes and high valleys throughout California and north to the middle of Oregon.

The black bark of this oak is twice as rich in tannin as hemlock bark. The wood is rich in colour and wavy grained, but lumbermen dislike it. It dries very slowly, and is likely to be perforated with "pin knots," which mar and weaken it.

Pin Oak, Swamp Spanish Oak (*Quercus palustris*, Linn.) —A graceful, pyramidal tree when young, becoming oblong and irregular, at length; 50 to 120 feet high; branches horizontal, short. *Bark* grey-brown, shining, smooth, becoming scaly on trunk; twigs red, tomentose. *Wood* hard, tough, strong, heavy, coarse grained, light brown, variegated. *Buds* small, acute, brown. *Leaves* alternate, 4 to 6 inches long, deeply 5 to 7-lobed with wide sinuses almost to the midrib, shining above, dull and pale beneath, scarlet in autumn. *Flowers* in May, with half-grown leaves; staminate, in hairy catkins, 2 to 3 inches long; pistillate on short hairy peduncles, with bright red stigmas. *Acorns* ripe in autumn of second year, $\frac{1}{3}$ to $\frac{1}{2}$ inch long, pale brown, streaked, broader than long and set in a shallow saucer-like cup, of close, reddish scales, which is lined with hair; kernel white, bitter. *Preferred habitat*, low, moist soil. *Distribution*, Massachusetts to Delaware; west to Wisconsin and Arkansas. *Uses:* Handsome rapid-growing tree for avenues or lawns. It has fibrous roots and so transplants easily. Wood used in construction, cooperage, for interior finish of houses, and for shingles and clapboards.

The tourist who visits Washington and takes the trolley rides recommended by the guide book must have noted the superb avenues of native trees that give character and dignity to the whole city. For long stretches a single species holds uninterrupted sway, and the distinctive traits of the various kinds are thus impressed upon the observer, even as he flies by them on the car. I remember the beautiful pin oaks on the way from the capitol to the navy yard. Only a few years ago they were little striplings from the nurseries. Now they are goodly shade trees, and the beauty of youth is still upon them. Each tree is a glistening pyramid of leaves, that dance as the breeze plays among them; for the leaf stems and the twigs are slender and flexible, and the blades, catching the wind, keep the treetop in a continual flutter.

211

The leaves are deeply cut into five or seven spiny-toothed blades that point forward. The leaves of scarlet oak, cut with about the same "waste of cloth," point outward and have more rounded sinuses than those of the pin oak.

The leaf might confuse us, but the pin-oak tree tells its name before one is near enough to see the leaf distinctly. The tree has a broad pyramidal form, with slender branches stretched out horizontally as far as they can reach. The spur-like little twigs that cluster on the branches throughout the treetop are choked to death by being crowded, but they remain, the "pins" that characterise this species of oak. When it gets old the pin oak loses some of its symmetry and beauty. It holds on to its dead branches, but there is a dignity in its bearing that is admirable, even in its decline.

The village of Flushing, Long Island, has proved through many years that the pin oak is an admirable street and shade tree. It is as easily transplanted as a box elder, so there is scarcely an excuse for not planting it. The flush on its opening leaves, the red flame that lights the tree in the autumn, and the dainty striped acorns in their scaly saucers—all combine to make an ornamental tree with scarcely a fault to set off its many horticultural virtues. The Europeans have cherished this tree for over a century. We Americans are just discovering it, and should make up for lost time.

Red Oak (*Quercus rubra*, Linn.)—A large, stately tree, 50 to 150 feet high, with columnar trunk and round, symmetrical head of stout, spreading branches. *Bark* greyish brown with red tinge, with wide furrows between ridges; twigs reddish. *Wood* red-brown, with darker sap wood, coarse grained, with well-marked annual rings and medullary rays; heavy, hard, strong. *Buds* reddish, pointed, $\frac{1}{4}$ inch long. *Leaves* alternate, 7 to 9-lobed, 5 to 9 inches long, 4 to 6 inches wide; lobes and sinuses both triangular in form; second pair from apex always largest; lobes irregularly toothed and bristly pointed; leaves variable in size and form; lining paler green, smooth at maturity; autumn colour deep red. *Flowers*, May, with half-grown leaves; staminate catkins, yellow, hairy, 4 to 5 inches long; pistillate, on short 2 to 3-flowered stems; stigmas, long, bright green. *Acorns* ripe second autumn; large, $\frac{3}{4}$ to $1\frac{1}{4}$ inches long; broad at base, in close-scaled, shallow saucer; kernel white, extremely bitter. *Preferred*

THE RED OAK (*Quercus rubra*)

This tree is lusty and beautiful throughout. The pointed buds promise what summer fulfils. The broad leaves have triangular lobes and sinuses. The lobes point forward more than outward. They are often 9 inches long and six inches broad. The second leaf shows the paler lining. The large acorns sit in saucers, much shallower than in other oaks. The furrowed bark has a reddish-brown colour

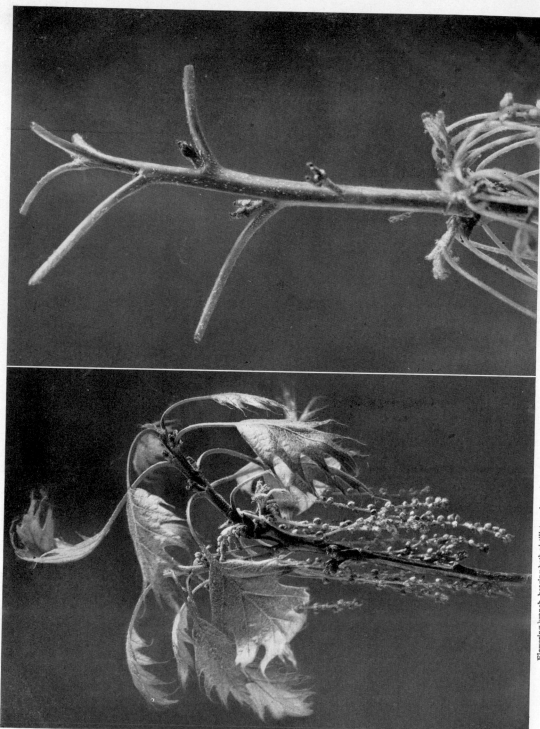

Flowering branch, bearing both pistillate and staminate flowers   Pistillate flowers shown at base of leaves.   (Leaves were removed to show flowers)

THE RED OAK (*Quercus rubra*)

The new shoots come out all pink and silvery, the leaves densely velvety. Paired acorns, half-grown, the nuts quite covered by the cups, show below the pendulous catkins. New acorn flowers appear in the angles of the leaves. Two seasons bring them to maturity

habitat, rich, well-drained stream borders. *Distribution*, Nova Scotia to Minnesota; south to Georgia, Tennessee and Kansas. *Uses:* A handsome, quick-growing shade and ornamental tree, easily transplanted and free from insect pests. Wood used in cooperage, cheap furniture, in construction and finish of buildings and for fuel. It is inferior to white oak. Bark rich in tannic acid, used in tanning leather.

There is no American oak more highly prized in Europe than the common red oak. It has been cultivated there for two centuries, and splendid specimens are pointed out with pride, especially in Belgium, Germany and England. It is the "champion oak" which flames in English parks when the foliage of native species falls without a hint of the brilliant colouring which we always expect in autumn woods.

The red oak is so common in our Eastern forests that we have not realised its worthiness as a street and ornamental tree. Surely it is a stately tree in the forest, and as noble and benignant a figure as the white oak where it has ample room to develop its round dome. It grows faster than any other native oak and in a greater variety of soils. It can be transplanted, even when 15 feet high, from the woods to a lawn, and not notice the change. After it becomes established a growth of a foot or more in height may be expected yearly, and an increase in diameter of an inch of wood in five years.

The shining leaves of red oak, though they are variable in form, are always cut oval and into triangular lobes which point forward, rather than outward. The sinuses are angled or rounded, but are not so broad as those of the black oak. These leaves are leathery and smooth, those of black oak are rougher. The bloom of red oak is more luxuriant than that of other oaks. The tree is fairly draped with its long yellow catkins, and the red stigmas shine out against the silvery pink of opening leaves.

The acorns of the red oak are unique. They are large, in pairs, on very short stalks, and the nut sits in a broad, shallow saucer covered with small, close-fitting scales. The acorn crop is two years in ripening, but the tree is so vigorous that there are usually nuts, or at least saucers, in evidence to identify the tree, if the leaves do not determine it with certainty. The under bark is red, while that of black oak is orange-yellow. This is another way to tell the two species apart at any time of year by the aid of a pocket knife.

Scarlet Oak (*Quercus coccinea*, Muench.)—Slender, symmetrical tree, 70 to 160 feet high, with graceful, curving branches and twigs, tapering trunk and round head. *Bark* brown or grey, rough, scaly, shallowly fissured; inner layers reddish; twigs green, scurfy, becoming red and smooth. *Wood* pale brownish red, hard, coarse grained, strong, heavy, of rapid growth. *Buds* pointed, hairy at tip, small, reddish. *Leaves* oval or obovate, thin, smooth, shining above, paler beneath, sometimes hairy tufted on veins, 3 to 6 inches long, 2 to 5 inches broad, with 5 to 7 spreading bristly pointed and subdivided lobes, with deep, rounded sinuses between; autumn colour scarlet; petioles slender, long. *Flowers* staminate catkins slender, reddish before maturity; pistillate with long stigmas bright red. *Acorns* biennial, $\frac{1}{2}$ to $\frac{3}{4}$ inch long, half covered by short-stalked cup, smooth, triangular, close-pressed scales, rounding in at the top; kernel white, moderately bitter. *Preferred habitat,* dry, fertile loam. *Distribution,* Maine to Florida, west to Minnesota, Nebraska and Missouri. Best development in lower valley of Ohio River. *Uses:* A favourite ornamental oak in this country and in Europe. Lumber used for same purposes as that of *Q. rubra*.

The splendour of our autumnal forests owes much to the foliage of the scarlet oak. The tree blazes like a torch against the duller reds and browns in the woods, and often keeps its brilliancy until after snow covers the ground.

There is no reason for confusing the black, red and pin oaks with this species. They are all heavy and coarse beside it. Their leaves are leathery compared with the papery thinness of these. In summer the scarlet oak lifts its young shoots, delicately pink above the last year's growth, and waves them like long, tapering plumes, set with skeleton leaves. Break a twig, and the smoothness and delicacy of the leaves strike you. Just a pale trace of fuzziness remains along the veins on the under side. The wide, rounded sinuses are cut nearly to the midrib, and the leaf flutters airily on a long petiole. The acorn differs from the black oak's in having its cup drawn tightly in at the top.

Though we have planted this tree less often than the red oak and pin oak in this country, it is coming to be recognised as

214

THE SCARLET OAK (*Quercus cocci..ea*)

No oak leaf is more exquisite in form and finish than this one. The tree becomes a torch of scarlet in the late autumn. The wood and the furrowed bark are tinged with red. The broad leaf on the budded twig is a freak

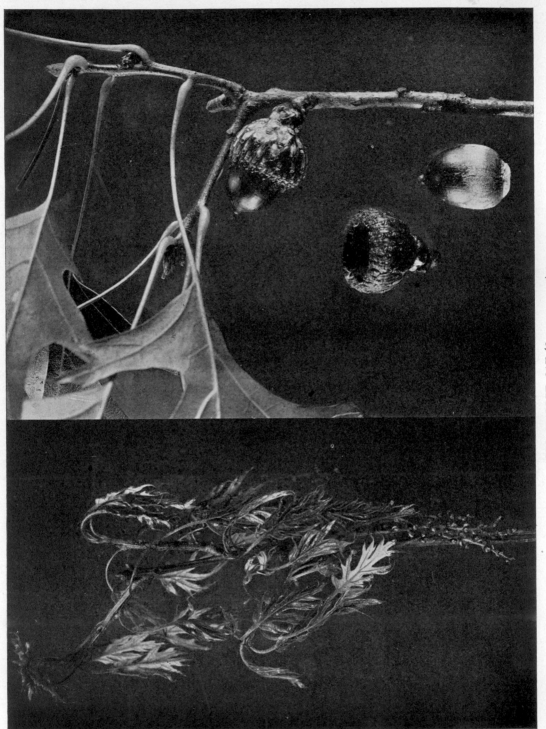

THE SCARLET OAK (*Quercus coccinea*)

The new shoot is a feathery spray of red and white velvet when the leaves and flowers come out. In autumn the foliage is brilliantly scarlet. The acorn cups are closely incurved at the rim as a rule. The kernel is white and rather bitter.

superior to both, while in hardiness and rapidity of growth it is the equal of either.

The **Texan Red Oak** (*Quercus Texana*, Buckl.), tallest of American oaks, and one of the handsomest, grows from Iowa to Indiana and south to Texas and Florida. It is closely related to the red and scarlet oaks, showing the characteristic acorns of the former and the leaves of the latter.

Possibly the giant red oak that stood on the borders of the Bayou St. Barb in Louisiana, fifty years ago, "44 feet in girth and tall according," was of this Texan species. *Quercus rubra* does not grow so far south.

Black Oak, Yellow Oak (*Quercus velutina*, Lam.)—A tree 70 to 90 feet, rarely 150 feet high, with narrow, open head of slender branches, occasionally wide spreading and short trunked. *Bark* usually very dark grey or brown, thick, with rough broken ridges and deep furrows; inner layers orange yellow, rich in tannin. *Wood* light reddish brown, coarse grained, with annual layers strongly marked and thin medullary rays, hard, strong, heavy, not tough. *Buds* large, pointed, angled, downy. *Leaves* alternate, 4 to 10 inches long, 2 to 6 inches wide, deeply cut into 7 to 9 broad, bristly toothed lobes with rounded sinuses, thick, almost leathery texture, lustrous, dark green above, smooth, or somewhat hairy, brownish beneath; petioles long, yellow, flattened; autumnal colour brownish yellow, rarely reddish. *Flowers*, May, with half-open leaves; hairy, reddish, stigmas bent back. *Acorns* biennial, solitary or in pairs, short stalked; nut ovoid, smooth, in cup of loose scales; rim fringed, not incurved; kernel yellow, bitter. *Preferred habitat*, rich, moist soil. *Distribution*, Maine to Florida; west to Minnesota, Kansas and eastern Texas. *Uses:* Rarely planted for ornament and shade. Wood used in cooperage, for furniture and in general construction; bark in tanning and dyeing.

Since early spring I have been watching life kindle and glow in the top of a grim old black oak. I knew the tree then by its black bark and its large, downy winter buds, and the velvety scurf on its young shoots. Still another sign, constant the year round, proclaimed this tree a black oak beyond question. Under the rough outer bark is an orange-yellow inner layer, easily reached by a little digging in one of the furrows. No other oak need be confused with this species if the observer carries a pocket knife.

215

This tree, though it was late March, was still holding some of its old leaves. On twigs destitute of leaves I found a leaf stem, here and there, frayed into many threads, showing how tough its fibres are.

My black oak leans up against a bluff, and thrusts its giant arms out over the wide roadway. One sided as the situation compelled it to grow, it is yet a majestic tree, "framed in the prodigality of Nature." From the path below I can just touch its lower limb with the ten-foot pruning shears; but by climbing the bluff I walk right into the treetop. Here I go to see things happen in the spring days.

The buds open and the shoots set with leaves push rapidly out. The whole treetop flushes crimson in the morning sunshine, and there is a "pale moonbeam's light" gleaming through it. Can it be dewdrops pearling the young leaves? I ask the question, and the tree answers it as soon as I get near enough to examine a spray. The red glow is from crinkly, half-awake, baby leaves, and their brilliance is softened by a silky covering of white hairs. This is especially thick on the under side, but the silvery mist over the treetop lasts only a day, or until the leaves are grown large and self-reliant enough to get on without such protection. Then the fuzz is suddenly shed from the upper sides of the leaves, but the under surfaces are more or less coated throughout the summer with a dull scurfy down.

The coarseness of the leaves is one trait that distinguishes the species from the red and scarlet oaks, whose leaves it often imitates in form. Crumple a leaf of each in your hands. The red oak is intermediate between the leathery, harsh texture of the black, and the thinness and delicacy of the scarlet. The incisions in black oak leaves are rounded and deep, their bristly lobes point outward as often as they incline forward.

The bloom of black oak may be profuse or scant; the tree has its "off years." As the leaves lose their red the flowers take up the theme, and glow with ruddy stigmas and fringed tassels of stamens among the half-grown foliage. The lustiest shoots set acorns—sometimes a pair under each leaf. While the new ones are swelling and forming their little basal cups, on twigs a year older ambitious acorns of a larger growth are hurrying through their second summer to be ready to fall in October.

This species is the type of the black or biennial-fruited oaks—

THE BLACK OAK (*Quercus velutina*)

The leaves have squarish lobes, coarse, rough texture and often brownish linings, with tufts of rusty hairs in the angles of the veins. They turn to dull red or brownish orange. The under bark is orange-coloured. The acorns sit in cups of loosely shingled scales which form a fringe at the margin. The buds are large, ovate, with a hoary covering of fine hairs

Flowering branch; A, Staminate flowers; B, Pistillate flowers

THE BLACK OAK (*Quercus velutina*)

The opening leaves are crimson, with silvery velvet linings and long white hairs above. Half-grown acorns are seen below the fringe of staminate catkins. The pistillate flowers are in the leaf angles a large group which takes two years to ripen an acorn crop. As a rule, these trees always show half-formed acorns on their terminal twigs in winter. The white or annual-fruited oaks never carry any over; they ripen their fruits and cast them in the autumn. Black oaks have bristly pointed leaves; white oaks have only curved lines on their leaf margins. These facts are well worth remembering.

Most people know an oak "just by the looks of it." Ask them *which* oak it is, and they can't be sure. The bark of the black oak, with its orange lining, is the key to its name. The woodsman knows that this oak leads the country as the source of tan bark. Only the chestnut oak comes near it in percentage of tannin. Beside tannin, there is in the inner bark the yellow dyestuff called *quercitron*, which, before the discovery of aniline dyes, was largely used in the printing of calicoes. The yellow bark was dried, then ground, and the powdery citron-yellow colouring matter sifted out of it. Besides the yellow tints and shades, it gave, with the addition of salts of iron, various shades of grey, brown and drab.

Black oaks would doubtless be planted oftener for shade and ornament but that there are so many other beautiful oaks to choose from. In the wild they are noble ornaments to the natural landscape.

For my giant black oak on the hillside I have developed a kind of personal regard that surprises me. It is the result of getting acquainted with the tree at successive seasons of the year. It has taken on individuality. It ought to have a personal name, not merely its tribal cognomen. I have learned to read the answers to my questions. I have acquired, therefore, the rudiments of a new language—for tree language is a code of signs which anybody can learn. It is astonishing how much of interesting personal and family history a tree will freely give in one year of friendly intercourse.

The **Turkey Oak** (*Quercus Catesbæi*, Michx.) grows most abundantly, and reaches 60 feet in height, in the high lands bordering bays and river mouths, along the coasts of South Carolina and Georgia. It follows the Gulf coast to Louisiana, but is rare west of Florida. It is an important fuel in the regions it inhabits, but is little known to lumbermen. Generally a small tree, 20 to 35 feet high, it may be distinguished from the

Spanish oak by the greater size and breadth of its leaves, and by the teeth that generally adorn the tapering, triangular lobes. The leaves are thick and stiff; those of Spanish oak are thin and flexible.

The **Spanish Oak** (*Quercus digitata*, Sudw.), of the Southern States, is a distinguished-looking tree, with tall trunk and broad, open head covered with downy-lined leaves of peculiar forms. The lobes are elongated, often curved, sickle-like, rarely toothed, and separated by deep, wide sinuses. From this extreme they often vary widely, showing broadly obovate blades, often with no lobes at all. The leaves droop from the twigs, giving the tree an unique expression.

It is a pity that this tree is not hardy north of lower New Jersey and Missouri. It is one of the handsomest of shade trees. The old plantations of the South are likely to show a few aged Spanish oaks. There are two forms of the tree. Beside the upland type, a white-barked one abounds in swampy land. This tree has leaves very deeply cut, which turn a splendid yellow in autumn. Lumbermen count its wood nearly equal to white oak. The upland form yields far less durable timber.

The range of the Spanish oak is from New Jersey to Florida and west to Missouri and Texas. It is most common in the South Atlantic and Gulf States, on the hills back from the coast.

The **Bear**, or **Scrub Oak** (*Q. nana*, Sarg.), is a shrubby tree that creeps in thickets over rocky barren ledges from Maine to Virginia and Kentucky. Its downy-lined leaves vary greatly in their size and lobing. They are obovate, with the three largest lobes at apex, and tapering to the base, with at least one pair of lesser lobes below the broad middle sinuses. There is a resemblance between these and the leaves of the post oak, although the sharp, holly-like spines that tip each lobe and the two sizes of acorns each tree shows in summer prove this species to belong in the black-oak class. The little acorns, which are bitter and set in shallow saucers, are abundantly produced, and bears fatten on them. The species is often effectively planted to adorn rocky areas in parks.

The **Black Jack**, or **Barren Oak** (*Q. Marilandica*, Muench.), is a black-trunked, contorted, spreading shrub, or a tree reaching the height of 50 feet. Its leaves are leathery, with brown fuzzy linings, and the upper surfaces are set with rough, stellate hairs.

Unripe fruit

A. Pistillate flowers   B. Staminate flowers

THE BEAR OAK (*Quercus nana*)

This is a little tree or a much-branching shrub. It covers rocky slopes with a handsome foliage mass. The flowers and half-grown acorns are in evidence in May.
Bears formerly hid in this underbrush and ate the acorns
The typical leaf form and the nearly full-grown acorns are here shown.

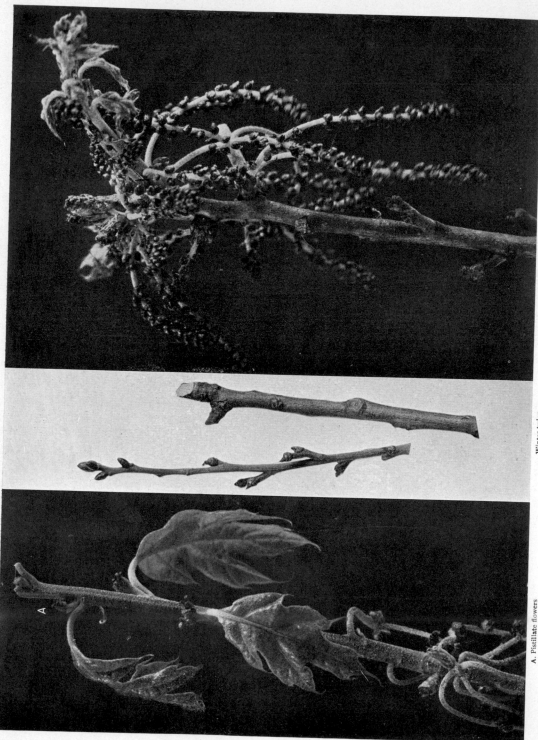

Staminate flowers

Winter twigs

A. Pistillate flowers

THE BEAR OAK (*Quercus nana*)

This species is variable in its leaf forms and its acorns. Pistillate flowers are shown among the new leaves. Winter twigs show buds and half-grown acorns. Flowers of both kinds are shown in bud, with opening leaves and half-grown acorns

The leaf broadens to its apex and ends in three indistinct lobes of variable size and form, whose ribs protrude into the bristly points that characterise the black oak group. The obovate or pear-shaped outline is constant, however the lobing may vary.

The function of this ragged little tree is to clothe sterile ground from New York to Nebraska, and south to Florida and Texas. What it lacks in beauty it makes up for in a certain admirable ruggedness of character. The leaves are not as other oak leaves, and the tree's habit is as handsome as one could expect considering the worthless ground assigned it by Nature.

The **Water Oak** (*Quercus nigra*, Linn.) is a good-sized tree, with a leaf of somewhat similar outline, but thinner texture than those of the black jack. It is a favourite shade tree in the Southern States. It grows naturally along the borders of streams and swamps, but is easily transplanted, grows rapidly and thrives in cultivation. Its shining leaves, blue-green above, paler below, vary from entire margins to lobing as deep as the average red oak shows. The acorn is a squat little nut in a shallow cup, set with fine scales.

Willow Oak (*Quercus Phellos*, Linn.)—A graceful, quick-growing tree, 60 to 80 feet high, with slender branches that form a conical, round-topped head. *Bark* rather rough, reddish brown, with scaly surface; young trees, smooth. *Wood* pale, red-brown, coarse grained, strong, soft, heavy; sap wood lighter in colour. *Buds* small, acute, brown. *Leaves* alternate, leathery, short petioled, 2 to 5 inches long, linear like willow leaves, but obtuse at apex and base; upper surface bright green and glossy; lower pale green, dull, smooth; autumn colour yellow. *Acorns* biennial, not numerous, solitary or paired on short stalks; nut $\frac{1}{2}$ inch across, hemispherical, downy, yellowish brown, set in shallow saucer-shaped cup; scales thin, ovate, dark reddish brown, hairy; kernel orange, bitter. *Preferred habitat*, low, wet borders of swamps. *Distribution*, New York to northeastern Florida (in the low maritime region just back from the coast); along the Gulf into Texas; north in low ground into Missouri, Kentucky and Tennessee. *Uses:* A fine shade and ornamental tree for Southern cities. Wood used in construction.

We think of oaks as being sturdy and rugged in their expression, leaving grace and delicacy to willows and birches, and such. Here is an oak whose leaves are willow-like in form, size and texture; and they hang on supple, pendant branches, like a willow's. The dainty acorns in their saucers are often needed to convince observers that the tree is truly an oak. But only the young trees are willowy in habit. The oak characters soon assert themselves.

Naturally, willow oaks grow on the margins of swamps, but they thrive as a street and shade tree, and are especially beautiful in the autumnal yellow of their foliage. A large tree grows in John Bartram's garden in Philadelphia; a small one seems to be holding its own without protection in the Arnold Arboretum at Boston, though its shoots are often nipped by frost.

The **Shingle Oak,** or **Laurel Oak** (*Q. imbricaria*, Michx.)— A tree 60 to 100 feet high, pyramidal, becoming round headed at length; branches slender. *Bark* pale brown, scaly; twigs smooth. *Wood* reddish brown, heavy, hard, coarse grained. *Buds* small, acute, brownish. *Leaves* deciduous, alternate, oblong, usually entire, 4 to 6 inches long, 1 to 2 inches wide, shining, dark green above, paler and pubescent beneath; petioles short. *Flowers* in May, with opening leaves, tomentose, greenish. *Acorns* biennial, ½ to ⅔ inch long, stalked, solitary or paired; nut broad, short, pointed; cup shallow, scaly, reddish; kernel bitter. *Preferred habitat*, rich bottom lands. *Distribution*, Pennsylvania to Georgia; west to Nebraska and Arkansas. *Uses:* Lumber for clapboards and shingles. A hardy and beautiful park tree.

The pyramidal shape of the young shingle oak and the horizontal and drooping postures of its slender branches remind us strongly of the pin oak. The "pins," however, are missing, as we will observe when the tree is bare; and the foliage in summer quickly corrects any false impressions. Even from a distance the foliage masses of the two trees differ distinctly. The clefts and angles that make so large a part of pin-oak leaves are all missing in those of the shingle oak. Willow or peach leaves are more like these plain-margined ones. The wayfaring man will never imagine this tree to be an oak until he sees the acorns.

The shingle oak grows quickly, as the long, leafy shoots in early summer prove. The star-shaped arrangement of the leaves on the short branches is most interesting, and there is a wavy curl in the margins, as if they would each turn aside to let the sunlight in to the branches less favourably situated. So little interference

THE SHINGLE OAK (*Quercus imbricaria*)

This tree has laurel-like leaves, destitute of lobes and bristly points. The squat acorns prove it an oak of the biennial group. The flowers consist of a fringe of staminate catkins, and solitary or paired pistillate flowers in the angles of the new leaves

THE SHINGLE OAK (*Quercus imbricaria*)

The glossy, elliptical leaves are unlike the typical oak leaf. The plump little acorns leave no doubt as to the family name of the tree. Half-grown acorns appear above the mature ones

is there that the tree is leafy to its central shaft, but the head is still open.

The shingle oak has a fashion of crossing with related species, and thus producing hybrids from seed. The black oak and this one are believed to be the parents of a rather widely distributed form, now called *Quercus Leana*. Crosses with the pin oak and the jack oak also occur.

The summer beauty of this tree is quite sufficient to commend it to all planters. It is covered in spring with pink and silver, the leaves before they expand are curled in tight little tubes. In summer they are leathery and shining. In autumn they change to rich reds, and the veins and midrib are touched with a more fiery hue. Truly, there is no season when the shingle oak is not handsome in any congregation of trees.

Another **Laurel Oak** (*Quercus laurifolia*, Michx.), with leathery leaves like laurel, grows to large size in swamp borders, and along streams in the coast regions, from Virginia to Louisiana. It is the common "water oak" of streets and yards, adorning them with its graceful columnar trunks and lustrous dark green, almost evergreen, foliage. Only the live oak, its near associate, exceeds it in beauty. It is commonest in eastern Florida, and here it reaches its greatest height. Unfortunately, it is not hardy in the North.

THE HISTORY OF OAKS

The oak was held sacred by the Greeks, Romans, Teutons and Celts. They venerated the living tree for its fruit which fed them, and for its lumber which housed them and served as their defence against their enemies. "Hearts of oak" were built into the Norsemen's ships that storms could not wrench apart. The triremes of the great navies of Greece and Rome were of oak timber. So were their great bridges, aqueducts and buildings— triumphs of architectural art and engineering skill. The very columns, with their flaring bases and capitals, were modelled from the trunks of oaks. The curves of the branches suggested their arches, and the leaves and acorns gave them designs for ornamentation.

The Druids held their most solemn rites under the sacred shade of their oak groves. The mistletoe was gathered on the coming in of the new year, and only a hook of gold was fit for this ceremony. Their Yule log was an oak tree cut down, drawn home and offered on the rude hearth as a sacrifice to Yaioul, the Celtic god of fire, in the feast of midwinter. It was through his favour that winter's icy grasp loosened, and the days began to lengthen.

Sleeping under the shade of an oak was counted a sovereign cure for paralytics. The benefits of such treatment must have depended upon the weather, for oaks in thunderstorms seem very prone to "draw the stroke." Shakespeare's famous apostrophe in "Measure for Measure" seconds the popular belief in his time; the opinion prevails among woodsmen to-day:

> "Merciful heaven!
> Thou rather with thy sharp and sulphurous bolt
> Split'st the unwedgeable and gnarled oak
> Than the soft myrtle."

There is a whole thunderstorm crowded into these lines.

Durability is a prime merit in oak timber. The oldest houses in England show their oak beams and panelling as sound to-day as ever. Shrines of the early kings carved in oak have not yet begun to show signs of age. "Antique oak" is imitated by staining to very dark colour the stock used in furniture manufactories. Genuine "antique oak" is a priceless treasure.

Bog Oak.—This oak, a favourite wood in the decorative arts, is obtained from trunks which have lain and blackened in the peat bogs of Ireland and England for untold centuries. These logs, exhumed, seasoned, and sawed into lumber, bring extravagant prices. Wholesale inundation of forests, due possibly to earthquakes, produced some of this bog oak. Tradition has it that, in 55 B. C., Cæsar's army, wintering in the land of the Britons, was set to cutting down the forests and dragging the logs into boggy districts. This was to keep the army under strict discipline, and to spite the unfriendly Britons. The camps and bridges the Romans built consumed many of the sacred oak groves, and the surplus, maliciously buried in the swamps, has been discovered and dug up centuries later. This wood is described by Evelyn as taking on a colour and hardness "emulating the politest ebony."

Structure of Oak Wood—Oak wood shows distinct annual rings, each made of a band of close grained, pale *summer wood*, and dark, open, porous layer of *spring wood*. Broad, shining bands of fibres extend in vertical plates from centre to bark in the tree. When the wood is properly sawed these shining *medullary*, or *pith rays*, show as irregular patches on the surface. Much of the beauty of polished oak depends upon these "mirrors," which are the largest when the wood is "quarter sawed"—that is, when sawed toward the centre of the log. Gnarled roots and tortuous branches of old oak trees furnish wood of curly grain which is highly prized for veneering.

Uses of Acorns.—Acorns vary in sweetness and edibility. They all contain food elements, and primitive peoples have used them as food. The Californian white oak (*Quercus lobata*) has a sweet acorn which the Indians bake, shell, and then grind into a coarse meal out of which bread is made. The New England Indian tribes ate the acorns of white oaks of various species, as did the tribes farther south. The Japanese and Chinese have species with edible acorns. In Europe the acorn crop is watched with great solicitude. The ancients believed that

> " . . . men fed with oaken mast
>   The aged trees themselves in years surpassed."

Quercus esculus was especially esteemed for food. The mast was also depended upon for the fattening of swine. English villagers still enjoy in many places the ancient "right of pannage," the privilege, granted them by some early king, of turning their hogs in autumn into the royal forests.

The acorn cups of *Quercus Valonia* are exceptionally rich in tannin, and are sifted out from the nuts and sold under the trade name, Valonia, to the best tanneries in Europe.

Oak bark is a staple tan bark the world over. The black and chestnut oaks in this country and the English oak in Europe are richest in tannin. Spent bark from the pits holds heat. It was formerly used in private greenhouses under the soil to force exotic fruits, especially pineapples, in England. It is now spread on race tracks, roadways, paths and sidewalks.

Insect Enemies.—Numerous insects and fungi prey upon oaks. Great caterpillars of our most beautiful night-flying moths devour the young foliage. Weevils infest the acorns, gall insects distort the leaves and twigs, scale insects suck the juices from the young branches. Certain of these enemies of the oaks have been turned to good account by man. The scale, Kermes, is a soft-

223

bodied creature, diminutive in size, but infinite in numbers. Its eggs are gathered and dried, much as the cochineal insects are, and a valuable scarlet dye is made of them. This industry belongs to the countries of southern Europe and northern Africa, where the Kermes is used for dyeing leather and wool. In France cosmetics are tinted with it.

Oak Galls.—"Oak apples" are abnormal growths on the leaves or twigs of oaks due to the presence of the larvæ of certain insects whose eating seems to poison the tissues and distort their development. An entomologist knows by the form of the gall what insect produces it. In ancient times people knew little of their causes—the "apples of Sodom" and "Dead Sea fruit" of history, sacred and profane, were galls of oaks. The "flea seed" of California oaks contain the young of a species of the genus Cynips. A glance into almost any oak tree just as the buds are opening will show delicate, wasp-like insects resting lightly for a moment on one leaf cluster after another, depositing eggs, one in a place, within the leaf substance. The beginnings of oak apples may be found as large as peas on leaves scarcely an inch long. John Gerard, the herbalist, writing in 1597, naïvely expresses the misconceptions and superstitious beliefs of his day in England.

"The gall tree," he explains at the outset, "is a kinde of oke." Then proceeding:

"The oke apples being broken in sunder about the time of their withering doe foreshew the sequell of the yeare, as the expert Kentish husbandmen have observed, by the living things found in them: as, if they finde an ant, they foretell plenty of graine to ensue; if a white worm like a gentill or maggot, then they prognosticate murren of beasts and cattell; if a spider, then (say they) we shall have a pestilence or some such like sickness to follow amongst men; these things the learned also have observed, and noted that before they have an hole through them they contain in them either a flie, a spider, or a worme; if a flie, then warre ensueth; if a creeping worme, then scarcities of victuals; if a running spider, then followeth great sicknesse or mortalitie."

Oak galls are rich in tannin, sometimes yielding as high as 77 per cent. They have always been used in various countries in tanning the finest skins, and in making inks and dyes. The Aleppo galls from northern Italy rank highest. The oldest documents in America show the ink still bright on the yellowing parchment, for it was made of oak galls and is practically permanent.

224

Dyes are equally lasting, in distinct contrast to the cheap aniline dyes in use nowadays, and the inks that fade in a year or two. Here is something startling. A writer in England three centuries ago thus recommends these galls to horse jockeys: "A handful or two of small Oak buttons, mingled with *Oats* given to *Horses*, which are *black* of *colour*, will in a few days eating alter it to a fine *Dapple grey*."

Truffles.—The truffles of commerce, famous in the French cuisine and well known to the gourmands in Rome's palmiest days, are edible fungi, somewhat like puff balls in texture and mode of growth. They grow as parasites upon the roots of various trees, including the Holm oak and the English oak. Limy soil is required by these fungi. They are produced in southern England and on the Continent, reaching their highest perfection in France and Italy. "The reputation of the truffle of Perigord is as old as the world!" In an impassioned ode to this delicacy, a famous Frenchman uttered this apostrophe:

"Noir diamant, perle de la Gascogne,
 Tous les gourmets vénèrent ton pays!"

Truffles bring astonishing prices in the markets of Europe. This fact alone quite justifies the planting of chalky lands to oaks. Yield of truffles is expected when the trees are a dozen years old, and it continues without abatement for twenty-five years if conditions remain favourable.

The truffle hunter, often a peasant woman, goes into the woods with a basket, a spading fork, and a dog or a pig, trained to help her. The truffle has a rich, strong odour which these animals detect by their keen sense of smell. The hunter keeps close to the animal, which soon begins a vigorous digging or rooting. It is at once interrupted. The eager quadruped is sorely disappointed, for he is a truffle connoisseur and a gourmand. His duty is to "point" the truffle only; the spading fork carefully unearths the precious tuber and it goes into the basket. Unless carefully tied or penned at night, these ill-used servants fare forth, and help themselves to these subterranean delicacies by the light of the moon.

Truffles are doubtless present on roots of beech and oak in our own woods. We have not yet taken time to discover and exploit them. Our epicures are satisfied with the canned and imported article. The delectable "beefsteak" fungus, which grows on the trunks of certain of our native oaks, is highly esteemed by those who know it, but most people cautiously despise all "toadstools," great and small.

The **Cork Oak** (*Quercus Suber*), native to the peninsulas of southern Europe, and to northern Africa, is a small evergreen oak, rarely over 30 feet high and 2 feet in diameter, which grows in forests on broken, unproductive land. The importance of these forests has never waned, because nobody has discovered or invented a satisfactory substitute for cork. In France and all other vine-growing countries the importation of cork is a great business. What wonder then that the people in the grape and wine belt of California rejoiced to find that the cork oak can be successfully grown on the otherwise unproductive foothills of the Sierra Nevada Mountains. It is a vast saving to raise their own bottle stoppers instead of importing them from the other side of the globe.

What a novel experience it would be to visit at harvest time one of those forests in Spain or Algeria which have for centuries furnished cork to the world! We should not say the business was carried on in a very economical or economic way, as we Americans count those things. There is not the rush and bustle of the Western World in those sleepy countries. Haste makes waste in growing cork and stripping it. The slowest-growing trees produce the best grade of cork, and they are not at their best till fifty years old. For the next fifty years they yield a thick coat of cork every ten years. Then the quality deteriorates, and the trees are cut down, the bark sent to the tan pit, and the charcoal burner takes the wood.

When the age of twenty-five years is reached it is time to strip off from the trunk the "virgin bark," a thin, hard, outer layer, which is rich in tannin, but bears no resemblance to cork. The removal of this layer sets the tree to forming a spongy layer, thick and entirely different from the first. This grows eight or ten years, when it is removed, and a second layer produced. The first is practically useless. The second stripping gives cork used by fishermen to float their nets with. The stripping goes on, each decade showing improvement in the quality of the cork until the fiftieth year brings it to its best state.

The stripping of cork is a particular job. Two opposite vertical cuts are made the full length of the trunk; then circular cuts at top and bottom are made, and the two rectangular plates of bark, each covering one-half of the whole trunk, are attached to it only by the alburnum, or "mother bark." It is a delicate matter to get the cork off and yet leave this under layer uninjured. Cork never grows again on spots that are bruised. Very carefully the wedge-shaped handle of the hatchet creeps along the edge of the plate and lifts it gradually off. The skill and patience required to do this must challenge our admiration. The harvest time comes in July or August. The curved plates of cork are scraped smooth, heated and flattened for transportation.

The flowering period of cork oaks is practically continuous in the warmer sections of Portugal. The acorns are annual from the early flowers, but the later ones are carried over, ripening in the second season. There are no less than three distinct crops of acorns, as the farmer folk well know. The fattening of hogs depends largely upon these acorns. There seems to be no distinct line drawn between annual and biennial cork oaks.

There is only one tree in the world whose bark ranks commercially with the cork oak, and it takes second place. It is the Cinchona, or Peruvian-bark tree, which is the source of quinine and related drugs.

Exotic Oaks in American Gardens.—The English oak (*Quercus Robur*) is the only oak native to the British Isles. It is the patriarch of the forest, noblest in any company of trees, fostered in its youth, cherished and revered in its old age, depended upon in its prime for its valuable products. The Briton to-day is as fervent a tree worshipper as his Druid ancestors were, but his love for the oak is stripped of superstition and tempered by intelligence. He is a practical man, and while he cherishes the gnarled oaks that adorn his private grounds and public parks, he has his oak forests for timber as his grain fields for bread. Sense and sentiment are both strong in him, but there is a proper balance between them.

The English oak is by no means confined to England. It is found all over Europe, where in earlier times it formed extensive forests. It is known in two forms, *sessiliflora* and *pedunculata*, varieties dependent upon the absence or presence of stalks of flower and fruit. With age these trees increase in breadth, more than in height, grow stout in trunk and limb, and the branches become extravagantly gnarled and twisted. The

227

prevailing belief as to the age of these oaks is expressed in Dryden's lines:

> "Three centuries he grows, and three he stays
> Supreme in state; and in three more decays."

There are trees still hale in England to-day which were old enough to cut for their lumber when William the Conqueror landed in 1066. Scientists estimate the limit of longevity among oaks at about 2,000 years.

The British oak grows indifferently in the United States except in California. Here it finds conditions most favourable and grows with great rapidity and vigour. Acorns planted in 1878 were grown into large trees in 1890—to the amazement of everybody.

The **Holm Oak** (*Quercus Ilex*), which skirts the Mediterranean coast of Europe, and seems to thrive best, even in England, when exposed to sea breezes, is the Ilex, famous in classical literature. Its evergreen leaves resemble those of the holly, whose generic name is Ilex. This is one of the most ornamental of the oaks, compact and regular in form, and beautiful in its glossy foliage the year round. Its acorns form one of the important edible sorts in Europe. The value of its mast alone would justify the planting of the Holm oak. It is also one of the truffle oaks, and its bark and the galls of one of its varieties are of the highest value in dyeing and tanning.

Turkey Oak (*Quercus cerris*), of Europe, is planted in our Southern States. It has somewhat the form and symmetry of the beech in its lusty youth. Its foliage is dark, with greyish linings; the acorn $1\frac{1}{2}$ inches long, with a large mossy cup that halfway swallows it. This is the "wainscot oak" of English builders.

Japanese and Chinese oaks feel at home in the Eastern States of America, and are now coming in, to the enrichment of our horticulture and the delight of landscape gardeners. The crispness and vigour of the foliage make these trees strikingly handsome. *Quercus variabilis* has leathery, dark green chestnut-like leaves, with white woolly linings. *Quercus dentata*, with toothed margins, in one variety cut into narrow fingers almost to the midrib, is notable for the size of its leathery, lustrous leaves. They are often a foot in length. Another Japanese favourite is *Quercus glandulifera*, a half-evergreen shrub, whose chestnut-like leaves are set with glandular teeth. This is half hardy when planted in New England.

228

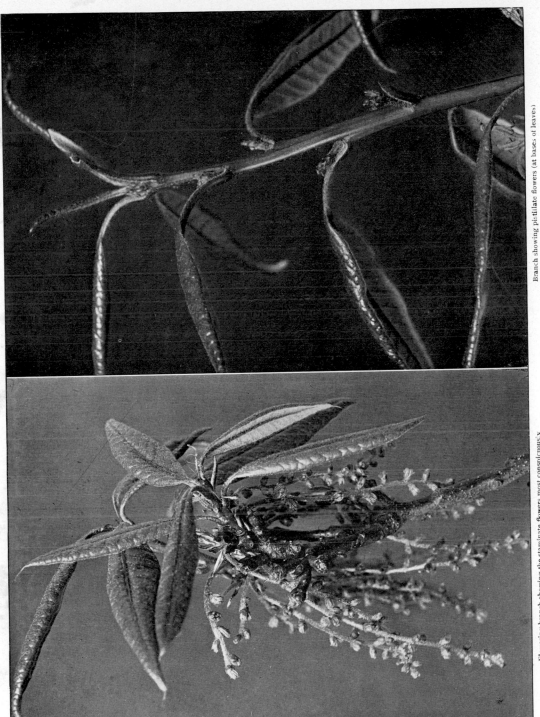

Branch showing pistillate flowers (at bases of leaves)

Flowering branch showing the staminate flowers most conspicuously

THE SHINGLE OAK (*Quercus imbricaria*)

Copious blossoms open with the leaves in May. The young shoots are covered with pink and silver; the leaves are rolled in tight little cylinders at first. The pistillate flowers are paired in the leaf angles. The catkins of stamens are clustered at the base of the season's growth. Half-grown acorns are to be seen below the catkins on side shoots

THE LANCASTER ELM (*Ulmus Americana*)

This noble specimen of our common white elm grows in a field near Lancaster, Massachusetts. The objects around it emphasise its great size. It shows what a roadside tree may become if it is let alone and given time and elbow room. It is the pride of the state it grows in. May the insects spare it long!

CHAPTER XXVIII: THE ELMS AND THE HACKBERRIES

FAMILY ULMACEÆ

1. Genus ULMUS, Linn.

TREES of horticultural and lumber value. *Leaves* alternate serrate, unequal at base, with strong ribs and short petioles *Flowers* greenish, inconspicuous, perfect. *Fruit* a dry nutlet with thin encircling wing, bearing two hooks at apex.

KEY TO SPECIES

A. Blooming before the leaves in spring.
  B. Twigs smooth.
    C. Branches corky winged.
           (*U. alata*) WAHOO or WINGED ELM
    CC. Branches not corky winged.
          (*U. Americana*) AMERICAN or WATER ELM
  BB. Twigs pubescent.
    C. Branches corky.   (*U. Thomasi*) CORK ELM
    CC. Branches not corky; leaves rough above; twigs and
        buds with coarse, rusty hairs.
           (*U. fulva*) SLIPPERY ELM
AA. Blooming late in summer or autumn.
  B. Leaves over 2 inches long, thin. (*U. serotina*) RED ELM
  BB. Leaves 1 to 2 inches long, thick.
          (*U. crassifolia*) CEDAR ELM

2. Genus CELTIS, Linn.

Valuable shade trees. *Leaves* simple, 3-nerved, serrate. *Flowers* polygamo-monœcious, axillary, small. *Fruit* sweet, succulent berry.

A. Leaves coarsely and sharply serrate; fruit large.
          (*C. occidentalis*) HACKBERRY
AA. Leaves entire or obscurely serrate; fruit small.
        (*C. Mississippiensis*) SUGARBERRY

229

3. Genus PLANERA, Gmel.

Water-loving trees of small size. *Leaves* elm-like, small, unsymmetrical. *Flowers* polygamo-monœcious, axillary, small, *Fruit* a dry drupe in crustaceous husk. (*P. aquatica*) PLANER TREE

1. Genus Ulmus, Linn.

The genus Ulmus has sixteen known species, distributed in all north temperate countries except western North America. Five species are native to our Eastern States and one to the Southwest; Europe has three, two of which extend to eastern Asia and northern Africa. Southern and central Asia have representatives. Elms are valuable timber trees, and have always been planted for shade and ornament. Many varieties have arisen in cultivation among the European species. So far the American species have shown few horticultural forms. The elms are distinguished by their simple, unsymmetrical, 2-ranked leaves, and their thin, circular, winged samaras. Their wood is tough, heavy and hard, with interlacing fibres which make it difficult to split.

White Elm, American Elm (*Ulmus Americana*, Linn.)— A tall, graceful, wide-spreading tree, 75 to 125 feet high, usually of symmetrical, vase shape, with slender limbs and pendulous twigs. *Bark* dark or light grey, rough, coarsely ridged; branches grey; twigs reddish brown. *Wood* reddish brown, with pale sap wood; coarse, hard, heavy, strong, cross grained, difficult to split, durable in water and soil. *Buds* acute, flattened, smooth; flower buds lateral, large. *Leaves* alternate, 2 to 6 inches long, obovate, doubly serrate, acuminate, unequal at base; smooth above when mature; ribs parallel. *Flowers*, March, before leaves, on slender, drooping pedicels in umbel-like clusters, perfect, greenish red, inconspicuous. *Fruit*, May, smooth, oval with thin ciliated circular wing, notched above to the nutlet. *Preferred habitat*, rich, moist soil. *Distribution*, Newfoundland to Florida; west to Rocky Mountains. *Uses:* Favourite shade and ornamental tree. Wood used for hubs, saddle trees, barrels and kegs, flooring, in boat and shipbuilding, flumes and piles. Indians used bark for canoes and ropes.

Up and down New England the trolley cars ply in a maze

of systems that becomes more complex every year. Buzzing like insistent and inquisitive bumblebees, they awaken the sleepiest hamlet, haling its inhabitants to the cities and unloading weary, city-bound mortals in the green country. They stir the torpid, stagnant pool of existence; they wake the old nomadic cravings of the primitive race. The most indignant farmer or villager, once he gets thoroughly awake, ceases to grumble; for his feet of clay the trolley gives him the wings of a bird.

I am not an idolater, I hope, and I would chiefly scorn to worship the almighty dollar. But the vast extent of picturesque country one can see for this sum by trolley in New England fills me with a surprise akin to awe.

The striking ornament of New England landscapes is the American elm. The countryside abounds with splendid specimens. They are the pride of cities and villages. Down fine old avenues arched over with their mighty arms the trolley cars take their noisy way. The Westerner stands astonished at the giant size of these trees, and wonders why he cannot match them at home. It is largely a matter of time. In the early days our ancestors took up the trees from the woods and planted them by their roadsides and about their dwellings. Memories of elms at homes—the beautiful *Ulmus campestris* in England and on the Continent—guided their choice. Trees twenty years old were transplanted with safety, for this elm has fibrous roots that keep near the surface of the ground. Then the busy home-makers let the trees alone. They had no time to prune and cultivate. The trees needed no such attention. The roots ranged freely in the virgin soil. The spreading tops were self-pruning—the strong limbs choked the weak ones, keeping an open, symmetrical head. Every year added to the tree's stature. It is a race of giants now, against whom insect hosts have come—the tussock moths, the elm-leaf beetle and the brown tail. No wonder the people have made the fight their own.

The elm is familiar to everybody—its vase-like form is in sight whenever we look out of a window. It grows everywhere east of the Rocky Mountains, and ignorance of it is a mark of indifference or stupidity. No village of any pride but plants it freely as a street tree.

The Etruscan vase form—a base gradually flaring to a round dome—is most common. The trunk soon divides into

231

three or four main limbs with slight but constant divergence as they rise. Their branches follow their example. The divisions are drawn downward by their increasing weight, and the extremities are pendulous, sweeping out and down with loads of foliage, luxuriant, but never heavy looking or ungraceful.

There are narrower elm forms: tall trunks whose limbs form a brush at the top, not unlike a feather duster. Such trees often replace lost outer limbs by a multitude of short leafy twigs, covering the trunks with foliage, thus forming what are known as "feathered elms."

The "oak-tree form"—wider and broader than the vase form—reminds one of the ample crown of an oak. But only the outline is suggestive. The limbs are curved, never angular and tortuous like the oak. Grace rather than strength is invariably the expression of the American elm. In good soil the terminal shoots attain great length, and it is not unusual to see an elm of vase shape with the droop of a weeping willow.

The leaves of the elm are two-ranked, the twigs plume-like. Every chink is filled with a leaf. Break off a branch that faces the sun, and you will be astonished at the twisting and contriving of the leaves, to present an unbroken surface of green. This is known as a "leaf mosaic," and is by no means confined to elms. Any roadside thicket shows the same habit in all its species.

I think, with all due regard for its summer luxuriance, and the grace of its framework in winter, the greatest charm invests the elm of the roadside in the first warm days of spring. The swelling buds are full of promise. A flush of purple overspreads the tree, while snow yet covers the ground. A tremendous "fall of leaves" ensues—for the tiny leaf scales that enclose the elm flowers are but leaves in miniature. The elms are in blossom; they are among the first in the flower procession that silently passes till the witch hazel brings up the rear in October. Then come the little green seeds, winged for flight. These ripen and are scattered before the leaves are open, and the growth of the season's shoots really begins. How much they miss who never see the elms in flower and fruit!

The English elm (*U. campestris*) is a strikingly different tree from its American cousin. Boston Common gives ample opportunity to contrast large specimens of the two species. Dignity is a characteristic of each. Each bears a luxuriant

THE AMERICAN ELM (*Ulmus Americana*)

This elm once had the characteristic fan top. It is "feathering" its trunk and lower limbs with little twigs to replace limbs cut off. The farther tree has had better treatment. The average elm needs no pruning

Winter buds   B. Fruit   A. Flowers not fully open

THE AMERICAN ELM (*Ulmus Americana*)

The leaf is unsymmetrical at the base, and has strong parallel ribs. The winter twigs show plump, blunt flower buds, larger than the slim, pointed leaf buds. In March the flowers appear, giving the bare tree top a warm, purplish colour. The pale-green seeds dangle in profuse clusters in May, falling before the leaves are full grown. Each seed has a circular wing with two incurving hooks at the top. Elm lumber is hard, tough, heavy and cross-grained The bark is grey and divided by deep furrows into scaly ridges

burden of leaves. The Briton is stocky; the American, airily graceful. One stands heavily "upon its heels," the other on tiptoe. One has a compact crown, the other an open, loose one. In October the English elm is still bright, dark green; the American elm has passed into the sere and yellow leaf.

The elm is the favourite tree of the hang bird, or Baltimore oriole, in America. In winter the deserted nests swing from the high outer limbs, where the leaves concealed them in nesting time. The English elm at home is the red-breast's tree. These birds build, not in the upper limbs, but in those that grow down near the trunk, and come earliest into leaf.

Classical literature proves the antiquity and the great importance of the elms of southern Europe. The Romans used elm leaves as forage for cattle. In the vineyards elms were planted to support the vines. The trees were well pruned so they should not overshadow the grapes. It was counted dangerous to give bees freedom to visit blooming elms, lest they become surfeited, and sicken as a result. In this opinion the early observers were evidently mistaken. Virgil discourses upon the successful grafting of oak upon elm, and describes swine eating acorns that dropped from the fruiting branches of this wonderful tree. Experiment long ago proved the fallacy of this report. In England the rustic still watches the elm for signal to sow his grain, relying on the old saw:

"When the elme leaf is as big as a mouse's ear,
Then to sow barley never fear."

The witch hazel (*Hamamelis Virginiana*) does not grow in England, but the wych elm was known in some regions by this name, because its leaf is hazel-like. Long bows were anciently made of its wood, and it was mentioned in the "Statutes of England."

Slippery Elm, Red Elm (*U. fulva*, Michx.)—Fast-growing tree, 60 to 70 feet high, with erect, spreading branches, forming a broad, open head. Twigs stout, rusty, downy. *Bark* brownish, rough, scaly. *Wood* strong, hard, heavy, coarse, reddish brown, durable in soil. *Buds* densely rusty, pubescent; large, blunt. *Leaves* alternate, deciduous, 2-ranked, broadly oval, 4 to 7 inches long, irregularly heart shaped at base, acuminate at apex, doubly serrate, strongly ribbed; on short, stout petiole;

surface rough both ways, stiff, harsh. *Flowers,* April, before leaves, fascicled, numerous, *Fruits,* May, rounded, hairy, only on seed, wing not ciliate, margined. *Preferred habitat,* fertile soil along streams. *Distribution,* lower St. Lawrence River, through Ontario to Dakota and Nebraska; south to Florida; west to Texas. *Uses:* Wood used as fence posts and railroad ties; for wheel hubs, sills and agricultural implements. Mucilaginous inner bark used to allay fever and inflammation.

The slippery elm disregards the laws of symmetry. Each limb strikes out for itself. It is not unusual to find a tree quite one sided in form. Shoots 6 feet in length are often seen as the growth of a single season, where a broken limb gives an ambitious bud a chance. The roughness of its foliage to the touch is one of the striking characteristics of this tree. The leaves are covered with harsh, tubercular hairs, and the crumbling of a leaf grates most unpleasantly on the ear. Then, there is a tawny pubescence on young shoots, and especially on the bud scales of this elm. In winter this is the best distinguishing mark of the red elm. The large flower buds are below the pointed leaf buds on the youngest shoots.

The bark is brownish grey, and rough alike on trunk and branches. Everything, in fact, about the slippery elm seems coarser than in its relatives. The leaves are often 8 to 10 inches long on vigorous shoots.

Under the bark is a mucilaginous, sweet substance that gives this elm its common name. What man lives who in the heydey of youth has not had the spring craze for slippery-elm bark, as surely as he had the chicken pox and the measles! The trees in every fence row show the wounds of many a jack-knife, for in the spring its cambium waxes thick and sweet and fragrant—to growing boys, a delectable substance that allayed both hunger and thirst. Fortunate for the longevity of the individual trees, the bark of the limbs is most easily stripped off, so many a veteran supplies boys to-day, which served as well a former generation. The bark, dried and ground, mixed with milk, forms a valuable food for invalids. Poultices are made of it to relieve throat and chest troubles. It is also useful in allaying fevers and acute inflammatory disorders. This bark, first used as a home remedy, has now an established place on the apothecary's shelf, and is used by physicians of both schools. The problem of the supply

THE SLIPPERY ELM (*Ulmus fulva*)

Note the bud at the tip of the upper twig. Its scales are coated with tawny hairs. The obovate or circular samaras are ripe in May. They are hairy only on the seed body; the wing is smooth. The belated buds produce leafy shoots. The leaves are large and very harsh when crumpled or stroked with the finger. They have the characteristic shape, straight ribs and saw-toothed margin of all elms. The bark is reddish brown and cleft into narrow, loose flakes by shallow fissures

THE ROCK OR CORK ELM (*Ulmus Thomasi*)

This tree has corky ridges on its twigs and shaggy bark on the older limbs. The trunk is deeply and irregularly furrowed. The leaf is small, oval, twice cut-toothed, lustrous and dark above, with soft down below

is a serious one. The tree grows fast and vigorously if only the boys give it a chance. The trees are becoming scarcer each year.

The **Rock** or **Cork Elm** (*Ulmus Thomasi*, Sarg.) has shaggy stout limbs like a bur oak's, and a rugged, stiff expression quite unusual in an elm. A look at the foliage is reassuring, for elm leaves vary but slightly in the different species. In spring the type of inflorescence is the best botanical character to depend upon.

The cork elm was discovered in the woods of western New York by David Thomas, who noted its corky bark and habit of bearing its flowers and fruit in racemes. He named the species *Ulmus racemosa*, as was most reasonable. It was discovered later that this name had previously been applied to a European corky elm; whereupon the name of its discoverer was substituted.

"Rock elm" and "hickory elm" refer to the hardness of its wood. It has in greater degree the good qualities of white elm lumber, and is counted the best of all elms by the wheelwright. Compact, with interlacing fibres, there is spring, strength and toughness in this wood which adapts it for bridge timbers, heavy agricultural implements, wheel stocks, sills, railroad ties and axe handles.

The best trees, 60 to 90 feet high, with trunks 2 to 3 feet through, grow in dry soil in lower Ontario and Michigan. The species occurs also in scattered localities west to Nebraska and Tennessee, and east as far as Vermont.

The **Winged Elm**, or **Wahoo** (*U. alata*, Michx.), is not an important timber tree, though its wood is used in the localities where it grows. Its leaves and the two thin, corky blades that arise on the branches are dainty, as befits the smallest of the elm trees. There is none of the ruggedness of the cork elm in the appearance of this pretty, round-headed tree. It rarely grows over 40 feet high, and is distributed from Virginia to Florida, and west to Illinois and Texas. Its small, winged samaras are each prolonged into two prominent incurving hooks at the apex. They hang in pendulous racemes. The tree is occasionally planted for shade in Southern cities, but it is not hardy in the North. "Wahoo" seems to be a term rather indiscriminately applied to elm trees in sections of the South. "Mountain elm" and "small-leaved elm" are significant popular names.

Two elms have leathery, almost evergreen leaves, and

235

bloom very late in the summer. One, found in Georgia and Tennessee, was confused with *U. Thomasi* until its flowers were found opening in the axils of the season's leaves in the month of September! This discovery set it apart as a separate species, and it was named from its red-brown wood, the **Red Elm** (*U. serotina*), by Professor Sargent. The specific name means *late*.

The **Cedar Elm** (*U. crassifolia*, Nutt.), of Arkansas, Texas and Mississippi, blooms in August. Occasionally this tree reaches a height of 80 feet, with broad, spreading limbs and slender, pendulous branches. It is a beautiful, graceful tree; its tiny leaves, close set on the winged twigs, form a dense head of lustrous foliage. Occasionally a second crop of flowers appears in October.

There seems to be no better reason for its common name than that it grows with cedars on the dry limestone hills of Texas. It is the common elm tree of that great state, and is sometimes planted as a shade tree. Its lumber is used for fencing and for wheel hubs, the better qualities being cut in the moist lowlands. In dryer situations it is scarcely worth cutting even for fuel.

2. Genus CELTIS, Linn.

The hackberries include fifty or sixty tropical and temperate zone species. Two are trees in North America, but future investigations may still further divide the group. They are trees of considerable value for shade and ornamental planting. Beside the two natives, three exotic species are in cultivation in the south, and a hardy Japanese species farther north. Of the former, one is from South Africa, one from the Mediterranean basin, and the third from China and Japan.

Hackberry, Nettle Tree, Sugar Berry (*Celtis occidentalis*, Linn.)—Tree, 50 to 125 feet, with slender trunk and round head, of very slender, bushy twigs and pendulous branches. *Bark* light brown or pale grey, broken into thick warts or scales by deep furrows; branches often corrugated and warty. *Wood* light yellow, heavy, soft, coarse, weak. *Buds* axillary, never terminal; acute, ovate, small. *Leaves* simple, alternate, ovate, $2\frac{1}{2}$ to 4 inches long, often fulcate, oblique at base, serrate above widest part, entire below it; thin, deep green, with downy lining; 3-nerved, from slim petiole; autumn colour yellow. *Flowers*, May, monœcious,

236

or mixed, greenish, axillary staminate, clustered at base of season's shoot; pistillate solitary, in axils of leaves, green, with spreading, 2-horned stigma. *Fruits*, September, oblong, thin, fleshed berry, $\frac{1}{4}$ to $\frac{1}{2}$ inch long, purple, sweet; hangs all winter. *Preferred habitat*, moist soil along streams or marshes. *Distribution*, Southern Canada west to Puget Sound; south to Florida, Tennessee, Missouri, Texas and New Mexico. *Uses:* Planted for shade and ornament. Wood used for cheap furniture and fencing.

It is easy to mistake the hackberry for an elm. The habit of the two trees leads the casual observer astray. It takes a second look to note the finer spray of the hackberry twigs, its more horizontal, less drooping branches. The warty bark is characteristic. The little axillary sugar berries are very different from elm samaras. There are few months in the year when fruits are not to be found, green or ripe, on the tree. They are the delight of birds throughout hard winters. A peculiarity of the foliage is the apparent division of the petiole into three ribs instead of a single midrib. Otherwise the leaf is elm-like, though smaller and brighter green than that of the American elm.

The hackberry is not familiarly known by people in the regions where it grows. Else it would be transplanted more commonly to adorn private premises and to shade village streets. There is no danger in digging up well-grown trees, for the roots are fibrous and shallow, and carry an abundance of soil with them.

The beauty of the hackberry's graceful crown is sometimes marred by a fungus which produces a thick tufting of twigs at the ends of branches. These are called "witches' brooms." Growths of similar appearance are produced by insects on other trees.

Celtis Mississippiensis, Bosc., is the warty-barked, round-topped hackberry of the Ohio and Mississippi valleys; a graceful tree, and much like *C. occidentalis*, but smaller. Its leaves are narrow and entire on the margins. The warts of its bark are very noticeable. The berries are orange red. This tree is quite as worthy of cultivation as its larger relative, and the people of Texas know it. The chief virtue of this species as a shade tree is that its foliage hangs on, with little dimming of its brightness, to the very edge of winter.

The European nettle tree (*C. Australis*) is supposed to have been the famous lotus of classical literature. Homer tells of the lotus eaters, who, when they tasted the sweet fruit, straightway forgot their native land, or could not be persuaded to return.

This innocent little tree, against which this charge has never been proved, bears a better reputation for the qualities of its wood. It is as hard as box or holly, and looks like satinwood when polished. Figures of saints and other images are carved out of it. Hay forks are made of its supple limbs. Rocky, worthless land is set apart by law for the growing of these trees. A seven-acre tract in the south of France yielded, according to Landon, 60,000 hay forks per annum, worth $5,000! Suckers from the roots, cut while small, make admirable ramrods, coach whip stocks, and walking sticks. Shafts and axle trees of carriages are made of the larger sticks; oars and hoops from these coppiced trees. This tree is widely scattered, from northern Africa through Europe, and on to India, where it is a shade tree and is planted for its leaves, which furnish fodder for cattle.

3. Genus PLANERA, Gmel.

Planer Tree, Water Elm (*Planera aquatica*, Gmel.)—Small tree, 30 to 40 feet high, with short trunk and slender, crooked branches forming a low, round crown. Twigs reddish. *Bark* thin, scaly, grey; inner layers red. *Wood* light, soft, fine grained, brown. *Buds* small, ovoid, scaly. *Leaves*, February to March; dull green, paler beneath, 2-ranked, elm-like, 2 to $2\frac{1}{2}$ inches long, unilateral. *Flowers* with leaves, monœcious or polygamous, axillary, in fascicles, small. *Fruit* 1-seeded drupe in dry, thin, horny, pericarp; seed shiny, black. *Preferred habitat*, inundated swamps. *Distribution*, North Carolina to Florida; west to Missouri and Texas. Rare.

This tree is interesting chiefly as a botanical remnant of its family. Several species of this genus once grew in Alaska and in the Rocky Mountains. Closely related forms are preserved in the tertiary rocks in Europe.

A. Pistillate flower   B. Staminate flower

THE HACKBERRY (*Celtis occidentalis*)

The leaf has three midribs instead of one, and many swollen, reticulated veins. Note the wide-spreading stigmas of the solitary axillary fertile flowers. The staminate flowers cluster at the base of the twig. The sweet, 1-seeded berries ripen to dark purple in late September and hang all winter, to the delight of the birds. Strange, warty excrescences are on the bark of trunks and limbs. The second trunk is of the smaller species, *Celtis Mississippiensis.* The third is var. *reticulata* of the latter species

THE RED MULBERRY (*Morus rubra*)

The short trunk sustains a broad crown of ascending limbs with zigzag twigs. The leaves are bluish green and thin. A complex system of ribs and veinlets make a prominent network of the leaf linings, and roughen the upper surfaces. The berries are purple and pleasantly sweet

CHAPTER XXIX: THE MULBERRIES, THE OSAGE ORANGE AND THE FIGS

FAMILY MORACEÆ

TREES of small or medium size, with milky sap. *Leaves* simple, alternate, deciduous, variable. *Flowers* minute, in axillary spikes or heads, diœcious or monœcious. *Fruit* compound, of many small fleshy drupes.

KEY TO GENERA AND SPECIES

A. Leaves toothed or lobed, with swollen, netted veins; fruit an edible, oblong berry.
    1. Genus MORUS, Linn.
  B. Fruit purple; leaves 3 to 5 inches long.
      (*M. rubra*) RED MULBERRY
  BB. Fruit black; leaves 1 to 2 inches long.
      (*M. celtidifolia*) MEXICAN MULBERRY
AA. Leaves entire; fruit globular.
  B. Fruit 4 to 5 inches in diameter, inedible.
    2. Genus TOXYLON, Raf.
      (*T. pomiferum*) OSAGE ORANGE
  BB. Fruit size of pea, ovate; tree habit parasitic.
    3. Genus FICUS, Linn.
    C. Leaves thick, yellow-green; fruit short stemmed.
      (*F. aurea*) GOLDEN FIG
    CC. Leaves thin, dark green, fruit long-stemmed.
      (*F. populnea*) POPLAR-LEAF FIG

The mulberry family comprises 55 genera and 925 species of temperate zone and tropical plants, of which the fig, genus Ficus, includes 600 species. The hemp, important for its fibrous inner bark, and the hop, are well known herbaceous members of the mulberry family. Hemp is a native of Europe and Asia, but has run wild here, and is now in cultivation throughout both temperate zones. Hops are used in the brewing of beer, and in the Old World as well as the New are raised as a staple field crop. The plant is native to both hemispheres.

Botanically, the mulberry family lies between the elms and nettles—strange company, but justified by fundamental characteristics. Three genera of this family have tree forms in America: Morus, the mulberry; Toxylon, the osage orange; and Ficus, the fig. Two native species of mulberry and three exotic species are generally cultivated for their fruit, their wood, and as ornamental trees. Weeping forms are much planted.

1. Genus MORUS, Linn.

Red Mulberry (*Morus rubra*, Linn.)—Large tree, 60 to 70 feet high, with dense, round head, fibrous roots and milky juice. *Bark* light brown, reddish, dividing into scaly plates; branches reddish; twigs grey, downy. *Wood* orange yellow, light, coarse grained, soft, weak, very durable in soil. *Buds* ovate, blunt, small. *Leaves* alternate, variable in form, 3 to 5 inches long, broad, acuminate, serrate, very veiny, often lobed and palmately veined; usually rough, blue-green above, pale and pubescent beneath, yellow in early autumn; petioles stout, long. *Flowers* monœcious or diœcious, variable, in stalked, axillary spikes, staminate flowers with flat, 4-lobed calyx and 4 incurved stamens that spread suddenly and lie flat on calyx, forming a cross as they mature; pistillate flower, a vase-shaped, 4-lobed calyx, with two stigmas protruding. *Fruit* fleshy calyx lobes, surrounding single seed; whole spike unites to form an aggregate fruit, sweet, juicy, dark purplish red. *Preferred habitat*, rich well-drained soil. *Distribution*, western Massachusetts to southern Ontario, Michigan, Nebraska, Kansas; south to Florida and Texas. *Uses:* Wood used in cooperage and for fencing. A worthy tree for ornament, but rarely planted.

The Chinese mulberry (*Morus alba*), with white fruit, holds a unique economic position, as its leaves are the chosen food of silkworms. No substitute has ever robbed this tree of its pre-eminence maintained for centuries, in its own field of usefulness. The hardy Russian mulberries are derived from *Morus alba*.

The red mulberry, discovered in Virginia in great abundance, inflamed the minds of early colonists who counted it one of the chief resources of the colony. A tree "apt to feede Silke-worms to make silke" promised truly "a commoditie not meanely profit-

240

able" in a new colony—made up of gentlemen. A Frenchman, reporting the abundance of these trees, mentions "some so large that one tree contains as many leaves as will feed *Silke-wormes* that will make as much *silk* as may be worth five pounds *sterling* money." But their sanguine hopes were not realised. The red mulberry is no substitute for the white species. Silk culture is still an Old World industry, even though white mulberries grow in this country.

Indians discovered that ropes and a coarse cloth could be woven out of the bast fibre of mulberry bark. The berries have some medicinal properties, and are eagerly devoured by hogs and poultry. The chief value of the tree lies in the durability of its wood, which commends it to the boatbuilder, the cooper, and to the man with fences to build.

One of the mulberry's chief characteristics is its tenacity to life. Its seeds readily germinate, and cuttings strike quickly, whether from roots or stems. Evelyn's instructions for propagating the European mulberry by cuttings are quaint and worth hearing. "They will root infallibly, especially if you twist the old wood a little or at least hack it; though some slit the foot, inserting a stone or grain of an oat to suckle and entertain the plant with moisture."

The **Mexican Mulberry** (*M. celtidifolia*, H.B.K.), with small, ovate leaves, somewhat like the hackberry's, and small black fruit, is found from western Texas to Arizona, and follows the mountains to Peru and Ecuador. It is a small tree whose wood furnished the early Indians with bows; and the Mexican often sets it out in his garden, for the inferior fruit is grateful in the hot, dry sections where berries are scarce.

The **Black Mulberry** (*M. nigra*), native of Persia, is the one cultivated in Europe for its fruit. It is occasionally grown in California and the Southern States, but is not hardy in the North. It has its name from its dark red, fleshy fruit, as well as its sombre foliage.

No mulberry is ranked among profitable fruit trees. The berries rarely appear in the markets, though the trees are common in gardens. The fruits are too sweet, and they lack piquancy of flavour. They ripen a few at a time, and may be gathered on sheets by shaking the trees. Planted in hog pastures, the fruit is highly appreciated as it falls. As an attraction for birds the tree justifies planting in towns, and in country yards and gardens. Some of our most desirable song birds build near mulberry trees which promise summer fruit for their families. When a bird basin is added with promise of water supply for drink and bath, the place will be chosen by many birds.

The **Paper Mulberry** (*Broussonetia papyrifera*, Vent.) is one of two or three oriental species of its genus. Its inner bark has long furnished a good grade of paper in its own country, Japan. In the United States it has a southern range, and is an ornamental of considerable popularity owing to the luxuriance of its foliage. But as a street tree it is less planted than formerly, for its habit of throwing up suckers makes it troublesome. It has escaped from cultivation in many places. In sheltered situations it is hardy to the city of New York.

2. Genus TOXYLON, Raf.

Osage Orange (*Toxylon pomiferum*, Raf.)—Handsome, round-headed tree, 40 to 60 feet high, with short trunk, sharp spines, fleshy roots and milky, bitter sap. *Bark* dark, scaly deeply furrowed; branches orange brown; twigs pubescent, *Wood* orange-yellow, hard, heavy, flexible, strong, durable in soil. takes fine polish. *Buds* sunk deep in twigs, blunt, all lateral; *Leaves* alternate, simple, 3 to 5 inches long, ovate, entire, taper. pointed, thick, dark green, polished above, paler and dull beneath, yellow in autumn; petioles slim, hairy, grooved; thorns axillary. *Flowers* diœcious, in June; staminate small, in peduncled racemes, terminal on leafy spur of previous season; greenish; pistillate in globular, many-flowered heads, axillary. *Fruit* globular, 4 to 5 inches in diameter, green, compound by union of 1-seeded drupes, which are filled with milky juice; seed oblong. *Preferred habitat*, deep, rich soil. *Distribution*, southern Arkansas, southeastern Indian Territory and southern Texas. Naturalised widely. *Uses:* Indians used wood for bows and clubs. Now used for posts, piles, telegraph poles, paving blocks, railroad ties; sometimes for interior woodwork of houses. Trees planted in parks and grounds for shade and ornament, also for hedges. Roots and bark yield yellow dye and tannic acid.

The Osage orange hedge marked one period in the pioneer's

work of taming the wilds of the Middle West. Farms had to be enclosed. Board fences were too costly, and were continually needing repairs. Fencing with wire was new and ineffectual, for barbed wire had not yet come into use; so hedges were planted far and wide. The nurserymen reaped a harvest, for this tree grows from cuttings of root or branch. All that is needed is to hack a tree to bits and put them into the ground; each fragment takes root and sends up a flourishing shoot.

It is a pity that this stock mostly came direct from Arkansas and Texas. A cold winter with little snow killed miles of thrifty hedge, just as it reached the useful stage. Sometimes the roots sent up new shoots, sometimes they didn't, and gaps of varying widths spoiled the appearance and the effectiveness of hedges throughout Illinois, Iowa, Missouri and Kansas. Then barbed wire was introduced, and wicked as it was, it defended the growing crops from free-ranging cattle as no other fencing had done. In most places the hedges were let alone on farm boundaries. These old hedgerows have become an important source of fence posts. No timber furnishes better ones. A row often produces twenty-five posts to the rod. These bring from 10 cents to 20 cents each in local markets, a fact which makes them a very profitable crop. The native Osage orange timber is all exhausted now; and as the old hedgerows are passing, systematically maintained plantations of Osage orange, grown for posts, promise to pay increasingly well. They ought to be largely planted in the tree's natural range. Occasionally a remnant of the first planting is met with as a fine roadside tree, glorious in its lustrous foliage, formidable thorns, and the remarkable green oranges that hang on the fruiting trees. It is a tree well worth planting for both ornament and shade, for it harbours few insects and has withal a unique character. It is a "foreign-looking" tree.

I had a personal experience with the Osage orange. "The leaves are food for silkworms"—so the nurseryman had told us— and we could have silkworms' eggs from Washington for the asking. Now, gingham aprons were the prevailing fashion for little girls on the Iowa prairies—princesses in fairy tales seemed to wear silks and satins with no particular care as to where they came from. Silkworms and Osage orange offered a combination, and suggested possibilities, which set our imaginations on fire. Lettuce leaves sufficed for the young caterpillars—then the little mulberry

243

bushes, but the lusty white worms so ghastly naked and dreadful to see, and so ravenous, we fed with Osage orange leaves, cut at the risk of much damage from ugly thorns and with much weariness. But what were present discomforts compared with the excellency of the hope set before us! Not Solomon in all his glory was arrayed as we expected to be. And the worms—while we loathed them, we counted them, and ministered to their needs.

At last our labours ended. They began to spin, and soon the denuded twigs were thickly studded with the yellow cerements of the translated larvæ, to the relief and wonder of all concerned. But even as we wondered, the dead twigs blossomed with white moths whose beauty and tremulous motion passed description. We were lifted into a state of exaltation by the spectacle.

"Whom the gods would destroy they first make mad." A hard-hearted but well-informed neighbour told us that the broken cocoons were worthless for silk. "You'd ought to have scalded 'em as soon as they spun up." Clouds and thick darkness shut out the day. We refused to be comforted.

This explains why the mere mention of the Osage orange tree, or the sight of a hedge, however thrifty, brings to my mind a haunting suggestion "of old unhappy far-off things."

3. Genus FICUS, Linn.

Figs belong to a genus of 600 species scattered over all tropical countries. The trees have peculiar flowers lining the inside of a fleshy receptacle so that the "fig wasps" that fertilise them have to crawl in through a small opening.

Dried figs are an important commercial fruit. These are from varieties of *Ficus Carica*, an Asiatic species. Smyrna figs are best for drying. They are extensively raised in California, and cured for market. Other varieties, better adapted for use as a fresh fruit, are grown in many Southern States. The figs we buy are mostly from Asia Minor. The dependence of the fig upon the ministrations of the little wasp is one of the most interesting and baffling chapters in the romance of science.

The rubber plant, vastly popular in this country as a pot plant, is a Ficus. So is the famous banyan tree of India, and the

THE OSAGE ORANGE (*Toxylon pomiferum*)

This handsome hedge tree has stout thorns and foliage of unusual lustre. The staminate flowers are borne in loose, head-like racemes. The pistillate flowers are in globular heads. They appear in June, after the leaves, on separate trees. The green, orange-like fruit is 4 to 5 inches in diameter, with many seeds and bitter, milky juice. The wood is very durable in contact with the soil

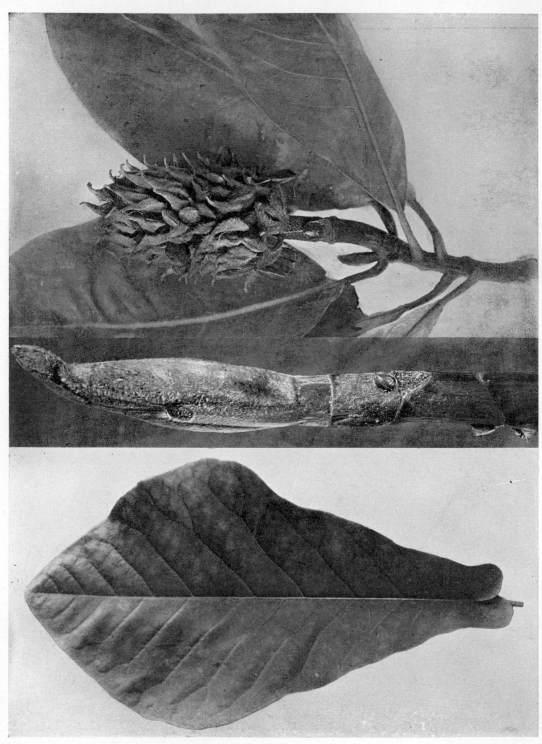

THE GREAT LAUREL MAGNOLIA (*Magnolia fœtida*)

The cone of furry capsules stands erect among the ever-green leaves. The scarlet seeds are hung out on elastic white threads until the wind carries them away

THE LARGE-LEAVED CUCUMBER TREE (*Magnolia macrophylla*)

The buds are stout and often two inches long. They are coated with silvery white hairs. The wrapping is the stipule, which falls in spring

THE EAR-LEAVED MAGNOLIA (*Magnolia Fraseri*)

The leaf of this tree has two ear-like lobes at the base. They broaden toward the apex, and are almost a foot long

sacred peepul tree of the Hindoos. Our native fig trees are sprawling parasitic forms, unable to stand alone.

The **Golden Fig** (*F. aurea*, Nutt.) climbs up another tree, which it strangles with its coiling stems and aërial roots. There is a famous specimen tree on one of the islands of southern Florida, which has spread by striking root with its drooping branches until it now covers with its secondary trunks an area of a quarter of an acre. It looks much like a banyan tree. More often in South Florida one sees this tree with a sturdy single trunk which has swallowed up the parasite that supported it in youth. Smooth as a beech trunk, with a crown of foliage more glossy than the live oak, this is a large and beautiful tree. The little yellow figs snuggle in the axils of the leaves and turn purple when ripe. They are succulent and sweet, and are sometimes used for jams and preserves.

Another interesting thing about *Ficus aurea* is that its wood is lighter than that of any other native tree. Its specific gravity is 0.26, which means that, bulk for bulk, this substance is only one-fourth as heavy as water. Most of our woods range between 0.40 and 0.80. The heaviest wood belongs also to a Florida tree, *Krugiodendron ferreum*, Urb., whose specific gravity, when seasoned, is 1.302.

The **Poplar-leaf Fig** (*F. populnea*, Willd.) is a rare parasite clambering up other trees on coral islands and reefs off the southernmost coast of Florida. Its thin, dark green leaves and long-stemmed fruits distinguish it from its near relative.

CHAPTER XXX: THE MAGNOLIAS AND THE TULIP TREE

FAMILY MAGNOLIACEÆ

TREES with soft, light wood, and fleshy roots. *Leaves* large, simple, alternate, entire. *Flowers* large, showy, perfect, solitary, terminal, all parts distinct. *Fruit* cone-like, compound, of many 1 to 2 celled follicles or keys imbricated upon a central spike.

KEY TO GENERA AND SPECIES

A. Leaves pointed at apex; seeds scarlet, berry-like.

    1. Genus MAGNOLIA, Linn.

  B. Foliage evergreen or nearly so.
    C. Leaf linings rusty pubescent. (*M. fœtida*) MAGNOLIA
    CC. Leaf linings silvery, smooth.

                (*M. glauca*) SWAMP MAGNOLIA

  BB. Foliage deciduous.
    C. Leaves scattered along branchlets.
      D. Flowers large, white; leaves 15 to 30 inches long.
        (*M. macrophylla*) LARGE-LEAVED CUCUMBER TREE
      DD. Flowers small, yellowish green; leaves 6 to 10 inches long. (*M. acuminata*) CUCUMBER TREE
    CC. Leaves in whorls on ends of branchlets.
      D. Bases of leaves tapering; calyx turned back.

            (*M. tripetala*) UMBRELLA TREE
      DD. Bases of leaves broadened into ear-like lobes; calyx not turned back.
          (*M. Fraseri*) MOUNTAIN MAGNOLIA
AA. Leaves cut off square at apex; seeds dry, in winged samaras.

    2. Genus LIRIODENDRON, Linn.

          (*L. Tulipifera*) TULIP TREE

1. Genus MAGNOLIA, Linn.

The magnolias include twenty species; twelve are found in eastern and southern Asia, two in Mexico, six in eastern North

America. Splendid as they are, tropical in foliage and magnificent in flower compared with everyday forest trees, the family is to-day but a shadow of its preglacial greatness. Forests of magnolias flourished in the midcontinental plains of Europe and America, extending northward even to within the Arctic circle. Fossil forests, uncovered by erosion and by volcanic forces that seam and split mountains apart, reveal the trunks and even the leaves and seed cones of these ancient trees. Amethyst Mountain, in Yellowstone Park, has such a story to tell, and European geologists can match it. Even in its decline, the magnolia family holds first rank among the ornamental trees of the North Temperate zone.

Magnolias are of peculiar interest because they have the largest flowers of any trees in cultivation. This is not saying that they are the showiest trees when in blossom, for an apple tree or a flowering dogwood may completely cover itself with blossoms. But the individual flowers of such trees are relatively small, while a magnolia blossom is often 6 inches, and sometimes a foot in diameter. Magnolias have several other points which make them a most attractive group; certain kinds bloom before the leaves in early spring; the flowers of most sorts are deliciously fragrant; the texture of the petals is notable, being thick, waxy and lustrous, and the colouring is exquisite. In many species the leaves are of extraordinary size, some exceeding a yard in length. In all, the foliage mass is luxuriant and tropical looking. Some have shining, leathery evergreen leaves—just the thing for Christmas decorations. Last, but not least, there are the curious cone-like fruits which make the trees so attractive in midsummer and autumn. As they ripen they take on rosy tints, and later they open in a peculiarly interesting fashion, and hang out their scarlet seeds on slender, elastic threads.

Magnolias are not hard to grow. The essential thing is to choose the right kinds and to put them in the best locations. As they are, first and last, ornamental trees and shrubs, they are usually grown as single specimens on lawns, and the placing of them is important. Such a tree should have room enough to attain its full development. A solid mass of evergreens is the most effective background for a fine symmetrical specimen, especially when it is in bloom. The soil should be rich and well

247

drained, with good supply of moisture, for these trees are heavy feeders.

Magnolias can be obtained from nurserymen as lusty young trees ready for transplanting. They cost from 75 cents to $1.50. There are both native and exotic kinds for North and South. I would strongly urge everyone to refrain from taking young magnolias from the woods. They are scarce enough there, and transplanting such trees requires more than a general knowledge of such work. It is much better to leave them where they are.

Magnolia, Great Laurel Magnolia (*Magnolia fœtida*, Sarg.) —A regular, conical tree, 50 to 80 feet high; trunk 2 to 4 feet in diameter; branches, strict, ascending. *Bark* thin, scaly, light brown or grey; on branches, smooth, pale grey. *Wood* hard, close grained, heavy, cream coloured turning to brown. *Buds* rusty pubescent, scaly; terminal, 1 to 1½ inches long. *Leaves* alternate, oval, 5 to 8 inches long, leathery, shining above, lined with rusty down, or smooth and dull green; persistent until second spring. *Flowers*, April to August; white, cup shaped, 6 to 8 inches across when spread; fragrant; solitary on end of twig; sepals three, petal-like; petals thick, waxen, 6 to 9; stamens, many, purple at base; pistils, many, crowded. *Fruit*, a rusty brown, oval cone, 3 to 4 inches long, pubescent; seeds flat, red, two in each cell, hung out on threads; ripe in November. *Preferred habitat*, rich, moist soil; swamp borders or river banks; sometimes on uplands. *Distribution*, North Carolina coast to Florida (Mosquito Inlet and Tampa Bay), west along Gulf coast to Brazos River Valley in Texas; north along Mississippi bluffs and bayous into northern Louisiana and southern Arkansas. *Uses:* Superb ornamental tree, hardy to Philadelphia. Branches cut for Christmas decorations. Wood used for fuel.

The magnolia that Linnæus named *grandiflora* is a kingly tree. It is not graceful, for its limbs are stiffly erect. Even the twigs and leaves are stiff, and in blossom the tree is like a great system of candelabra, each terminal bud containing a single flower. But look at a fine specimen tree as it stands in a Southern garden new-washed by a night rain. Each leaf of the dark pyramid of green reflects the sunlight like a blade of polished metal. This lustrous foliage mass is just the foil to set off the purity of the white flowers. Each is like a great camellia or a water lily, with waxen petals, enclosing the purple heart.   William Bartram likened them to great white roses, and declared that he could see them distinctly a mile away.   The blossoms, when fully open, are from 7 to 8 inches across, as a rule.   There is a horticultural variety called *gloriosa*, the flowers of which Mr. Berckmanns says are 14 inches in diameter.   In southern California there are double and ever-blooming varieties exploited by nurserymen, and there are no more popular ornamental trees than these.   Unfortunately, this magnolia has one drawback—its flowers have a heavy odour which is disagreeable to many people. Another is this: They cannot be shipped as cut flowers, for the slightest bruise of the waxy petals produces a brownish discolouration.   This is the species that furnishes the splendid evergreen foliage that is shipped North for Christmas decoration, and is used for similar purposes in the South.   The upper surface of each leaf is a dark, lustrous green; the lining of rusty-red fuzz is shed when the leaf is old.   Negroes go into the woods and cut down large trees and small to strip them of their leafy branches.

The comparative uselessness of its wood has until now been the saving of the species.   This new industry already threatens its extermination in many sections of the South.

In cultivation this magnolia is oftenest seen as a small tree, from 20 to 50 feet high, planted on lawns and in parks or lining avenues.   In the forests of Louisiana, where it reaches its greatest perfection, it stands 80 feet high, with a trunk 4 feet thick. Professor Sargent calls it "the most splendid ornamental tree in the American forests."

The **Swamp Bay** (*Magnolia glauca*, Linn.)—A splendid tree 50 to 75 feet high, or a shrub of many stems. *Bark* grey or brown, smooth. *Wood* soft, pale reddish brown, weak. *Buds* silky, $\frac{1}{4}$ to $\frac{3}{4}$ inch long. *Leaves* persistent in the South, deciduous in the North; smooth, lustrous, bright green, with silvery lining minutely hairy; blades oblong-lanceolate or ovate, 4 to 6 inches long, blunt at apex and base, margin entire, petiole short, stout. *Flowers* globular, 2 to 3 inches across when spread, creamy white, fragrant, of 9 to 12 broad concave petals. *Fruit* oval, dark red, smooth, $1\frac{1}{2}$ to 2 inches long; seeds $\frac{1}{4}$ inch long, flattened. *Preferred habitat*, swamps and pine-barren ponds. *Distribution*, Florida to Texas and Arkansas; north along Atlantic coast to

New York; isolated stations in Suffolk County, Long Island, and near Gloucester, Massachusetts. *Uses:* Valuable ornamental tree or shrub in American and European gardens. Branches sold for decoration of houses and churches. Cut flowers hawked on city streets. Wood used for broom handles and for small wooden utensils.

The swamp bay is remarkable for its range, which extends from Gloucester, Massachusetts, to Florida, and westward to lower Arkansas and the Trinity River in Texas. On the rich "hammocks" elevated above the cypress swamps and pine forests of middle Florida this magnolia is a tree of slender trunk but often 50 to 75 feet high. Leaves, flowers and fruit proclaim it a magnolia. The smooth, silvery linings distinguish the leaves from those of the other evergreen magnolia. The small globular flowers and the smooth, diminutive fruits further identify it. From Bay Biscayne northward along the coast, following the pine barrens and swamp borders, this fugitive species becomes gradually dwarfed and its leaves become deciduous. In New Jersey it is a shrub, vigorous and tropical looking, for the region, but very unlike the sub-tropical representatives of the species. On Long Island there is a station of this bay in Suffolk County. A few remaining plants are known still to exist in a swamp near Gloucester, Massachusetts, the only place north of the latitude of New York which has any recollection of native magnolias growing wild near by. I wandered through that Gloucester swamp, just east of the station named Magnolia, in a vain quest for the remnant of the colony. I was told that the only person who knew where the survivors grew was "the Hermit," who formerly made his living by digging up young plants and selling them. Thrifty garden specimens in Gloucester and other points on Cape Ann came originally out of this swamp. The colony is now practically extinct.

Swamp bay flowers are globular and small for a magnolia—only two or three inches across—but delightfully fragrant.

One of the sights on the streets of Philadelphia and New York in May is the street Arab hawking the blossom clusters. A flower with a half-open bud in its whorl of leaves costs ten cents. An absurd custom prevails among these flower venders. They "open" the globular blossoms by springing back the curved petals. The finest flowers are produced by cutting back

SWAMP MAGNOLIA (*Magnolia glauca*)

Upper one is the seed pod and seed

the tree and letting the suckers grow up thickly around the stump. These bear flowers of unusual size, and clean, handsome leaves.

Professor Gifford recommends the systematic planting of swamp lands in New Jersey to this species of magnolia as a profitable enterprise. He would prune with care, so as to produce the finest leaves and flowers. The blooming period covers several weeks. Cut flowers and leafy branches command good prices in the markets. Waste land near large cities can be transformed and beautified by this means, and become a source of income to the owners at small outlay. The prunings are salable for house decoration at holiday time.

The swamp bay is also called white bay, sweet bay and beaver tree. Beavers used its soft wood for their lodges in earlier times. The English call it laurel magnolia.

Sweet bay it is called because its foliage is somewhat like that of the bay tree of the Old World, which is commonly grown in tubs by florists and is much used in this country for porch decoration. This is *Laurus nobilis*, the "laurel" of the ancients. The sweet bay of the swamps grows well in gardens if only the soil is moist. But it is safer and in every way more desirable to get plants of it from nurserymen.

Large-leaved Cucumber Tree (*Magnolia macrophylla*, Michx.)—A broad, round-headed tree, 30 to 50 feet high, with slender trunk and stout branches. *Bark* thin, smooth, grey, minutely scaly. *Wood* light, close textured, pale brown, weak; sap wood thick, yellow. *Buds* terminal, $1\frac{1}{2}$ to 2 inches long, blunt, covered with white silky hair; axillary small, flat. *Leaves* 16 to 30 inches long, obovate, rounded or acute at apex, broadened at base into ear-like lobes, or deeply cordate, margin entire; upper surface bright green, lining silvery white; petioles stout, 3 to 4 inches long, veins prominent. *Flowers* 10 to 12 inches across, bowl shaped, made of 6 white fleshy petals much broader than the 3 sepals. Inner petals with purple spot at base. *Fruit* almost globular, 2 to 3 inches long, turning red at maturity. Seeds $\frac{2}{3}$ inch long. *Preferred habitat*, deep, fertile valleys, protected from wind. *Distribution*, foot hills of Alleghany Mountains in North Carolina, south to middle Florida, and west to southern Alabama, to northern Mississippi and Louisiana, and in central Arkansas; range not continuous, trees occur in small, detached groups.

251

Uses: Cultivated as an ornamental tree in Europe and America. Hardy to Boston.

This species excels all other magnolias in the size of its leaves and flowers. The leaves are almost a yard long. In fact, no tree of simple leaf approaches it outside of the tropics. It is the remarkable size of its leaves and flowers that commends this tree to planters. Of beauty we cannot credit it with quality to match its size. A flower as big as a man's head is sure to be lacking in delicacy. There is a dash of purple at the base of the inner row of petals. The wind lashes the broad leaves into ribbons early in summer, and every twig or leaf that touches a petal mars it with a brown bruise. So the flowers soon spread wide open and become discoloured. Two fine young specimens stand in front of the Museum of the Arnold Arboretum, Boston. The protection of the building and the border planting are not sufficient to defend these trees from the common fate of all plants which offer an unusual expanse of leaf surface in a region where winds are frequent and strong. Though but a dozen feet high these trees have already bloomed freely. The silvery leaf linings tend to obscure the white flowers in spite of their extraordinary size.

People who desire to plant this magnolia do well to shelter it from wind and cold. At best it is but half hardy in the North. It is a curiosity. Prominent situations are better filled by species of tried hardiness, whose beauty is admitted to be a joy at any season.

Cucumber Tree (*Magnolia acuminata*, Linn.)—Pyramidal tree of spreading habit, 60 to 100 feet high, with trunk 3 to 4 feet in diameter. *Bark* furrowed, thick, coated with brown scales. *Wood* weak, light, yellowish brown, close grained. *Buds* silky, pointed, terminal ones longer, larger. *Leaves* longer than wide, entire, heart-shaped base, acute apex, 6 to 10 inches long, thin, yellow green, sparsely hairy below; yellow in autumn; petioles 1 to 2 inches long. *Flowers* inconspicuous because yellowish green, bell shaped, terminal, erect, sepals 3, short, reflexed; petals 6 with long, tapering bases; stamens numerous, pistils numerous on central receptacle. *Fruit* compound, of many coalesced follicles, distorted by abortion of many; seed scarlet, berry-like, hangs out of 2-valved follicle on elastic thread when ripe. *Preferred habitat*, rocky uplands near streams; low mountain ranges. *Distribution,* western New York and southern Ontario to Illinois, Kentucky and Arkansas; mountain slopes of Pennsylvania south to Tennessee, Alabama and Mississippi. *Uses:* Ornamental tree planted in Europe and America to a limited extent. Wood is used for flooring and other general purposes. Good stock upon which to graft less hardy magnolias.

The cucumber tree is the hardiest species of native magnolias. Its great leaves betray its sub-tropical affiliations. No tree but the catalpa can match it in the North, and this does not venture by itself farther than the latitude of southern Indiana. Against the foliage mass of oaks and elms and maples the great clean leaves of the cucumber tree form a striking contrast. They are silky at first, but when mature keep only a fringe of hairs on the veins beneath. In autumn the tree turns yellow before the leaves drop. The elevated leaf scars almost encircle the silky winter buds.

Cucumber trees make less show in the period of blossoming than other magnolias. The yellowish-green tulip-like flowers, though large, are scarcely distinguishable at a little distance from the new leaves by which they are surrounded. They are neither beautiful nor pleasantly fragrant. The elongated fruits look like pale green cucumbers at first, but are soon distorted in form by the failure of many of the carpels to set seed. The fleshy green cone flushes pink, and later turns red as autumn approaches. In September each mature carpel splits open and two scarlet seeds hang out, each on an elastic thread. The wind buffets them until they dangle several inches below the conical fruit. Then a gust tears them off, and if they fall in moist leaf mould or on the damp border of a stream, young cucumber trees spring up from this planting.

The cucumber tree is not yet appreciated as a shade and avenue tree in the Northern States. It has few faults and many virtues. It grows vigorously from seed and after transplanting. The digging and planting must be carefully managed, as the fleshy roots of all magnolias are brittle. Since the tree is comparatively rare in the northern part of its range, nursery stock or seed should be planted rather than stripling trees from the woods.

The **Yellow Cucumber Tree** has been cultivated in gardens for over a century. It has bright yellow blossoms, and dark, almost evergreen leaves. In the wilds of central Alabama and the Blue Ridge of South Carolina has been found the yellow-flowered prototype of this garden form. It is named for its broad, heart-shaped leaves, var. *cordata*, of *Magnolia acuminata*. In cultivation the variety has been considerably modified.

Umbrella Tree (*Magnolia tripetala*, Linn.)—A round-topped or conical tree 30 to 40 feet high, of irregular habit, with stout contorted branches and twigs. *Bark* thin, grey, smooth, with bristly warts. *Wood* close, soft, pale brown, weak; sap wood yellow. *Buds*: terminal, purplish with pale bloom, pointed, 1 inch long; lateral, round, short, reddish brown. *Leaves* 16 to 20 inches long, obovate, acute, entire, tapering narrowly to the stout petiole, smooth, thin, bright green. *Flowers* white, cup shaped, of unpleasant odour, 4 to 5 inches deep, soon spreading open, the 3 sepals recurved. *Fruit* elongated, smooth, 2 to 4 inches long, rose coloured when ripe; seeds $\frac{1}{2}$ inch long. *Preferred habitat*, swamp borders and banks of mountain streams. *Distribution*, Pennsylvania to southern Alabama, northeastern Mississippi and southwestern Arkansas. Nearly to the coast in South Atlantic States. *Uses:* An ornamental tree in temperate regions of Eastern States and Europe.

The flower of this magnolia is surrounded by an umbrella-like whorl of leaves. The whole tree, indeed, suggests an umbrella, so closely thatched is its dome with the glossy leaves. The twigs have a peculiar habit of striking out at right angles from an erect branch, then turning up into a position parallel with the parent branch. This feature, combined with the inevitable forking of each twig that bears a flower, gives the branches angularity and tends to destroy the symmetry of the dome.

The three recurved sepals are the distinctive feature of the flower. The whole tree is smooth, except when its young shoots unfold. The silky hairs are soon shed. Altogether, this is one of the trimmest and handsomest of our native magnolias. It attains large size in the Arnold Arboretum, proving it hardy in southern New England.

Ear-leaved Magnolia, Mountain Magnolia (*Magnolia Fraseri*, Walt.)—Tree 30 to 40 feet high, with small, broad crown above slender, often leaning trunk. Branches stout, angular, erect. *Bark* thin, brown, smooth, with warty patches. *Wood* brownish yellow, weak, soft. *Buds* smooth, purplish; terminal

1 to 2 inches long; axillary very small. *Leaves* obovate, acute, with ear-shaped lobes at base, 10 to 12 inches long, bright green, smooth, whorled near end of branchlet. *Flowers* creamy white, fragrant, spreading, 8 to 10 inches across, petals narrowed at base. *Fruit* oblong, 4 to 5 inches long, bright rose at maturity; carpels with long horny tips, seeds ⅜ inch long. *Preferred habitat*, well-drained soil along mountain streams. *Distribution*, valleys of Appalachian Mountains from Virginia and Tennessee to Georgia, Alabama and northern Mississippi; abundant in South Carolina along headwaters of the Savannah River. *Uses:* Cultivated in gardens of Eastern States and in Europe. Hardy to New England.

The eared leaves of this tree and the prominent horns that decorate its brilliant seed cones readily distinguish it from the preceding species, which it resembles in habit and in the whorled leaf arrangement. The two are alike in their adaptability to culture far outside of their natural range. Each has proved successful as a hardy stock upon which to graft half-hardy exotic varieties. Planted in the Northern States, these trees seem to hold their own even with *M. acuminata*. A peculiarity of the mountain magnolia, umbrella tree and large-leaved cucumber tree is that the foliage of all three falls without any perceptible change of colour. The leaves are pretty much frayed and blemished before falling.

THE HARDY EXOTIC MAGNOLIAS

There are sixteen species of magnolias worth cultivating in this country, six of which are natives. Two of these natives and five exotics have proved hardy as far north as Boston. The others are not to be depended upon north of Washington, D. C. It is plain that they reach their highest development in the Southern States.

Whenever you see a magnolia in the North blossoming before the leaves you may be sure that it is an exotic species; and if the flowers are coloured you may be equally sure that it is a hybrid belonging to a group of which the type is *Magnolia Soulangeana*. This hybrid is a cross between *Magnolia Yulan* and *Magnolia obovata*, and it is most interesting to compare these two with their offspring. Both parents came from China and Japan, where they grow wild. All of our important exotic species are

natives of the same countries, except *M. Campbelli*, which comes
from the Himalaya Mountains.

The Yulan magnolia (*Magnolia Yulan*) has pure white,
fragrant flowers, which are bell shaped and fully 6 inches across.
It is a hardy tree which grows about 50 feet high. For centuries
it has been a favorite in Japanese gardens. The purple magnolia,
Magnolia obovata, is only a shrub, and it cannot endure our
northern winters. It blooms in May or June—later than the
Yulan—and its flowers are relatively small and almost scentless.
The outside of the flowers is purple, and it is from this that the
hybrids get their shades of pink and rose and crimson.

It can be readily understood what a triumph it was to cross
these two species successfully, for the hybrids are hardy, large-
flowered and fragrant; and they present several new and most
desirable colours. In this group are the following: *Alexandrina,
grandis, Lennei, Norbertiana* and *speciosa*. They are all small
trees, excellent for setting in city yards and in other prominent
places, for after the blossoms the fruits and foliage are both
decorative.

The starry magnolia (*Magnolia stellata*) is also a very fine
species for home grounds, as it blooms in March and April
and is one of the earliest of the flowering shrubs. Not only is
it the earliest magnolia, but it is wonderfully precocious,
beginning to bloom when scarcely 2 feet high. Unlike most
magnolias, its flowers are star shaped, opening out flat instead of
forming cups or bells. When open the flowers measure 3 inches
across. They are made of sixteen to eighteen narrow petals—
twice as many as most magnolias have. There is a variety, *rosea*,
with petals flushed with pink outside.

Magnolia Kobus, a large tree from Japan, is at present of
interest only to connoisseurs. Though one of the hardiest of
the exotics, it does not yet bloom profusely. Its white flowers
are star shaped, 4 or 5 inches across. They open in April or May.

TENDER EXOTIC MAGNOLIAS

Magnolia parviflora, a little known species from Japan, is
hardy in Salem, Massachusetts, where a handsome tree, the
largest in this country, blooms freely. Its white flowers have
few petals, but in form and texture they are exquisite.

THE SWAMP MAGNOLIA (*Magnolia stellata*)

The elliptical, silver-lined leaves and the small, globose fruits adorn this tree after the bloom is past. The winter buds are silky; the twigs are marked with circular lines. This species is an evergreen tree in the South and a deciduous shrub in the North

1 Winter bud   2 Fruit and leaves   C. Fruit   D. Fruit further advanced
A. Under side leaf   B. Upper side leaf

THE UMBRELLA TREE (*Magnolia tripetala*)

This tree has an umbrella-like whorl of oval leaves at the end of each branch. The white flower has its three sepals turned back. The pointed terminal bud is smooth and purplish

THE CUCUMBER TREE (*Magnolia acuminata*)

The winter buds are thickly coated with white hairs. The blunt terminal bud contains a flower. The leaves are ovate, thin, bright green, with pale linings

3 Winter bud   4 Leaves   5 Winter bud   6 Winter bud   [7 Leaves and flower
A. Under side   B. Upper side

A. Seed cases detached from axis

THE TULIP TREE (*Liriodendron Tulipifera*)

The tree frame is one of unusual symmetry and stateliness, the columnar trunk extending far into the crown. The winter twigs end in flattened buds, enclosed in a pair of stipules. The conical fruits, made up of flat-winged seed cases attached to a central spike, persist over winter, and are gradually loosened by the wind

Campbell's magnolia (*M. Campbelli*) is at once the most beautiful and the most difficult of cultivation of all our tender exotic species. It is the glory of the high mountain valleys of the Himalayas, where at very high altitudes it is a great tree. But in this country it cannot endure cold winters, and even in the extreme South it does not grow as it does at home. However, it is a splendid magnolia, and some day we hope to see it—a tree 80 to 100 feet high—covered, before the leaves appear, with its rosy bells. It is, or should be, to the Southern States what the Soulangeana group is to the North, for its petals are coloured pink or crimson, shading from the pale interior to the deeper colouring on the outside. The flower cups are from 6 to 10 inches in diameter and sweet scented.

The rest of the tender exotic species bloom after the leaves appear. Of these, the best, by all odds, is *Magnolia hypoleuca*, a tall tree which is notable because it is used so extensively in the manufacture of the lacquered wares for which the Japanese are famous. It is readily distinguished from all the species so far described by the dash of scarlet in the centre of its white blossoms. This colour is on the filaments of the stamens, and not on the petals. Another strikingly beautiful feature of this tree is the silvery linings of the leaves, which are much larger than those of the swamp bay. The latter species shows far less brilliant contrast in its foliage mass than does this exotic.

Another species with crimson-centred flowers is Watson's magnolia (*M. Watsoni*), a small tree, with blossoms 5 or 6 inches across. These have a decided odour of allspice.

The dwarf magnolia (*M. pumila*), a native of China, grows only 4 or 5 feet high, as a rule, and has white flowers which exhale a perfume like that of a ripe pineapple. This is especially strong at night. The flowers are small—only an inch or two in diameter —but the shrub is widely found in Southern gardens, probably because of its fragrance and the foliage, which is evergreen. Its period of bloom is long, and under glass it becomes everblooming. The purple magnolia (*M. obovata*) is also grown in the South, but I see no reason why it should be. Surely it is inferior to its noted offspring, which embody all its good traits and are, besides, far easier to grow.

257

HOW TO TELL MAGNOLIAS WHEN IN FLOWER

A simple key for the tree lover; free from technicalities and especially designed for use out-of-doors:

Blooming before the leaves.
    Colour of flowers pure white or nearly so.
        Shape of flowers bell-like..................YULAN
        Shape of flowers star-like.
            Petals 9 to 18, pink streaked outside..STELLATA
            Petals 6, pure white................KOBUS
    Colour of flowers pink to purple outside.
        Size of flowers large, 6 to 10 inches.
            Hardy ....SOULANGEANA
            Tender ....CAMPBELLI
        Size of flowers about 3½ inches.............OBOVATA

Blooming after the leaves.
    Colour of flowers greenish...................ACUMINATA
    Colour of flowers white, with conspicuous colour
            in centre.
        The petals purple-spotted at base..........MACROPHYLLA
        The stamens with scarlet filaments.
            Leaves mostly clustered at the ends of
                branches....................HYPOLEUCA
            Leaves scattered along the branches..WATSONI
    Colour of flowers, pure white.
        Size of flowers small (1 to 3 inches across).
            Shrub or tree, 10 to 70 feet high......GLAUCA
            Shrub, usually 4 or 5 feet high.......PUMILA
        Size of flowers large, 6 to 9 inches across.
            Foliage evergreen....................FŒTIDA
            Foliage deciduous.
                Leaves eared at base................FRASERI
                Leaves not eared at base..........TRIPETALA

2. Genus LIRIODENDRON, Linn.

Tulip Tree, Yellow Poplar (*Liriodendron Tulipifera*, Linn.) —A stately tall tree, 80 to 200 feet high, with trunk 5 to 10 feet in diameter, the crown conical at first, spreading in old age. *Bark* close, thick, intricately furrowed, brown. *Wood* light, soft, brittle, weak, easily worked, pale brown with narrow, white sap wood. *Buds* reddish with pale bloom, elongated, blunt. *Leaves* 5 to 6 inches long and wide, 3 or 4 lobed with shallow

258

sinuses, apex truncate or concave, base truncate or heart shaped; margin entire, dark green, leathery, smooth, lustrous above, paler beneath; autumn colour, yellow. *Flowers* tulip-like; 1½ to 2½ inches across, sepals 3, greenish, recurved; petals 6, yellow, with orange splash near middle; stamens numerous with large yellow anthers; pistils numerous, imbricated around central receptacle. *Fruit* in September, seeds in dry, winged samaras that fall early from the persistent central spike. Few seeds fertile. *Preferred habitat* deep, rich soil. *Distribution,* Vermont to Florida; west to Illinois, Arkansas, Mississippi and Alabama; maximum size and greatest abundance in the lower Ohio Valley and on mountain slopes of North Carolina and Tennessee. *Uses:* A valuable shade and ornamental tree. Lumber used in boat-building, construction and interior finish of houses, for shingles brooms, small woodenwares, and wood pulp. Postal cards are made of "poplar" pulp. Bark yields an important tonic drug.

A grove of young tulip trees is most beautiful, I do believe, in the dead of winter. It is not hard to find the old seed tree, whose family of varying ages and sizes stand in close ranks all about. A young tulip is singularly straight and symmetrical, compared with the young of chestnut, dogwood and oak. It takes on very early in life the tree habit of later years. The shaft is tall and grey and smooth, crowned with an oval head of ascending branches, clean and handsome throughout.

The winter twigs, with their oblong terminal buds, are worth looking at. The leaf scars are prominent, and a narrow ridge encircles the twig at each scar. Spring tells the meaning of these lines, when the leafy shoots unfold. Cut across the terminal bud, and its contents exhibit all parts of a flower—or, if the tree be too young to bloom, the little leaves are revealed, packed away to wait for spring.

Two green leaves with palms fastened together form a flat bag that encloses the new shoot after the bud scales fall in spring. Hold it to the light and you see a curved petiole and leaf. The bag opens along its edge seam, and the petiole straightens up, lifting the leaf, which has its halves folded on the midrib. At the base of the petiole stands a smaller flat green bag. The leaf grows and takes on its mature, dark-green colour, while the basal palms of its protecting stipules shrivel and fall away. Their work is done. The place of their attachment is the ring scar.

259

Within the second bag is the second leaf. The stem lengthens, mounting this little bag far above the first leaf before it opens to let out the second. So the growing point conceals itself, but grows on, unfolding a new leaf and expanding the shoot, node by node, until the growth of a whole season is accomplished. Suckers from the roots of a tree often exhibit unusual exuberance of growth, and hold the stipules at each joint as two broad, leafy blades, throughout the season.

The "chopped-off" ends of the leaves of the tulip tree set it apart from others at any season. Sometimes there are two shallow basal lobes, like those the maples have. Occasionally the apex is concave. Always the surface is shining, and turns to gold with birch and chestnut and hickory in the autumn.

The flowers are showy and handsome, with dashes of orange on their greenish-yellow corollas to attract the bees. The plan of the flower is much like the magnolias' until the central spike reveals its seeds. Magnolia seed vessels split up the back at maturity. Tulip capsules are dry and do not open. A flat wing rises above the angular, 2-celled seed box. The outer keys loosen and fly away on the early autumnal breezes. These seeds are rarely fertile. Before winter is fairly come the shingled seeds that formed the tulip cone have all been carried off, and the pencil-like receptacle remains erect on the end of the twig.

The tulip poplar is a beautiful lawn and shade tree. It is a favourite in Europe. Only far-away China has a sister species in the genus Liriodendron. It is a pity that this stately native tree is not better known in cultivation in its own country. It needs the same care we bestow on magnolias in transplanting, for its roots are fleshy and tender. There is no season when the tree is not full of interest and beauty, no matter what its age.

CHAPTER XXXI: THE PAPAW AND THE POND APPLE

FAMILY ANONACEÆ

THE custard apple family contains fifty genera, all tropical and mostly confined to the Old World. The family characteristics are exemplified by the two genera with a single species in each, which invade the warmer parts of the United States—vanguard of the West Indian host of many species. These trees have small use as ornamentals in a region rich in handsomer species. Their fruits have small horticultural value.

KEY TO GENERA AND SPECIES

A. Trees with straight trunks; fruit simple, banana-like.
>   1. Genus ASIMINA, Adans.
>> (*A. triloba*) PAPAW

AA. Trees with trunks bulging at base; fruit compound, of many united pistils.
>   2. Genus ANONA, Linn.
>> (*A. glabra*) POND APPLE

1. Genus ASIMINA, Adans.

Papaw (*Asimina triloba*, Dunal.)—Slender, spreading trees or shrubs, 20 to 30 feet high. *Bark* thin, fibrous, dark brown, blotched with pale grey, beset with warts and a network of shallow grooves. *Branches* grooved, reddish brown. *Wood* light, coarse grained, weak, soft. *Winter buds* small, flat, pointed, densely hairy, red. *Leaves* alternate, simple, clustering near ends of branches, obovate, tapering slenderly to base; 8 to 12 inches long, 4 to 5 inches broad, thin bright green above, paler beneath, on short petiole. *Flowers* in April, solitary in axils of last year's leaves; stamens in globular mass; pistils, many,

261

on disk; sepals 3, green, downy; petals, 6, veiny, purplish red, ill-smelling. *Fruit*, 3 to 5 inches long, like a thick, shapeless banana, skin wrinkled and brown; flesh yellow, sweet, insipid. Ripe in September and October. Seeds, large, hard. *Preferred habitat*, rich bottom lands. *Distribution*, Southern States and north into Kansas, Michigan, western New York and New Jersey. *Uses:* Planted for ornament and for a curiosity. Fruit, indifferent. Wood, inferior. Bark, used for fish nets.

This dainty little "wild banana tree" of the North is more interesting than it is useful, I am bound to confess. Its great leaves spread in umbrella whorls like certain magnolias, covering the upturned branches with a dense thatch of green. These leaves give the tree a tropical look, hinting at the fact that this is a fugitive member of a large family that belongs in the regions of no winter.

The papaw is not devoid of beauty in its blossoming time, though the flower resembles, and is not more conspicuous than that of the wild ginger that cowers in the woods. In April, the opening leaf buds have scarcely cast their scales when the wine-coloured flowers appear, set at intervals upon the twigs. Then the leaves come out lined with a red fuzz, which intensifies the rich colour of the whole tree. The bees find the flowers worth visiting, but their odour is unpleasant to most people. Twigs and leaves share this disagreeable characteristic, and the fruits repeat it in autumn.

The papaw's soft pulp, in its green banana-like envelope, is delighted in by the Negro of the South. It is sold in the markets, but is too sweet and soft to be really enjoyed by more fastidious people. One must get used to the pungent papaw taste, and then only the yellow-fleshed fruits are fit to eat. These are improved by hanging on the tree until they get a sharp bite of frost. The name, *Asimina*, means "sleeve-shaped fruit," and *triloba* refers to the three-parted flower.

The **Melon Papaw** (*Carica Papaya*, L.), which has had its name borrowed by the species just described, is a tropical tree that grows wild in southern Florida, and is often seen in greenhouses farther north. It grows like a palm, with tall stem and leaves rosetted at the top. The bark is silvery white, the leaves lustrous, long stalked, deeply cleft, and often a foot across. The flowers are waxen and yellow, and on the pistillate trees are succeeded by melon-like fruits, sometimes as large as a man's head, clustered at the base of the leaf rosette. This is the papaw exploited in certain patent medicines. It belongs to the passion-flower family.

The botanical explorer, William Bartram, wrote in 1790: "This admirable tree is certainly the most beautiful of any vegetable production I know of." The fruits are eaten raw, or made into conserves. The leaves are used by the Negroes as a substitute for soap in washing clothes. But they are especially valued as a means of making tough meat tender. The fleshy leaves are bruised, then wrapped up with the meat and laid aside. A solvent called *papain*, which the leaves contain, soon breaks down the tough connective tissues.

2. Genus ANONA, Linn.

The **Pond Apple** (*Anona glabra*, Linn.) is our only other arboreal representative of the custard apple family. It grows in the swamps of southern Florida, and in the West Indies. Its fruits are heart shaped, 4 to 6 inches long, smooth, and when ripe the thick stem pulls out, leaving the creamy, custard-like flesh set with hard seeds next to the large central cavity. The fruit is fragrant when ripe, but not of such quality as would warrant the cultivation of the little tree. The West Indian *Anona muricata* is the Soursop sold on Southern fruit stalls. Some hopeful horticulturists believe the pond apple may in time rival the soursop as a fruit.

CHAPTER XXXII: THE LAURELS AND THE SASSAFRAS

FAMILY LAURACEÆ

AROMATIC trees with handsome wood. *Leaves* simple alternate, punctate, entire. *Flowers* small, unconspicuous, yellowish green, clustered. *Fruit*, a 1-seeded berry.

KEY TO GENERA AND SPECIES

A. Leaves evergreen, entire.
    B. Calyx lobes persistent on the fruit.

1. Genus PERSEA, Linn.

    C. Flower stalks short, smooth; bark red.
        (*P. Borbonia*) RED BAY
    CC. Flower stalks long, pubescent; bark dull brown.
        (*P. pubescens*) SWAMP BAY
  BB. Calyx lobes not presistent on the fruit.
    C. Flowers in long-stemmed, sub-terminal panicles; berry small, blue-black.

2. Genus OCOTEA, Aubl.

        (*O. Catesbyana*) LANCEWOOD
    CC. Flowers in short-stemmed axillary umbels; berry large, yellow-green.

3. Genus UMBELLARIA, Nutt.

        (*U. Californica*) CALIFORNIA LAUREL
AA. Leaves deciduous, entire or 2-3 lobed.

4. Genus SASSAFRAS, Nees.

        (*S. Sassafras*) SASSAFRAS

The laurel family has forty genera, most of them tropical. Of the six North American genera, four are arbourescent. Three of these have broad evergreen leaves; the fourth is deciduous. All have 1-seeded berries, following inconspicuous, yellowish-green flowers. Three of these genera are monotypic; one has two species. All but the sassafras produce handsome, ornamental wood, used in inlay work and for interior finish of houses.

1. Genus PERSEA, Linn.

Red Bay (*Persea Borbonia*, Spreng.)—A shapely, narrow headed tree, 50 to 70 feet high, with numerous stout, erect branches and angled branchlets. *Roots* yellow, fleshy. *Bark* thick, red, furrowed and cut into broad, flat, scaly ridges; branches greenish. *Wood* hard, heavy, strong, bright red. *Buds* woolly, red, small. *Leaves* evergreen, 3 to 4 inches long, broad, entire, oblong to lanceolate, tapering at base and apex, thick, bright green, lustrous, glaucous beneath, turning yellow; petioles stout, short, brown. *Flowers* small, white, axillary, in few flowered clusters. *Fruit* blue or black, shiny berries, ½ inch long, 1-seeded, with persistent calyx lobes. *Preferred habitat*, stream and swamp borders. *Distribution*, Virginia to Texas near coast; north to Arkansas.

The red bay is a handsome tree deserving more extensive cultivation for its clean, leathery foliage, which is red when it opens and yellow before it dies. The brilliant dark green mass is lightened in summer by the pale leaf linings. The red bark probably gives the name its distinguishing adjective. The leaf is not unlike that of *Laurus nobilis*, the familiar tub laurel of hotel verandas.

This lover of rich, wet soil is occasionally discovered growing wild among long-leaf pines in dry, sandy loam—a most encouraging fact for anyone who wishes to grow the tree in ordinary well-drained soil. The berries are handsome but not showy. The wood was once used for boatbuilding, but is now devoted to interior house finishing and fancy articles of furniture. It is comparatively rare in use.

The **Swamp Bay** (*P. pubescens*, Sarg.) is a slender tree, rarely 40 feet high, that frequently crowds out all other under-growth in pine barren swamps along the coast from North Carolina to Mississippi. Its densely woolly opening shoots and leaf veins, and the dull brown bark distinguish it from the previous species, as do also the long stalks on which the flowers and berries are borne.

The **Avocado**, or **Alligator Pear** (*P. gratissima*, Gærtn.), grows wild in the West Indies, Brazil, Peru and Mexico. It is cultivated in Florida and southern California. The berry in this species has the size and the shape of a Kieffer pear. It has smooth, greenish-purple skin, and a yellow pulp, soft and oily like marrow, surrounds the single giant seed. The flavour is peculiar, and strangers to it have to acquire a liking for it. When this preliminary step is taken, they often become extremely fond of it. It is usually cut in two like a melon, and eaten as a salad, dressed with vinegar, salt and pepper.

The abundant oil expressed from these pears is used in soap making and for illumination. The seeds yield a black dye that is converted into an indelible ink. The growing of the trees is easy and profitable. They begin to fruit in about five years from seed.

2. Genus OCOTEA, Aubl.

The **Lancewood** (*Ocotea Catesbyana*, Sarg.) is a little evergreen laurel tree 20 to 30 feet high, much like the swamp bay in flower and fruit. But its shoots are smooth, its leaves thin and lanceolate, and the lobes of the calyx have dried away under the berry. The flower stalks are bright red. The reddish-brown bark is warty. This tree is common on the shores and islands of the lower end of Florida, from Cape Canaveral on the east around to Cape Romano. It is abundant and of largest size near Bay Biscayne.

3. Genus UMBELLARIA, Nutt.

The **California Laurel** (*Umbellaria Californica*, Nutt.) is frequent among the broad-leaved maples in the forests of southwestern Oregon. It is a lover of wet soil, growing 80 to 90 feet high in rich bottom lands. It climbs the western slopes of the Sierra Nevada and extends to the San Bernardino Mountains in southern California, reaching altitudes of 2,500 feet, but keeping generally along waterways.

The beauty and stateliness of this tree impress all those who look with eyes that see upon the varied forest flora of California. It is strikingly handsome in a land full of handsome trees. Its willow-like leaves are lustrous and rich in an aromatic oil, which causes them to burn even when piled green on a campfire. The flowers, small but fragrant, bloom in December and January. The plum-like purple fruits which fall in autumn have the peculiar habit of keeping their integrity long after the pit has germinated in the leaf mould under the tree. The plantlet has the distinction of being provided with a fresh fruit lunch which does not decay and disappear until well into the following summer.

The tree is planted in parks and gardens of California, and in southern Europe. Its wood is esteemed one of the most beautiful and valuable in the forests of the Pacific coast. It is used for interior finish of houses and for furniture. It is close, firm, hard and strong, rich brown, with pale thick sap wood. From the leaves an aromatic oil is extracted, and a fatty acid from the fruit.

4. Genus SASSAFRAS, Nees.

Sassafras (*Sassafras Sassafras*, Karst.)—Tree, 30 to 50 feet high; rarely, in the South, 100 feet high with trunk 6 to 7 feet in diameter; top, flat or round, loose, open, irregular. *Roots* fleshy, aromatic, deep, throwing up suckers. *Bark* spicy aromatic, thick, dark brown, reddish, scaly and broken by shallow fissures into broad flat ridges; twigs, smooth, striated, green, mucilaginous. *Wood* dull brownish yellow, soft, weak, coarse, brittle, durable in the soil. *Buds* ovate, acute, greenish, aromatic. *Leaves* alternate, petiolate, sometimes opposite, 4 to 6 inches long, dull yellow-green, pale beneath, with entire margin; autumn colour orange; shapes vary: (a) ovate, (b) mitten shape, with one side lobe only, (c) 3 lobed, with a thumb on each side—the three shapes all on the same tree. *Flowers* in May, diœcious, pale yellow, in corymbose racemes on separate trees; staminate, with 9 stamens mounted in 3 rows on the 6-lobed calyx, minute glands, orange coloured, at base of inner whorl of 3 stamens; pistillate, with 6 abortive stamens in one row about single erect pistil. *Fruit* soft, oblong, smooth, dark blue, on thickened scarlet calyx and pedicel. *Preferred habitat*, rich, sandy loam, borders of woodlands and peaty swamps. *Distribution*, southern Vermont west through Michigan and Iowa to Kansas. south to Florida and Texas. *Uses:* Wood makes posts and rails, boats and ox yokes. Bark of roots used as medicinal tea. Oil of bark used to flavour medicines. Valuable ornamental for its berries and brilliant autumn colouring. Attracts birds.

Who has not nibbled the dainty green buds of sassafras in winter, or dug at the roots for a bit of their aromatic bark? Or who has not searched among the leaves for "mittens"? Surely they are people whose youth was spent in regions that knew not this little tree of the fence corners and woodland borders. And they have missed something very much worth while out of their childhood.

Then there is the great green caterpillar with the Cyclopean black eye transfixing the culprit who dares disturb him on the soft silk mattress he has spun for himself on a sassafras leaf. When he is hung up like a mummy we have dared to carry him home, to learn that the "eye" is only a big black spot made to scare away birds, no doubt, which are looking for worms. Did you never see the glorious swallow-tail butterfly that comes out of that plump chrysalis in a day or two? Then you have, indeed, missed another joy, for no tiger of the jungle is more richly banded with black and yellow than this ranger of the meadows; in form and colouring and motions he is as beautiful as the flowers that supply him with nectar.

But there is the sassafras tree. When the butterfly is still in its tiny green eggshell, hidden by a provident mother in plain sight on the face of an opening leaf, the delicate greenish yellow flowers come out. The starry calyxes are alike on all the trees. But the stamens are all on one tree, nine in each flower, prominent, with bunchy glands at the bases of the inner ones. Plainly these flowers have pollen making for their duty. The pistillate flowers, with a row of abortive stamens at the base of the central style, grow in numbers on another tree. Here in autumn come the birds, even before the blue berries have softened on their coral pedestals. To leave them till they ripen would be to lose them to some other bird.

The glory of the autumn foliage of the sassafras is like the glory of a sunset—all mingled with purple and red and gold. The three forms of leaves that fascinated us in summer time are here yet, but the shining treetop is the unit now, and we do not look for individual leaves.

The wood of sassafras is light and tough, and makes good

THE SASSAFRAS (*Sassafras Sassafras*)

The roadside specimen is often shrubby, but it rises in favorable situations into a stately tree. In autumn the foliage turns to scarlet and gold

B. Pistillate flowers   A. Staminate flowers

THE SASSAFRAS (*Sassafras Sassafras*)

The leaves show three different shapes, all on the same twig. The yellow flowers are borne on separate trees. The blue berries are handsome on their coral-red stems, the delight of birds in late September. The plump green aromatic buds are good to nibble on a winter's walk

fishing rods. Durable in the soil and in water, it is used for posts and rails, and for boats and barrels. The bark, especially of the roots, is strong in a volatile oil used to flavour medicines. The bark itself is sold in drug stores, and people buy it in spring and make sassafras tea "to clear the blood." The leaves and twigs yield a mucilaginous substance which is used in the South to give flavour and consistency to gumbo soups. The useful properties of its various members are as nothing when compared with the beauty and desirability of the living tree, which is beautiful throughout the year—as a towering tree or a roadside sapling.

CHAPTER XXXIII: THE WITCH HAZEL AND THE SWEET GUM

FAMILY HAMAMELIDACEÆ

TREES with slender twigs and fibrous roots. *Leaves* simple, opposite, deciduous. *Flowers* with parts in four's, perfect or unisexual. *Fruits* woody 2-valved, 1, to 2-seeded capsules.

KEY TO GENERA AND SPECIES

A. Leaves obovate, unequal at base; flowers perfect, autumnal.
> 1. Genus HAMAMELIS, Linn.
> > (*H. Virginiana*) WITCH HAZEL

AA. Leaves star shaped, symmetrical at base; flowers monœcious, staminate in terminal racemes, pistillate in axillary long-stalked heads, in early summer.
> 2. Genus LIQUIDAMBAR, Linn.
> > (*L. Styraciflua*) SWEET GUM

The relationship of the witch hazel and sweet gum is not obvious to the general observer. In fact, the common characters are such as only the keen eye of the botanist detects. The 2-horned woody capsules joined together in the sweet gum seed ball is morphologically the same type as the solitary woody 2-lipped seed capsule of the witch hazel.

Eighteen genera compose the subtropical family, Hamamelidaceæ. Two genera, each with a single species, are native to North America. There are two or three species of Hamamelis in Eastern Asia. The four species of Liquidambar include one Mexican and two Asiatic species beside our own sweet gum.

1. Genus HAMAMELIS, Linn.

The **Witch Hazel** (*Hamamelis Virginiana*, Linn.)—A small tree, or usually a stout shrub, rarely 25 feet high. *Bark* light brown, scaly or smooth. *Wood* close grained, hard, heavy, brownish red, with thick, white sap wood. *Buds* sickle shaped, pale brown, hairy, enclosed in leafy stipules. *Leaves* alternate, unsymmetrical, strongly veined, oval or obovate, wavy margined, or coarsely serrate, 4 to 6 inches long, rusty-hairy at first, yellow in autumn, often hanging all winter. *Flowers* in autumn, clustered, greenish, with 4 yellow ribbon-like petals. *Fruits* ripe in autumn, a 2-beaked, 2-celled, woody capsule that opens explosively; seeds, 2, black, shiny. *Preferred habitat*, low, rich soil or rocky stream banks. *Distribution*, Nova Scotia to Nebraska, south to Florida and Eastern Texas. *Uses:* Valuable ornamental. Bark, twigs and leaves used in making extract for rubbing bruises.

There is nothing in the forest west of the Mississippi Valley that quite compensates the Easterner for the absence of the witch hazel, familiar to every lover of the woods in his half of the continent. Not that it is a very important tree, in any practical sense, but it is an integral and familiar part of the woods it frequents, filling in the bare places with undergrowth and exhibiting interesting and unusual habits. It is the most inconspicuous tree in the woods in spring. Its opening leaves are coated with rusty hairs, which the botanist finds interesting because they branch into star-shaped tops. But to the casual observer these leaves look old and dingy, compared with the bright green foliage about. And no sign of bloom adorns the witch hazel while the impressive flower pageant is passing. Only the curious, lifting a branch and looking in the axils of last year's leaves, will see little curved stems each capped by a cluster of green-grey cups, dull from their winter's contact with the elements. On the newer shoots, and at the bases of leafy side spurs cluster tiny green balls no larger than pin heads. A few brown pods, dry and empty, drop to the ground, as the wind shakes the tree.

All through the summer the witch hazel tells its secrets only to the thoughtful and keen-eyed observer. The side branches send out twigs of varying lengths. The longest and thriftiest of these are near the extremity of the limb, where the best light is, and the most room. Here the broad leaves spread their faces toward the sun, and under them little green buttons assert themselves, rending apart the cups that easily contained them in spring.

Every tree has its supreme moment of beauty. This usually comes when the foliage is in its prime, or when the flower buds burst in spring. The witch hazel is an exception to all rules. When the crisp autumnal atmosphere warns all plant life to get ready for winter the witch hazel trees put a new construction on the message. As if by magic, all up and down through the woods they burst into bloom, each flower bravely flaunting four delicate petals like tiny yellow streamers. The woods are fairly sprinkled with these starry, gold-thread blossoms, and a rare fragrance breathes upon the languid October air. The ripening leaves second and intensify the colour of the flowers, which often thickly fringe the outstretched twigs, and cover up the green buttons.

Ah! here is another surprise the witch hazel has to offer. These buttons, so precious to the tree, contain the seeds developed from the flowers that bloomed last year. It has taken a full year to ripen them. Each pod has two cells, with a shiny black seed prisoner in each. The frost gives the signal, and the pods fly open with a snap, freeing the seeds, and ejecting them with surprising force. Dry, cold weather will discharge the whole seed crop in a few days. They shoot in every direction, and to a distance sometimes of twenty feet from the foot of the tree. But warm, wet weather delays their game. The pods are close and glum. There is no spring in them till they are dry again.

It is a far cry from March to October; from furry tassels of blossoming aspens and willows to the witch hazel in its yellow blossoms bringing up the rear in the great annual procession of the flowers. In fact, the witch hazel practically bridges the chasm of winter, for at no time does the cold cause all the flowers to fall. Their yellow petals curl up like shavings; but they often stay till spring.

A witch in old days was a person who did or said things not conventional. Our witch hazel has defied the ancient laws of the calendar—a very dreadful thing! So it comes honestly by its name; and one is inclined to ignore the accepted etymology that the word "witch," or "wych," in Old English, means "weak," and refers to the sprawling habit of the tree. Surely the observer cannot miss seeing little weazen witch faces grinning at him from all possible angles of the tree, their yellow cap strings flying in the wind, as if in defiance of the rumour that the days of witchcraft are past.

The English "wych hazel" is an elm. In the mining regions it would be counted the height of folly to sink a shaft without first determining with a hazel wand where the rich veins of coal or metal are. No more would one think of digging a well until the same divining rod pointed to the hidden springs. Our American witch hazel is credited with all the occult powers of the Old World tree from which it gets its name. In hamlets and country neighbourhoods not too close to the currents of modern life we may still meet old fellows who can "water witch," and a goodly number of neighbours who believe in his powers.

Billy Thompson's well goes dry and he sends in haste for Old Andy. Promptly, but with no undignified haste, the old man goes out into the woods that join his "clearin'." He chooses a forked twig whose Y stands north and south, for the rising and setting suns must have sent their rays through its prongs as it grew. Carefully the leaves are removed, as they drive to Billy's place, where the whole family and a neighbour or two await them. A solemnity settles on the company as the supple twig is grasped by its two forks, thumbs out, knuckles down, and the stem of the Y is thrust forward. Holding it as rigid as his trembling old hands are able, Andy paces with dignity over the ground that Billy has chosen as a convenient site for the new pump. He shakes his head as the stubborn wand keeps its position. "There's no use diggin' thar." Billy is disappointed, but convinced.

Old Andy stumbles along and the wand points downward. It is most emphatic. Back he comes across the same spot, and down goes the wand again. He moves away—even to the other side of the barn—then returns and the sign is repeated over the exact spot indicated before. "D'ye see his wrist move?" asks a doubter, nudging his neighbour, and speaking under his breath. But it is not a time for levity. All eyes are on the seer who announces with proper dignity: "Thar's the place, Billy. The signs is plain. You'll git a good spring-fed well if you go deep enough." And nobody has the hardihood to dispute his word.

Hamamelis water, or extract of witch hazel, in a variety of brands, is for sale in every country and city drug store. There is widespread faith in its soothing and curative powers when rubbed on bruises and sprains, and applied to burns. Strangely enough, the Indians taught white folks to use it. But chemical analysis has failed to discover any medicinal properties in bark or leaf. Druggists will concede that the alcohol in these decoctions is the most effective agent. The patented preparations cost more than the ordinary witch hazel that the druggist makes up, and there is an impression that the higher-priced kinds are "stronger." They probably have a higher percentage of alcohol.

Below is given the "national formulary" which manufacturing druggists follow in the United States. It is published that anyone may know just how the extract is extracted, and what is added to the witch hazel.

(*Aqua Hamamelis*) EXTRACT OF WITCH HAZEL

Hamamelis roots and twigs . . . . 10 lbs.
Water . . . . 20 pts.
Alcohol—6 per cent. . . . . 1½ pts.

Place Hamamelis in a still, add the water and alcohol, and allow the mixture to macerate twenty-four hours. Distil ten (10) pints by applying direct heat, or preferably by means of steam.

2. Genus LIQUIDAMBAR, Linn.

The **Sweet Gum** (*Liquidambar Styraciflua*, Linn.)—A large tree 75 to 140 feet high, with straight trunk and short, slender branches, forming a pyramidal or oblong head. *Bark* reddish brown, furrowed, scaly, on old trunks; on young trees, ashy grey, with hard, warty excrescences; twigs, pale, usually with corky wings, which continue to grow for years. *Wood* bright reddish brown, striped with black, straight, close grained, lustrous when polished, hard, heavy, not strong. *Buds* acute, reddish and hairy at tips, small. *Leaves* 5 to 7 inches, long and broadly cleft into 5, rarely 7, triangular-pointed lobes, which are finely saw-toothed; with resinous sap, lustrous when mature, streaked crimson, and yellow in autumn. *Flowers* after leaves, monœcious; staminate in terminal, hairy racemes, 2 to 3 inches long, set with head-like stamen clusters; pistillate in solitary swinging balls from axils of upper leaves; stigmas conspicuously twisted. *Fruits* dry, swinging balls, 1½ inches in diameter, of the hardened, 2-horned capsules. Single seed, winged, ½ inch long in some cells. Most of the cells filled with minute, aborted seeds. *Preferred habitat*, low wet woodlands. *Distribution*, Connecticut to Missouri; south to Florida and Texas; also in Mexico and Central America. *Uses:*

THE WITCH HAZEL (*Hamamelis Virginiana*)

The gold-thread blossoms appear with the ripening fruits in October and November. The 2-valved capsule flies open and explosively discharges the two seeds. The leaves are unsymmetrical and strongly ribbed, and turn yellow in autumn. In spring the undeveloped fruits appear clustered on side shoots, awaiting the summer, which will mature them. The buds are naked, the outer covering becoming the first leaf. The spiny galls are produced by an insect

THE SWEET GUM (*Liquidambar Styraciflua*)

The woody seed balls are made of two horned capsules which open to discharge the winged seeds. The tree spreads its limbs in platforms of shade, the shining leaves turning to fiery colours in autumn. Occasionally a tree is free from corky ridges on its twigs and branches

Valuable ornamental and shade trees. Lumber used for railroad ties, paving blocks, shingles, fruit boxes, spools; choice pieces known as "satin walnut," used for veneering furniture and for interior finishing of houses. Dyed black, it imitates ebony, in picture frames and cabinet work.

The sweet gum is probably more closely linked with plantation life in the South than any other tree. It grows in the swamps, and many a slave hugged the slender shaft of a leafy gum tree while he waited all day for the north star to point him the way to freedom. Here the 'possum and the 'coon found similar refuge from hunters and their dogs; and it was a hollow gum tree that old "Nicodemus, the slave," was buried in to be waked in time for the great jubilee! As a child, I lived in a state north of the range of the most intrepid liquidambar tree. I recall with great vividness an old ex-slave's description and eulogy of the tree, and the song he sang, full of the exaltation his dearly bought freedom always roused in him—especially the thrilling chorus:

> "Da's a good time comin', 'tis almos' heah,
> Hit's bin long, long on de way:
> Run 'n' tell 'Lijah t' hurry up, Pomp',
> Meet us at de gum tree, down in de swamp;
> Wake Nicodemus to-day!"

Travellers in the bayou country of the Mississippi Valley can easily verify the statement that a hollow gum tree is large enough to entomb a man. Giants exist there to-day, standing in rich bottom lands, or on soil that is inundated a part of the year, whose trunks, 15 feet or more in girth, carry their tops 150 feet into the air. These trees, often bare of branches for half their height, look like great columns set amid the tropical vegetation, and towering high above most of their neighbour trees. In its northern range the tree sacrifices size but not beauty.

It is good to take a whole year to get acquainted with the sweet gum, and it doesn't really matter when one begins. The seed balls swing on the trees in winter, looking like the buttonballs of the sycamore. A second glance shows the paired "cows' horns" above the gaping pods, and the crowded, undeveloped seeds shake out like sawdust. An easier way to identify the tree is by the narrow blade-like ridges of bark that in most cases adorn the twigs. Strangely, these are on the upper side of horizontal twigs, and all around the vertical ones. The shading of olives and greys and browns in these corky ridges reminds one of the banding of an agate. Now and then you come upon a gum tree whose twigs are all smooth.

Farther down, the branches have warty bark, broken into rough, horny plates. This gives the tree its name, "alligator-wood." Then the grey of the big branches gives way to the red-brown of the trunk; the shallow fissures and scaly ridges give a finer texture to this oldest bark than the limbs give us reason to expect.

In summer time the leaves of the sweet gum are our sure guide to its identity. "Star-leaved gum," it is often called. There is no other tree whose leaf so closely resembles a regular, six-pointed star with one point missing where the petiole is fastened on. These leaf stems are long and flexible—a very important fact in analysing the beauty of the sweet gum tree in full leaf. The large shining blades flutter on their stems,

> "Continuous as the stars that shine
> And twinkle in the Milky Way."

They fairly dazzle the beholder, as the polished leaves of the tulip tree always do.

But the summer garb of the sweet gum tree is pale and monotonous compared with the radiant beauty of its October foliage. Wherever gum trees grow, there the autumn landscape is painted with the changeful splendour of sunset skies. The leaves do not seem to dry and wither as maples and dogwoods do. They give up their bright green for the most gorgeous shades of red. "The tree is not a flame—it is a *conflagration!*"

Often one sees a fence-row thicket of young gum trees all burning low with dull crimsons as if their fires sullenly smoulder, and might at any moment burst into the clear orange-red flame that consumes a neighbour tree. Afterward, the foliage may turn to those browns and lilac tones assumed by ash trees, but as a rule the ground is littered with the leaves before they fade—they "die like the dolphin."

The sap of the sweet gum is resinous and fragrant. It is easy to find this out by crushing a leaf or bruising a twig. Chip through the bark of a tree and an aromatic gum accumulates in the wound. In the Northern States this exudation is scant, but it becomes more plentiful as one proceeds south. The most copious flow is from trees in Central America. This gum is known to commerce as "copalm balm," large quantities of which are shipped to Europe from New Orleans and from Mexican ports each year. A Spanish explorer in Mexico described in 1651 "large trees that exude a gum like liquid amber." This was the beginning of the trade. Linnæus later gave the name "liquid-ambar" to the whole genus, which contains four species. Besides our American tree there is a species in eastern Asia, not yet well known, and a very important species, *L. orientalis*, which forms forests in Asia Minor. Long before the Christian era the fragrant gum *storax*, or *styrax*, of these trees was used as incense in the temples of various oriental religions. Later it had its place also with frankincense and myrrh in the censers of the Greek and Roman Catholic churches. It was used then, as it is now, as a healing balm, as a medicinal drug and as a perfume.

The American gum is believed to have the same properties as the oriental storax, and it is manufactured into medicines, perfumes, and incense. As a dry gum, it is the standard glove perfume in France.

First and last, it is not the products of the sweet gum tree that should first commend it to the American people. It is the tree itself, beautifying by its growth the landscape of which it is a part. More and more we are realising the value of native things in landscape gardening. There is a lesson for the American (who would not learn it at home) as he hunts in European gardens and nurseries for trees to plant on his estate. Among the finest and most valued trees abroad is his own native *Liquidambar Styraciflua*, all the more esteemed because there is no European species.

The name "gum tree" is also applied to our tupelos, and to certain species of Eucalyptus, natives of Australia.

CHAPTER XXXIV: THE SYCAMORES

Family Platanaceæ

Genus PLATANUS, Linn.

LARGE, ornamental, deciduous trees with smooth limbs from which whitish bark peels in irregular flakes. *Leaves* simple, alternate, palmately lobed. *Flowers* monœcious in pendant heads. *Fruits* swinging, many-seeded balls, hanging all winter.

KEY TO SPECIES

A. Fruits solitary, rarely 2; leaves with shallow sinuses, broader than long; seeds blunt.
$\qquad$ (*P. occidentalis*) SYCAMORE
AA. Fruits 4 to 6 on each stem; seeds pointed.
$\quad$ B. Leaves with triangular lobes and deep sinuses.
$\qquad$ (*P. racemosa*) CALIFORNIA SYCAMORE
$\quad$ BB. Leaves with variable lobes, often finger-like and 8 to 10 inches long. $\quad$ (*P. Wrightii*) ARIZONA SYCAMORE
AAA. Fruits 2 to 4 on each stem; seeds pointed; leaves deeply lobed, broader than long. (Exotic.)
$\qquad$ (*P. orientalis*) ORIENTAL PLANE

There are six species of the genus Platanus found in the Northern Hemisphere, and equally divided between the Old and New Worlds. The geologist finds evidences of much wider distribution for our sycamore than it now enjoys. The Arctic regions from Greenland west bore forests of these trees, and so did central Europe before the Glacial Epoch. The plane tree of Europe extends east to India.

The trees are all characterised by brittle, smooth bark of light colour, except on old trunks. The flaking off of this bark in irregular plates, leaving the white under layer exposed, enables the most casual observer to recognise the trees of this family by sight. The broad leaves, lobed like a maple's, and the hanging seed balls are striking characteristics.

A. Pistillate flowers   B. Staminate flowers

THE SWEET GUM (*Liquidambar Styraciflua*)

The star-shaped leaves and the corky ridges on the twigs are distinguishing characters. The flowers appear in May after the leaves. The staminate are in racemes at the ends of the twigs. The pistillate are in heads on long stems from leaf axils

A. Pistillate flowers   B. Staminate flowers   C. Fruit of previous year

THE SYCAMORE (*Platanus occidentalis*)

The broad leaf is strongly veined and toothed, yellow green with a pale lining. Its petiole has a conical hollow base which protects and conceals the growing bud. Winter shows the bud and its encircling leaf scar. The flowers are in heads, staminate dark red, lateral; pistillate greenish red and terminal. They open in May with the new leaves. The stipules form a sheath with a leaf-like frill around the top. The seed balls dangle on flexible stems. A central, bony cone is covered with dart-like seeds, each flying away on a hairy parachute. Sycamore bark is reddish brown on the lower part of the trunk, and broken into small plates. Above and on the limbs it comes off in thin, irregular flakes of considerable size, exposing the pale-green or white under-bark. This gives the tree a mottled and weird appearance, especially in winter

Sycamore, Buttonwood, American Plane Tree (*Platanus occidentalis*, Linn.)—A large, stately tree, 75 to 150 feet high, with tall trunk and loose, broad head and mottled green and white limbs. *Bark* dark reddish brown on trunk, breaking into small scaly plates; smooth and thin on branches, olive green, flaking off in irregular plates, exposing whitish inner bark. *Wood* light reddish brown, hard, heavy, with prominent satiny pith rays. *Buds* conical, with hood-like scales, covered by hollow base of leaf stalk, and encircled by a single leaf scar. *Leaves* deciduous, alternate, simple, 5 to 6 inches long, 7 to 9 inches broad, 3 to 5 lobed, with broad, shallow sinuses and wavy-toothed lobes; yellow green above, paler beneath, and fuzzy on veins; yellow in autumn and papery; petiole short, with hollow, dilated base; stipules, a sheath, tubular, flaring into ruffle-like border. *Flowers*, May, monœcious, in globular heads on flexible stems; staminate axillary, deep red; pistillate terminal, pale green tinged with red, with long stems. *Fruit*, dry pendulous balls, solitary or rarely two on a single peduncle, 1 inch in diameter, made of a close-set, pointed akenes. *Preferred habitat*, borders of streams and rich bottom lands. *Distribution*, southern Maine to north shore of Lake Ontario; west to Minnesota and Nebraska; south to Florida and Texas. *Uses:* Excellent shade and ornamental tree, especially in cities and towns. Wood is used for furniture and inside woodwork of houses; also for butchers' blocks and tobacco boxes.

The "hoary antlered sycamore" in our damp woods is a tree that the stranger will never forget after his first introduction to it. There is only this one native tree with such strange, crazy patchwork on its branches. These patterns in dull olives and dingy white show themselves from any reasonable distance in winter, and the grey balls dangling from the twigs are another sure means of identification. In the summertime the thickest foliage never quite conceals the scarred trunk and excoriated branches, splotched as if with whitewash to the utmost twigs. Moulting is a continuous performance during the buttonwoods' growing season. Even in winter flakes of bark may be picked up on the snow blanket that protects the roots. This tree seems utterly lacking in the power to stretch its bark fibres and fill in the chinks to fit the growing limbs. Instead, with the first rift sycamore bark loosens, separates, and lets go, leaving only the inner layers between the tender cambium and the cold outdoors. It is the sycamore's way.

Have you ever looked out of a car window at the sycamores and white birches that streak the dull winter woods with light? It is a strange sight, calculated to stir the dullest imagination. The birches stand together, and keep each other in countenance. They do not seem to mind being looked at, but flaunt their tattered ribbons of bark without self-consciousness. The sycamores stand alone, as a rule. Except in young trees, the limbs are tortuous, reaching out in many directions without much regard for symmetry. One often stands on the verge of a stream, and leans far out as if contemplating a plunge. The rush of the train makes of these solitary trees pallid, spectral figures, that dart past the windows—hunted outcasts, lepers in the tree community, fleeing before invisible pursuers. It is a satisfaction to find each tree back in its place when we come again that way.

Quite a different tree from the distressed-looking specimen in colder New England is the buttonwood of more congenial soil and clime—a stalwart, large-limbed tree of colossal trunk, which lifts its head high above its forest neighbours, and shelters great oaks and maples under its protecting arms. The weird, irregular top is singularly free from small branches, but in summer the broad leaves are so disposed as to soften the harsh lines. The open-boughed buttonwoods of the little city of Worcester, Massachusetts, noted for their stately beauty early in the century just finished, well illustrate this kindly ministry of the leaves.

The buds of the sycamore deserve our close attention in the autumn. Leaves are fading; at first glance we note that there are no buds in their angles. How is next year's growth provided for? Look again! The leaf loosens in your hand and lets go its hold on the twig. Its stem ends in a hollow cone. There on the twig is a plump bud that grew all summer under the protecting base of that leaf. Two or three little hoods each bud wears to protect it, now the leaf is gone. The outer one is of leathery texture, without seams, and the delicate inner ones fit close, so there is no danger. The leaf never abandons its ward until it is safe to do so.

The little frilled sheathing stipules are well worth looking for on young shoots of the sycamore in spring. So are the balls that hang in the treetop, first in May as the two separate kinds of flower heads; later when the surviving pistillate ones change to hard brown seed balls, banging against neighbouring limbs until the flexible stems are worn to shreds, and the pointed seeds are loosened and wafted away on their hairy parachutes. Most of the seeds die, of course, but Nature sees to it that here and there a sycamore seed falls on good ground; and a young sapling lifts its broad palms next year above the spot.

Some people object to sycamores because the leaves as they unfold cast off their fuzzy covering of branched hairs, which are irritating to the mucous membrane of the eyes and throat. Most of us have never heard of this trouble before, and have lived comfortably in the neighbourhood of sycamore trees for years. Happily, this moulting period of the leaves is very brief. A more serious obstacle to the planting of these trees is their susceptibility to a fungous disease. The young leaves often look scorched immediately upon opening. A second crop of inferior size and vigour may replace them. Examine an affected leaf, and you find black specks along the veins. These are the outward signs of inward trouble, which is too deep-seated to be reached by any fungicidal spray. Let us hope that time will show a cure, for the sycamore is one of the trees that grows rapidly and flourishes amid the dust and smoke of city streets. How few kinds of trees there are, after all, that stand by to shelter and encourage city-bound humanity through the hot summer days, making fresh green oases in burning brick-and-mortar deserts!

The **California Sycamore** (*P. racemosa*, Nutt.) bears its button balls in a series of four to six strung on the tough, fibrous stem. The leaves have the same general outline as those of its Eastern relative, but the lobes are slenderly triangular, and deeply cleft by sinuses of about the same size and shape. This beautiful Western tree was long confused with *P. occidentalis*, for its bark is white, and in habit and size the two are similar. A comparison of the leaf and the fruit easily enables one to distinguish them.

The **Arizona Sycamore** (*P. Wrightii*, Wats.) is a sycamore which looks like *P. racemosa* in fruit and leaf, but the lobes of the latter are much more finger-like, and measure often 8 to 10 inches in length. These trees are strikingly beautiful objects, growing to large size on cañon sides and stream borders, rising far above the evergreen oaks and pines of the semi-arid regions, each tree a refreshing dash of verdure in a weary land.

The **Oriental Plane Tree** (*P. orientalis*, Linn.) is the species best known in Europe, and is coming to be very popular in this country. It is a shapelier tree than our own, more compact in habit, with larger leaves, and three or four seed balls are strung on each long stem. So far it seems almost immune to fungous diseases, a very important consideration to the planter. This is the plane tree of the Greek writers, in groves of which Plato walked and discoursed—a tree held in worshipful esteem by the ancients for its stateliness and beauty. On occasions they poured wine upon its roots and decked its limbs with jewels and gold. Xerxes halted his unwieldy army for days that he might contemplate to his satisfaction the beauty of a single tree. He had its form wrought upon a medal of gold to help him to remember it the rest of his life. Xerxes never did things by halves.

Certain venerable plane trees in Europe are estimated to be 4,000 years old. Very few species of trees attain a greater age. These patriarchs are giants as well. They measure as much as 40 feet in trunk diameter, though they are so perforated by decay that counting rings is impracticable even when the tree falls. These old trees are at best but shattered ruins, supported in their senile age by columns and braces—melancholy figures, indeed, renewing feebly each spring by their few leaves the youth they had spent and quite forgotten centuries before the dawn of civilisation. It is almost pitiful that they should live on.

Quaintly does John Parkinson, "Apothecarye of London," write of plane trees in the year 1640: "They are planted by the waysides and in market places for the shadowes sake onely." Quite sufficient justification for any tree in any age, that it tempers the heat of the sun in places where men must congregate. "For the shadowes sake" is a phrase worth remembering! John Parkinson seems to have been a poet as well as an apothecary.

The generic name of these trees comes from the Latin *platus*, which means "broad." It refers to the breadth of the leaf. A species *platanoides* is found in many genera; it means "like the sycamore." The swamp white oak sheds its bark in sheets. In the Norway maple the shape of the leaf is much like that of the sycamore.

The common name of this tree has had an interesting history. The original sycamore was a fig tree of the ancients—Pharaoh's fig, they called it in Egypt. Their strong mummy cases were

282

built of its wood. Its scientific name is *Ficus Sykomorus*. In Europe, the great maple, *Acer Pseudo-platanus*, is called sycamore. In America, our sycamore is *Platanus occidentalis*. Botanists try to teach Europeans to call their tree the sycamore maple and Americans to call theirs the buttonwood; but in spite of their efforts the old names stick. The traveller who meets abroad all three of these sycamores—a fig, a plane, and a maple—all different but known by the same common name, is ready to side with the botanists, for his head is in a whirl. Common names may do well enough till all the trees are met with in the same region. Then trouble and confusion are constant.

CHAPTER XXXV: THE APPLES

FAMILY ROSACEÆ

Genus MALUS, Hall.

TREES which are parents of cultivated apples. *Leaves* simple, alternate, deciduous. *Flowers* showy, perfect, fragrant, in terminal cymes. *Fruit* fleshy, enclosing papery 5-celled core.

KEY TO SPECIES

A. Leaves smooth at maturity; flowers rose pink.
    B. Blades of leaves ovate, blunt, minutely serrate, thin.
                (*M. coronaria*) WILD CRAB APPLE
    BB. Blades of leaves narrow, pointed, coarsely toothed, leathery.
             (*M. augustifolia*) NARROW-LEAVED CRAB APPLE
AA. Leaves tomentose beneath; flowers pale.
    B. Fruit flattened, 2 to 4 inches in diameter.
      C. Stems slender. (Exotic.)
                (*M. Malus*) COMMON APPLE
      CC. Stems stout   (*M. Soulardi*) SOULARD'S APPLE
    BB. Fruit not flattened, $\frac{1}{2}$ to $1\frac{1}{2}$ inches in diameter.
      C. Flowers white.   (*M. rivularis*) OREGON CRAB
      CC. Flowers pink.   (*M. Ioensis*) IOWA CRAB

The genus Malus is native to the whole of eastern Asia. We have four native species. Our cultivated crab apples and the hundreds of orchard varieties have their ancestral home somewhere in Asia Minor. For centuries horticulturists have been at work improving wild apples. In Europe and in America the effort is to get better fruit. In the Far East the aim has been to produce the finest flowering trees. The results are both advantageous to the horticulture of the world.

Closely allied to apples are the other pome fruits, pears and quinces. Neither are native to America, though they are widely cultivated here.

PRAIRIE CRAB APPLE (*Malus Ioensis*)

Wild Crab Apple (*Malus coronaria*, Mill.)—A low, bushy tree, with thorny angular twigs, rarely 30 feet high. *Bark* reddish brown, scaly. *Wood* heavy, fine grained, weak, reddish brown. *Buds* small, blunt, bright red. *Leaves* ovate or triangular, 3 to 4 inches long, half as broad, velvety beneath, blunt pointed, sharply serrate, often lobed near base; petioles 1½ to 2 inches long. *Flowers* May to June, after the leaves, in 5 to 6 flowered umbels, perfect, white to deep pink, spicy, fragrant—1 to 2 inches across. *Fruit* flattened, yellow, 1 inch in diameter; flesh hard, sour. September. *Preferred habitat*, upland woods, in moist, rich soil. *Distribution*, Ontario to Minnesota; south along Alleghanies to Alabama; Nebraska to eastern Texas; New York to South Carolina. *Uses:* An ornamental, flowering tree. Fruit made into jellies and preserves. Wood used for levers, tool handles, etc.

The wild, sweet-scented crab apple! The bare mention of its name is enough to make the heart leap up, though spring be months away, and barriers of brick hem us in. In the corner of the back pasture stands a clump of these trees, huddled together like cattle. Their flat, matted tops reach out sidewise until the stubby limbs of neighbouring trees meet. It would not occur to anyone to call them handsome trees. But wait! The twigs silver over with young foliage, then coral buds appear, thickly sprinkling the green leaves. Now all their asperity is softened, and a great burst of rose-coloured bloom overspreads the treetops and fills the air with perfume. It is not mere sweetness, but an exquisite, spicy, stimulating fragrance that belongs only to wild crab-apple flowers. Linnæus probably never saw more than a dried specimen, but he named this tree most worthily, *coronaria*, "fit for crowns and garlands."

Break off an armful of these blossoming twigs and take them home. They will never be missed. Be thankful that your friends in distant parts of the country may share your pleasure, for though this particular species does not cover the whole United States, yet there is a wild crab apple for each region.

In the fall the tree is covered with hard little yellow apples. They have a delightful fragrance, but they are neither sweet nor mellow. Take a few home and make them into jelly. Then you will understand why the early settlers gathered them for winter use. The jelly has a wild tang in it, an indescribable piquancy of flavour as different from common apple jelly as the flowers are in their way more charming than ordinary apple blossoms. It is the rare gamy taste of a primitive apple.

Well-meaning horticulturists have tried what they could do toward domesticating this *Malus coronaria*. The effort has not been a success. The fruit remains acerb and hard; the tree declines to be "ameliorated" for the good of mankind. Isn't it, after all, a gratuitous office? Do we not need our wild crab apple just as it is, as much as we need more kinds of orchard trees? How spirited and fine is its resistance! It seems as if this wayward beauty of our woodside thickets considered that the best way to serve mankind was to keep inviolate those charms that set it apart from other trees and make its remotest haunt the Mecca of eager pilgrims every spring.

The wild crab apple is not a tree to plant by itself in park or garden. Plant it in companies on the edge of woods, or in obscure and ugly fence corners, where there is a background, or where, at least, each tree can lose its individuality in the mass. Now, go away and let them alone. They do not need mulching nor pruning. Let them gang their ain gait, and in a few years you will have a crab-apple thicket. You will also have succeeded in bringing home with these trees something of the spirit of the wild woods where you found them.

The **Narrow-leaved Crab Apple** (*Malus angustifolia*, Michx.), smaller in all its parts than the common wild crab apple, but closely resembling it in all but its leaf, is found on the Atlantic coast from New Jersey to Florida, and west to the Mississippi. It extends also to western Pennsylvania and eastern Tennessee, overlapping the range of the other species in these regions. Its leaves are leathery, almost evergreen, dark and shiny, with dull, often fuzzy linings. They are small, narrow, and blunt pointed at both ends.

The **Oregon Crab** (*Malus rivularis*, Rœm.), a white-flowered species with ovate, taper-pointed leaves, grows in dense thickets along streams in the coast region from northern California well into Alaska. Its young growth is covered with a grey pubescence. The apples are oblong, rarely over $\frac{3}{4}$ inch long, and few people beside Indians consider them worth gathering for food.

THE WILD CRAB APPLE (*Malus coronaria*)

In late May the tree is a mass of pink, spicy, fragrant flower clusters and bright green leaves. The flat little apple ripens in September, but it is not mellow. It is waxy to the touch, and has the gamy taste a wild apple ought to have

THE NARROW-LEAVED CRAB APPLE (*Malus angustifolia*)
The leaves of this tree are narrowly oval, acute at both ends, smooth and leathery

THE PRAIRIE CRAB APPLE (*Malus Ioensis*)
The woolliness of the leaf-linings and all the young growth is very noticeable in this species. The leaves are often much elongated. The apples are globular or somewhat oblong

The **Prairie Crab Apple** (*Malus Ioensis*, Britt.) is the species found from Wisconsin to Oklahoma. It has only recently been distinguished from *M. coronaria*, which its flowers closely resemble. Its leaves are shorter and oval in shape, with deep, irregular teeth, and linings of silky white down. The dull green apples are of good size, larger than the other native crabs, and are not at all flattened. It is the woolliness of all the young growth in summer that will chiefly distinguish this tree.

The double-flowered form of this crab apple, *Malus Ioensis flore pleno*, is one of the most beautiful of ornamental trees. Its flowers are not so numerous as to overload the tree, and each blossom, in its setting of green leaves, has all the delicacy of a pink tea rose, exquisite in form, in shading, and in fragrance.

The **Soulard Apple** (*Malus Soulardi*, Britt.) may confuse us. It is a hybrid of *M. Ioensis* and the common apple, as caped from orchards—the trees that come from apple seeds and are not grafted. Such are our good-for-nothing roadside "wilding" trees, with gnarly fruit nobody can eat.

The Soulard apple occurs locally from Minnesota to Texas. It is large leaved and stout of stature, with pink-flushed blossoms, like an orchard apple tree. But its woolly surfaces are often roughly rusty; its fruit is a flat crab apple on a stout stem, larger, sweeter and more edible than one expects it to be. Because this species is hardy and disposed to vary and improve in the quality of its fruit in cultivation, horticulturists consider it a distinctly promising apple for the coldest of the prairie states. Several varieties have already been produced from it.

The **Wild Apple** (*Malus Malus*, Britt.), native to southern Europe and Asia, is the parent of our cultivated apples. It is the apple of classical literature, inseparably associated with the growth of civilisation, and cultivated for the improvement of its fruit for unnumbered centuries. Our orchard trees, which renew their youth every spring in fuzzy leaves and fragrant pink and white blossoms, are direct descendants of this ancient species. Myth and folk-lore and written history all tell how this fruit, more than any other—the simple, wholesome, uncloying fruit of the north temperate zone—is interwoven with the life of the people. Read in the Song of Solomon: "As the apple tree among the trees of the wood, so is my beloved among the sons." And as a symbol of exquisite joy attained through the senses, "the smell of apples" is named with the odours of spikenard and camphire and bundles of myrrh. Read the classics, ancient and modern. Fancy the story of the fall of Troy or the legend of William Tell with the apple left out!

If we would know what this wild European apple is like we may get a good idea by planting an apple seed, and watching the tree that springs from it. Or we may save time by examining a wilding tree in the fence corner, planted perhaps by the hand that threw away an apple core years ago. Suppose it was the seed of a fine desert variety of apple. Its offspring will not bear the same variety and quality of fruit. It is almost sure to "revert to the wild type." That is, the fruit of it will be small, sour and gnarly, just such apples as the orchard tree would have borne if it had not been grafted or budded while it stood in the nursery row.

But there are exceptions to every rule. There are varieties of apples—a very few—that "come true from seed." Such is *La Belle Fameuse*, the ruddy-cheeked, white-fleshed "Snow" of the Northeastern States—the domestic apple of the Canadian French. Up and down the valley of the St. Lawrence this apple tree grew in the gardens of the early settlers. The seeds were carried and distributed by neighbours, by migrant traders, but chiefly by the Jesuit missionaries whose hope was that the homesick habitant should grow to love the land of his adoption. And they were not disappointed. Generations passed, and the tree became an intimate part of the home life of New France. Drummond, poet of the habitant, describes the old-fashioned garden, modelled on the typical one of precious memory in sunny France:

> "Dat house on de hill, you can see it still,
>   She's sam' place he buil' de firs' tam' he come;
>   Behin' it dere's one leetle small jardin,
>   Got plaintee de bes' tabac Canayen,
>   Wit Fameuse apple, an' beeg blue plum."

It was a hard life, and the touch of poetry and luxury brought into it by these fruit trees was not lost on the appreciative habitant. He had his domestic animals, and the home flowers about his door—"the leetle small jardin"—and he was comforted in the land of the long, cold winters. His apple trees were as much a part of his establishment as the dog and cow and team of horses. He cherished them next to his family and his religion. In fact, they were a part of both, if he could have analysed his feeling for them.

While the French in Canada were still planting seeds of their beloved Fameuse apple as their fathers had done before them, noting no change in the character of the fruit except when a tree bore handsomer and finer-flavoured apples than any tasted before, a strange and interesting story was unfolding itself in the valley of the Ohio River. A picturesque character calling himself Johnnie Apple Seed wandered up and down, with no apparent object in life but to plant apple seeds. Queer as he was, the motive that actuated him was nobly altruistic. He was doing what he could to turn the desert into a garden. He had the strange notion that grafting and pruning trees was a wicked practice. He lived to see his trees in bearing over a vast territory. But it is to be hoped that he never realised to what a degree his philanthropy failed. They were mostly "Apples of Sodom" that came as a harvest. Where he had planted seeds of Baldwins and Greenings and Bellflowers grew trees bearing apples with strange, crabbed looks, mongrels of varying degrees of insipidity. They were largely seedling trees of varieties that did not come true. They stubbornly exemplified the rule of which the Fameuse is an exception.

Do you know the romance of the Newtown pippin? If you have seen one of these matchless apples and sunk your teeth into its mellow substance I need not tell you of its sprightly flavour, its absolute fulfilment of your ideal of what an apple ought to be. What is its pedigree?

Two centuries ago a chance seed fell near a swamp on the outskirts of the village of Newtown, Rhode Island. A seedling tree came up, and was ignored, as such trees are, until some vagrant passing by saw and tasted the first apples it bore. And the very golden apples of Hesperides they were for the village and the countryside! Cions of this tree became the parents of great orchards in the Hudson River Valley. Up and down the coast among the colonies they were scattered.

In the year 1758, Benjamin Franklin, our representative in England, received a box of Newtown pippins, and he gave some to his distinguished friend, Peter Collinson. Thus were American apples introduced with éclat to the attention of the English. The trees did poorly in English orchards, but the fruit in London markets grew in popularity. In 1845 the orchard of Robert Pell, in Ulster County, New York, which contained 20,000 pippin trees, yielded a crop which brought in the London market $21 per barrel. The tables of the nobility were supplied with these apples at the astonishing price of a guinea a dozen—forty-two cents apiece!

And yet, almost within the memory of men now living, the old tree still stood on the edge of the swamp, and men came from far and near—even from over seas—to cut cions from the original Newton pippin tree.

Here and there in the history of horticulture are other instances where Nature seems to rise superior to her own laws by creating valuable seedling varieties. The "Wealthy" apple was a chance discovery in a Minnesota nursery row. It is the parent of one of the noblest varieties of the Northwest States—a worthy mate for the Newtown pippin. Other sorts of apples have sprung from crosses between known varieties. These are hybrids—seedlings, one of whose parents contributed the pollen that fertilised the flower on another tree. From the seed thus set the new tree comes, different from each parent tree, but having some traits of each.

In these two ways—by seedlings and by hybrids—new varieties have arisen, and others will come on. But each is uncertain—a problem for the scientist, not the apple grower. To plant seeds for an orchard would be the utmost folly. The quick and sure way to get and keep a good variety is to graft other trees with cions of the desired kind. Fertilising the soil, and thorough tillage, greatly improve the health of a tree, and the quality and size of its fruit. But they do not change a Baldwin into a Greening. It may be possible, however, to produce a superior individual tree, whose characters, perpetuated, give rise to an improved "strain" of the variety. Soil, climate and treatment all emphasise individual differences in trees and in their fruits. There is no law in Nature so inexorable as the law of Constant Variation.

Our little hard-fleshed, slender-stemmed garden crab apples are an interesting race. The Siberian crab (*Malus baccata*), of northern Asia, is the parent species. The larger sorts are probably from crosses of this with *Malus Malus* in some of its varieties.

Japan has given us some wonderful flowering apples, small

trees and shrubs. *Malus floribunda* is probably as glorious a sight in bloom as any tree that ever grew. After these splendid blossoms we can but marvel again at the crop of fruit that succeeds them. Some of these apples are handsome and good to eat, but of the various species I have seen no fruit grows larger than a cherry!

The **Pear** (*Pyrus communis*, Linn.), also a native of Europe and Asia, is a close relative of the cultivated apple, and ranks high among orchard fruits. We have no native species, but numerous valuable varieties have originated in this country.

The **Quince** (*Cydonia vulgaris*, Pers.) is a dwarf tree from Europe, whose hard-fleshed, apple-like fruit has been used for centuries in marmalades and jellies. It is seen in old gardens in the East—one or two trees are the customary number. Occasionally one sees a quince orchard. It is an old-fashioned fruit, indeed; the demand for it is small, but steady. The Japanese quince, *C. Japonica*, is a splendid flowering shrub, with inedible fruit. Hedges are often seen of it, ablaze with great rose-coloured flowers before the leaves are out in spring—a sight, indeed, worth going miles to see.

The **Medlar** (*Mespilus Germanica*, Linn.), a pretty tree native to central Europe, is occasionally planted in gardens for the curiosity aroused by its peculiar, apple-like fruits. The core is exposed at the blossom end, as if the flesh had not quite reached around it. After frost has bitten them, and they have lain all winter, these medlars soften, and are not unpleasant to eat. They also are made into preserves.

CHAPTER XXXVI: THE MOUNTAIN ASHES

FAMILY ROSACEÆ

Genus SORBUS, Linn.

SMALL trees of good habit, with ornamental foliage, flowers and fruit. *Leaves* alternate, 7 to 17 leaflets, serrate. *Flowers* small, white, in many-flowered flat corymbs. *Fruit* small, red, berry-like.

KEY TO SPECIES

A. Buds sticky; shoots smooth.
    B. Leaflets taper pointed, pale green.
                    (*S. Americana*) AMERICAN MOUNTAIN ASH
    BB. Leaflets abruptly pointed, dark green.
              (*S. sambucifolia*) ELDER-LEAVED MOUNTAIN ASH
AA. Buds woolly; branchlets and petioles pubescent; leaflets
    blunt pointed, dull green. (Exotic.)
    (*S. Aucuparia*) EUROPEAN MOUNTAIN ASH or ROWAN TREE

The handsome foliage and showy clusters of flowers and fruits make this a favourite genus of trees and shrubs for ornamental planting. There are about thirty species of Sorbus, widely distributed over the Northern Hemisphere and chiefly inhabitants of mountain slopes. Their contentment with poor soil and exposed situations make them valuable for the covering of broken ground, where they show to the best advantage. In autumn the red berries are matched by the ruddy foliage. Birds often depend on the berries for food in snowy winters. On a lawn a mountain ash is a neat and very decorative little tree at all seasons.

Mountain Ash (*Sorbus Americana*, Marsh.)—A small tree, attaining 30 feet, with slender spreading branches, forming pyramidal head. *Bark* smooth, brown or grey, with large lenticels like those on cherry; taste bitter. *Wood* pale brown, close grained, weak. *Buds* reddish, pointed, glutinous. *Leaves* pinnate, 6 to 12 inches long, alternate; petioles red; leaflets 13 to 17, lanceolate, dark yellow-green, pale beneath. *Flowers* creamy white, perfect, small, in broad, compound, flat-topped corymbs, after the leaves in May and June. *Fruit* small, scarlet, berry-like, with thin flesh and bony seeds. Ripe in September and hang on all winter. *Preferred habitat*, rich, moist soil. *Distribution*, Newfoundland to Manitoba; south along mountains to Tennessee and North Carolina. *Uses:* Planted for its red berries and fern-like foliage. Fruit used in home remedies.

The way to see our American mountain ash at its best is to take a leisurely October drive through the wooded uplands of New England or lower Canada. Along the borders of swamps, or climbing the rocky bluffs, with the wild plums and the straggling beeches, this frail scarlet-berried ash leaps up like a yellow flame, and the broad discs of its fruit gleam among the leaves like red embers in a grate. There is no handsomer leaf at any season than this one, on its red stem, its pointed leaflets dainty and slim as a willow's.

I have wondered that people prefer to plant in their gardens the European species. But I find it is not all the deep-seated craving for imported things. The American tree languishes in warm, dry climates and in the protected situations we are apt to choose. It shows a distinct preference for cold, unsheltered places, exposed to winds, where its growth is stunted. Though its range extends into the Southern States, it always keeps to high altitudes.

The Elder-leaved Mountain Ash (*Sorbus sambucifolia*, Rœm.) is even more daring in its fight with the elements. It climbs higher on the mountains, and ranges from Labrador to Alaska, following the Rocky Mountains to Colorado. In the East, it goes no farther south than Pennsylvania. The same species inhabits Japan and eastern China,

This species has showier flowers and fruit clusters than *S. Americana*. In the large area where their ranges overlap, these two can be best distinguished by their leaves. This Western mountain ash has darker green foliage, of abruptly pointed leaflets. The fruits have five large, erect calyx points at the blossom end. These points are small on the berries of the other species, and are bent inward until they lie flat.

All through the summer the graceful, elder-like foliage of the Western mountain ash makes it a tropical-looking tree among its north temperate forest neighbours, though it is rarely more than 15 feet in height. Its open, pyramidal head gives each leaf a chance. After the leaves have fallen, the twigs still hold up their broad discs of scarlet berries that cling until winter is well past.

The **Rowan Tree** or European mountain ash (*Sorbus Aucuparia*, Linn.) is the one people usually plant on their lawns in this country. This trim, round-headed tree is very conventional and well-behaved compared with its country cousins back in the hills. Long discipline at the gardener's hands has made it what it is. In the craggy highlands of Scotland and Wales it leads a wild life, and is there quite different from the familiar garden tree. Strange legends and superstitions, centuries old, cluster around the rowan in all rural sections of Europe. They are preserved in the folklore and the literature of many languages. The tree, its berries, a leafy spray, or a bit of its wood—all were considered to be effectual charms to exorcise evil spirits, and to undo their work. The rowan was planted at the gates of churchyards, and by cottage doors; and leafy twigs were hung over the thresholds. Crosses of "roan" wood, given out on festival days, were worn as amulets, and were tacked up over the doors of houses and barns. Milkmaids, especially, depended on them for the defeat of the "black elves" who tried to make their cows go dry, and, unless prevented, got into the churns, and then the butter would never come! We shall look upon this pretty tree with new interest, and perhaps a mild kind of awe, knowing how it has been regarded by our ancestors.

It may be known at any season by the woolly fuzz that whitens buds, twigs and the linings of leaves. The leaflets are small, dull green, with blunt points, and the margins have double teeth, large and small. The flowers and fruits are larger than those of our native species, and more showy.

Mountain ash berries at best are a poor, insipid sort of fruit. But as they hang on the trees very late, birds eat them with apparent satisfaction. During periods of deep snow, these trees are often the sole reliance of our hardy winter residents—the one bar between them and starvation.

The farther north a tree can grow, the more likely it is to have near relatives in the Old World. One mountain ash of Japan can be distinguished only with difficulty from our own; and some

THE MOUNTAIN ASH (*Sorbus Americana*)

The flat, crowded cluster of tiny white flowers is set in a whorl of the dark-green leaves in May or June. The red berries ripen in September and remain all winter. The foliage is bright yellow in autumn. The twigs are red; so are the waxy buds above the prominent leaf scars. The white breathing pores show distinctly on the smooth bark

THE SERVICE-BERRY TREE (*Amelanchier Canadensis*)

This solitary tree grows on the edge of a plowed field. Tillage and elbow room enable it to spread out like a luxuriant cherry tree. Its bloom appears in April, when most trees are still bare. Its berries are the delight of the birds in June

authorities consider our two species but varieties of the rowan tree of Europe, which extends its range well into Asia. Intermediate forms, growing wild with the two American species, show how each is apt to vary, and how very close is their relationship. All species are supposed to have sprung from a common ancestor not very long ago.

CHAPTER XXXVII: THE SERVICE-BERRIES

FAMILY ROSACEÆ

Genus AMELANCHIER, Med.

SLENDER, pretty trees often cultivated. *Leaves* simple, alternate, deciduous, *Flowers* white, numerous, in racemes. *Fruits* small berry-like, with 4 to 10-celled core.

KEY TO SPECIES

A. Leaves ovate, finely saw-toothed; fruit flattened, red to purple.
  B. Fruit ⅓ to ½ inch across; leaves sharp pointed.
      (*A. Canadensis*) SERVICE-BERRY
  BB. Fruit about ⅓ inch across; leaves blunt pointed.
      (*A. obovalis*) LONGLEAF SERVICE-BERRY
AA. Leaves broad, coarsely toothed on apical half, blunt; fruit ½ to 1 inch across, blue-black.
      (*A. alnifolia*) WESTERN SERVICE-BERRY

The genus Amelanchier occurs in southern Europe, northern Africa, China and Japan, and in southwestern Asia as well as in eastern and western North America. It includes few species, all delicate and pretty in foliage and flower, planted for ornament in many countries. Dwarf varieties are raised for their fruit. The flowers cover the slender branchlets before the leaves appear. The sweet berries feed the birds. Our Western service-berry has especially large and juicy fruits.

June-berry, Service-berry, Shad-bush (*Amelanchier Canadensis*, T. & G.)—A slender, round-headed tree, rarely 40 feet high, usually less than 20 feet. *Bark* smooth, purplish brown, with pale lenticels. *Wood* heavy, hard, dark brown. *Buds* pointed, brown, inner scales elongate in spring. *Leaves* alternate, oval or oblong, serrate, tapering, smooth; 3 to 4 inches long, midrib grooved above and ridged underneath. *Flowers*, April, before leaves, white in loose, drooping racemes, with silky bracts, 1 inch across with 5 narrow, long petals. *Fruit*, June, a red, juicy, sweet berry, with 10-celled core. *Preferred habitat*, rich, upland soil, borders of woods. *Distribution*, Newfoundland to the Dakotas, south to the Gulf. *Uses:* A desirable park or lawn tree; wood occasionally used for tool handles, etc.

Do you wait until you are sure of finding violets a-plenty before you take the time to go to the woods? Then you miss a rare and most delightful experience. Go two weeks earlier this year, and you may see the little June-berry tree put on her bridal veil. The larger trees which stand about with naked branches are but a background to set off the charms of this modest woodland beauty. It is not simply by contrast with the barrenness around it that this tree delights the beholder. The soft, graceful, feathery clusters and the individual, starry blossoms would be attractive at any season. But that flowers so delicate should unfold so early, while yet winter lingers, is a marvel that goes straight to the heart. You break the sprays that lean toward you as if in invitation, and carry them home with a sense of personal gratitude. What makes one feel a glow of warmth when looking at this tree? The sharp spring air does not justify it. There is a faint undertone of colour that takes off the chill of the white cloud of blossoms. Looking close we see that the strap-shaped bracts are red, a pair of them below each flower, and the tinge is deepened by the red-brown of the silky infant leaves, which hang limp and helpless, their two halves folded on the midrib, and quite obscured by the mass of bloom.

In summer the leaves are not distinctive. They are daintier than those of the apple and pear, and have not the hydrocyanic acid odour of the foliage of plums and cherries. The twigs lack the thorns characteristic of the hawthorns. So, by elimination, we may be able to identify this tree among the multitude of its relatives.

The fruit cluster is a good clue all summer long, though the birds take the berries so promptly that it is exceptional good luck if you find a ripe one on the tree. But the long branching stems which bore the sweet morsels are held out empty, or with dry, undeveloped berries upon them, longer and looser in structure than the racemes of the cherry group.

Showy as it is in blossom, the June-berry is never a self-assertive tree. Its flowers are gone as suddenly as they came, and the little tree quite loses its identity when the forest wakes and covers itself with a dense thatch of green. Cloistered thus, and cut off from the benefits of wind and sun, no wonder that the tree ordinarily rises little higher than a thrifty shrub.

The **Dwarf June-berry**, or **Swamp Sugar Pear** (*A. obovalis*, Ashe), has its young leaves and tender shoots covered with dense white wool until quite matured. The flowers are smaller than those of its sister species, and crowded in shorter, denser racemes. The fruit is juicier and of richer flavour, and eagerly sought by children and birds. The tree bears the name, long-leaf service-tree in some localities, and in others, shad-bush. The Indians noted that these trees blossomed along the banks of tide-water streams about the time that the shad came up to spawn. The colonists adopted this name. Naturally, it is not used in the inland states, where shad are seen only in fish markets. This June-berry frequents swamps and stream borders, ranging from New Brunswick to Florida and Louisiana, and west to Minnesota and Missouri.

The **Western Service-berry** (*A. alnifolia*, Nutt.) has a thick, roundish leaf, broad and toothed, which makes it a handsome foliage tree. Its large, juicy, fine-flavoured berry commends it to horticulturists as worthy of cultivation. It grows over a vast territory which extends from the Yukon River south through the Western States, and east to Ontario, Michigan and Nebraska.

Widely distinct as is this species from *A. Canadensis* when individuals from distant localities are compared, these differences become less marked as each species is studied nearer and nearer the regions where their ranges overlap. It is believed that in these two we have the offspring of a single species which came from the North, and, spreading east and west on the slopes of the Rocky Mountains, became modified by climate into two distinct species as we see them to-day. Comparisons of specimens taken at regular intervals on both sides of the mountains form a most interesting chain of evidence to support the theory of a common origin. Fossils of the Glacial Period show clearly the characteristics of the ancestral type.

THE SERVICE-BERRY (*Amelanchier Canadensis*)

A well-tilled specimen spreads like an apple tree. The flowers appear in April before the leaves spread themselves. The fruit is a juicy berry, which the birds love. It is ripe in June

THE ENGLISH HAWTHORN (*Cratægus Oxyacantha*)

This deeply cut leaf differs from those of most hawthorns; the coral red fruits lead almost anyone to identify the tree as a hawthorn. Numerous cultivated forms of this species are used as hedge plants or as ornamental trees in this country. The flowers are abundant, white or rose-coloured

CHAPTER XXXVIII: THE HAWTHORNS

Family Rosaceæ

Genus CRATÆGUS, Linn.

Small trees or shrubs, with rigid, thorny branches. *Leaves* simple, alternate, deciduous, stipulate, serrate, often lobed. *Flowers* perfect, usually white, in corymbs on short side twigs. *Fruits* drupe-like pomes, with hard nutlets containing the seeds. *Wood* hard, tough, reddish, close grained. *Uses:* Ornamental trees and hedge plants; wood used for tool handles and mallets.

KEY TO GROUPS AND TO SPECIES

A. Nutlets not grooved in front.
  B. Leaf veins extending to points of lobes; not to sinuses.
    C. Petioles short; leaves obovate, wedge shaped at base.
      D. Corymbs many-flowered.
        E. Leaves leathery, dark green, shining above; fruit almost globular, nutlets 1 to 3, ridged on back.

I. Group CRUS-GALLI

        F. Stamens 10, anthers rose colour; leaves thick, fruit dull red; spines stout, 4 to 6 inches long.
                (*C. Crus-galli*) COCKSPUR THORN
        FF. Stamens 20, anthers yellow; leaves thin; fruit orange red; spines slender, 1 to 1½ inches long.   (*C. Mohri*) HAW
        EE. Leaves membranaceous or firm; veins strong; fruit usually dotted; nutlets 2 to 5, strongly ridged on back.

II. Group PUNCTATÆ

        F. Fruit oblong, yellow or red, ½ to 1 inch long, with large, pale dots; stamens 20.
                (*C. punctata*) DOTTED HAW

299

FF. Fruit globose, $\frac{1}{3}$ to $\frac{1}{2}$ inch long, dull red, with small pale dots; stamens 20, yellow.   (*C. collina*) HAW

DD. Corymbs few-flowered; flowers with leaves in February, stamens 20 to 25, with large, dark-red anthers.

III. Group ÆSTIVALES

(*C. æstivalis*) MAY HAW

CC. Petioles long, slender, scarcely glandular; leaves membranaceous to leathery, narrow at base; corymbs many-flowered; fruit oblong to subglobose, $\frac{1}{8}$ to $\frac{5}{8}$ inches in diameter.

IV. Group VIRIDES

Fruit flattened, under $\frac{1}{3}$ inch in diameter, bright scarlet or orange.   (*C. viridis*) HAW

CCC. Petioles long, slender, glandular at apex.

D. Leaves broad at base; corymbs many-flowered.

E. Fruit flattened, $\frac{1}{2}$ to $\frac{5}{8}$ inch in diameter, green, with glaucous bloom, becoming dark purple-red and lustrous; leaves blue green, smooth.

V. Group PRUINOSÆ

Leaves elliptical   (*C. pruinosa*) HAW

EE. Fruit short oblong or obovate, $\frac{1}{2}$ to $\frac{5}{8}$ inch long, scarlet to purple, leaves membranaceous.

VI. Group TENUIFOLIA

Leaves blue-green, rough.

(*C. apiomorpha*) HAW

EEE. Fruit 1 inch in diameter, red or yellow, flesh thick, juicy; corymbs downy.

VII. Group MOLLES

F. Stamens 20, anthers yellow; leaves broad and thick; fruit scarlet, downy.

(*C. mollis*) RED HAW

FF. Stamens 10, anthers yellow.

G. Fruit crimson, velvety, flattened.

(*C. Arnoldiana*) SCARLET HAW

GG. Fruit orange red, lustrous.

(*C. submollis*) RED HAW

FFF. Stamens 10, anthers rose colour.

Fruit short oblong, bright crimson, shining.

(*C. Ellwangeriana*) SCARLET HAW

EEEE. Fruit oblong, ¾ inch long, red, pulpy, lustrous; leaves lobed; anthers red.

VIII. Group FLABELLATÆ

Stamens 5, rarely 6 to 8; leaves yellow-green. (*C. Holmesiana*) HAW

EEEEE. Fruit nearly round, ¾ inch long, greenish red, calyx prominent; stamens 20, anthers rose coloured.

IX. Group DILATATÆ

Flowers 1¼ inches across, few; leaves 2 to 3 inches long and broad, with deep side lobes. (*C. coccinioides*) HAW

DD. Leaves wedge shaped at base.

E. Corymbs many-flowered; leaves dark green, lustrous above, fruit ½ to ¾ inch long, nutlets 2 to 3, ridged on back.

X. Group COCCINEÆ

Thorns 1½ inch long, brown, stout; fruit crimson, dry and sweet, leaves 2 to 3 inches long. (*C. coccinea*) SCARLET HAW

EE. Corymbs few-flowered; leaves membranaceous.

F. Fruit ½ inch long, green or yellow; nutlets 3 to 5, rounded at ends, strongly ridged at back; leaves yellow-green.

XI. Group INTRICATÆ

Fruits 2 to 4 in clusters, erect, flat, rusty, reddish green, stamens 10, pale yellow. (*C. Boyntoni*) HAW

FF. Fruit ¼ inch long, red or orange; nutlets 3 to 5 but slightly grooved on back; stamens 20, anthers rose coloured; leaves thin, sharply lobed.

XII. Group PULCHERRIMÆ

Fruit bright red. (*C. opima*) HAW

FFF. Fruit ½ to ⅝ inch long; nutlets 3 to 5, narrowed at ends, strongly ridged on back; bracts large; calyx lobes leaf-like; stamens 20, anthers yellow; leaves dark, lustrous, leathery.

XIII. Group BRACTEATÆ

Fruit bright red. (*C. Ashei*) HAW

301

CCCC. Petioles, leaves and corymbs conspicuously glandular; corymbs few-flowered; fruit ½ to ¾ inch long, flesh hard, dry; branches zizag.

XIV. Group FLAVÆ

Bark deeply furrowed; leaves diamond shaped, thick, shining, with short winged petiole; corymbs velvety, with 3 to 6 flowers, stamens 10, anthers yellow; fruit late, dull orange red, flattened. (*C. aprica*) HAW

BB. Veins of leaves extending to sinuses as well as to points of lobes; corymbs many-flowered; stamens 20.

C. Fruit flattened to oblong, pea size, scarlet; nutlets 2 to 5, prominently ridged at back; anthers rose coloured or purple.

XV. Group MICROCARPÆ

D. Leaves round, deeply 5 to 7 cleft. (*C. apiifolia*) PARSLEY HAW

DD. Leaves heart shaped. (*C. cordata*) WASHINGTON THORN

CC. Fruit flattened, ⅓ to ½ inch long, red, blue or blueblack nutlets 3 to 5, obtuse at ends, slightly ridged at back; leaves dark and lustrous.

XVI. Group BRACHYACANTHÆ

Leaves lanceolate; thorns stout; fruit bright blue. (*C. brachyacantha*) POMETTE BLEUE

AA. Nutlets grooved in front.

B. Fruits ¼ to ½ inch long, erect, lustrous, orange or scarlet; nutlets 2 to 3, blunt at ends, ridged on back; leaves downy below.

XVII. Group TOMENTOSÆ

C. Fruit pear shaped, translucent, orange red, leaves 2 to 5 inches long, grey-green, tomentose below; thorns 1½ inches long, slender. (*C. tomentosa*) PEAR HAW

CC. Fruit, pea-like, crimson, leaves 2 to 3 inches long, dark, lustrous, tapering; thorns 2½ to 4 inches long, curved. (*C. macracantha*) LONG-SPINE HAW

BB. Fruit nearly globular, ½ inch long, black; nutlets 5, blunt at ends, faintly ridged on back; stamens 20; leaves leathery.

XVIII. Group DOUGLASIANÆ

Leaves variable in form, fruit many in a cluster, lustrous, sweet. (*C. Douglasii*) BLACK HAW

The hawthorns are a shrubby race of trees, under-sized, as a rule, with stiff, zigzag branches, set with thorns. The leaves are simple, alternate, deciduous, usually cut into sharp lobes, and saw teeth. The flowers are generally white, and set in terminal corymbs on side branchlets. The fruits are drupe-like pomes, with bony nutlets containing the seeds. As a rule fruits are red; in a few species they are orange; still fewer, yellow, blue or black. The flesh is generally mealy and dry. The nutlets are joined at their bases, and are variously grooved and ridged.

The stamens are normally five in a circle, set alternate with the petals. There may be five pairs, similarly placed. Or fifteen may occur, in two rows, twenty in three, or twenty-five in four circles. These are the typical arrangements. When not in fives, some stamens have failed to develop. The number of stamens, their arrangement and the colour of their anthers, is considered by Professor Sargent an important clue to relationship. The grooves and ridges on the nutlets form another constant and significant character on which his classification is based.

The generic name, Cratægus, is derived from *kratos*, the Greek word for strength, and refers to the hard, tough wood.

The centre of distribution for the hawthorns is undoubtedly the eastern United States. From Newfoundland to Mexico they abound in great variety. A few species are found on the Pacific coast and in the Rocky Mountains. Europe and Asia have a few.

It is remarkable that trees so conspicuous as these should until lately be so little known. Linnæus named four American species. Professor Sargent described fourteen only in Vol. IV. of "The Silva of North America." In Vol. XIII., the supplement, issued in 1900, seventy-three species were added to those described in Vol. IV., bringing his total up to eighty-seven. In his "Manual" published in 1905, Professor Sargent describes and gives rank as species to 128 hawthorns native to the United States. These are divided into eighteen groups by characters set forth in the key. I have chosen a typical species to illustrate each group, and added only such others as have distinction and horticultural promise. The fact that Professor Sargent knows this genus better than anyone else has been my reason for borrowing his key almost unchanged.

The whole story of the hawthorns and their relationships cannot be told by any man now living. Nor can present knowledge and opinion on the subject be considered as final. It takes time to test the stability of species. Thousands of seeds have been collected from haws and planted in the nurseries of the Arnold Arboretum. Probably no such undertaking was ever projected and carried out. What is it all about? Take an example.

A new kind of hawthorn was found growing wild on a hillside within the very gates of the Arboretum. It was evidently related to *C. mollis*, but was considered sufficiently distinct to deserve rank as a new species. Professor Sargent called it *Cratægus Arnoldiana*. A keen-eyed scientist found the same species growing wild along the river banks at Medford, Massachusetts. Does it grow elsewhere? Nobody knows, yet. Seeds from both groups are growing in the nursery. They have shown their foliage. They will be set out in due time, and ultimately will produce flowers and fruit for comparison with the parent trees. If they are alike and "true to type," the inference is that the species is distinct—set off by clear-cut characters from its near relatives. If, on the other hand, these seedling trees closely resemble *C. mollis*, rather than their own parents, the variability is evidence against their deserving a distinct name and a place among species. Their seeds must be planted, and seedling trees brought to bearing. What will their testimony be? How will they compare with their parents and grandparents?

It takes years of careful study to find out these things. Accurate records must be kept; each tree has its pedigree and biography written in full in the card catalogue, and a prophecy of its value in cultivation.

Perhaps there are not so many species as are now described. One student of the genus thinks that the virgin forests kept hawthorns suppressed. The clearing of the land gave them a chance. The multitude of forms now seen, he thinks may be seminal variations, due to the more favourable auspices under which the seedling trees now grow. Until recent years, nobody was making observations on the subject. Now, in many regions, this scientific study is being carried on—independently or in conjunction with Professor Sargent. The outcome will be a large body of knowledge regarding the genus.

The horticulturist is beginning to realise the value of the hawthorns. The showy flowers and fruits, the vivid colouring of autumn foliage, and the striking character expressed in winter

SCARLET HAW (*Cratægus coccinea*)

by the rigid branches and their menacing thorns, give most of these little trees attractiveness at all seasons. Many species are handsome and effective as hedge plants. Fine individual trees for lawn planting are furnished by others. Hawthorns are quick to grow in any soil and situation, and they show the most remarkable improvement when encouraged by tillage and a little fertilising. They do well in heavy clay. They are transplanted easily when young, from the wild; but having tap roots are hard to dig, and less sure to survive transplanting when older. They come readily from seed, though as a rule requiring two years to germinate.

I. CRUS-GALLI

Cockspur Thorn (*Crataegus Crus-galli*, Linn.)—A small, handsome tree, 15 to 25 feet high, with stiff branches in a broad, round head. *Thorns* axillary, stout, often curved, brown or grey, 3 to 4 inches long, often becoming 6 to 8 inches long and branched when old. *Bark* grey or brown, scaly, branchlets smooth, green, becoming brown, then grey. *Wood* brownish red, close grained, hard, heavy, takes satiny polish. *Buds* small, scaly, brownish red. *Leaves* thick, leathery, lustrous, dark green above, paler beneath, 1 to 4 inches long, obovate; acute or rounded and serrate at apex; entire below middle and tapering to the stout petiole; veins netted; stipules paired, strap shaped, or obliquely ovate, falling early. Autumn colours orange and scarlet. *Flowers*, May to June, after leaves, in racemose corymbs, loose, many-flowered, with smooth stems, blossoms spreading, white, $\frac{2}{3}$ inch across; sepals and petals 5; stamens 10, with rose-coloured anthers; styles usually 2. *Fruit*, October, remain till spring, almost globular, $\frac{1}{2}$ inch long, dull red, with dry, thin, mealy flesh; calyx lobes dry and spreading at apex; nutlets 2, deeply grooved on back. *Preferred habitat*, rich soil of low hill slopes. *Distribution*, Montreal region to southern Michigan; south to Delaware and Pennsylvania; along Appalachian foothills into North Carolina. *Uses:* Cultivated as an ornamental and in hedges in Europe and America. Wood used for tool handles, levers, etc.

Wherever a cockspur thorn is planted, in open lawn with elbow room, or in a crowded shrubbery border, it keeps its character, and gives the passerby a distinct impression of something new and different. It is like an interjection met in the even swing of a long sentence.

There are vigour and strength expressed at any age by the tree's rigid, zigzag branches, armed with long, sharp spurs. The thorns strike downward, as a rule, on horizontal branches. The leaves stand up "on tiptoe," as if to keep out of the way. Indeed, they might be taken for weapons themselves, they are so thin, and keen edged, and shining. From the ground up, on young trees, the bark is bright and polished, varying from red to brown and grey.

The flowers are late, coming out in showy clusters when the full-grown leaves make a lustrous background. The fruits make little show until ripe, for the leaves are rarely touched by fungous or insect injuries, and in the fall, when the fruit begins to flush, the foliage takes on the colours of flame. The dull red clusters glow with a subdued warmth on the branches all winter. The birds let them alone.

So all year long the cockspur is a beautiful ornamental tree, and a competent and popular hedge plant. It is the favourite American thorn in Europe and at home, known for two centuries, and named by Linnæus, one of the proud old "first families" of the genus Cratægus.

Cratægus Mohri, Beadl., is a slender thorn tree, close of kin to the other cockspurs, as we recognise by its shining leaves, slender spines and thin-fleshed fruits, with nutlets deeply grooved on the back. It belongs to the group of cockspur thorns whose flowers and fruits are borne on pubescent pedicels. There are twenty stamens, with yellow anthers, set in three rows.

This straight thorn tree has spreading and rather pendulous limbs, and short, shiny, brown spines. Its range centres in Alabama, whence it extends into Georgia, Mississippi and Tennessee. Its favourite situations are moist, level woodlands.

It promises to be for the South what *C. Crus-galli* is in the Northeastern States—a handsome, useful ornamental and hedge tree.

II. PUNCTATÆ

Dotted Haw (*Cratægus punctata*, Jacq.)—A broad, round-headed tree, 20 to 30 feet high, with horizontal branches, and

306

1 Leaf, under side   2 Leaf, upper side   3 Fruit   4 Fruit cut to show seeds   5 Seeds from one fruit

THE COCKSPUR THORN (*Cratægus Crus-galli*)

Copious white bloom conceals the leaves in early June. The thorns are slender and strong, becoming 6 to 8 inches long and branched on old limbs. The leaves are leathery and polished, narrowly obovate, 1 to 4 inches long

THE RED HAW (*Cratægus mollis*)

The large red haws, which ripen in early September, are fuzzy around the base of the incurving calyx tips. The fruit stems and leaf linings are pubescent. In spring the new growth is thickly coated with white hairs

THE DOTTED HAW (*Cratægus punctata*)

The pale dots on the fruit give this tree its name. The grey-green leaves taper narrowly to the petioles. The prominent, depressed veins and the long, straight spines are shown in the upper plate

THE SCARLET HAW (*Cratægus pruinosa*)

The lower right-hand picture shows the broad-based leaf with its lobed margin and the short, stout spines. The leaves are blue-green, and the unripe fruit has a hoary bloom upon it

rigid twigs. *Thorns* straight, slim, 2 to 3 inches long, brown or grey. *Bark* thin, dark brownish red, in long, plate-like scales, branches brown to pale grey; twigs pubescent at first, soon becoming smooth. *Wood* red-brown, hard, close-textured. *Buds* plump, small, scaly, shiny. *Leaves* obovate, acute or obtuse at apex, 2 to 3 inches long, narrowed to short petiole; sharply serrate, sometimes lobed, entire toward base; pubescent at first, smooth at maturity, except on veins below, leathery, grey-green, orange and scarlet in autumn. *Veins* prominent, depressed above. *Flowers*, May, when leaves are half grown, in thick, flat, many-flowered corymbs on pale tomentose stems; calyx hairy, corollas spreading, white, $\frac{1}{2}$ to $\frac{3}{4}$ inch across, stamens 20, with rose-coloured or yellow anthers, styles 2 to 5, hairy at base. *Fruit* falls in October, short-oblong to sub-globose, $\frac{1}{2}$ to 1 inch long, yellow or red; marked by white dots; flesh thin, dry; calyx lobes flattened; nutlets 5, ridged on back. *Preferred habitat*, rich, moist upland soil. Farm thickets. *Distribution*, Quebec to Detroit; western New England, along mountains to northern Georgia, Tennessee and North Carolina; west to Ohio and Illinois. *Uses:* Valuable ornamental hawthorn.

The large, pale dots on the fruit of this haw give it its name, *punctata*. Very strangely, some trees produce yellow fruit, and have flowers with yellow anthers; while red is the rule in both anthers and fruit.

The dotted haw is a handsome, long-thorned tree, with obovate, strongly veined leaves, whose colour in autumn is like fire. The fruit is brilliant, too, hanging in full clusters long after the leaves drop.

Cratægus collina, Chapm., which resembles *C. punctata* and *C. Crus-galli* in habit, has yellow-green foliage, and the dull red fruits are flattened globes, containing five grooved and ridged nutlets. Sometimes the branches are set with formidable, branched thorns, 6 inches long. It is quite common for the trunk to be corrugated and buttressed at the base.

This tree grows along the foothills from West Virginia to central Georgia, and west half way across Tennessee and Alabama. It reaches an altitude of 2,500 feet. It is an early species, blooming in April when the leaves are scarcely opening, and ripening its fruit in September. The flesh is yellow and thin, mealy and insipid.

III. ÆSTIVALES

May, or Apple Haw (*C. æstivalis*, T. & G.)—A round-headed, compact tree, with stout trunk, 20 to 30 feet high. *Thorns* 1 to 1½ inches long, stout, sharp; often absent. *Bark* thin, fissured and broken into plate-like scales, dark reddish brown. Twigs rufous pubescent, soon becoming smooth and grey or brown. *Wood* heavy, Close grained, light brown, weak. *Buds* plump, small, scaly, brown. *Leaves* elliptical, irregularly wavy-toothed and serrate above the middle, entire and tapering to pubescent petiole; 1½ to 2 inches long, dark green, leathery shining above, with rusty hairs on veins beneath. *Flowers* with the leaves in February or early March, 2 to 5 in simple corymbs, corolla 1 inch across, white; calyx tips ruddy; stamens 20 to 25, anthers large dark rose. *Fruit*, May, 1 to 3 in cluster, flattened globes, fragrant, pleasantly sub-acid, juicy, thick fleshed, calyx lobes large, curved back; nutlets 3 to 5, with deep grooves and ridges on back. *Preferred habitat*, moist, sandy soil. *Distribution*, Florida to Texas and Arkansas. *Uses:* Handsome tree for ornamental planting. Fruit sold in Louisiana markets, and made into preserves and jellies.

IV. VIRIDES

Haw (*C. viridis*, Linn.)—A round-headed tree, 20 to 35 feet, with tall, often fluted trunk, and spreading branches. *Thorns* slim, pale, under 1 inch long; usually wanting. *Bark* brown, ashy grey or orange, checked into plate-like scales. *Leaves* ovate or obovate, acute at apex and base, serrate and lobed above middle, usually entire below; dark green, lustrous above, pale and dull beneath, scarlet in autumn; veins strong; petioles slender. *Flowers*, March to May, with leaves, in smooth corymbs, white, ¾ inch across, stamens 20, anthers yellow, styles 5. *Fruit* bright scarlet in pendant clusters, flattened globose, pea-size, thin, dry flesh; nutlets 5, scarcely ridged. *Preferred habitat*, low ground along streams. *Distribution*, Savannah River to western Florida, through Gulf States to eastern Texas; north to St. Louis; forms thickets in Louisiana. *Uses:* Valuable ornamental tree, for the brilliance of its autumn foliage and winter fruits.

The trunk of this species attracts attention, sometimes by its form, always by its colour. Its vivid fruit hangs throughout the

HAW (*Cratægus Boyntoni*)

Few-fruited, erect clusters of reddish-green haws; oval leaves ined with some pubescence; short petioles, winged near the leaf; and straight thorns an inch or two long characterise this species

HAW (*Cratægus apiomorpha*)

Rough, blue-green leaves, ovate-oblong on long petioles; drooping fruit clusters purplish-red in September; calyx spreading over the angled fruit distinguish this species

THE SCARLET HAW (*Cratægus Arnoldiana*)

This tree is vigorous in habit; its new growth is downy. Even the ripe fruits are velvety. The flowers come out in May after the broad, ovate leaves are spread

THE PARSLEY HAW (*Cratægus apiifolia*)

The deeply cut leaves distinguish this tree

winter, making up in quantity what it lacks in size. Rare in the East and North, yet it is hardy in the Arnold Arboretum.

V. PRUINOSÆ

Scarlet Haw (*C. pruinosa*, K. Koch.)—Small tree, 15 to 20 feet high, spreading irregular head of horizontal limbs. *Thorns* numerous, stout, straight, 1 to 1½ inches long. *Bark* grey, thin, in loose scales. *Wood* hard, heavy, close grained. *Buds* small, blunt, scaly. *Leaves* ovate or elliptical, acute, lobed and serrate, except on entire base; dark blue-green, smooth, leathery, paler beneath; 1 to 1½ inches long, on slender petioles; autumn colour orange. *Flowers*, May, white, 1 inch broad, in few-flowered corymbs, stems long smooth; stamens 20, with long, rose-coloured anthers; styles 5, tufted. *Fruit* sub globose, ½ to ⅝ inch in diameter, with erect calyx, green with hoary bloom until ripe, then purplish red and lustrous with pale dots. Nutlets 5, deeply ridged, enclosed in dry, thick flesh. *Preferred habitat*, limestone soil of slopes. *Distribution*, Vermont to southern slopes of Appalachian Mountains; west to Illinois and Missouri. *Uses:* Valuable ornamental tree over wide territory.

There is a pale bloom on the green fruit of this tree, which wears off at length, and the skin becomes shiny and dark, purplish red. The leaves, too, have a bluish green cast through the summer, but turn to orange at last. This is one of the handsome native thorn trees, a long time confused with *C. coccinea*.

VI. TENUIFOLIÆ

Haw (*C. apiomorpha*, Sarg.)—A pyramidal tree, 10 to 25 feet high, with short trunk. *Thorns* short, straight, slender, grey, 1 to 1½ inches long. *Bark* dark grey, cracking into plates which show yellow under layer. *Leaves* oblong-ovate, pointed at apex, serrate almost to petiole, irregularly lobed above middle, thick, leathery, lustrous, blue-green, paler beneath, membranaceous and hairy when opening, 1½ to 2½ inches long, petioles slender. *Flowers*, May, in many-flowered corymbs, with hairy stems, small, white, stamens 5, anthers pink, styles 3 to 5, tufted. *Fruits*, September, in drooping clusters of 3 to 5; pea size, obovate, bright, red-purple; calyx large, spreading, deciduous, flesh thin, acid, succulent; nutlets 3 to 5, with one low ridge on back. *Preferred habitat*, dry borders of woodlands. *Distribution*, near Chicago.

VII. MOLLES

Red Haw (*C. mollis*, Scheele.)—A tree 25 to 40 feet high, tall trunk; round head, branchlets stout. *Thorns* stout, brown, 1 to 2 inches long, shining. *Bark* grey to brown, thin, in plate-like scales; branches ashy grey; twigs coated with pale hairs. *Wood* hard, heavy, brown. *Buds* small, blunt. *Leaves* thick, firm, rough above, dark yellow-green, 3 to 4 inches long, broadly ovate, acute, serrate, with 4 to 5 pairs of pointed lobes above middle; base entire; lining, pale, pubescent; petioles slender, hairy, stipules leaf-like, toothed on vigorous shoots. *Flowers*, May, 1 inch across, in hairy, many-flowered corymbs, with prominent bracts; disc, red, calyx hoary, red-tipped, stamens 20, with pale yellow anthers, styles 4 to 5. *Fruits*, August and September, few in a cluster, drooping, scarlet, downy, globular, or nearly so, ¾ to 1 inch in diameter, marked with dark dots; calyx lobes large, erect, falling as fruit ripens, nutlets 4 to 5, faintly ridged, in thick, mealy yellow flesh. *Preferred habitat*, rich bottom lands. *Distribution*, Ohio to Dakota, Nebraska and Kansas.

This red haw is the type of a large group containing a dozen related species. Ample in size, fine in form and colouring, there is but one fault the landscape gardener can find. The red fruits fall early in the autumn.

Scarlet Haw (*C. Arnoldiana*, Sarg.)—A broad, open-headed tree, 15 to 20 feet high, with ascending branches and slender, zigzag, orange-brown branchlets, downy at first. *Thorns* stout, shining, brown, 2 to 3 inches long. *Bark* dark grey, with thick scales on trunk; branches pale grey, smooth. *Leaves* broadly ovate, with shallow lobes, sharply serrate almost to petiole; covered at first with matted white hairs, at maturity lustrous, dark green above, paler beneath and smooth except on slender veins, 2 to 3 inches long and the same broad; petioles ¾ to 1½ inches long. *Flowers*, May, in broad, compound corymbs; stems velvety; corolla ¾ inch across; stamens 10, anthers pale yellow, large; styles 3 to 4, densely tufted. *Fruit*, August, September, soon falling, few in a cluster, erect, nearly globular, bright crimson, ¾ inch long, velvety, with large, pale dots; flesh thick, juicy, pleasantly acid; nutlets 3 to 4, ridged. *Preferred habitat*, dry banks. *Distribution*, Arnold Arboretum in Boston, and Medford, Massachusetts.

The discovery of this handsome hawthorn, not long ago, growing wild within the gates of the Arnold Arboretum, was an event of considerable importance to horticulture; for this tree, laden with its large crimson fruit in August, is a wondrous sight. Added to their beauty, these fruits are juicy, and have a pleasant piquant flavour, for which they deserve especial mention.

In winter, the tree may be known by the remarkable zigzag of its ascending branches. In habit and foliage it is thrifty and handsome. The fruit ripens and begins to fall in August, but a goodly quantity remains to brighten the fading leaves well on into October.

The tree has been found growing wild near Medford, Massachusetts, and is now often seen in cultivation about Boston.

Red Haw (*C. submollis*, Sarg.)—Tree 20 to 25 feet high, with round, handsome head, branchlets slender. *Thorns* slender, curved, brown, shining, 2 to 3 inches long. *Bark* pale greyish brown, scaly; twigs, tomentose, branches orange brown. *Leaves* ovate, acute, with doubly serrate, pointed lobes above middle; base cuneate, serrate, becoming entire near slender, downy petiole; 2½ to 3½ inches long, almost as wide, pubescent at first, becoming smooth, except on veins beneath, and rough above. *Flowers*, May, in compound, pubescent corymbs, white, 1 inch across, with 10 stamens, anthers pale yellow, styles 3 to 5, tufted at base. *Fruits* ripe and falling in early September; in slender, copious clusters, lustrous orange red, pear shaped, with pale dots, ¾ inch long, with prominent, erect calyx lobes; pedicels slender, velvety; nutlets 5, slightly ridged, in thin, mealy flesh. *Preferred habitat*, rich soil of woodland borders. *Distribution*, Quebec to Penobscot Valley in Maine; to eastern Massachusetts; also near Albany, New York.

This Eastern species was long considered identical with the preceding one. It is now distinguished by well-defined characters. It is not so densely downy as *C. mollis*. The leaves are smaller, more deeply lobed, and usually wedge shaped at base. The fruits are smaller and pear shaped. The branchlets are orange brown. The flowers have ten stamens; *C. mollis* has twenty. *C submollis* is one of the showiest and best species for ornamental purposes.

Scarlet Haw (*C. Ellwangeriana*, Sarg.)—A handsome tree, 10 to 20 feet high, with ascending branches, forming a round head. *Thorns* 1½ to 2 inches long, stout; tree often unarmed. *Bark* light grey, scaly; twigs green, with pale hairs. *Leaves* oval, acute, sharply serrate almost to base, with 4 to 5 acute lobes, rough above, paler beneath, light green, thin, 2½ to 3½ inches long; petioles pubescent, slender; veins strong. *Flowers*, May, in velvety-stemmed corymbs; calyx, hairy, with stalked glands; corollas 1 inch across, white; stamens 8 to 10; anthers small, rose coloured. *Fruits* ripe and falling in September, on smooth stems, oblong, bright crimson, shining, 1 inch long, ¾ inch wide, flesh thin, sour, juicy; nutlets 3 to 5, ridged. *Preferred habitat*, rich woodland soil. *Distribution*, about Rochester, New York. *Uses:* A handsome ornamental tree.

The preceding species is worthily named in honour of the founder of the Arboretum. Another distinguished patron of horticulture and forestry, George Ellwanger, is remembered in the name of this species. A single tree which stands in the Mount Hope Nurseries of Ellwanger & Barry, at Rochester, New York, has been for years the wonder and admiration of visitors and the pride of its owners. In the woods about Rochester this species is quite common. It is counted by Professor Sargent "one of the largest and most beautiful hawthorns in the Northern States."

VIII. FLABELLATÆ

Red Haw (*C. Holmesiana*, Ashe.)—Tall tree, 20 to 30 feet high, with stout ascending branches; head irregular and open, or compact. *Thorns* thick, 1½ to 2 inches long, scattered far apart. *Bark* grey or nearly white, scaly. *Leaves* oval or ovate, acute or acuminate, sharply lobed and doubly serrate; thick and firm, nearly smooth, distinctly yellow-green at maturity, 1½ to 2 inches long, with strong midribs and long petioles. *Flowers*, May, cup shaped, ½ to ¾ inch across, in loose corymbs; stamens 5 to 8, anthers large, deep reddish purple. *Fruits* September, falling soon, crimson, oblong, ½ to ⅔ inch long, with reddish, incurved calyx lobes; nutlets 3, distinctly ridged, flesh mealy, acid, dis-

THE SCARLET HAW (*Cratægus coccinea*)

This is one of the old, well-known, ornamental thorns which flowers copiously in early May and ripens its large red fruits in late August. Unfortunately, they soon fall

THE RED HAW (*Cratægus mollis*)

This handsome thorn tree is hoary in spring with white, matted hairs upon its new shoots. One flower cluster is shown below. Each flower has 20 pale yellow stamens

THE HAW (*Crataegus coccinioides*)

The broad leaves with squarish bases, the erect fruit clusters and the conspicuous flaring calyx lobes of the greenish-red fruits distinguish this vigorous species. The thorns are short and stout

agreeable. *Preferred habitat,* rich, moist hillsides. *Distribution,* Montreal to southern Ontario; coast of Maine, central and western Massachusetts, Rhode Island, western New York, eastern Pennsylvania. Largest in Worcester County, Massachusetts. *Uses:* Handsome tree for ornamental planting.

This is the largest hawthorn in eastern New England. Its scaly bark is often almost white. Its leaves are more distinctly yellow than green—greenish yellow, to speak accurately. The lustrous crimson fruit makes a gorgeous autumn contrast with bark and foliage.

Scattered over pasture land, these lusty young trees are cropped by cattle, which manage to avoid the infrequent thorns. By degrees, the girth of the tree widens, in spite of the pruning thus administered. The terminal shoot finally rises above the reach of any yearning tongue. It branches, and lifts above the dome-like basal part a flourishing top that grows loose and free in striking contrast to the compact close-clipped base. Many of these pasture trees have this hour-glass form.

IX. DILATATÆ

Red Haw (*C. coccinioides,* Ashe.)—A tree 10 to 25 feet high, with broad dome of stout, spreading branches. *Thorns* 1½ to 2 inches long, straight, stout, purplish red. *Bark* dark brown, scaly; branches light grey. *Leaves* broadly ovate, acute, sharply serrate, with deep pointed lateral lobes, 2 to 3 inches long, lustrous yellow-green, at first; becoming dull, dark green later; thin, turning to orange and bright red in fall; petioles bright red, ¾ to 1 inch long. *Flowers,* May, in compact corymbs, with prominent, serrate bracts, with red glands; corolla 1¼ inches across; stamens 20, anthers large, rose colour; styles 5. *Fruits,* October, falling gradually; clusters erect; haws globose, flattened at ends, lustrous, dark red, with pale dots; calyx conspicuous, red at base; flesh thick, reddish, pleasantly acid; nutlets 5, small, slightly ridged on back. *Preferred habitat,* dry woods. *Distribution,* St. Louis, Missouri, to eastern Kansas. *Uses:* Desirable ornamental thorn tree.

The very large leaves of this tree obscure the compact fruit clusters, and its ornamental character is not so obvious until the leaves turn. I recall one tree, a fine, lusty specimen, loaded with fruit in late September. There was a cockspur on one side, an *Arnoldiana* on the other. Both were bidding high for attention, one with its crimson fruits, the other with its splendid foliage and flashing thorns. A flush of rose pink covered the middle tree, the fruits turning to red. There was more delicacy of colouring and moderation here, which made the two trees alongside seem rather common and gaudy by contrast. Sometimes soft colours appeal strongly as a relief from more vivid ones. Out of this period the tree passes to its flaming October garb, in the midst of which the shining fruits are a dark crimson, and even the twigs and spines burn red or purple.

X. COCCINEÆ

Scarlet Haw (*C. coccinea*, Linn.)—A shrubby round tree, 10 to 20 feet high, with short trunk, and stout, ascending branches. *Thorns* stout, shining, 1 to $1\frac{1}{2}$ inches long, brown. *Bark* dark red-brown, scaly; branches grey. *Leaves* elliptical or obovate, acute at both ends, serrate and acutely lobed on sides; $2\frac{1}{2}$ to 3 inches long; veins prominent; petioles 1 inch long, tinged with red. *Flowers*, May or June, in broad corymbs with downy stems; corollas $\frac{1}{2}$ to $\frac{3}{4}$ inch across; stamens 10, anthers small, yellow. *Fruit*, October, falling soon; sub-globose to oblong, $\frac{1}{2}$ inch in diameter, deep crimson, with dark dots; calyx red, spreading; flesh sweet, dry, thin; nutlets 3 to 4, distinctly ridged on back. *Preferred Habitat*, well-drained soil, along low hills and banks of salt marshes. *Distribution*, Newfoundland to Connecticut, along the shore, and along St. Lawrence to western Quebec. Var. *rotundifolia*, a shrub, New England into Pennsylvania.

This scarlet thorn, the one that Linnæus named, has very uncertain botanical and geographical limits. Those forms found west of Quebec are now excluded, and many that were counted mere varietal forms are now promoted to specific rank. These changes in classification are the result of recent studies of the genus in various regions. The true *coccinea* is one of the old well-known ornamental thorns, a favourite in the Northeastern States.

XI. INTRICATÆ

Haw (*C. Boyntoni*, Beadl.)—Narrow or round-headed tree, 15 to 20 feet high, with tall, straight trunk, often a many-stemmed shrub. *Thorns* numerous, slender, straight, $1\frac{1}{2}$ to 2 inches long, sometimes branched when old. *Bark* grey, often brownish, scaly. *Leaves* broadly ovate, acute, irregularly lobed, finely serrate, thin, firm, yellow-green at maturity; smooth, 1 to $2\frac{1}{2}$ inches long; petioles stout, short, with red glands. *Flowers*, May, in 4 to 10-flowered corymbs, smooth, corrollas $\frac{3}{4}$ inch across, stamens 10, anthers pale yellow; styles 3 to 5, tufted. *Fruit* ripe and falling in October, in erect clusters of 2 to 4; each a flattened globe, rusty reddish green, with dark dots, $\frac{1}{2}$ inch in diameter; calyx spreading, falling off before fruit ripens; flesh thin; nutlets 3 to 5, distinctly ridged. *Preferred habitat*, stream borders and uplands. *Distribution*, Appalachian foothills, to 3,000 feet elevation; southern Virginia and southeastern Kentucky to northern Georgia and Alabama.

XII. Pulcherrimæ

Haw (*C. opima*, Beadl.)—Small tree 20 to 25 feet high, with open, oval head, above a slender, spiny trunk. *Thorns* slender, straight, shining, 1 to $1\frac{1}{2}$ inches long. *Bark* nearly black at base; ashy grey on limbs. *Leaves* ovate, acute, sharply saw-toothed, lobed above middle, thin, firm, pale beneath. *Flowers*, few in clusters $\frac{2}{3}$ inch across, stamens 20, anthers purple. *Fruit* in October, persistent, small, few, bright red, mealy. *Preferred habitat*, clay soil in woods. *Distribution*, about Greenville, Alabama.

XIII. Bracteatæ

Haw (*C. Ashei*, Beadl.)—Tree 15 to 20 feet high, with pyramidal head. *Thorns* slender, 1 to $1\frac{1}{2}$ inches long. *Bark* scaly, grey or brown. *Leaves* broadly ovate to obovate, about 2 inches long, finely serrate, blunt at apex, tapering to base. *Flowers* in May, 3 to 10 in cluster on hairy stems, $\frac{3}{4}$ inch across, stamens 20, anthers yellow. *Fruit*, October, bright red, 1 inch long, dotted, thick fleshed. *Preferred habitat*, clay soil of fallow land. *Distribution*, near Montgomery, Alabama.

XIV. Flavæ

Haw (*C. aprica*, Beadl.)—Tree 15 to 20 feet high, or many-stemmed shrub. *Thorns* straight, slender, chestnut brown,

315

1 to 1½ inches long. *Bark* dark grey, deeply furrowed, with plate-like scales; branchlets brown to ashy grey. *Leaves* obovate or rhomboidal, acute or rounded, serrate, often faintly lobed at apex, entire at tapering base; thick, shiny, dark yellow-green at maturity, paler beneath, 1½ to 2 inches long and wide; petioles short, winged. *Flowers*, May, 3 to 6 in corymbs, velvety stems, corollas ¾ inch across, stamens 10, anthers yellow. *Fruit* late to ripen, 2 to 3 in cluster, ½ inch in diameter, slightly flattened, dull orange red; calyx spreading, red tinged at base; flesh juicy, yellow, sweet; nutlets 3 to 5, ridged. *Preferred habitat*, dry woods of foothills. *Distribution*, southwestern Virginia, through western North Carolina, eastern Tennessee, northern Georgia and Alabama. Common at 1,500 to 3,000 feet above sea level.

Its contorted branches and dark, furrowed bark give this tree a picturesque appearance that matches well the wild, broken foothills it covers in thickets of considerable extent. Inured to high altitudes and exposed situations, yet it grows thriftily in the Arboretum at Boston. It is a striking tree in late autumn, when its leaves turn to purple, and the twigs are illuminated by the thickly clustered, orange-red fruit.

XV. Microcarpæ

Parsley Haw (*C. apiifolia*, Michx.)—Tree 15 to 20 feet, with horizontal, zigzag, twisted branches, forming irregular, wide, open head. *Thorns* stout, straight, brown, 1 to 1½ inches long. *Wood* hard, heavy, reddish brown, with satiny lustre. *Leaves* broadly ovate to round, with 5 to 7 lobes, separated by deep sinuses, and sharply toothed margins to the broad, entire base; bright green, smooth above, 1½ to 2 inches long; petioles slender, long. *Flowers*, March to April, ½ inch long, in hairy, dense corymbs; stamens 20, anthers bright rose colour, styles 1 to 3. *Fruits*, October, persistent for several weeks, oblong, ¼ to ⅓ inch long, scarlet; nutlets 1 to 3, grooved. *Preferred habitat*, stream borders, hummocks in pine barrens and swamp margins. *Distribution*, coast region from Virginia to Florida; westward to Arkansas and Texas. *Uses:* One of the finest and most abundant hawthorns in the valley of the Mississippi. Its graceful, parsley-like leaves at once distinguish it from other species. The flowers and fruit are small, but abundant and very handsome.

Washington Thorn (*C. cordata*, Ait.)—Vigorous tree, compact, 25 to 40 feet high. *Thorns* numerous, slender, 1 to 2 inches long. *Leaves* triangular, 1 to 3 inches long, with 3 to 7 acute lobes, serrate, cordate at base, thin, shining, vivid red in autumn; petioles slender, long. *Flowers*, May, many in corymb, ⅓ inch across, styles 5, stamens 20, anthers. *Fruits*, September, small, flat, scarlet, shining, hanging late into winter. *Preferred habitat*, moist woods. *Distribution*, Virginia to Alabama, to Illinois. *Uses:* A desirable ornamental and hedge thorn.

This species comes nearer than any of its relatives to the typical heart-shaped leaf, hence its Latin name. As the upper course of the Potomac River is the northernmost limit of its natural range, we may guess that it takes its common name from the capital city.

Very early, the Virginians sent the seed of this thorn to friends at home, so that it has long adorned European gardens. In the colonies, it was extensively planted for hedges. It proved hardy in all the Middle States, and is now naturalised by escape from old hedges in New York, Pennsylvania and Delaware. The compact habit of the tree, and the great multitude of its slender spines make it useful as a hedge plant. Besides, it is thrifty and grows rapidly. The flowers and berries make up in numbers for their small size. When the bright green foliage turns to vivid reds in the fall, the tree has already been conspicuous for some weeks by its coral red berries, which persist often till spring.

XVI. BRACHYACANTHÆ

Hog's Haw, Pomette Bleue (*C. brachyacantha*, Sarg. & Engelm.)—Tree 40 to 50 feet high, trunk 18 to 20 inches in diameter, with handsome, compact head, of stout grey branches. *Thorns* numerous, short, stout, curved, ⅓ to ⅔ inch long. *Bark* dark brown, deeply furrowed, scaly. *Leaves* lanceolate to rhomboidal, acute, serrate, sometimes distinctly lobed above middle, dark green, lustrous, firm, 1 to 2 inches long, on short petioles; stipules triangular, often 1 inch long. *Flowers*, May, ⅓ inch across, in compound corymbs; petals orange colour as they fade; stamens 15 to 20. *Fruits*, August, falling soon, flattened globes, ⅓ to ½ inch in diameter, bright blue, with pale bloom; flesh thin; nutlets 3 to 5, faintly grooved on back. *Preferred habitat*, rich, moist soil of stream borders. *Distribution*, southern Arkansas to western Louisiana, and to the Sabine River valley in Texas. *Uses:* Handsome ornamental in south temperate regions; not hardy in Massachusetts.

This is the only blue-fruited haw in the world. This unique character alone must commend it to planters. The stout, curving thorns, the lustrous foliage, the abundant flowers, and the large blue fruit—all make this one of the best ornamental species. On the wet prairies of western Louisiana, this tree forms dense thickets which are quite the dominating feature of the woods.

XVII. Tomentosæ

Pear Haw (*C. tomentosa*, Linn.)—A tree 15 to 20 feet high, forming a flat, wide head. *Thorns* scattered, slim, straight, 1 to 1½ inches long; or wanting. *Bark* dark brown, furrowed; branches grey, twigs hoary tomentose, becoming dark orange colour. *Leaves* ovate, acute at apex and base, 2 to 5 inches long, shallowly lobed and coarsely serrate, thin, firm, grey-green, persistently tomentose below; petioles stout, winged; veins prominent; autumn colour orange and scarlet. *Flowers*, March to June, ½ inch across, in broad, downy corymbs, ill-scented; stamens 20, anthers rose or yellow. *Fruits*, October, in erect, many-fruited clusters, persisting all winter, dull orange red, translucent, pear shaped, ½ inch in diameter; flesh thick, sweet, juicy; nutlets 2 to 3, ridged on back; grooved on ventral face. *Preferred habitat*, low, rich soil. *Distribution*, Troy, New York, to eastern Pennsylvania, central Tennessee and northern Georgia; west to southern Minnesota and south to southeastern Kansas. *Uses:* Valuable ornamental for its brilliant autumnal colours and persistent fruits.

This is one of the most widely distributed of our native haws. It is cultivated to some extent, but not as it deserves. With the development of horticulture, it will get recognition from nurserymen and from the tree-planting fraternity in general.

Long-spine Haw (*C. macracantha*, Kœhne.)—Tree 10 to 15 feet high, or spreading shrub. *Thorns* numerous, curved, slender, 2½ to 4 inches long, shining. *Bark* pale, close textured; branchlets reddish, lustrous. *Leaves* oval or obovate, 2 to 3 inches long, 1 to 2 inches wide, acute at both ends, shallowly lobed, and

THE WASHINGTON THORN (*Cratægus cordata*)

The leaves are in general heart-shaped at base. The charm of this old-fashioned hedge tree is its formidable thorny armament and the brilliant red of its erect fruit clusters which remain all winter

HAW (*Cratægus pruinosa*)

This tree has blue-green foliage, and a hoary bloom on the unripe fruits, which at length turn purple and become shiny

THE PEAR HAW (*Crataegus tomentosa*)

The downy leaf with its winged petiole, and the many translucent pear-shaped fruits held erect in a thick cluster, distinguish this species. It sometimes has slender thorns 1 to 1½ inches long; oftener the tree is unarmed

THE LONG-SPINE HAW (*Crataegus macracantha*)

Stout thorns 3 to 4 inches long make this a handsome and formidable tree. The leaves have depressed veins and the stout petioles are not winged. A leaf with its axillary thorn is shown beside the pear haw leaf and fruit in the next picture

sharply serrate; dark green, often red when opening, leathery, lustrous in late summer; petioles short, red, stout. *Flowers*, May, ¾ inch across, in compound, velvety corymbs; stamens 10, anthers yellow. *Fruits*, September, falling before winter, in erect clusters, globular, pea size, hairy at tips, till ripe, then lustrous, crimson; flesh dry; nutlets 2 to 3, ridged on back, with irregular depressions on face. *Preferred habitat*, rich, uplands; limestone soil. *Distribution*, from Montreal region through New England south to eastern Pennsylvania; westward to northern Illinois and southern Wisconsin. *Uses:* For ornamental planting.

Its many very long thorns make this a strikingly ornamental tree. The leaves are handsome, and the fruits though small are blood red and conspicuous.

XVIII. DOUGLASIANÆ

Black Haw (*C. Douglasii*, Lindl.)—Round-headed tree, 30 to 40 feet high, or many-stemmed shrub, with slender, stiff twigs. *Thorns* stout, acute, ¾ to 1 inch long, red, becoming grey. *Bark* red-brown in oblong, scaly plates. *Wood* hard, tough, heavy, rose coloured, with satiny grain. *Buds* blunt, ⅛ inch long, scaly, shining, brown. *Leaves* obovate to oblong-ovate, acute, finely serrate, on irregular incised lobes; occasionally with two deep sinuses nearly cutting the blade in two; base tapering to short, stout petiole; smooth, dark green, leathery, paler beneath; 1 to 4 inches long. *Flowers*, May, ⅓ to ½ inch across, in leafy cymes; stamens 20, anthers pale, small; styles 2 to 5, short. *Fruits* black, ripe in August to September, soon falling, globose or oblong, in many-fruited clusters, lustrous, ½ inch long; flesh thin, sweet; nutlets slightly grooved on back and front. *Preferred habitat*, moist soil of coast and stream borders. *Distribution*, coast of Puget Sound, Oregon, and California; east on mountains to Montana and Idaho, and south to Colorado and New Mexico. Occurs also in the upper peninsula of Michigan.

This black-fruited thorn tree of the West has been successfully introduced into cultivation in the Eastern States, and proves hardy along the Atlantic seaboard to Nova Scotia. It is well worth cultivating wherever it will grow.

The **English Hawthorn** (*C. Oxyacantha*, Linn.) is the best known Cratægus in the world. It grows wild in Asia and Europe, and when it first came into cultivation no man knows. Englishmen will tell you it has always formed the hedgerows of their snug little island, and the sweetness of the blossoms will be one of the last things to fade from the exile's memory. Snowy white, and pink and rose coloured, the "blossoming May" turns the whole countryside into a garden, with linnets and skylarks filling the fields and lanes with music. "Oh! to be in England, now that April's there!" Browning's poetry is sometimes obscure, but here is a line that needs no explanatory note for any of his countrymen.

The leaf of the English hawthorn is deeply cut, like our parsley haw, in the type species. But this species we shall rarely see. It has been so long in cultivation that the improved horticultural varieties are legion. These are much in evidence in American gardens, where they are usually grown as single specimens, for their showy flowers and coral-red fruits.

CHAPTER XXXIX: THE PLUMS AND THE CHERRIES

FAMILY ROSACEÆ

Genus PRUNUS, B. & H.

TREES with bitter, astringent sap, containing hydrocyanic acid. *Leaves* simple, alternate, generally serrate. *Flowers* in clusters, perfect, white, with parts distinct. *Fruit* a fleshy, 1-seeded drupe, with smooth skin and stone.

KEY TO SPECIES

A. Flowers axillary, in sessile umbels; fruit with oval, flattened stone. **Plums**
 B. Fruit red or yellow, without bloom.
  C. Leaves broadly elliptical, taper pointed, dull green, thick; twigs thorny.
   D. Petioles bearing 2 glands near base of leaf; pit much compressed. (*P. nigra*) CANADA PLUM
   DD. Petioles without glands, pit thick.
       (*P. Americana*) WILD RED PLUM
  CC. Leaves broadly oval, finely serrate, leathery; pit grooved at back. (*P. subcordata*) PACIFIC PLUM
  CCC. Leaves lanceolate, thin shining; petioles glandular; pit thick.
   D. Twigs stout, stiff, usually thornless; leaves broad; fruit thick skinned.
       (*P. hortulana*) WILD-GOOSE PLUM
   DD. Twigs slender, supple, thorny; leaves narrow; fruit thin skinned.
       (*P. angustifolia*) CHICKASAW PLUM
 BB. Fruit blue or black, with pale bloom, small.
  C. Petioles not glandular at apex.
   D. Leaves lanceolate to ovate, long pointed.
       (*P. Alleghaniensis*) ALLEGHANY SLOE
   DD. Leaves oblong or obovate, blunt pointed.
       (*P. umbellata*) BLACK SLOE
AA. Flowers axillary, in umbels; fruit small, red, shining, globular. **Bird Cherries**

B. Leaves lanceolate, taper pointed; fruit sour.
                (*P. Pennsylvanica*) WILD RED CHERRY
BB. Leaves obovate, blunt pointed; fruit bitter.
                (*P. emarginata*) BITTER CHERRY
AAA. Flowers in terminal racemes; fruit globose.
                                    Wild Cherries
B. Trees small, blooming early; leaves broad, abruptly
    pointed.
    C. Fruit red, puckery; sap rank smelling.
                (*P. Virginiana*) CHOKE CHERRY
    CC. Fruit purple, mild, edible.
                (*P. demissa*) WESTERN CHOKE CHERRY
BB. Trees large, blooming late, leaves oval to lanceolate,
    taper pointed; fruit black, sweetish.
                (*P. serotina*) WILD BLACK CHERRY
AAAA. Flowers in lateral racemes; leaves persistent; fruit
    globular.   **Cherry Laurels**
B. Fruit thin fleshed, dry.
    C. Flowers in autumn; fruit brown.
                (*P. sphærocarpa*) WEST-INDIAN CHERRY
    CC. Flowers in spring; fruit black; leaves with entire
        margins.   (*P. Caroliniana*) CHERRY LAUREL
BB. Fruit thick fleshed, juicy; leaves ovate, entire, or
    obscurely spiny serrate.
                (*P. integrifolia*) ENTIRE-LEAF CHERRY

The genus Prunus includes trees with stone fruits, and has its representatives well distributed over the Northern Hemisphere. In its wild forms it is not as well known, perhaps, as in those varieties that horticulture has brought to high perfection and importance as fruit trees. There are over one hundred species, including many shrubby ones. Of this number about thirty occur in North America, only half of which assume tree form. All of these but the wild black cherry are small trees. Nevertheless the wood of most of them is valuable, being close grained and durable. Their fruits furnish food and medicinal substances. Beside the cherries and plums of others countries, the peach, apricot and almond belong to this genus. Important flowering varieties of each are to be added to this list of valuable introduced stone fruits.

THE PLUMS

Wild Red, or Yellow Plum (*Prunus Americana*, Marsh.)—A graceful little tree, 15 to 20 feet high, with thorny limbs. *Bark*

THE CANADA PLUM (*Prunus nigra*)

Note the spurs and the broad, abruptly pointed leaves. The sour, hard-fleshed orange fruits have flattened pits. They are ripe in August

THE CANADA PLUM (*Prunus nigra*)

The white, fragrant flowers open in early spring and turn pink in fading. The stiff zigzag branches beset with spiny stubs interlace, forming impenetrable thickets

thick, grey. *Leaves* oval, taper pointed, sharply toothed. *Flowers* in April, before the leaves, in lateral umbels. *Fruit* globose, red or yellow, with pleasant taste, but covered with leathery, acid and puckery skin. Pit, with two sharp edges. *Preferred habitat,* moist woods and river banks. *Distribution,* New York to Texas and Colorado. *Uses:* Good stocks on which to graft less hardy varieties. Deserves planting as an ornamental, and cultivation to improve its fruit.

In the woods that bordered the prairie watercourses were occasional open spaces, often swampy in times of high water. Here the wild plum took possession and spread into dense thickets. The timber land about was owned by farmers who lived on the prairies, but the plums belonged by common consent to the community at large, just as did the nut trees and the wild grapes.

In April these plum thickets were white with bloom. Bees hung over the nectar-laden blossoms, as if intoxicated. Indeed, the fragrance was so sweet it was overpowering; and in hot weather the nectar often fermented and turned sour before the petals fell. It was good luck if a brisk wind were blowing when plum blossoms opened, for experience had taught that

> " You need a breeze
> To help the bees
> To set a crop of plums."

After the bloom, thoughts of plums were banished until the days grew shorter and the autumn haze settled on the woods. Then came a sharp frost one night, and everybody knew what the signal meant.

"Do you calculate to go a-plummin' this fall?" The question was quietly put in father's judicial tones, but it sent an electric thrill from head to toes of every youngster. Mother's reply sent an answering current, and the enthusiasm of the moment burst all bounds. "Well, you'd better go this afternoon. I can spare the team and wagon, and I guess John is big enough to drive. There's no use in goin' at all if you can't go right off."

So mother and the children rode out of the yard, she sitting with her young driver on the spring seat, the rest on boards laid across the wagon box behind. What a jouncing they got when the wheels struck a stone in a rut! But who cared for a trifle like that? John's reckless driving but brought nearer the goal of their heart's desire.

A lurid colour lightened the plum thicket as it came in sight. The yellow leaves were falling and the fruit glowed on the bending twigs. Close up the wagon is drawn; then all hands pile out, and the fun really begins. "How large and sweet they are this year!" Mother knows how to avoid the puckery thick skin in eating plums. The youngsters try to chew two or three at once and their faces are drawn into knots. But they soon get used to that.

Now the small folk with pails are sent to pick up ripe plums under the trees, and warned against eating too many. "Remember last year," says mother—and they remember. The larger boys spread strips of burlap and rag carpet under the fullest trees, in turn, and give their branches a good beating that showers the plums down. With difficulty the boys and girls make their way into the thicket; but torn jackets and aprons and scratched knuckles can be mended—such accidents are overlooked in the excitement of filling the grain sacks with the ripe fruit. How fine "plum butter" will taste on the bread and butter of the noon lunch when winter comes and school begins! (The Pennsylvanian's love for "spreads" on his bread leavened the West completely.)

Other neighbours have come, and started in with a vim. It seems unreasonable to take any more. The bags are full, and there are some poured loose into the wagon box. Besides, everybody is tired, and John shouts that the hazel nuts are ripe on the other side of the log road.

A great grapevine, loaded with purple clusters, claims mother's attention. There will probably be no better chance for grapes this fall, and the sun is still an hour high. John chops down the little tree that supports it, and the girls eagerly help to fill the pails with the fruit of the prostrate vine, while John goes back to command the hazel-nut brigade and see that no eager youngster strays too far.

Mother's voice gives the final summons, and the children gather at the wagon, tired but regretful for the filled husks that they must leave behind on the hazel bushes. A loaded branch of the grapevine is cut off bodily, and lifted into the wagon. The team is hitched on, and the happy passengers in the wagon turn their faces homeward.

Such was the poetry of pioneer life. Pleasures were simple,

primitive, hearty—like the work—closely interlinked with the fight against starvation.   There was nothing dull or uninteresting about either.   The plums and grapes were sweetened with molasses made from sorghum cane.   Each farmer grew a little strip, and one of them had a mill to which everyone hauled his cane to be ground "on the shares."

Who will say that this "long sweet'nin'" was poor stuff, that the quality of the spiced grapes suffered for lack of sugar, or that any modern preserves have a more excellent flavour than those of the old days made out of the wild plums gathered in the woods?   And this is also true: There is no more exhilarating holiday conceivable than those half days when mother took the children and "went a-plummin'."

The **Canada Plum** (*Prunus nigra*, Ait.), which grows from Newfoundland to Manitoba, and extends its range into the northern tier of states, is called by Professor Waugh a variety, *nigra*, of our common wild plum, instead of a separate species, as the earlier authorities have set it down.   The tree has a narrow head, formed of stiff, angular branches.   The leaves are broad and large, with abruptly sharpened points.   Flowers and fruit are larger than in the common plum; the petals turn pink before they fall.   It is valuable to the North, furnishing the settler a relish for his hard fare until his orchard comes into bearing. It forms an excellent stock on which to graft cions of species which are not hardy on their own roots through long Northern winters.   It is a tree well worth planting about one's premises, as in some bare fence corner that needs brightening in early summer, and in August and September when the bright orange-coloured fruit shows its colour against the leafy background. In winter the framework of the tree is picturesque by the angularity of its thorny twigs.

The **Chickasaw Plum** (*Prunus angustifolia*, Marsh.) is the wild plum of the South.   Its narrow leaves are shiny and strangely trough-like, instead of flat.   The small, round fruit is soft and sweet, more like a cherry than a plum.   One often sees it planted near houses, and the crop in the woods is marketed by the Negroes. It is unexcelled for jellies and preserves.

The **Wild-goose Plum** (*Prunus hortulana*, Bailey) is a natural hybrid between the species, *Americana* and *angustifolia*. It is supposed to have originated in Kentucky.   It grows wild

325

from Maryland to Texas—a tall, straight-limbed, thornless tree, with thin, oblong, flat leaves, and thick-skinned, juicy fruit. It is a better fruit tree than either of its parents, and has given rise to several varieties of garden plums of which the Miner and the Wayland are familiar types. The Miner group are commonly seen in Northern orchards; the Waylands in the South.

The little beach plum of the Atlantic coast, the sloes of the Alleghanies and the South, the leathery-leaved Pacific plum, and the sand plum of the semi-arid plains are all distinct species. There is scarcely a region of the country that has not its own wild plum; and each species shows a tendency to improve under cultivation.

The **Alleghany Sloe** (*Prunus Alleghaniensis*, Port.) is a black-fruited little wild plum found growing on the slopes of the mountains of this name wherever the soil is wet enough. The abundant fruit is gathered in fall to make preserves and jellies, and is often seen in local markets.

The **Black Sloe** (*P. umbellata*, Ell.) is highly esteemed for the same purposes farther south. It follows the coast from South Carolina to Mosquito Inlet, Florida, and from Tampa Bay into Louisiana, thence north into Arkansas.

Exotic Plums

The old-fashioned New England garden with its fine plums—damsons, green gages, and the like—points us back to the time when the colonists came to the New World and brought the fruit trees they had known in the Old. These common plums are varieties of the woolly-twigged, thick-leaved European *Prunus domestica*, and they still do well in the Northeastern States and on the Pacific slope.

The native plums, improved greatly in the past half century have proved the best for the prairie states and for the South.

Now a fine Japanese plum, *Prunus triflora*, hardy, prolific and generally immune from the black knot, a fungous disease of native plums, gives promise of thriving in the South and in the Middle West. Its fruit is large and handsome and keeps well, though in quality it is not considered equal to the European varieties. Crosses between the Japanese and the native American plums promise well. Prune raising as an industry was old in

THE WILD GOOSE PLUM (*Prunus hortulana*)

THE WILD RED PLUM (*Prunus Americana*)

THE CANADA PLUM (*Prunus nigra*)

THE BEACH PLUM (*Prunus maritima*)

The white flowers are succeeded by little globular, sweet fruits, coated with a pale bloom. This scraggly seaside plum is always shrubby

THE WILD-GOOSE PLUM (*Prunus hortulana*)

This is a natural hybrid between the wild red plum and the Chickasaw plum. The leaves are large, thin and flat, and the fruit is thick-skinned, sour and juicy. It is the parent of the Miner and Wayland groups of garden plums

ALLEGHANY SLOE

(*Prunus Alleghaniensis*)
The winter buds of this little black-fruited plum

Europe before it came to us. Now France ranks second to California. Prunes are dried plums. Only certain sweet and fleshy species can be profitably dried.

Peaches, almonds, nectarines and apricots, all stone fruits, and Old World relatives of plums, have been introduced into cultivation here. The almond, with its dry, woody flesh, is commercially the most valuable species in the genus. Bitter almonds yield almond oil and hydrocyanic acid. The pit of the sweet almond is one of the most important nuts.

THE CHERRIES

The **Wild Red Cherry, Bird,** or **Pin Cherry** (*Prunus Pennsylvanica*, Linn.)—A slender, narrow or round-headed tree, 20 to 40 feet high, with regular, horizontal branches. *Bark* smooth, shining, reddish brown, with conspicuous rusty lenticels on branches; on trunk broken into thin, curling, horizontal plates. Twigs red. *Wood* pale, close grained, soft. *Buds* small, brown, sharp, often clustered. *Leaves* slender, pointed, finely saw-toothed, with wavy edges and shining, smooth surfaces. *Flowers* white, few in lateral clusters on long stems. *Fruit* globular, clear red, size of a pea, sour. *Preferred habitat*, rocky woods. *Distribution*, Newfoundland to Georgia; west to Rocky Mountains. *Uses:* Valuable nurse trees to hardwoods in the natural reforesting of burned areas. Fruit made into cough medicine.

It is hard to find what a hard-headed, practical person would call a sufficient excuse for this tree's existence. It has no timber value, and the horticulturist has little interest in it as a fruit tree. But I consider that it has many uses. It is beautiful, with satiny bark and leaves that catch and reflect the light, providing itself with a sort of nimbus of glory, winter or summer. The wavy leaf margins, fluttering in every breeze, seem to shake the light off as they do the drops of rain.

It is no small boon to a bleak ravine and to the people who live near it that this tree should spring up and clothe both sides with verdure. With the leaves, come clustered, nectar-laden flowers, whitening the tree, and calling the bees. Then comes the harvest, and who can see without real emotion a bird cherry, gemmed on all its twigs with these clear, ruby fruits, and the birds holding high carnival among the shining leaves? The

327

cherries are small and sour, to be sure, but the birds pick every one. By them, the pits are scattered far and wide, and seedlings spring up each year, in fence corners, on rocky hillsides, and in the paths of forest fires. Wherever such a tree appears we may be sure it was planted by birds.

This wild cherry, it is acknowledged by foresters, renders a distinct service to the country by furnishing shade under which valuable hardwoods and other kinds of timber trees can make a strong start. By the time the nurse trees are no longer needed they are gone, for the bird cherry is a fast-growing, short-lived tree.

Wild Black Cherry, Rum Cherry (*Prunus serotina*, Ehrh.) —A large, spreading tree with oblong head and sturdy, rough trunk; branches drooping. *Bark* dark brown (grey in the South), checked into rough plates, shedding horizontally in curling sheets on branches; bitter taste. *Wood* reddish brown, hard, light, strong, easily worked, close, lustrous grain. *Buds* brown, slender, scaly. *Leaves* narrowly oblong, tapering, 2 to 5 inches long, alternate, finely serrate; dark green, shining above, paler beneath; bitter; yellow in fall; petioles slender, short. *Flowers*, May, small, white, in racemes 2 to 4 inches long. *Fruits*, September, flattened, pea sized, purple, bitter and sweetish aromatic; skin thick. *Preferred habitat*, moist, alluvial soil. *Distribution*, Ontario to Dakota; south to Florida and Texas. *Uses:* A most valuable lumber tree; handsome, quick-growing shade and ornamental tree; the fruit, roots and bark yield a tonic drug.

The black cherry is a substantial citizen in any community of trees. In an astonishingly short time the sapling becomes a tree, low trunked, great of girth, and crowned with a dome of graceful, pendulous branches.

The satiny brown bark reminds us of the birches. It has the same slit-like horizontal "breathing holes," and the birches' way of shedding its bark. But a taste, or even a sniff of a twig, or a bit of bark, will decide the point. The cherry birch, which is the species most likely to be confused with the black cherry, has a pleasantly aromatic flavour. The bark of the cherry is bitter as gall.

In old-fashioned home remedies, in patent medicines, and in the prescriptions of regular physicians cherry extracts and decoctions are often met. No spring tonic is seriously expected to rid us of "that tired feeling" unless the tang of wild cherry is there.

THE BIRD CHERRY (*Prunus Pennsylvanica*)

The white flowers spread a feast for the bees in May and the ruby fruits for the birds in June. The tree lover finds beauty in the dainty foliage all summer long, and in the satiny brown bark all winter

THE CHOKE CHERRY (*Prunus Virginiana*)

Very broad leaves, rank, disagreeable smell of bark and bruised leaves, and puckery, harsh fruit that is red or yellow until almost dead ripe—these traits distinguish this species. The flowers are beautiful in May, and the fruits from June until they turn black in August.

Cherry brandies and cordials are put away against an emergency, and cherry bounce is a good old-fashioned beverage that long ago got into the story books. Old settlers, frugal as they were wise, simply chewed the opening buds in the spring "to purify their blood," and to save doctors' bills at the same time.

The chief value, however, of this cherry is its wood. It is beautiful enough when polished to compete in popularity with mahogany and rosewood. Its rich, lustrous brown deepens and softens with age. Woodwork in sumptuously built houses, parlour cars and steamships is often done in cherry. Fine furniture is made of it. Small pieces are used in inlay work, for tool handles, and the like. It is so costly that it is largely used in veneering cheaper woods. A sharp look on unfinished edges of chairs, bureau drawers and similar articles will detect this. Birch furniture, which is much cheaper and more crude in colour, is often sold under the name of "solid cherry" or "solid mahogany."

As a shade and ornamental tree the black cherry is charmingly unconventional. It is somewhat wayward in habit and sparse in foliage, but it carries neither trait to extremes. The foliage mass is carried with the grace of a willow, for the leaves are narrow and pointed, and they hang on slender petioles.

While the opening leaves are still red the flowers come on, in dainty, erect racemes that bloom from the bottom upward to the top. The heavy fruits invert the clusters, and remain until late summer. They are sweet and not unpleasant in flavour, eaten before they are thoroughly ripe by birds and by children.

The **Choke Cherry** (*Prunus Virginiana*, Linn.) is a miniature tree, as a rule, rarely growing higher than a thrifty lilac bush except in the region between Nebraska and northern Texas. Its shiny bark, racemed flowers and fruit, and the odour of its leaves and bark may lead one to confuse it with a black cherry sapling. But this mistake need not occur. The leaves and bark of the black cherry are aromatic and pungent, and the taste is bitter. The choke cherry exhales an odour that is rank and disagreeable beside being pungent, and the taste is intensified in the same unpleasant way. The leaves of choke cherry are nearly twice as broad as those of *P. serotina*, and abruptly pointed; its fruit, until dead ripe, is red (or yellow), and so puckery, harsh and bitter that children, who eat the black cherries eagerly, cannot be persuaded to taste choke cherries a second time.

329

The birds are not so fastidious. They strip the trees before the fruit turns black. It is probably by these unconscious agents of seed distribution that the choke cherry has become so widely scattered. From the Arctic circle to the Gulf of Mexico, and from the Atlantic to the Rocky Mountains it is found in all wooded regions.

The **Western Wild Cherry** (*P. demissa*, Walp.) occurs west of the Rocky Mountains, and on to the Pacific. Closely related to the Eastern choke cherry, it differs in having thicker leaves and sweeter, scarcely astringent fruit. It is easy to believe that these Western trees belong to the Eastern species, but are modified by climatic conditions into a new form. Where their ranges meet, it is hard to distinguish the two species.

THE CHERRY LAURELS

The cherry laurels are ornamental native species, so named because of their waxy green leaves. They have handsome but not showy fruits. They deserve and are receiving recognition by nurserymen. Californians bring their beautiful spiny-leaved evergreen islay and plant it in their gardens as an ornamental tree, or set it close for screens and hedges.

The European cherry laurels, strange evergreen relatives of our plums and cherries, are often seen as tub plants for porch decorations in this country. They are easily mistaken for the Old-World sweet bay, *Laurus nobilis*, which is also set in tubs for the same purposes.

CULTIVATED CHERRIES

The **Sour, Pie Cherry** (*Prunus Cerasus*, Linn.), which often escapes from old gardens and spreads by suckers into roadside thickets, is a European immigrant. It is believed to be the parent of our cultivated sour cherries. It is a low-headed, spreading tree with no central "leader" among its branches, with grey bark, and stiff, grey-green, ovate leaves, and white flowers in scaly side clusters opening before the leaves are fully out. The cherries are soft, small and red.

Two groups of these sour cherries are recognised in cultivation: (1) The early, light-red varieties with uncoloured juice, of which the Early Richmond is a familiar type; and (2) the late, dark-red varieties with coloured juice, of which the English Morello is a well-known example.

The **Sweet Cherry** of Europe (*Prunus Avium*, Linn.), has given us our cultivated sweet cherries. Wild seedlings in fence corners are called Mazzards. They have brown bark, and grow tall and pyramidal around a central stem, often attaining great age and size—very different in habit of growth from small, short-lived sour cherry trees. The leaves are broad, doubly toothed, sharp pointed, and limp in texture. The flowers are much like those of the preceding species, but they open later, when the leaves are out. The cherries are more or less heart shaped and generally sweet.

Beside the Mazzards, which are inferior in fruit, there are the Heart cherries in cultivation, two groups of them: (1) Those with firm flesh, and (2) those with soft, juicy flesh; and the Dukes, which have light-coloured, acid flesh. The Hearts are variously coloured—some red, some black, others yellow.

CHERRIES IN JAPAN

Everybody admires, in a casual way, the crisp, dainty blossoms of our garden cherries, and the large, rosy ones of certain European ornamental varieties often seen in American gardens. But until one goes to Japan he cannot realise how beautiful a blossoming cherry tree can be, nor what it is really to *love* the flowers. The native species, *Prunus Pseudo-Cerasus*, has been specialised in the direction of beauty, according to the ideals of Japanese artists. Grace of line and delicacy of texture and colour have been patiently worked for—not in flowers alone, but in leaf, in branch, and even in bark. The whole tree crowned with its blossoms is the ideal toward which patience and artistic skill have successfully striven for centuries.

"Spring is the season of the eye," says a Japanese poet. The third month is cherry-blossom time, and as the gardens burst suddenly into the marvellous pink bloom all eyes and thoughts are fixed upon them. The passionate love for *Sakura*, the cherry, symbol of happiness, lays hold on all classes alike. In a quiet ecstasy of joy the Japanese people turn out in holiday attire to view the wondrous spectacle. It is a great national fête, a time of universal rejoicing.

CHAPTER XL: THE POD-BEARERS

Family Leguminosæ

Trees of high ornamental and timber value. *Leaves* compound (except in Cercis), alternate, deciduous. *Flowers* sweet, pea-like, or regular. *Fruit,* a pod.

KEY TO IMPORTANT GENERA AND SPECIES

A. Foliage simple; flowers rosy, pea-like.

1. Genus CERCIS, Linn.

B. Leaves heart shaped.   (*C. Canadensis*) REDBUD
BB. Leaves kidney shaped.   (*C. Texensis*) TEXAS REDBUD
AA. Foliage compound.
     B. Leaves twice compound; flowers regular.
       C. Branches thorny; foliage fleecy.

2. Genus GLEDITSIA, Linn.

D. Pods 12 to 18 inches long, pulpy, many-seeded.
         (*G. triacanthos*) HONEY LOCUST
DD. Pods 4 to 5 inches long, without pulp, many-seeded.   (*G. Texana*) TEXAN HONEY LOCUST
DDD. Pods oval, 1 to 2-seeded, without pulp.
         (*G. aquatica*) WATER LOCUST
   CC. Branches thornless; foliage and pods coarse.

3. Genus GYMNOCLADUS, K. Koch.

       (*G. dioicus*) KENTUCKY COFFEE TREE
BB. Leaves once compound; flowers pea-like, showy, in racemes, pods thin.
   C. Leaves with spiny stipules.

4. Genus ROBINIA, Linn.

D. Blossoms white; shoots smooth.
       (*R. Pseudacacia*) LOCUST
DD. Blossoms pink; shoots hairy.
     E. Shoots clammy.   (*R. viscosa*) CLAMMY LOCUST
   EE. Shoots not clammy.
       (*R. Neo-Mexicana*) NEW MEXICAN LOCUST

THE BEACH PLUM (*Prunus maritima*)

Note the thick, reticulated veins of the leaves. The little plums, scarcely bigger than cherries, have a very pleasant flavour. They are purple or yellow

THE CANADA PLUM (*Prunus nigra*)

The white flowers turn pink as they fade. The bark is rough, scaly, and greyish

THE RED BUD (*Cercis Canadensis*)

The dainty, low-headed tree covers its bare branches in early April with rosy magenta flowers of the sweet pea type. The broad, heart-shaped leaves are smooth and firm, resisting insect and fungus injuries, to turn bright yellow before they fall. The thin pods contain several hard seeds

CC. Leaves without spiny stipules; flowers white, in loose clusters.

5. Genus CLADRASTIS, Raf. (*C. lutea*) YELLOW-WOOD

The family Leguminosæ, to which our pod-bearing trees belong, is one of vast size and economic importance, and of world-wide distribution. There are nearly 450 genera and over 7,000 species. Peas, beans, lentils, clover—all plants that bear simple, 2-valved pods after the flowers—are included. By this sign they are easily recognisable when in fruit. Besides food stuffs, the pod-bearers yield rubber, balsams, oils, dyestuffs, good timber, and a long list of ornamental plants. The grass family, which includes the chief forage and grazing plants, the grains and sugar cane, is the only one that ranks higher than the legumes in service to the human family.

The pod-bearers are the only plants that have the power to abstract nitrogen from the air and store it in their stems and roots. The rotting of these parts restores to the soil that particular plant food which is most commonly lacking and the costliest to replace. The cheapest way to put nitrogen into the soil is to plough under green crops of clover, cowpeas, or other legumes. They improve the texture and therefore the moisture-holding capacity of the soil; commercial fertilisers do not. Legumes grow on poor soil and make it rich.

American pod-bearing trees belong to several different genera, with one or more species in each. With few exceptions they have handsome pinnate foliage, and showy flowers in drooping clusters. These characters, combined with an admirable form, give these trees prominence as ornamentals wherever they will grow. Their pods are often highly decorative in summer and winter. The thorns of certain species give the trees character and distinction. Several valuable lumber trees are included in the family. In North American forests seventeen genera of pod-bearers are native. These include over thirty species. Beside these, several exotic species are met with in cultivation.

1. Genus CERCIS, Linn.

The genus Cercis, including seven species of shrubs and trees, is distributed in Asia, Europe and America. We have two tree forms and one shrubby species, native to California.

Red Bud, Judas Tree (*Cercis Canadensis*, Linn.)—A dainty tree, sometimes 40 to 50 feet high, oftener much smaller, with broad, flat head of slender, smooth, thornless, angular branchlets. *Bark* reddish brown, furrowed deeply and closely, broken into small, scaly plates; twigs brown or grey. *Wood* heavy, hard, close grained, weak, red-brown. *Buds* inconspicuous, axillary, scaly, blunt. *Leaves* simple, entire, broadly heart shaped or ovate, alternate, deciduous, on long, slender, smooth petioles which are enlarged at apex; autumn colour yellow. *Flowers*, April, before the leaves, in axillary fascicles, pea-like, ½ inch long, rose pink to purplish; numerous, conspicuous. *Fruit* a pod, thin, pointed, flat, smooth, lustrous, purplish, stalked, 2 to 3 inches long, many-seeded. *Preferred habitat*, borders of streams, under other trees. *Distribution*, New Jersey to western Florida, Alabama, Mississippi, Texas; Ontario to Nebraska and south. Maximum size, Arkansas to Texas. *Uses:* Important hardy ornamental tree. Grown in Europe. Flowers sometimes eaten as a salad.

The early-blooming trees and those of small size will ever be held in affectionate regard. Here is one of the most charming of them all—a dainty, low-headed tree skirting the woodlands in the North, often growing farther south in dense thickets, under the taller trees. It wakes with the shad-bush and the wild plum and covers its bare twigs with a profusion of pea-like rosy magenta blossoms in clusters that hug the branch closely, and continue to open until the leaves have unfolded.

The hardiness of the redbud commends it to planters in the Northeast, as well as in the warmer parts of its natural range. It is widely cultivated as a flowering tree. After the flowers, the glossy, round leaves are beautiful, as are also the dainty, pale green pods, which in late summer take on their purple hue. The foliage, unmarred by the wear and tear of a season of growth, turns to bright yellow before it falls.

A further merit of the redbud tree is that it begins blooming when very young. It should be in every shrubbery border. Some people prefer the double-flowered form offered by nurserymen. A variety, *pubescens*, called the downy redbud, grows wild from Georgia westward.

The **Texas Redbud** (*Cercis Texensis*, Sarg.) is commonly seen as a low shrub, forming thickets on the uplands of eastern Texas. Occasionally it reaches 40 feet in height. The leaves

334

are leathery, but in the characters of flower and fruit the tree is much like its Northern relative.

The European redbud, which grows also in Asia Minor, is stigmatised by tradition as the tree on which Judas Iscariot hanged himself. Our little tree has had to share the name, and in many places it is the "Judas tree" to-day. It is a pity to keep alive a notion so ghastly. The most beautiful redbud is a Chinese species (*C. Chinensis*, Bunge), with very large and abundant pink flowers. Its leaves are bordered with a clear or white rim.

2. Genus GLEDITSIA, Linn.

The genus Gleditsia has ten species or more, three of which are native to the eastern half of the United States. Japan and China have three or four species between them; Asia Minor and northern Africa have representatives. The oriental species are cultivated by the Japanese and Chinese, and have been introduced into European and American plantations. The wood is durable and strong. The trees are ornamental and easy to grow. In Japan the pulp of the green pods is used instead of soap.

Honey Locust, Three-thorned Acacia (*Gleditsia triacanthos*, Linn.)—A large, handsome tree, 70 to 140 feet high, with rigid, horizontal branches; trunk 3 to 5 feet in diameter. *Bark* rough, dark, deeply furrowed; twigs brown, smooth. *Thorns* in second year, 3-pronged, single, or in close-set clusters. *Wood* reddish brown, heavy, durable, hard. *Buds* clustered, nearly hidden in winter; spine bud some distance above axillary buds. *Leaves* 7 to 8 inches long, alternate, once or twice pinnately compound, soft, velvety, and pink when opening, changing to dark green with paler linings; yellow in autumn. *Flowers* inconspicuous, regular, in small greenish racemes, staminate and pistillate racemes separate on the same or on different trees. *Fruits* purple, curving, flat pods, 6 to 18 inches long; seeds 10 to 15, hard, flat, brown. *Preferred habitat*, rich woods. *Distribution*, New York and Pennsylvania to Mississippi and Texas; Ontario to Michigan and Arkansas. *Uses:* Ornamental and shade tree much cultivated. Good hedge tree. Wood used for wheel hubs, fencing, and for fuel.

335

Unlike its relative, the yellow locust, this tree is strikingly handsome and full of character in winter. Its bark, from root to twig, is brown and "alive-looking," though no buds are in sight, and the bark furrows are deep on a large tree. There is all the difference in the world between a dead grey and a lively brown. The locusts well illustrate this difference.

The honey locust has angular branches, slender and wiry, which extend far out in horizontal planes. These branches shine as if they were polished. The three-pronged thorns give an added asperity to the demeanour of the tree. The rattling pods are purple and shiny. They curve and cluster on the topmost limbs, and long defy the efforts of the wind to dislodge them.

The thorns of the honey locust are thorns indeed—modified branches that branch again, and are rooted in the very pith of the twig that bears them. The "thorns" of the yellow locust are prickles—merely skin deep. Occasionally a leaf appears on the side of a young thorn to strengthen the evidence that the thorn is a branch changed to a special form to serve a special use. But the thorns stop growing when they reach about a foot in length, and remain indefinitely in their places, ranging along the branches or clustered on the trunk, even encircling it in some instances with the most formidable *chevaux-de-frise*—a barrier to the ambitions of climbing boys, and to cropping cows which like the taste of locust foliage. There is a thornless variety which is the delight of boys who climb for the sweet pods in summer time.

The foliage mass of the honey locust is wonderfully light and graceful. New leaves with a silvery sheen upon them are constantly appearing; some once, some twice compound, on the same tree. The colour of them is a clear, intense emerald. The pods in midsummer show many shades of changeable red and green velvet against the leaves, and are as beautiful in form as in colour and texture.

In this stage of growth the pods contain a sweet, edible pulp which later dries and turns bitter. An Old-World tree has pods that are thicker but otherwise resemble those of the honey locust; these sweetish pods are sold on the streets of New York as "St. John's Bread," and are believed to be the locusts eaten by John the Baptist in the wilderness.

Staminate Flowers

Winter Bud

THE HONEY LOCUST (*Gleditsia triacanthos*)

The main thorn bears two side spurs. On old branches there is often much sub-branching, and the thorns reach a foot in length. Staminate and perfect flowers are borne in separate, greenish racemes on the same tree in June. The leaves (much enlarged in the lower plate) are made up of many leaflets. Frequently they are twice compound

THE YELLOW LOCUST (*Robinia Pseudacacia*)

The angled, fluted twigs are swollen at the joints, and the winter bud is buried under the leaf scar. Two spines stand guard at each leaf base, as a rule, but occasionally a tree is unarmed. The white, fragrant flowers appear in early June, after the leaves. The pods hang on all winter. The bark is deeply furrowed and dark brown. The tree is a dead-looking, unattractive one in winter. It is the prey of a destructive borer

The curving, S-shaped pods of the honey locust hang on the tree until winter, when the wind whirls them along over the icy ground until they lodge. Here the seeds eventually soften and germinate, and saplings spring up far from the parent tree. The range of this tree is extensive, but it has nowhere a very plentiful growth. The wood is not as well known nor as fully appreciated as it deserves. The claims of the tree for ornamental planting and for shade are granted by enterprising nurserymen. It is a handsome park tree, and thrives in almost any soil. It is hardy, and endures heavy pruning. This character combined with its thorns make it one of the best of our native hedge plants. It is necessary to soften the hard seeds in hot water before planting, else they will not germinate until the second year.

Unlike most of the pod-bearers, the honey locust has greenish, inconspicuous flowers, not of the pea-blossom form. The bees find them, as they are fragrant and nectar laden. The "honey" mentioned in the name is not in the flower but in the half-ripe fruit.

The **Texan Honey Locust** (*G. Texana*, Sarg.), with the characters given in the key, has so far been found only in one grove near Brazoria, Texas. It is a large, thornless tree, with thin, smooth bark.

The **Water Locust** (*G. aquatica*, Marsh.) is a small, flat-topped, irregular tree which grows best in the swamps just west of the lower Mississippi. It is found sparingly from South Carolina through the eastern Gulf States, and north as far as the Ohio River. The tree can easily be recognised by its brown polished thorns which are 3 to 5 inches long, pointed and stiff, and sometimes flattened, like the blade of a sword. The two lateral thorns arise close to the base of the main one.

The pods, which are usually but 1-seeded, are oval and pointed, and much more thickly clustered than those of *G. triacanthos*. The wood is coarse and inferior to other locusts, though it is heavy, hard and strong, and has been put to many uses.

3. Genus GYMNOCLADUS, K. Koch.

The genus Gymnoclodus has one species in China and another in eastern North America. Both are bare-limbed, clumsy members of a family which boasts many graceful trees. The pulp in the heavy pod is used in China for soap. Our tree is planted for shade on city streets, and for the sake of its peculiar, great pods, which hang on the bare limbs all winter. The characters of the genus are embodied in the native species.

Kentucky Coffee Tree (*Gymnocladus dioicus*, K. Koch.)— A narrow, round-topped tree with tall trunk, 75 to 100 feet high, with stout, thornless twigs. *Bark* grey, deeply furrowed; ridges scaly. *Wood* light brown, soft, heavy, coarse, strong, durable. *Buds* scaly, half hidden in the twig. *Leaves* twice pinnate, 1 to 3 feet long, 1 to 2 feet broad, of 40 to 60 oval leaflets, dark green, smooth; petioles stout, long, enlarged at base; autumn colour, clear yellow. *Flowers*, June, diœcious, regular, greenish white, in racemes staminate, 3 to 4 inches long; pistillate 10 to 12 inches long, somewhat hairy. *Fruit* a thick-walled, purple pod, 6 to 10 inches long, 2 inches wide, dark red, short stalked; seeds several, bony, globular, $\frac{1}{2}$ inch in diameter, in sweetish, sticky pulp, bitter at maturity. *Preferred habitat*, rich, moist soil. *Distribution*, New York to Minnesota and Nebraska; south to Pennsylvania, Tennessee, Arkansas and Indian Territory. *Uses:* A good street and shade tree. Wood used for fencing, in construction and rarely in cabinet work.

The Kentucky coffee tree is one of the rarest of American forest trees. It ranges widely, but is nowhere common. It is remarkable for its dead-looking frame, which holds aloft its stiff, bare twigs in spring after other trees are clothed with new leaves. But at length the buds open and the leaves appear, twice compound, and often 3 feet long. The basal leaflets are bronze green while the tips are still pink from having just unfolded. This stately tree, its trunk topped with a close pyramid of these wonderful leaves, is a sight to remember. Often the trunk is free from limbs for 50 feet or more.

The flowers of the coffee tree are greenish purple and inconspicuous, borne in erect racemes or loose panicles on separate trees. The pistillate trees are burdened with their clumsy pods in the autumn. They are so heavy as to inflict a painful bruise if they strike a person in falling. The pioneers of Kentucky made out of the seeds a beverage to take the place of coffee. We may well wonder how they ever ground these adamantine beans, and how they ever drank a beverage as bitter as it must have been.

4. Genus ROBINIA, Linn.

Trees of the genus Robinia have slender, angled branchlets usually set with paired prickles which are the spiny stipules of leaves, past or present. The leaves are once compound, and have the habit of closing and drooping when night comes or when rain begins to fall. The pea-like blossoms are in showy clusters; the pods are thin valved, opening when ripe, but slow to fall from the tree.

Four species belong to the United States; of these three are arbourescent. Three more occur in Mexico. Other countries are without native species, so they borrow of us. Streets, parks and gardens, in various parts of Europe, are planted with our black locust. The genus contains one of the good lumber trees of this country, and some of our handsomest flowering trees.

Locust, Yellow Locust, Black Locust (*Robinia Pseudacacia*, Linn.)—A tall, slender tree, 40 to 80 feet high, with erect branches forming an oblong head. *Bark* rough, dark grey, deeply furrowed; twigs smooth, silvery, downy, becoming reddish brown. *Wood* brownish yellow, hard, coarse grained, heavy, strong, very durable in contact with soil. Buds pointed, silky, all but tip hidden. *Leaves* 8 to 14 inches long, alternate, odd-pinnate of 9 to 19 leaflets, silvery, downy when young, later, pale beneath, dark green above, turning yellow in early autumn. Stipules in pairs, spiny, persistent, becoming thorny. *Flowers*, May to June, in axillary, drooping racemes, white, fragrant, pea-like, of good size. *Fruit* thin, brown, smooth, 4 to 8-seeded pods, hanging on through the winter. *Preferred habital,* gravelly soil on mountain slopes. *Distribution,* Pennsylvania to Georgia, west to Iowa and Oklahoma. Naturalised in New York, New England, and west of Rocky Mountains. *Uses:* Planted as a shade and ornamental tree. Wood exceptionally durable and strong. Used in ship-building, for mill cogs, posts, ties, wagon hubs and spokes, and especially for tree nails. Excellent fuel. Bark has tonic properties.

The locust is a beautiful tree in its youth, and being a rapid grower, becomes sturdy and spreading in a few years. But its twigs and branches are brittle, the wind breaks them, and the symmetry of the crown is soon lost. An old locust is a dead, scraggly-looking object for half the year. Coarse, ragged bark

339

covers trunk and larger branches. The twigs show no sign of buds. These trees have a fashion of hiding their winter buds in the wood of the twig, as the sumachs do. The pods hang on all winter, chattering in the wind, and calling attention to the hopelessly untidy appearance of the tree as a feature of the landscape.

Whatever may be urged against it—and it surely has its faults—the locust redeems itself in the late spring. The delicate leaf spray is silvery as it unfolds, changing to dark green as the masses of white fragrant bloom are shaken out. From a little distance the green leaves are obscured by the flowers; it is as if a white cloud rested on the treetop, heavy with perfume and alive with bees. One rarely sees, even in spring, a sight more beautiful. It is the supreme moment in the life of this tree.

A very interesting habit of the locust is the folding of its leaflets and the drooping of its leaves on rainy days and on the approach of evening. The sensitive plant, a near relative, shrinks away and folds its leaves whenever it is touched. It is believed the locust's habit of "cuddling down" avoids excessive loss of moisture and heat. Parkinson, writing of the tree in 1640, noted "each leaf foulding itself double every evening upon Sunne setting, and opening again upon the rising." Some years before, the cultivation of locusts had been introduced in Europe by Vespasian Robin, whose name the genus bears. Great plans were made a century ago for the growing of these trees to supply the British Navy with shipbuilding timbers. The plan never reached the magnitude its promoters desired; yet the locust is to be met with more often in European gardens and forests than any other American tree. The leaves are a common forage for cattle.

Unfortunately for us, the locust borer has put an end to raising this valuable timber in any but the mountainous parts of its natural range. Lumbermen well know there is no more profitable timber crop, except when the locust borer attacks it. The wood is riddled by these, even to the twigs, and no effective means of combating them is known. For this reason, the cultivation of the tree has been abandoned in the regions where this insect has appeared. In Europe, locusts seem to be comparatively free from insect injury.

The extreme hardness of locust wood is due to crystals, called *rhaphides*, formed in the wood cells. These hard mineral deposits soon take the edge off of saws and chisels.

As an ornamental tree, the chief drawback of the locust is its unsightliness when bare of leaves. The fact should he added that the leaves come late and fall early. The tree sends up suckers freely from the roots, which unfits it for planting on lawns. There are sixteen varieties of this tree known in cultivation. With all its faults they love it still; the American people plant locusts for the borers to distort.

The prickles that arm these trees are not thorns at all. They are but skin deep, like prickles of rose and gooseberry bushes. But they persist and become quite formidable. They are merely stipules of the leaves. Each pair of leaflets has a pair of tiny spines guarding the base. But they are transient, falling with the leaf. Thornless trees often occur in groves of locusts.

The **Clammy Locust** (*Robinia viscosa*, Vent.) is a little, rough-barked tree that grows wild in the mountains of North Carolina. It is a favourite garden ornament, for it has delicate feathery foliage and the shaded pinks of its close flower cluster make a combination of form and colour no artist can resist. The calyxes are dark red, and all the new growth shines with the sticky substance that exudes from the covering of glandular hairs, and gives the tree its name. The spines are inconspicuous.

The **New Mexican Locust** (*Robinia Neo-Mexicana*, Gray) rarely rises higher than a shrub in the Southwestern semi-desert regions. Its tender shoots are covered with glandular but not viscid hairs. The flowers are rosy and handsome. The twigs are armed with short, stout, recurved spines.

The **Bristly Locust** (*Robinia hispida*, Linn.), a garden shrub with large crimson flowers and bristly hairs covering its shoots, is probably the most common locust in cultivation.

5. Genus CLADRASTIS, Raf.

The genus Cladrastis is "Queen of Beauty" among the pod-bearers. It is represented by one species in the eastern United States and another in Manchuria. The name, from two Greek words, refers to the brittleness of the branches.

The **Yellow-wood**, or **Virgilia** (*Cladrastis lutea*, K. Koch.), is native to the limestone hillslopes of Tennessee, Kentucky and North Carolina, but even here it is very rare. It is cultivated,

341

however, and good specimen trees may be seen in nurseries and in private grounds in the East. It is hardy as far north as New England and Ontario, and is one of the most desirable native ornamental trees.

It is a small tree, rarely reaching 50 feet in height, with wide, graceful head of slender, pendulous branches, grey bark as smooth as that of a beech, and four little winter buds enclosed in the hollow base of each leaf stem. The leaves are compound, a foot long, of seven to eleven oval, broad leaflets, diminishing in size toward the base, pale beneath, and turning a clear yellow in the autumn.

The flowers are large, white, pea-like, fragrant, and borne in drooping, terminal clusters, often a foot long. The pods are thin, smooth, few-seeded. Virgilia is the garden name of this tree. It is called so in the nursery catalogues. The wood is yellow, and its sap yields a dye of that colour.

These are the botanical characters of the yellow-wood. One can easily identify it. But to remember the tree, to have it indelibly impressed upon the memory, one must see it in blossom. It is a "shy bloomer"; at least it never blooms in two successive years, and rarely does it cover itself with flowers oftener than twice or three times in a decade. That is quite enough to justify planting it as a lawn tree, with evergreens for a background—a frame for the picture when it comes.

The virgilia is always beautiful. But in wealth of bloom, as I saw it in the gardens and parks about Boston in the summer of 1904, it surpassed all other trees. Every twig ended in a long, loose raceme in which each pure white blossom had room to reach its full development—to get its fill of light and sun and air. The weight of the flowers made every twig bend outward and downward. Each tree was overspread for days with this marvellous veil of white, and out of each came all day long the low murmur of contented bees.

The tree is rare and local, hanging over mountain streams and edging the woodlands of its range, the highlands of western North Carolina, eastern Tennessee, central Kentucky and northern Alabama. Its beauty is much enhanced by cultivation. The handsome foliage turns yellow before it falls, and all through the summer and on through the autumn the pendant clusters of dainty pods are highly ornamental.

THE NEW MEXICAN LOCUST (*Robinia Neo-Mexicana*)

This desert locust has short, curved spines on its twigs, and its new growth bears glandular but not viscid hairs. The flowers are rosy

THE CLAMMY LOCUST (*Robinia viscosa*)

Glandular hairs cover all the new shoots of this tree. The sticky exudation is shiny, making the stems look wet. The flowers are beautifully shaded from deep to pale pink

THE YELLOW-WOOD (*Cladrastis lutea*)

This tree is "Queen of Beauty" among the pod-bearers. Smooth bark like that of the beech, a wide, graceful head of slim, pendulous branches, and broad, polished leaflets are but a proper background for the white blossoms. They occasionally cover the tree like a cloud in June, fleecy and fragrant for miles. The delicate pods are thin and contain few seeds

The virgilia has no bad habits; it is hardy in the climate of Boston; it thrives in many different soils; it is easily propagated by seeds or root cuttings; it is a handsome lawn or park tree at any season of the year. It ought to be in gardens up and down the land—increasingly planted wherever a beautiful native tree is desired and appreciated.

SOME LITTLE-KNOWN POD-BEARERS

Brief mention may be made here of a number of relatives of our locust trees which are little known because they are restricted to small areas distant from the Eastern States whose forests we know somewhat better than those of other sections of this great continent. They are omitted from the key to avoid making it too complex for easy use.

The **Horse Bean,** or **Retama** (*Parkinsonia aculeata,* Linn.), native to the valleys of the lower Rio Grande and the Colorado, is a small, graceful tree with drooping branches, which are clothed with strong spines, long leaf stems set with many pairs of tiny leaflets, and bright yellow, fragrant perennial flowers. In the tropics the tree is ever-blooming. In Texas it rests only in midwinter. The pods are long, and constricted between the seeds. As an ornamental hedge plant this tree has no equal in the Southwest.

The **Small-leaf Horse Bean** (*Parkinsonia microphylla,* Torr.) has its leaf stems as well as leaflets much reduced. It grows in complexly gnarled form in the deserts of Arizona and California. The yellow flowers are much smaller than those of the preceding species; the few-seeded beaked pods, larger. This little tree or shrub has its branches sharpened into stout thorns, which have green bark.

The **Cat's Claw** (*Zigia Unguis-cati,* Sudw.), of southern Florida, has persistent, twice pinnate leaves, each division bearing but two leaflets. A pair of spines guards the base of each leaf. The flowers are in compound panicles; the pods long, thin, and contorted in ripening. The shape of the petals is described by the tree's name.

The **Texan Ebony** (*Zigia flexicaule,* Sudw.), of southern Texas and Mexico, is a beautiful, acacia-like tree, with feathery leaves, racemed, creamy, fragrant flowers and large, woody pods, not quite so large as those of honey locust. These pods are cooked and eaten when half grown. The ripe pods are roasted, and ground to make a substitute for coffee. The wood is valuable in fine cabinet work, and for posts and fuel. It deserves the attention of gardeners and foresters in all warm temperate countries. Professor Sargent considers it the most valuable ornamental tree native to Texas.

The **Huisache,** or **Cassie** (*Acacia Farnesiana,* Willd.), belongs to a great tropical suborder of the pod-bearers which is widely distributed over the earth. The valuable blackwood of Australia belongs to it and *Acacia Arabica*, of Egypt and southern Asia, which yields the bulk of the gum arabic of commerce. Valuable timber, tan barks, dyes, perfumes and drugs are yielded by acacias. As ornamentals, the trees rank very high.

The huisache grows wild in the Rio Grande Valley, and has become established in Florida and the other Gulf States, having escaped from cultivation. It is a small, spiny tree, with graceful, spreading branches, and pendulous twigs covered with feathery twice pinnate leaves. The flowers are numerous, bright yellow, in heads, and very fragrant. The thick pods contain two rows of flattened seeds. In Italy this species is cultivated for its flowers, which are used in the making of perfumes. It is cultivated in gardens the world over, and has generally established itself in the warmer parts of every continent. It yields tannin, gums and valuable lumber.

The **Cat's Claw** (*Acacia Wrightii*, Benth.), of western Texas, is less graceful than the huisache, and more often seen as a shrub. The yellow flowers are borne in finger-like close racemes. The pods are large, flat and irregular, with small, oval seeds. The leaves are twice pinnate; the spines, short and recurved.

The **Cat's Claw** (*Acacia Greggii*, Gray), of the region from western Texas to California, differs from *A. Wrightii* in having its pods twisted, and its seeds larger and circular in outline.

The **Frijolito,** or **Coral Bean** (*Sophora secundiflora*, DC.), is a small, slender, narrow-headed tree, with persistent, locust-like leaves, and fragrant, violet-blue flowers in small, one-sided racemes. The pods are silky white, pencil-like, and the seeds are bright scarlet. The tree grows wild in cañons in southern Texas and in New Mexico, and is highly recommended by Professor

344

Sargent for cultivation throughout the South.   It is a close relative of the famous Japan pagoda tree, *S. Japonica*, of universal cultivation.

The **Sophora, or Pink Locust** (*Sophora affinis*, T. & G.), local in Arkansas and Texas, is a small round-headed tree, with deciduous leaves, pink flowers and small black pods, tightly constricted between the globular seeds.

The **Leucæna** (*Leucæna Greggii*, Wats.) is a spineless little tree, with fine, twice-compound foliage like the acacias, and white flowers, whose structure ranks it with the mimosas.   Its shoots and petioles are powdered white.   The tree is cultivated from the West Indies to southern California.   It is found wild near Key West, Florida, and in western Texas.

The **Chalky Leucæna, or Mimosa** (*Leucæna pulverulenta*, Benth.) grows as a handsome, round-headed tree near the mouth of the Rio Grande River in Texas.   Its leaves and young shoots are thickly covered with white down when young.   The feathery foliage and white flowers and fruit commend it to cultivators.

The **Green-barked Acacia** (*Cercidium floridum*, Benth.) is a little, gnarled tree, rare in western Texas, whose leaves are locust-like, but reduced to very tiny size in the dry air.   The whole tree is invested with smooth, green bark which serves the office of foliage.   The spiny twigs are sparsely set with regular yellow flowers throughout the summer, with pointed, few-seeded pods, yellow and papery, coming on after them.   It is, on the whole, a striking looking tree, and good to see in the desert.

The **Sonora Ironwood** (*Olneya Tesota*, Gray) is a small tree, with hoary, spine-beset twigs and locust-like flowers, leaves and seed pods.   It has very hard wood.   In the deserts between Arizona and Lower California it is a most beautiful object when in bloom.   It sheds its red bark in flakes after the manner of the buttonwood.

The **Jamaica Dogwood** (*Ichthyomethia Piscipula*, A. S. Hitch.) grows in southern Florida, a conspicuous and beautiful tree when the great clusters of pink pea-like blossoms hang on the bare branches.   The slender brown pods have four wide, papery, longitudinal frills.   The hard wood is used in boatbuilding, and the bark of the roots contains a drug like opium.   The natives of the West Indies have from ancient times used this bark to stupefy fish they were trying to capture.

345

The **Mesquite, or Honey Pod** (*Prosopis juliflora*, DC.) is one of the wonderful plants of the arid and semi-arid regions. It is found as a tree 60 feet high along the rivers of southern Arizona. It ranges from Texas to southern California, and north to Colorado and Utah. In arid situations it becomes a low shrub, often with little to show above ground. But the roots develop to amazing size. There is a central tap root that goes in search of water, sometimes 60 feet below the surface. Secondary roots go out in all directions, and form a labyrinth of woody substance, which in quantity furnishes the treeless region with building and fencing material and good fuel. Oxen drag the mesquite out by the roots, and it is cut into posts, railroad ties and frames for the adobe houses.

The leaves are like those of our honey locust, but much reduced in size. The tree furnishes little shade. But young shoots, leaves and the greenish, fragrant flowers which come in successive crops from May to July, are all cropped eagerly by cattle. So are the long, slim, sweet pods which are also used as food by Indians and Mexicans. The sharp, spiny branches of this shrub make it a good hedge plant, and the complex root system makes it invaluable for the holding of sand dunes. Altogether the mesquite is one of the most useful trees in the silva of this country. Aborigines in the American desert might well worship it as the Hindoos do a related species.

The **Screw Bean,** or **Screw-pod Mesquite** (*Prosopis pubescens*, Benth.), with hoary foliage, grows in the same region, and differs from the true mesquite chiefly in having its pods spirally twisted.

CLAMMY LOCUST (*Robinia viscosa*)

CHAPTER XLI: THE LIGNUM-VITÆ

FAMILY ZYGOPHYLLACEÆ

THE **Lignum-vitae** is *Guaiacum sanctum*, Linn.—The chief reason for mentioning this tree is that its wood is one of the toughest and hardest known to commerce. It is very close grained, and varies from dark green to yellowish brown. It is used for sheaths of ships' blocks, pulleys, cogs and other bearings in machinery, and also for tenpin balls. The heart wood, chipped and heated, yields a medicinal gum.

The tree grows on the Bahamas, the Antilles and the Florida Keys. It is squatty and gnarled, but beautiful in its silvery bark, little, lustrous, ash-like leaves and delicate blue flowers which keep on opening for weeks. The fruit is a little fleshy 5-celled capsule of bright orange colour.

The West Indian *Guiacum officinale*, Linn., ranks with the species just described in commercial importance. No distinction is made between the two woods in the trade.

CHAPTER XLII: THE PRICKLY ASH AND THE HOP TREE

FAMILY RUTACEÆ

THE rue family is best known through the genus Citrus, which includes oranges and lemons. It is a large botanical group of trees and shrubs, all of which have bitter aromatic sap, and an oil distributed in glandular dots all over the leaves.

The **Prickly Ash, or Toothache Tree** (*Fagara Clava-Herculis*, Small) has all the characteristics suggested by its names. Its compound leaves resemble those of the ash except that these alternate on the twig, while ash leaves are always opposite. The twigs are set with sharp prickles, each raised on a corky base. In Arkansas, where the tree forms thickets of considerable extent, it is also called "tear-blanket" and "wait-a-bit"!

There is an acrid, resinous juice in the twigs, leaves and bark which is used as a stimulant in medicine. The bark of the roots is especially bitter. The Negro in the South chews a piece of prickly ash bark to cure the toothache. "Sting-tongue" and "pepperwood" he calls it, for it produces a burning sensation and a copious flow of saliva. Possibly it is as a counter-irritant only that it relieves the pain. Belief in its curative powers is widespread; the collecting of its bark has almost exterminated the species along the southeastern coast.

The prickly ash in its best estate looks like a well-grown apple tree, and often grows over 40 feet in height. It is found along streams in sandy soil from Virginia to Florida and west to Texas and Arkansas. As a rule it is under 25 feet in height. The small, greenish flowers are clustered on the ends of branches. The birds are fond of the aromatic seeds which hang out of the seed cases in the autumn.

The prickly ash of the North is *Fagara Americanum*, a shrub found on mountain slopes from Quebec west to Nebraska and Missouri, and south to Virginia. It will easily be recognised by its abundant prickles and bitter taste. Its leaves have fewer leaflets than the Southern species, and the flowers are borne in small, sessile clusters in the axils of last year's leaves.

Fagara flava, Kr. and Urb., is the "satinwood" so much sought for in the West Indies. It once grew on all the Florida Keys, but is now extinct on all but three of them. Its wood has a beautiful satiny lustre when polished, and when fresh sawed has the odour of the true satinwood of the East Indies.

Fagara Fagara, Small, is a shrubby tree of this genus which is found growing in southern Florida and along the Texas coast. It is known as the wild lime.

The **Hop Tree**, or **Wafer Ash** (*Ptelea trifoliata*, Linn.) is a pretty, slender tree, widely distributed over this country. From Ontario its range covers the Eastern States from New York to Florida, throughout the Gulf States and north in the forests of the Mississippi Valley into Michigan and Minnesota. A related species, *P. angustifolia*, found in Mexico, Colorado and California, also occurs in South Carolina and Florida.

It is interesting to ask why this little tree has been so successful in the American forests. We go to the tree for an answer. It chooses to grow in the shadow of taller trees. The seeds are plentiful and vigorous, so bitter no animal eats them, and they are winged for long flight. These are reasons enough for its success in life. Besides, the roots send up suckers.

Warned of its scattering habits, one hesitates to introduce it into a garden. But look at that one! A neighbour has planted it among the high shrubs that form the background of his fine perennial border. From a little distance the pale green fruit masses against the dark foliage remind one of a hop vine in its midsummer glory, but genuine hops are quite unlike the elm-like discs on this hop tree. There is a satiny sheen on the dainty leaves that make us desire a tree of it for the foliage alone. They look like ash leaves reduced to three leaflets, and given an extra polish by way of compensation. Clean and shiny and circular, the seeds are models of form and finish, and in their tropical abundance they remain to adorn the tree even after the leaves fall. There is no question but that a hop tree finds its best setting in a shrubbery border, especially where the surrounding greens need lightening. In such company it is a continual delight.

Ptelea was the ancient name of the elm—its seeds look like

349

our elm keys, grown large and plump and smooth. These are sometimes used instead of hops in the brewing of beer, for there is a tonic, bitter principle contained in all parts of the tree, especially in the bark and fleshy roots.

The flowers of the hop tree are numerous in terminal clusters, but they are so small and green they are rarely noticed. They appear in May and June.

Baretta (*Helietta parviflora*, Benth.)—This small tree or shrub grows nowhere but along the lower Rio Grande River in Texas. Its 3-parted leaves, bitter bark and winged seeds suggest its relationship to the other members of the rue family. Its winged seeds, four on a stem, suggest maple keys in miniature.

Torch Wood (*Amyris Elemifera*, Linn.)—Slender as is this little south Florida tree, it is prized for fuel, for its wood is hard and close grained, and full of an aromatic oily balsam. Its twigs are often burned to give a perfume in the room. The leaves are much like those of the box elder, opposite and of three leaflets.

CHAPTER XLIII: THE PARADISE TREE AND THE AILANTHUS

FAMILY SIMARUBACEÆ

THE **Quassia,** or **Paradise Tree** (*Simaruba glauca*, DC.) is the nearest American relative of the ailanthus tree, which is no stranger to inhabitants of the Eastern States. It grows in lower Florida and in the West Indies—a low, round-headed tree whose graceful, pinnate leaves are dark red when they first appear, soon becoming dark green and shining above, and pale beneath. For weeks in spring the immense loose clusters of tiny yellow flowers spread like a delicate veil over the treetop. Staminate and pistillate trees both bear panicles often 2 feet across.

In the autumn the fertile tree burns bright with the scarlet fruit, which are full grown as early as the end of April. These remain all summer, turning purple, and falling in autumn. They are as large as wild plums.

This is one of the most beautiful trees in tropical gardens, as its name implies. A related species in the islands of the Caribbean Sea yields a tonic drug, *quassin*, used in the treatment of malaria. The Florida tree has bitter sap, and it is popularly believed that to drink water from a cup made of its wood is a cure for chills and fever.

The **Ailanthus** (*Ailanthus glandulosa*, Desf.) is an immigrant from China which has sprung into popularity as a city street tree. A Long Island nurseryman introduced the tree in 1820. New York City and Brooklyn planted the saplings extensively. Smoke and dust do not seem to injure their great, fern-like leaves. They throve in sterile and worn-out soil, shading hot pavements and clothing waste places with verdure.

Then came the blossoming, and the inch worm! The staminate trees had a rank odour, and the pollen annoyed people with catarrh. Caterpillars revelled on the luxuriant foliage, and dropped upon passersby. A tide of feeling against these trees

351

swept the cities. An effort was made to get rid of them. But no such effort can be made unanimous. The caterpillar nuisance was soon controlled by the birds. It was found that only staminate trees are malodorous, and the blossoming period is soon over. Pistillate trees can be guaranteed to planters by taking cuttings for nursery stock from pistillate trees only. The ailanthus is now rated at its real value. It is certainly a luxuriant tree and especially adapted for city planting. The dead, stiff appearance of the tree in winter is forgiven when spring sets the sap astir once more.

Ailanthus leaflets are plain margined except for a tooth or two near the base. The long leaves resemble those of the sumachs. The opening leaves and later the ripening fruit clusters exhibit most beautiful variations of rich colour—pinks, reds and bronzes. Somebody is sure to harbour a seedling tree whose pollen fertilises the pistillate flowers of a whole neighbourhood. A fruiting tree in late summer looks like a great hydrangea.

The vigour of ailanthus seedlings is amazing. Suckers ten feet high shoot up in one season. They appear in the most unexpected places. The tilting rafts on which the seeds are borne carry them with the wind, and lusty young trees come up in crannies of city back yards, covering unsightly objects with their graceful plumes of green. I have seen seedlings throw up leafy shoots 8 feet long and an inch through, bearing leaves nearly a yard long—all in one season. But these are youngsters, growing in exceptionally rich soil. Such lusty growers are peculiarly subject to accidents. The wind breaks off limbs, and the trunks become riddled with decay.

Short-lived as ailanthus trees are, they soon replace themselves. Their popularity is not likely to decline. The traveller in Europe will find them in evidence in the parks and along the boulevards of Paris and other cities. In Peking they are favourite shade and ornamental trees, for the ailanthus is the Chinaman's "Tree of Heaven."

An effective use of the ailanthus is to plant a few seeds along a fence or boundary line. Cut back the young trees to a few feet high each spring, and a beautiful leafy screen will result.

CHAPTER XLIV: THE MAHOGANY AND THE GUMBO LIMBO

I. FAMILY MELIACEÆ

THE **Mahogany** (*Swietenia Mahogani*, Jacq.) is the true mahogany whose heavy, brownish-red wood is so highly valued by the makers of elegant furniture. In Central America and in the West Indies it grows to great size, and is remarkable in having huge buttresses extending out from the base of its lofty trunk. In the Florida Keys it attains but medium size, and the greed of lumbermen usually sacrifices the half-grown trees. It is known as "Madeira," and is used in boat building.

Nurserymen in Florida and southern California offer small mahogany trees for ornamental planting. The potted specimens bloom when quite young. The tree has graceful, slender branches, delicate, shiny, ash-like leaves, and light sprays of tiny white flowers. The fruits are heavy, brown, 4-valved capsules as large as lemons and full of winged seeds.

The wood, beside being beautiful in colour and in pattern of grain, becomes richer in tone with age, and seems impervious to decay. The finest grades of this wood grow on upland limestone soil. The Florida trees do not furnish this first-grade lumber.

The **China Berry, Chinese Umbrella Tree,** or **Pride of India** (*Melia Azederach*, Linn.), is a relative of the mahogany. It came from China into European and American gardens long ago. It grows easily from seed, and rapidly becomes a most admirable shade tree. In April it bears a profusion of fragrant, lilac-coloured flowers, succeeded by yellowish berries. The leaves are bright and luxuriant, and remain so until late in the autumn, when they are gradually shed.

The variety *umbraculiformis* is the one most commonly planted. It is known as the Texas umbrella tree. The only fault I find with this tree is the shortness of its trunk and the

353

density of its leaf thatch. It cuts off the life-giving breezes too often and too well. The native Floridian's one-story house set low in the midst of his garden soon has its windows and doors choked by the "China trees" that were set too close to each other and to the house.

2. FAMILY BURSERACEÆ

The **Gumbo Limbo** (*Bursera Simaruba*, Sarg.), sole arborescent species of the single genus of its family represented in the United States, is a tree very commonly met with in southern Florida. It is the only native tree that sheds its leaves in the autumn. This habit it shares with the ubiquitous China tree of the Southern garden. Winter reveals a round-headed tree, with stout horizontal limbs, trunk and branches covered with reddish-brown bark, which peels off in thin flakes of irregular sizes. The soft wood easily falls a prey to disease and insect injury; a tree 50 feet high often falls to pieces from these causes. The species reminds one of willows in its ability to sprout from the stump and from fragments of any size set in the ground. Fence posts are soon clothed in verdant foliage if cut from a gumbo limbo tree and driven at once. Screens and hedges are made by sticking twigs into the ground.

Gumbo limbo is a popular street and lawn tree; its ash-like leaves, very new and fresh, make a grateful summer shade.

The flowers appear with the leaves in early spring. They are borne in lateral elongated clusters; the individual blossoms are imperfect and inconspicuous in size and colour, the two sorts on separate trees. The fruit looks like a green berry as it develops, but it breaks in ripening in a dry, 3-valved pod, each cell of which contains two triangular red seeds.

Beside its horticultural uses, the tree is valuable for a resinous gum which exudes from wounds in the trunk. This is made into varnish, and was formerly used in the treatment of gout. The Florida "cracker" makes tea of the leaves when "store tea" is not at hand.

354

CHAPTER XLV: THE SUMACHS AND THE SMOKE TREE

Family Anacardiaceæ

1. Genus RHUS, Linn.

SMALL trees or shrubs with stout, pithy branchlets, and viscid, usually milky, juice. *Leaves* alternate, usually pinnately compound. *Flowers* minute, greenish, polygamo-diœcious, in compound panicles. *Fruit* a small, dry drupe.

KEY TO SPECIES

A. Leaves pinnate, of 9 to 31 leaflets, deciduous.
    B. Fruit whitish, in loose, drooping, axillary panicles.
                     (*R. Vernix*) POISON SUMACH
    BB. Fruit red, in erect, compact terminal panicles.
        C. Branches, fruit clusters and leaf stalks densely
           hairy; leaflets 11 to 31; juice milky.
                   (*R. hirta*) STAGHORN SUMACH
        CC. Branches, fruit clusters and leaf stalks pubescent;
           rachis winged; leaflets 9 to 21; juice watery.
               (*R. copallina*) DWARF SUMACH
AA. Leaves simple, evergreen.
           (*R. integrifolia*) WESTERN SUMACH

The sumachs form a temperate zone genus of a great tropical family, comprising fifty genera and 400 species. There are about 120 species of the genus Rhus; they are most abundant in South Africa. Sixteen species are found in North America, only four of which are ever trees. Of these, none compare in economic importance with the sumach cultivated in southern Europe, whose leaves contain 25 to 30 per cent. of tannic acid, and are regularly gathered and dried, and used in the tanning of fine leathers. The pistachio-nut tree, from Asia Minor, now cultivated in southern California, is a relative of our roadside sumachs, as is also the turpentine tree of southern Europe. They belong to the genus Pistacia, and are both commercially important.

The Japanese lacquer tree (*Rhus vernicifera*, DC.) exceeds all other species in value; its sap is the black varnish used in making lacquered wares. Each year about 130,000 gallons of this valuable substance are gathered in Japan and China. Each little tree yields but a few ounces, and is killed by the draining process. The acrid juice of *R. Vernix*, our poison sumach, is milky and turns black on exposure to the air, forming a substance very much like the lacquer varnish.

Staghorn Sumach, Hairy Sumach (*Rhus hirta*, Sudw.)— A low, flat-topped tree, 30 to 35 feet high, with branches stout, erect, forked many times, and densely velvety. *Bark* smooth, brown; hair on branches soft, long, and changing from pink to green the first year; later, dark, short; shed the third or fourth year. *Wood* light, coarse, soft, brittle, but satiny when polished, green streaked with orange. *Buds* pointed, in summer covered by leaf base, in winter almost buried. *Leaves* pinnate; leaflets 11 to 31, narrow, pointed, serrate, dark green above, pale to white beneath; velvety; autumn colours scarlet, orange and purple. *Flowers*, June, inconspicuous, greenish, in dense, conical, hairy clusters, the two sorts on separate trees. *Fruit* tiny, globular acid drupes, densely hairy, red, in large, compact panicles, which remain through the winter. *Preferred habitat*, uplands and gravelly banks. *Distribution*, southern Canada to Winnipeg; south to Georgia and Mississippi. *Uses :* Planted as an ornamental for its foliage and fruit. Wood used for walking sticks, and for inlaying boxes, tabourettes and other fancy articles. Twigs used as pipes to draw maple sap from the trees.

This largest of Northern sumachs is constantly seen on railroad embankments, in fence rows, and along the highways of wooded regions. In the summer its fern-like foliage covers all the ugliness of the most unsightly bank, and lifts among the green its fine clusters of ruddy or pink blossoms. In the fall these are lost sight of amid the glory of the leaves, which turn to all shades of orange and purple and red. For weeks they flame and glow in the soft autumn sunshine, then fade and fall, and the bare antlered branches, like candelabra, hold aloft the pointed red fruit clusters which burn on with gradual abatement to the middle of winter.

The glory of the staghorn sumach's colouring makes it one of the most desirable of ornamental trees for fall and winter

356

Fruit

THE STAGHORN SUMACH (*Rhus hirta*)

Foliage, fruit, and all the younger branches of this much-forked sumach tree, are densely clothed with stiff hairs. The petioles dilate at the base, and their detachment leaves a circular scar. The winter bud is capped by this conical leaf base, and it never sees the light until the leaf falls. The foliage turns to vivid red in autumn. The fruits persist late into the winter, after the leaves have fallen. The species is an admirable cover for rocky slopes

THE POISON SUMACH (*Rhus Vernix*)

White berries in drooping clusters, growing with smooth foliage of brilliant autumn colouring in swampy ground set apart the deadliest of the sumachs. Touching the plant is far worse than handling poison ivy. The twigs are pale grey in winter, dotted thickly with lenticels (breathing pores)

THE DWARF SUMACH (*Rhus copallina*)

This tree is shrubby in the North. The new growth is coated with fine, silky down. The leaves are lustrous and smooth above, and lined with soft hairs. The central leaf stalk is wing-margined between the pairs of leaflets. The twigs are brown and marked with breathing pores. The prominent leaf scars give the twigs a zigzag appearance.

A. Pistillate flowers   B. Fruit cluster   Staminate flowers

THE SMOOTH SUMACH (*Rhus glabra*)

This is rarely a tree at all, but is familiar as a roadside shrub. The foliage and flower cluster are smooth, the stems coated with a pale bloom. The ruddy leaves and fruit glow brightly against duller backgrounds in autumn and winter. A pleasant beverage is made of the acid fruits. This is one of the best sumachs for decorative planting, especially for autumn effects colour effects. Its habit of spreading by root suckers makes it objectionable for planting except in situations where the trees can spread unchecked, and the massed effect of the foliage can be enjoyed at some distance. The fern-like leaves are much larger if the plants are cut back severely each spring. For screen and border shrubs this species is very satisfactory.

The **Dwarf, Black,** or **Mountain Sumach** (*Rhus copallina,* Linn.), is the soft, velvety species, fully as handsome, if not quite as large, as the preceding one. It grows all over the eastern half of the United States and beyond the Mississippi to the foothills of the Rocky Mountains. Usually a shrub, it rises to 30 feet in height in the mountains of Tennessee and North Carolina. It is the latest of all the sumachs to bloom. Its long pinnate leaves are lined with soft hair, and the central leaf stem is winged on each side between the pairs of leaflets. These are the most beautiful leaves to be found in the sumach family. They turn in autumn to dark, rich reds.

In the South, the leaves are gathered in summer in considerable quantities, for they are rich in tannin, and when dried and pulverised, are used for tanning leather. A yellow dyestuff is also extracted from them.

The **Poison Sumach** (*Rhus Vernix,* Linn.), "one of the most beautiful, but unfortunately the most poisonous of the sumachs," ranges from New England to Minnesota, south to Georgia, and across to Texas. It is more to be dreaded than the poison ivy, or the poisonwood of Florida, both of which are near relatives. Though widely distributed, it always grows in swampy land, and as its leaves and flowers proclaim it a sumach, people ought to learn to suspect it because of its habitat. Only red-fruited sumachs are safe to touch. This species has greyish-white berries. The clusters droop; in harmless sumachs they stand erect.

White berries in drooping clusters in swampy ground warn the collector to pass the poison sumach by, no matter how alluring its brilliant foliage. There is certain poisoning for those who are rash enough to touch it.

The **Western Sumach, or Mahogany** (*Rhus integrifolia,* Benth. & Hook.), is entirely different, of course, from the true mahogany, a lumber tree of the tropics. This is a low, stout-

357

berries. It grows from Virginia to Florida and west to Texas and Arkansas. The Indians made their famous "Black Drink" by boiling the leaves of this tree. This nauseating beverage was persistently drunk for several days with the notion that the system was thoroughly cleansed by the process. This purification was a yearly ceremonial in which the whole tribe took a part.

The **Swamp**, or **Meadow Holly** (*Ilex decidua*, Walt.) grows in wet soil throughout the South, its northern limits being Virginia and Kansas. Generally a shrub, it becomes a tree 30 feet high in Texas, Arkansas and Missouri. The thin brown bark is covered with warty outgrowths. Its most striking characteristic is the silvery grey bark of its twigs. The deciduous leaves are tapering at the base and blunt, often notched, at the apex. The red berries are flattened.

The **Mountain Holly** (*Ilex monticola*, Gray.) has a thin, serrated leaf that might be mistaken for a cherry or plum leaf, except that it is usually larger. This is one of the handsomest of the tree hollies. Its fruit is as large as a cherry. Unfortunately, leaves and fruit fall early, so they cannot be used for decoration. The tree is found in mountain woods from New York to Alabama, following the Appalachian chain to its southern limits. The species is shrubby except in the two Carolinas.

THE SWAMP HOLLY (*Ilex decidua*)

This deciduous holly has silvery-grey bark on its twigs, and the orange-red berries last until spring

THE MOUNTAIN HOLLY (*Ilex monticola*)

The leaves and fruit fall early, which cuts the species off of the decorator's list. In summer and autumn it is one of the handsomest of the tree hollies

THE EVERGREEN HOLLY (*Ilex opaca*)

This familiar leaf and berry grow in the South. The handsome specimen tree was photographed in Fairmount Park, Philadelphia. It is half-hardy at Boston

Winter Buds

Fruit

THE BURNING BUSH (*Evonymus atropurpureus*)

Both flower and fruit present a Maltese cross. The four pinkish-purple valves split open, showing a shining scarlet sac in which the seed lies. The fruits remain until midwinter. The oval leaves turn yellow before falling

CHAPTER XLVII: THE BURNING BUSH

Family Celastraceæ

Evonymus atropurpureus, Jacq.   This dainty little American tree skirts the edges of deep woods from western New York to Montana, and south to Florida and Arkansas.   The foliage is not noticeable, and the tree might be mistaken for a wild plum, except for its fluted ash-grey bark.   The close observer will see that the leaves are opposite.   The flowers in their axillary clusters spread flat their four purple petals to support a square platform that bears the stamens and pistils.   They are succeeded by equally strange-looking fruits.   Four flattish lobes, deeply separated, turn to pale purple as they reach full size. The whole fruit is one-half inch across in October.   The purple husk parts and reveals the seed, enveloped in a scarlet outer coat that fits it loosely.   The delicate pale lining of the purple envelope makes harmony between the two stronger colours, and the plum-coloured twigs and yellow leaves contribute to make this indeed a burning bush, that glows brighter as the advancing winter opens all the husks and displays the scarlet seeds.   No brighter dash of colour can be added to gardens or shrubbery borders than this tree, which shows its beauty chiefly in the dead of winter.   It does not require botanical knowledge to recognise that the climbing false bittersweet, *Celastrus scandens,* is a very near relative.

The European Evonymus is called spindle tree, for its wood has long been used in making spindles, knitting needles, and other small articles requiring hard, close-textured wood.   Toothpicks and skewers are made of it, and the English often call the tree prickwood for this reason.   Our species is locally known as the wahoo.   Chinese and Japanese species are now planted in American gardens, both tree forms and some notably valuable shrubbery and climbing species.   Two other members of the same family are found in America.

Gyminda Grisebachii, Sarg., is a relative of the wahoo which

F. Lobes of leaves blunt, pubescent beneath; margins wavy.

(*A. Floridanum*) SUGAR MAPLE

FF. Lobes of leaves sharp, smooth beneath; margins toothed.

(*A. Saccharum*) SUGAR MAPLE

EE. Leaves green beneath, pubescent.

F. Branchlets slender; leaves thin, bright yellow-green.

(*A. leucoderme*) SUGAR MAPLE

FF. Branchlets stout, orange coloured; leaves thick, drooping, dull green.

(*A. nigrum*) BLACK MAPLE

DD. Corymbs on short stalks; leaves 3-lobed, pale and pubescent beneath; lobes with large rounded teeth.

(*A. grandidentata*) LARGE-TOOTH MAPLE

AA. Leaves pinnately compound, leaflets 3 to 5; flowers diœcious. (*A. Negundo*) BOX ELDER

Opposite leaves palmately veined and lobed, and paired keys with long wings—these characters are the hallmark of the maple family the world over. No amount of "improvement" blots these out of the most ultra new variety. No other tree has both leaves and fruits likely to be confused with a maple's.

The genus Acer comprises between sixty and seventy species, well scattered over the Northern Hemisphere. China and Japan are the original home and the centre of population for them, having about thirty native maples. Twelve species are found in the Himalayas, and twelve in Europe and Asia Minor. Nine are native to North America. Of these, two are on the Pacific coast, one among the Rocky Mountains, five in the eastern half of the continent, and there is one species "at large."

Red or **Scarlet Maple, Swamp Maple** (*Acer rubrum*, Linn.)—A spreading, symmetrical tree, 80 to 120 feet high, oftener less, slender with erect branches. *Bark* flaky, in plates, dark grey; paler branches; twigs red. *Wood* pale, brownish red, hard, close grained. *Buds* opposite, blunt, red; flower buds clustered on side spurs. *Leaves* variable in size, 3 to 6 inches long, not so wide; with 3 to 5 triangular lobes, separated by triangular sinuses; margins twice cut-toothed; lining whitish, often downy; petioles long, slender, often red; autumn colours scarlet and crimson. *Flowers*: pistillate red, staminate orange,

Staminate flowers

Pistillate flowers

THE RED MAPLE (*Acer rubrum*)

The tree frame is gracefully symmetrical; the twigs slender and studded with the plump buds. The flower clusters set the twigs aglow in March. The pistillate flowers thrust out red-forked stigmas. The staminate contain yellow stamens only. Both sorts may occur on the same tree or on different ones

THE RED MAPLE (*Acer rubrum*)

Triangular lobes and sinuses and irregular saw teeth indent the margins of red maple leaves. The linings are nearly white, and fuzzy along the veins. The dainty red keys swing gracefully below the leaves, and fall in late April or May. The winter buds are red. They are set opposite in pairs in earliest spring before the leaves; on same or different trees. *Fruit*, May, smooth, paired samaras, 1 inch long; wings divergent, hung on slender pedicels, 3 to 4 inches long, seed germinating immediately; rarely the next spring. *Preferred habitat*, swampy ground, borders of streams. *Distribution*, Eastern States to Wisconsin, Nebraska and Texas. Most common in lower Mississippi Valley. *Uses:* Valuable ornamental and shade tree. Wood used for gun stocks, tool handles, oars, furniture and miscellaneous woodenwares. Excellent for fuel. Occasional curly and bird's-eye logs used for veneering in cabinet work.

> "The maple puts her corals on in May,
> While loitering frosts about the lowlands cling,
> To be in tune with what the robins sing,
> Plastering new log huts 'mid her branches grey;
> But when the autumn southward turns away,
> Then in her veins burns most the blood of spring,
> And every leaf, intensely blossoming,
> Makes the year's sunset pale the set of day."
> —*Lowell.*

Who shall know the red maple better than this poet of New England? Yet it must be a sadly belated tree that blooms in May. Her May corals are the dainty keys which swing in graceful clusters from the twigs, each one red as any cock's comb.

It is fine to watch the spring come on in a region where the red maple grows. Late in March a rosy cloud lies on the wooded marshes and stream borders. Up the hillsides the same colour tells where there is a clump of these trees. The grey branches glow with their "crimson broidery" long before any but the poplar trees and pussy willows show their blossoms.

Go as early as you will to examine these maple flowers, the bees are there before you. Their motive is a selfish one, but while they swing from one bell to another in quest of nectar they dust with pollen the red forked tongues of the fertile flowers. This insures the setting of seed. The reddest flowers are the fertile ones; the sterile ones, fringed with yellow stamens, are orange coloured. The two sorts are isolated on separate branches; often on separate trees. As the leaves appear, the colour deepens. The lengthening bud scales and the opening leaves are deep crimson at first. Then come the ruddy fruits, which set the trees aglow, and which fall in early summer, leaving only the red veins of the leaves to bear the colours of the tree until late

August or September. Then of a sudden the tree stands clothed in scarlet! It was not so yesterday. And one by one the leaves fall while yet fresh and smooth.

There is no more desirable tree for the home grounds, for parks and roadsides than the red maple. It is quick and sure to grow in the East if the soil is moderately rich and moist. Young trees are trim as beeches in their snug pale grey bark. The frame of the tree is admirably adapted to resist breaking in the wind. The branches are short, numerous, erect, not heavy, nor spreading enough to be torn loose from the trunk as the silver maple's so often are. The tree is beautiful at all ages and through all seasons, and it has no bad habits.

As it comes quickly from seed in the woods, there can be no objection to taking up woodland saplings for home planting. Or they may be obtained from nurseries. If seeds are desired, collect and plant them in early summer; they will not, as a rule, germinate if kept until the following spring. Nature gives helpful suggestions. The woodland carpet and the neighbouring cornfield show a forest of tiny red maples under six inches high by the middle of summer.

Unfortunately, the silver maple, a quick, cheap and sure grower, has been exploited by nurserymen to the overshadowing of the claims of its handsomer but more exacting relative. It is rare to see a red maple in the upper valley of the Mississippi, though its natural range covers these states to western Iowa, and along the lower course of the Ohio River and following the "Father of Waters" it becomes a dominant tree in wet land. Nurserymen near Chicago complain that it is hard to get good seed; that the tree grows very slowly at first, and the dangers of drought and hard winters make the cost of one red maple equal to that of ten silver maples. One of these days people will realise that it is ten times more beautiful. Then the study of its preferences and peculiarities will pay the nurseryman, and the tree will be more generally and successfully planted to supersede the silver maple in the moist soil and humid air of the North Central States. It is a foregone conclusion that a swamp-loving tree would die of thirst on the plains. Nebraska and Kansas have tried in vain to introduce it.

Nobody knows what red maple log is going to reveal the beautiful curly and bird's-eye grain when sawed into boards.

The sharp eye of the lumberman detects it, and the boards are put aside. They are worth far more than plain, sound lumber of the same species. Hard maple and red maple are the kinds most likely to display this variation from straight grain. Some lumbermen boast that they can "spot" the standing trees; others declare that there is no outward sign that is dependable. Injury to the bark tends to set a trunk to sprouting. Often a multitude of small twigs cover a considerable area, close together, and have only vigour enough to keep their terminal buds poked outside the bark—sometimes not even that—but they still 'live. Each is the centre of a series of wood rings which are revealed when cut and polished as "birds' eyes" of the maple that veneers a bureau or a dressing table. Curly grain is not so easily accounted for. The wood fibres are longer than in straight grain, and lie upon each other in ripples. Beech often shows this grain, as well as maples and birches. There seems to be no explanation of the cause and method of its formation. In beauty curly maple often excels the more striking "bird's-eye" wood.

To saw a bird's-eye log in the ordinary way would be to lose most of the beauty of the grain, which can be got only by tangential sawing. A special method used is to take short lengths to a saw which cuts a thin layer from the surface of the revolving log. Thus a thin, spiral sheet that will measure one hundred or more feet when spread out can be pared from a single log section before the saw reaches the central pith. Steamed and pressed this veneer wood shows every eye it ever had.

Silver Maple, Soft Maple (*Acer saccharinum*, Linn.; *Acer dasycarpum*, Ehr.)—A large tree, 80 to 120 feet, with wide spreading top, trunk soon dividing into long limbs, ending in slender, drooping twigs. *Bark* reddish brown, furrowed, surface roughly scaly; twigs reddish, smooth. *Wood* hard, pale brown, close grained, brittle; easy to work. *Sap* sweet. *Winter buds:* leaf buds pointed, red, in pairs; flower buds blunt, red, clustered at nodes. *Leaves* 4 to 7 inches long, deeply 5-cleft by narrow sinuses, irregularly toothed; smooth, pale green, white beneath, pubescent along veins; yellow in autumn; petioles long, red, flexible. *Flowers*, March to April, before leaves, greenish yellow, without petals, on spurs or in axils of last year's leaves; fertile and sterile on different branches or often on separate trees. *Fruit*, May, in pairs of winged samaras, 1½ to 3 inches long, on short

371

pedicels, pubescent and green when young, becoming smooth; germinating soon after they fall. *Preferred habitat*, rich, moist soil. *Distribution*, Newfoundland to Dakota; south to Florida and Oklahoma. Rare on Atlantic seaboard and on mountains. *Uses:* Popular ornamental and shade tree, especially useful west of Mississippi River. Wood used for flooring and cheap furniture. Sap boiled occasionally for sugar.

The silver maple is a tree to count upon, if one is in search of a suitable species to plant on a Western prairie that has uncertain rainfall. It has ingratiated itself with people living farther east, who might better choose elms and other maples. It is a lazy man's tree, for it comes vigorously from seed, and bears transplanting, even when there are radical changes in soil and in climate to be met. It is a rapid grower, soon giving ample shade. But rapid growth implies brittle, weak wood, as a rule. Slow-growing trees like elms should always be alternated with soft maples, to replace them after their brief race is run.

The habit of a tree must be considered when choosing a place to plant it. It is unwise to plant silver maples close to a house, as they have great horizontal spread, and the long, weak limbs are easily broken by ice and wind storms. Old trees are often cut back to a few main stubs above the trunk. A new top is soon formed by suckers that rise from the stubs, but the tree's symmetry is forever lost.

Local names often confuse the two Eastern early blooming, early fruiting maples. They may easily be distinguished by their mode of growth, flowers, fruits and leaves. Red maple limbs are small and rarely droop; those of the silver maple curve downward, but the twigs ascend. The brilliant colour belongs to the red maple; the deep-cleft, silver-lined leaves to the silver maple. The little, smooth, long-stemmed keys of the red species differ distinctly from the large, short-stemmed fruits of the other, which are woolly until almost ripe. In winter even, buds and twigs of the red maple are vividly red.

The **Broad-leaved Maple, Oregon Maple** (*Acer macrophyllum*, Pursh.)—A large, stout-limbed tree, 100 feet high, with compact head and drooping lower branches. *Bark* brown, furrowed and with plate-like scales; twigs reddish, with milky juice. *Wood* reddish brown, soft, light, close grained, susceptible of a satiny polish; often having curly and bird's-eye grain. *Winter*

THE SILVER MAPLE (*Acer saccharinum*)

The long limbs and the weakness of wood and bark combine to make this quick-growing species a prey to winds. The top continually needs corrective pruning. The twigs bear opposite leaves and buds. It is a good tree—but there are many better ones to be had as easily, if one wishes to plant trees

Pistillate flowers (enlarged)   Staminate flowers (enlarged)

THE SILVER MAPLE (*Acer saccharinum*)

The flowers come out before the leaves in March or early April. They may be on separate, or on the same trees. The red-forked tongues of the pistillate flowers soon wither, and the horns of the keys rise. The staminate flowers are yellow. The keys are more or less spreading. They are fuzzy until nearly ripe. They fall in May or earlier, and must germinate forthwith or they die. The deeply cut leaves are silver-lined

buds: axillary small; terminal larger, red, scaly. *Leaves* deeply cut, by deep, narrow sinuses, into 5 lobes, each of which has wavy margin, indented into secondary lobes; petioles 10 to 12 inches, slender; blades 8 to 12 inches broad and long, dark green, lustrous above; paler beneath; turn orange-yellow in autumn. *Flowers* yellow, fragrant, in long racemes in late spring. *Fruits* paired samaras, ripe in autumn; 1½ inches long, with hairy nutlets, but smooth wings, slightly divergent. *Preferred habitat,* banks of streams and rich bottom lands. *Distribution,* south coast of Alaska to San Diego, California. *Uses:* Valuable ornamental and timber tree. Wood used for furniture and interior finish.

The great leaves that distinguish this species make it a favourite on the Pacific slope. Unfortunately it is not hardy north of Philadelphia, and does better in Europe than in our Eastern States. It really is happiest in the bottom lands of southern Oregon, where it forms forests and attains tremendous proportions. One must see it at home in order to appreciate this maple.

John Muir, writing of the western slopes of the Cascade Mountains, says: "In a few favoured spots the broad-leaved maple grows to a height of a hundred feet in forests by itself, sending out large limbs in magnificent interlacing arches covered with mosses and ferns, thus forming lofty sky gardens, and rendering the underwoods delightfully cool. No finer forest ceiling is to be found than these maple arches."

The wood of the broad-leaved maple ranks highest of all deciduous lumber trees on the west coast. It is equal to the best maple of the Eastern States.

The **Vine Maple** (*Acer circinatum,* Pursh.) grows from British Columbia into northern California, and from the low bottom lands to an altitude of 1,000 feet, but always along streams. In the lowlands it throws up several stems from the root, which droop as they grow as if their weight overcame their strength. Branches that spring from these prostrate stems strike root, and soon the interlacing trunks and the branches they bear cover the ground to the exclusion of everything else.

The vine maple's leaf is thin and almost circular, with a heart-shaped base, and 7 to 9 triangular, cut-toothed lobes, uniform in size and shape. In summer they are green, with prominent veins and veinlets, and pale linings. In autumn they turn to orange and scarlet. The flowers are borne in terminal umbels, and the samaras are smooth, with widely divergent wings.

Sugar Maple, Rock, or **Hard Maple** (*Acer Saccharum,* Marsh.; *Acer saccharinum,* Wangh.; *Acer barbatum,* Michx.)—A large, handsome tree, 75 to 120 feet high, with many upright limbs forming an oval or oblong head. *Sap* sugary. *Bark* grey, deeply fissured. *Wood* reddish brown, close grained, tough, hard. *Leaves* broad, 4 to 5 inches across, 3 to 5-lobed, each lobe with straight sides and peaked apex, which has 3 to 5 prominent teeth with curved sinuses between; thin, dark green above, paler lining; turn to yellow, orange and red in the fall. *Flowers,* with the leaves in late spring, on long stems, in hairy, thick clusters, without petals, greenish; monœcious or polygamous. *Fruits,* October, 1 to 1½ inches long, smooth, in pairs, on stems, 1½ to 2 inches long, with wings only slightly diverging. *Preferred habitat,* rich, moist soil in valleys or uplands. *Distribution,* Great Lakes to Newfoundland; south along mountains to Florida; west to Nebraska and Texas. *Uses:* Best of all maples as lumber and shade trees. Wood used for flooring, interior finish of houses, saddles, furniture, boats, shoe lasts, all turned wares and fuel. Shows occasionally curly grain. Sap makes maple sugar.

The sugar maple is one of the most characteristic and valuable trees in the eastern forests of America. It leads all the other maples—it is the reliable, conservative member of the family, slower than many of them, and less brilliant, but with staying qualities—an absolutely dependable tree. Soft maples come and go. These come and stay—standing always "proud and tall under their leafy crowns." They are hardy, clean and vigorous. They turn gradually to gold and reds in the fall, and drop their burden of foliage without haste.

Hard maple lumber outranks all other species, and as fuel it is surpassed only by hickory. Its ashes yield potash and alkali in large percentages. Fresh unleached hard maple ashes are highly esteemed as fertiliser for orchards and vegetable gardens.

Wise men were they who set hard maples along the boundary lines of their farms in earlier days. They now have avenues to be proud of. And they have also a source of revenue, for these low-branched, isolated trees give abundant flow of sap in the early spring.

THE SUGAR MAPLE (*Acer Saccharum*)

This tree leads all the other maples—it is the reliable, conservative member of the family. Beautiful for shade and ornament, it yields sugar, lumber and fuel of high quality, and finally its ashes make the best of fertilisers

1 Winter buds   2 Flowering branch: **A.** Staminate flower; **B.** Pistillate flower   3 Fruiting branch

THE SUGAR MAPLE (*Acer Saccharum*)

The blossoms appear in May; the soft, hairy flower clusters are greenish. Some flowers (pistillate) thrust out forked tongues. Others (staminate) extrude a bunch of stamens. The leaf is thin and dark green with pale lining. The smooth, plump seeds ripen in October. The twigs are slender and smooth and dotted with pale, breathing pores

The **Black Maple, or Black Sugar Maple** (*Acer nigrum*, Michx.), is now counted a distinct species, but was long regarded as a variety of *Acer Saccharum*. The best year-round character to look for is the orange colour of the stout branchlets. The tree's head is less compact and has a duller, darker green foliage mass than that of the hard maple. The leaves vary much in size and shape, but in general have three pointed lobes with broad, shallow sinuses and scantly toothed or unbroken margins; the basal sinus is often closed by the overlapping of its sides. The leaf is usually green on both sides, and smooth, with hairy tufts along the principal veins below, and on the petioles. The drooping of the leaves is very noticeable, as if the stout petioles were too weak to support their burden. The samaras differ from those of the previous species in having more widely divergent wings.

The black maple predominates over *A. Saccharum* in the Western prairie states. It is the sugar maple of South Dakota and Iowa. In the East, it is a rare tree. It ranges from Montreal to Ontario and to the Dakotas, and from New Hampshire and Vermont south to lower Virginia, Kentucky, Missouri and eastern Kansas. It is an admirable shade and sugar tree, and its wood has the characteristics of the rock maple.

The **Florida Maple** (*Acer Floridanum*, Pax.) is smaller than our Northern hard maple, and differs from it in its small 3-lobed leaves, with blunt or faintly 3-lobed apexes, and pale, hairy linings. The fruits are also small. This tree varies considerably, and grows along streams and swamps, throughout the Gulf States.

The **Large-toothed Maple** (*Acer grandidentata*, Nutt.) resembles the last species, but its leaves are leathery and have very wide sinuses and very short petioles. It is found on the mountains from Montana to Mexico.

The two species named above are considered by some authors to be varieties of the Eastern rock maple.

THREE LITTLE MAPLES

There are a few members of the great maple family which do not share the lofty aspirations of the majority. They are to be sought in thick forests of mixed hardwoods, and they do much to make our walks through such a wood delightful. With the viburnums and the ground hemlocks they spread their leafy branches "amidst the cool and silence," and the sun rarely looks in upon them.

The **Mountain Maple** (*Acer spicatum*, Lam.) is usually shrubby in habit; very rarely it reaches 30 feet in height, and a maximum trunk diameter of 6 to 8 inches. Its green bark is not striped, a character which at any season distinguishes it from the striped maple. The lobes of its leaves are taper pointed, and their margins coarsely saw-toothed. The petioles are long and slim and scarlet throughout the summer. The flowers are small, greenish yellow with long, narrow petals; they are clustered in racemes that stand erect in the axils of the fully-expanded leaves. The fruits hang in clusters, the little samaras but slightly divergent, and showing clear red in the summer. In autumn they are brown, while the foliage takes on brilliant shades of yellow and scarlet. After the leaves fall the grey, downy twigs are bright with the winter buds only.

The **Striped Maple,** or **Moosewood** (*Acer Pennsylvanicum*, Linn.) grows from a shrub to a tree 40 feet high, best always in the shade of taller trees and usually in rocky woods that cover mountain slopes. It has green bark that breaks as the stems increase in diameter into a network of furrows, which expose a pale under layer, and make the green appear to be delicately striped with white. Sometimes the stripes are dark brown.

The leaf of this maple is unusually large, often 6 inches in length. It is about as broad as it is long, with three triangular lobes, whose points form the leaf's broad apex. There are faint suggestions of two basal lobes sometimes, but not always. The margin is finely serrate, and the petiole grooved. In the autumn the leaves turn yellow. The yellow, bell-like flowers in long, pendulous racemes appear among the leaves in May. The samaras are larger than those of the mountain maple, and the wings in each pair are more widely divergent.

The striped maple is most brilliant in colouring when its bud scales lengthen in late April, and the rosy, down-covered leaves appear. The stems and unfolding shoots are delicate and beautiful enough to repay an artist for making a pilgrimage each spring to the place where this budding maple blushes unseen. It is hard to make people believe that all this exquisiteness of

THE STRIPED MAPLE (*Acer Pennsylvanicum*)

The pendant flower cluster, the larger leaf, its finely serrate margin and the white striping of the tree's green bark set this tree apart from the one beside it. The seed cluster is heavier, and each key has a pit on one side of the seed case. The branchlets are smooth, the mountain maple's pubescent

THE MOUNTAIN MAPLE (*Acer spicatum*)

The racemes of flowers are held erect in this species. The samaras hang down and the pairs diverge but little. The leaves are coarsely toothed and rarely over 4 inches long. The bark of trunk and limbs is greenish. The full-grown fruit turn red in July. They fall in early winter. The twigs and buds are red

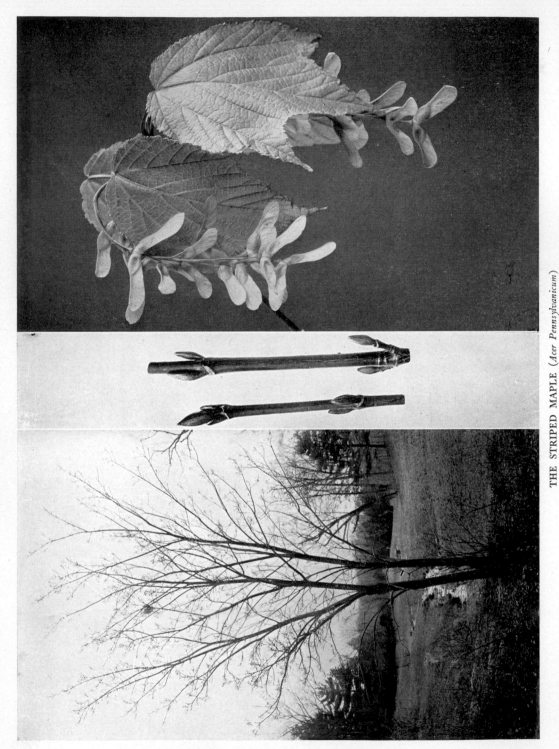

THE STRIPED MAPLE (*Acer Pennsylvanicum*)

This little tree is charming in winter, with its dainty, pointed buds and green bark delicately pencilled with white lines. Yellow leaves and graceful seed clusters adorn the tree in autumn. Each key has a pit on one side of the nutlet

line and colour and texture can be revealed by "a common maple that grows wild in our woods."

The name, moosewood, calls attention to the fact that in the north woods the green shoots are browsed by the deer and moose. "Goose foot" is from the shape of the leaf; "whistle-wood" from the easy slipping of the tough bark in early spring.

This little tree is rare in cultivation, though it is more interesting and beautiful even than many an expensive exotic. One may easily transplant a seedling from the neighbouring woods, and it thrives in good garden soil if not too dry. A shady corner is best, but there is a good specimen growing in the sunniest part of a garden I know.

The **Dwarf Maple** (*Acer glabrum*, Torr.) is a shrub or low tree of bushy habit which grows on the western mountains from Canada to Arizona and New Mexico. The leaves are variable, one type being a three-lobed, cut-toothed form not unlike the red maple leaf; the other extreme is a compound leaf made of three oval, coarsely toothed leaflets. They vary in diameter from one to five inches. The flowers are usually on separate trees as in the box elder. The fruits as well as the leaves are smooth and small, with wings that spread but little. They are often ruddy during the summer.

Box Elder, Ash-leaved Maple (*Acer Negundo*, Linn.)— A quick-growing, sturdy tree, 50 to 70 feet high, with irregular spreading top. *Bark* greyish, regularly furrowed; twigs purple, glaucous. *Wood* soft, white, weak, close grained. *Buds* opposite, blunt, reddish. *Leaves* opposite, compound, of 3 to 5 pinnate leaflets, irregularly toothed and lobed; smooth, pale beneath; yellow in autumn. *Flowers* open with leaves on separate trees, fertile, greenish, in drooping racemes, sterile, in clusters on pink, silky pedicels. *Fruits* narrow, flat, winged samaras, 1½ to 2 inches long, in pairs, clustered in drooping racemes; ripe in September, but hanging until early spring. *Preferred habitat*, rich, moist soil, by streams or along borders of swamps. *Distribution*, Vermont to Montana; south to Florida and west to Colorado and Utah. Rare east of Appalachian Mountains. *Uses:* Much planted for shade and ornament. Wood inferior; used for cooperage and small woodenwares.

There are two things remarkable about the box elder: its geographical range, natural and acquired, and the variation of

377

altitudes it will endure with cheerfulness. Out of a certain number of nursery trees you may plant a row rising gradually from low bottom land to an altitude of 6,000 feet above sea level, and they will all thrive.

It is the nature of mankind to love box elders for growing where most trees refuse. In the treeless regions people had no time to experiment with uncertain trees. Their land, taken up under the homestead laws, had to show so many acres of woodland at the end of a certain time. So box elders and cottonwoods and soft maples went in, because they could best be depended upon to grow. The windbreak behind the settler's house and the shade trees in front were of these same trees. They grew, but they didn't do well.

In the Middle West the quick growth and youthful prettiness of the box elder have led people to keep on planting it, though the early day of planting for shelter belts and windbreaks is past. The result is that in many a village the majority of its trees are unsightly, broken-down box elders and willows, with a few fine elms, hard maples and ashes to redeem it. It is high time the habit of planting the inferior, temporary kinds of trees was overcome.

In the interests of village improvement and the fostering of a love for better trees I went out to reason with a neighbour who had come over to beg a few trees to plant in front of his new house. He was digging a volunteer box elder out of our blackberry patch, when I expostulated, offering him some handsome young elms instead. 'Twas throwing words away. "I told yo' paw I'd ruther have box elders, an' he said I could."

"But why wouldn't you rather have the elms? You can see yourself that the finest trees in town are elms."

"Yes, they're harnsome trees—elms is; but it's the shade I want. I always noticed that box elders, big or little, has the coolest shade of any trees they is."

Before such subtle distinctions I was dumb.

JAPANESE MAPLES

I have said tnat Japan is the ancestral home of the maples. Two-thirds of the forest trees in the islands to-day belong to the genus *Acer*. The artistic and skilful Japanese gardeners have

THE STRIPED MAPLE (*Acer Pennsylvanicum*)

The bell-shaped flowers with bright yellow petals hang in graceful clusters below the opening leaves about the last week in May. Pistillate and staminate flowers are in separate clusters on the same tree

THE VINE MAPLE (*Acer circinatum*)

This leaf is almost circular in outline. The tree strikes root with its prostrate limbs, thus forming an impenetrable jungle. It grows in the Northwest

THE JAPANESE MAPLE
(*Acer palmatum*, var. *dissectum*)

The leaf of this variety has been reduced by cultivation to a mere skeleton

THE DWARF MAPLE (*Acer glabrum*)

This tree is variable in its leaf forms, even to producing compound leaves. They vary also in size. It is smooth throughout. Often it bears flowers separately, like the box elder. It is native to the mountainous West

developed a great number of beautiful garden varieties. These are dwarf forms, almost without exception, low and usually spreading in habit, as if to show to best advantage the wonderful form and exquisite colouring of the foliage and fruits.

Acer palmatum and *A. Japonicum,* with their varieties, show all possible gradations from a broad palm to the merest skeleton of a leaf. The Japanese worship beauty such as these garden maples show; and in the autumn when each careful gardener has brought his maples to their utmost perfection, a grand national fête is celebrated. The people dress for a holiday, and go forth "to view the maples." It is a day of picknicking, combined with mushroom gathering and a sort of æsthetic jubilee —as much a time for rejoicing as the spring jubilee of the cherry blossoms. Japanese maples are among our most beautiful exotics. They are quite at home in American gardens, and there is nothing like them. Well might we turn pilgrims like the Japanese, and by much planting and close watching come to know and appreciate them.

Acer Japonicum, the type, is throughout the season a uniform rich dark purple. *Acer Nikoense,* a large species, has vivid scarlet autumnal foliage. Other species of maples are imported from eastern Asia, and one or two each from the Himalayas, the Caucasus and North Africa. But the Japanese lead them all.

The European Maples

The **Sycamore Maple** (*A. pseudo-platanus*) is the most important hardwood tree in Europe. It ranks with our hard maple, and with a Himalayan species of great lumber value. It is the wood out of which deal tables are made.

In America, where it is planted to some extent, it is thrifty but short lived. It may be known by its thick 5-lobed, sycamore-like leaves, with crenate margins, and the long, pendulous racemes of flowers or keys, which may be found at any season on good-sized trees. It is chiefly set as a street tree, but its head is rather too spreading to use except on wide avenues.

The **Norway Maple** (*A. platanoides*) is a round-headed tree, of dense foliage which turns yellow in the fall. It is one of our best exotic maples, growing rapidly and to great size. Its broad, 5-lobed leaves are remotely toothed, and smooth and

379

green on both sides. A broken petiole or growing shoot exudes a milky juice. The flowers are yellow, in flat clusters, followed by thin, paired samaras whose wings spread in opposite directions. As the flowers open after the leaves, the samaras are late in ripening, and they germinate the following spring. Seeds of this species may be gathered and shipped without losing their vitality, as do the two "soft maples."

The Norway maple has proved itself an exceptionally good species for the Middle West. In any region, it holds its leaves much later than other maples, which is a strong argument in its favour, for they are still perfect when they fall.

There was a time in Rome's luxurious days when men went mad over tables made of curly maple. Not of the sycamore maple, the standard hardwood of Europe to-day, but of the lesser maple, *Acer campestris,* the maple of the field. It out-ranked even the precious Arrah, or citron-wood, in popularity among the Imperial "smart set." The best trees grew on the nether slopes of the Alps; and the curly wood came from trees disfigured with knobs and swellings. There were two kinds: one, dark, which came in logs large enough to saw into tables; the other, white, far more beautiful, but always in such small-sized pieces that only curious and dainty articles could be made of it. Often it was worked down so thin that when polished it was transparent, and showed its beautiful patterns as if they were in a pane of glass.

"The Pavonaceous maple" was that rare grain whose elegant curls and undulations imitated the eyes of a peacock's tail. Workers in maple wood ranked with jewellers and goldsmiths. They made tables with the most beautiful colours and patterns revealed by their polished tops. For such a table Cicero paid ten thousand sesterces. It showed curious "spots and macula-tions" in the natural grain which imitated the colours and shapes of tigers and panthers! One of the Ptolemies had a circular table three inches thick and four feet and a half in diameter for which he gave its weight in gold! Fifteen hundred thousand sesterces—$60,000—paid by this emperor for a single table, probably represents the limit to which this extravagance was carried.

A common phrase, which we use without understanding its meaning, originated at this time. The women matched their husbands in lavish expenditures. "When the men at any time reproached their wives for their wanton extravagance in pearl and other rich trifles, they were wont to retort, and *turn the tables* upon their husbands." Evelyn, from whom I quote, makes this statement on the authority of Pliny.

CHAPTER XLIX: THE BUCKEYES

FAMILY HIPPOCASTANACEÆ

Genus ÆSCULUS, Linn.

TREES with ill-smelling bark and soft wood. *Leaves* palmately compound, opposite, large. *Flowers* perfect, large, showy, in panicles. *Fruit* a nut; one or two of them in a 3-celled, 3-parted husk.

KEY TO SPECIES

A. Flowers yellow; leaflets 5 to 7.
    B. Husk spiny or rough; stamens long.
        (*Æ. glabra*) OHIO BUCKEYE
    BB. Husk smooth; stamens short.
        (*Æ. octandra*) SWEET BUCKEYE
AA. Flowers white; leaflets 5.
    B. Fruit smooth, pear shaped.
        (*Æ. Californica*) CALIFORNIA BUCKEYE
    BB. Fruit spiny, globose. (Exotic.)
        (*Æ. Hippocastanum*) HORSE CHESTNUT
AAA. Flowers red; leaflets 5; fruit smooth.
        (*Æ. austrina*) BUCKEYE

There are but few of our native tree families whose leaves are set opposite upon the twigs. The horse chestnut family is one of them. This is an important family trait, wherever it occurs; it is shared by the ashes, maples, dogwoods, catalpas, viburnums and elders. Of these six the first and last have compound leaves. So a tree with opposite and compound leaves, if a native, is almost sure to be an ash, an elder or a buckeye. Ash and elder leaflets are always distributed in pairs along the sides of the main leaf stalk. The buckeyes all bunch their leaflets at the end of the leaf stem. They are *palmately* compound, while those of the ash are *pinnately* compound. This simple and easy mode of identifying opposite-leaved trees is set forth more graphically in the Key to the Families.

Buckeyes are distinguished by large winter buds, showy flowers in pyramidal racemes, large handsome foliage, and large nuts in 3-valved husks.

Every continent of the Northern Hemisphere has its buckeyes. There are eleven species in all. Of these America has four in her own right; the horse chestnut of Asia Minor is much oftener planted in this country than the native kinds. Indeed this species is the most cosmopolitan of trees, being found in the parks of cities in all regions where the climate permits it to thrive. It is a hardy immigrant, springing up spontaneously in some sections of our Eastern States.

The name "buckeye" is traceable to the brown nut marked with white, which suggested to somebody's fancy the eye of a deer. "Horse chestnut" employs the word *horse* to indicate that the fruit, which resembles the familiar edible chestnut, is unfit for human food. One nibble will prove to anyone its rank quality. These nuts lie untouched by squirrels through the most trying of winters. A strange circumstance is that the name Æsculus was the classical name of an oak tree, and it is very similar in form to the Latin word which means *edible*. Acorns formed an important part of the diet of primitive peoples, but it is hard to imagine an edible horse chestnut. Bitter, astringent bark and seeds are characteristic of the whole family.

In Mexico and Central America grow two species of the genus Billia, trees with three leaflets instead of five or seven. Otherwise, the trees are like the buckeyes, and are included in the family. The maples with their opposite leaves are near relatives of the buckeyes.

Ohio Buckeye, Fetid Buckeye (*Æsculus glabra*, Willd.) —Tree 20 to 70 feet high, with small, spreading top; odour fetid; twigs brown, pubescent, becoming smooth. *Bark* grey, broken into plates. *Wood* white, shading into brown sap wood, light, soft, and difficult to split. *Winter buds* pointed, ⅔ inch long, not resinous; scales elongating to 2½ inches in spring, becoming light coloured. *Leaves* opposite, yellow-green, of 5 (rarely 7) obovate, smooth leaflets. *Flowers* April and May, in terminal clusters, small, pale, yellow-green. *Fruit*, October, 1 to 1½ inches in diameter, globular, 3-valved, very prickly when green, becoming less so when ripe; nut brown, with pale spot on side. *Preferred habitat*, moist woods along river banks. *Distribution,*

Alleghany Mountains from Pennsylvania to Alabama; west to Michigan and Oklahoma. *Uses:* Wood used for artificial limbs and small wares.

This tree was found most abundantly in Ohio by the botanical explorer, Michaux, and though it grows more plentifully farther west, Ohio will always be called "the Buckeye State." The tree is gradually becoming rarer, for the strong, disagreeable odour exhaled by its bark impels people to cut it down. There is nothing about the tree to offset this disadvantage. Its flowers are inferior to those of other species. Only the special use to which its wood is put—the making of artificial limbs—seems to justify this ill-favoured tree in the eyes of practical people. Its vigorous nuts are too bitter to be eaten, and thus it seems to be well fitted to hold its own in the woods.

The **Yellow, Sweet,** or **Big Buckeye** (*Æsculus octandra,* Marsh.), grows on mountain slopes of the Alleghanies, from western Pennsylvania south into Georgia and Alabama, and west to Iowa and Texas. It is a handsome large tree, with leaves of five slenderly elliptical leaflets, more or less pubescent below and on the veins above. The showy yellow flowers are elongated into tubes. The husks of the nuts are smooth. This species lacks the disagreeable odour of the Ohio buckeye, and its nuts, though distasteful to people, are eaten by cattle. Paste made from these nuts is preferred by bookbinders. It is strong in two senses: it holds well, and destructive insects will not eat it.

The **California Buckeye** (*Æsculus Californica,* Nutt.) is a close, wide-topped tree, 30 to 40 feet high, with leaves much like the horse chestnut's, large, compact clusters of white or rose-coloured flowers, and smooth pear-shaped fruits. Its winter buds are pointed and resinous. The upper Sacramento Valley is its northern limit. It is found along the coast and on the western slopes of the Sierras as far as Los Angeles County. It is occasionally seen in European gardens.

A red-flowered buckeye (*Æsculus austrina,* Sarg.) has but recently been assigned a place among the species of this genus. It is a small tree, often scarcely more than a shrub. Its thin bark is pale, the leaves have five leaflets, but the distinctive character is the bright red flower cluster, with stamens protruding from the tubular corollas. Later, the pitted husk of the fruit, and the two thin-shelled nuts within it are good characters.

THE BOX ELDER (*Acer Negundo*)   **THE BLACK MAPLE** (*Acer nigrum*)

    The only maple with a compound leaf is this one. The opposite buds   A winter twig
and leaves and the key fruits are family characteristics. These keys load the
leafless pistillate trees well into winter. The wind scatters them, but the curved
stems persist until summer

Fruit and leaf   Winter buds

THE OHIO BUCKEYE (*Æsculus glabra*)

Five smooth leaflets compose each leaf. The flowers are yellowish green, with stamens curved and extended. They open after the leaves in May, and the 3-valved spiny husk liberates the nut in October. The wood is used for artificial limbs

The tree occurs from Missouri to Texas and from near Memphis, Tennessee, to northern Alabama.

Æscula carnea is a garden species produced by crossing our shrubby red buckeye, *A. Pavia*, with the horse chestnut, *A. Hippocastanum*. The handsome hybrid tree is 20 to 30 feet high, with leaves like the horse chestnut and flowers flesh coloured to scarlet. The colour is derived from the smaller species, but size, foliage, waxy winter buds, and slightly prickly fruit, as well as its hardiness, come from the larger one. This is one of the most desirable kinds for ornamental planting.

The **Horse Chestnut** (*Æsculus Hippocastanum*, Linn.) came originally from southern Asia, and has for centuries been a favourite tree for avenues and parks in Europe. In America it grows with even greater vigour than in the Old World. It is one of the trees commonly planted in the Eastern States, and has escaped from cultivation in many places.

Longfellow's "spreading chestnut tree" was a horse chestnut. He called the tree by the name popular in England, where the word "horse" is ordinarily left off. The most aged and imposing specimen trees are to be seen in our Eastern cities, or near them. The trees reach their best development in more open country away from choking dust and smothering pavements. It is by no means the most desirable of trees, but it improves on acquaintance.

If you are in a city with a bare horse-chestnut tree outside your window, look at it. See the great varnished brown buds that tip the stout twigs. There are small buds on the sides in pairs, but these are evidently subordinates. The twigs are generally forked. This tells that a flower cluster came out of an end bud and the growth of the twig had to be carried up by a pair of side buds. The whole treetop is a great complex system of candelabra—each main branch curves up, then down, then up again to hold all its tips erect.

In late winter a subtle change comes over the horse-chestnut buds. They glimmer with an unwonted light as if warned from within of a great change about to take place. When the warm days come they swell and loosen their waxy scales, showing the silky grey down that lines them, and the close-packed leaves inside. If one would see a miracle he must watch the quick unfolding of the leaf bundle, the lifting of the pale green silvery

385

tent and the spreading of the young leaves into erect umbrellas all over the treetop. During this brief period the trees are enchanting. I wish every house-pent human being could stop work and sit with folded hands and absorb the beauty and inspiration of this spectacle. A brief hour and it is over; the leaflets rise and go about their duties, leaving with us only a memory of their hour of adorable appealing babyhood.

The horse-chestnut tree in bloom is a superb sight—"a pyramid of green supporting a thousand pyramids of white!" Each blossom of the dense cluster has in its throat dashes of red and yellow, and the curving, yellow stamens are thrust far out of the ruffled border of the corolla. If they were rare flowers, they would be admired as orchids are now.

Few of the flowers set seed, as few have perfect pistils. The cluster does quite enough if it matures one or two burs. In fall the small boy assails the trees, knocks off and husks the smooth brown nuts, and how glowing and soft are the colours of them! They are "Conquerors" in games which recur as regularly among town children in the autumn as do games of marbles and the flying of kites in the spring.

The fall of the horse-chestnut leaves is a sudden and absolute surrender. When the time comes, the leaflets and the stem that bore them fall separately. The leaf has evidently expected to come apart, for the joints are perfect: there is no tearing nor breaking involved in the process.

The base of the leaf stalk leaves a scar on the twig which is strikingly like the print of a horse's hoof. This may have given its name to the tree. Or was it, as Gerarde explains, "for that the people of the east countries do with the fruit thereof cure their horses of the cough, shortness of breath, and such like diseases"? More probably the coarse, large, uneatable nuts are responsible; many rank-growing plants unfit for human food are similarly named, e. g., horse mint, horse nettle, horse sugar.

The great fault of the horse chestnut is that it is continually dropping something. The bud scales first make a considerable litter; then the flowers fall like snow. The unripe fruits drop in all stages, and the leaves that choke to death in the crowded interior turn rusty yellow and drop all summer. It also casts too dense a shade, and in some regions is stripped of its foliage by caterpillars covered with tufts of white hairs—the larvæ of the tussock moth. Few people who take thought will choose this tree when elms and hard maples can be had for planting.

FAMILY SAPINDACEÆ

Some interesting relatives of the buckeyes are to be found in the soapberry family, which comprises over one hundred genera, chiefly tropical plants. The leaves are alternate, and the fruits are drupes or capsules. Five deserve mention here.

The **Spanish Buckeye** (*Ungnadia speciosa*, Endl.) is a small tree with alternate ash-like leaves and profuse clusters of rose-coloured flowers. It grows on cañon sides and along streams in Texas and New Mexico. Few trees surpass it in beauty when blooming. The fruit is shaped like an inverted top, deeply 3-lobed, and contains three shiny seeds smaller than buckeyes.

The **Soapberry** (*Sapindus Saponaria*, Linn.) has the distinction of bearing "sope berries like a musket ball that washeth as white as sope." So writes an early explorer of southern Florida. The berries produce a good lather in water. The Asiatic sort have long been used for washing silks and rare woollen fabrics, such as cashmere shawls. The stem of the ash-like leaf is winged with a narrow, leaf-like web throughout its length, as is that of our familiar smooth sumach of the roadside thickets.

The **Wild China Tree** (*Sapindus marginatus*, Willd.)—A tree of medium size which grows from Louisiana to Kansas and southern Mexico, has leathery leaves with wingless stems, and yellow berries which have the same saponaceous principle. This tree is especially valuable for its wood, which is tough and hard, and divides into plates, or annual layers. These are separated, stripped, and woven into baskets to use in gathering the cotton crop.

The **Ironwood**, or **Inkwood** (*Exolhea paniculata*, Radlk.), grows on the southeast coast of Florida. It is a small tree whose hard red wood is used for piles and boats, because it seems to be immune from the attacks of the ship-worm. Its leaves have

2 to 4 oval leaflets. The minute flowers are in panicles, and the fruit is a juicy, 1-seeded, purple berry.

The **White Ironwood** (*Hypelate trifoliata*, Schwartz.)— A rare species on the Umbrella Keys, and in Cuba and Jamaica, it is esteemed as timber and devoted to boat building. Its wood, though hard, is far from white. The leaves have three obovate leaflets; the minute flowers are succeeded by sweet, black berries, each enclosing a thick pit.

CHAPTER L: THE BUCKTHORNS

FAMILY RHAMNACEÆ

Genus RHAMNUS, Linn.

ORNAMENTAL trees and shrubs, with bitter juice. *Leaves* simple, alternate, entire or toothed. *Flowers* inconspicuous, greenish, in axillary clusters. *Fruit* berry-like, black or red.

KEY TO SPECIES

A. Leaves deciduous. (Eastern.)
> (*R. Caroliniana*) INDIAN CHERRY

AA. Leaves evergreen, or nearly so. (Western.)
B. Length, $\frac{1}{3}$ to $1\frac{1}{2}$ inches, holly-like.
> (*R. crocea*) EVERGREEN BUCKTHORN

BB. Length, 1 to 7 inches, deciduous or persistent.
> (*R. Purshiana*) CASCARA BUCKTHORN

The buckthorns are small, ornamental tree and shrubs. There are sixty species of them, widely distributed in the Northern Hemisphere, with a few tropical species, and representatives in South Africa and Brazil.

Of our three natives, the Indian cherry is rarely seen in cultivation. When people plant buckthorns they order them of nurserymen who offer the vigorous English *Rhamnus cathartica*, a clean-leaved, handsome, thorny shrub, beset in autumn with black berries clustered close to the twigs. Its fruit yields a valuable medicinal principle, oftenest sold in the form of a syrup. The bark furnishes a yellow dye. Another European buckthorn, *R. frangula*, appears in our shrubbery borders, its shining leaves brightened by large red berries. The wood of this species makes valuable charcoal for gunpowder.

Morocco leather is dyed yellow with the berry of a French buckthorn. Painters get their "China green" from two Chinese species. Jujube paste is made from the fruit of a member of this family. The "Lotus-eaters" of ancient literature are now

389

believed to have tasted—to their undoing—the fruit of one of the buckthorns.

Indian Cherry, Yellow Buckthorn (*Rhamnus Caroliniana*, Walt.)—A slender, spreading tree, 25 to 35 feet high, or a tall shrub; branches thornless. *Bark* ashy grey, blotched with black, shallowly furrowed; branches grey. *Wood* hard, light brown, close, brittle. *Buds* pointed, small. *Leaves* deciduous, alternate, elliptical, acute, faintly serrate, 2 to 5 inches long, yellow-green above, paler beneath; veins yellow. *Flowers* small, in axillary umbels, April to June. *Fruits*, September; berry-like, 2 to 4-celled drupes, with dry, sweet, black flesh, red before it ripens. *Preferred habitat*, rich bottom lands and limestone hillsides. *Distribution*, Long Island to Florida; west to Nebraska and Texas. *Uses:* Sometimes planted as an ornamental for its bright berries. Not hardy North.

The **Cascara Buckthorn** (*R. Purshiana*, DC.) grows from Puget Sound through California, and east to Colorado and Texas. It is extremely variable in size, adapting itself to different regions and climates with great facility. In the cañons of the Sierras it becomes a tree 40 feet high; on the exposed mountain sides and on the arid coast of California it dwindles to a prostrate shrub. Its elliptical leaves are usually evergreen or half evergreen; the fruits turn red on ripening, then black.

It is from the bark of this tree that the drug, *Cascara Sagrada*, is obtained. The species and its varieties are planted in shrubberies for their pretty foliage and bright fruits. Forms with deciduous leaves are hardy in Massachusetts gardens.

The **Evergreen Buckthorn** (*Rhamnus crocea*, Nutt.) grows on the western slopes of the Sierra Nevada Mountains in California, south of the upper valley of the Sacramento River. It is more often a shrub than a tree, and commonly forms thickets on the shaded sides of ravines. Its leaves are almost round and spiny-toothed, glossy green above and coppery beneath. Its scarlet, pea-like fruits are sweet and edible. This buckthorn is frequently seen in gardens in California. It is not hardy in the North, but deserves introduction into the Southern and Middle States.

Numerous related genera belonging to the buckthorn family are found in the Southern States and in California. Among them are trees of unusual interest which deserve brief mention here.

SCARLET HAW (*Cratægus Arnoldiana*)

Branch taken from type species in the Arnold Arboretum, Boston

Some are remarkable for the hardness of their wood, others for their flowers.

The **Red Ironwood** (*Reynosia septentrionalis*, Urb.), called also "Darling plum," grows wild in southern Florida, and is cultivated to some extent for its fruit. It is a pretty little tree, clothing its heavy, hard wood with bright red bark. The purple or black plums are sweet and of pleasant flavour.

The **Bluewood**, or **Logwood** (*Condalia obovata*, Hook.), grows in thickets in the valley of the Rio Grande River in Texas and is especially esteemed as fuel. It burns with an unusually fervent heat. Its leaves are dry and leathery, obovate, entire, and scarcely an inch long. Its twigs end in sharp thorns. The sweet berries ripen, turning blue, then black, during the long summer. The wood is red, but yields a bluish dye. It is an entirely different tree from the logwood of commerce, *Hæmatoxylon Campechianum*, which grows in Central America and the West Indies and yields a colouring matter used in calico printing and in the preparation of lake pigments.

The **Black Ironwood** (*Krugiodendron ferreum*, Urb.) grows plentifully in second-growth timber in southern Florida and in the West Indies. Its velvety green twigs are covered with small, oval, leathery leaves, and in autumn with solitary black berries. The bark is pale grey.

This species is notable for having the heaviest wood of all American trees. A cubic foot of it weighs 81.14 pounds. Its specific gravity is 1.3020. The ashes, after a stick burns, weigh $8\frac{1}{3}$ per cent. of the original weight, proving a remarkably high percentage of mineral substance in the wood.

The **California Lilac**, or **Blue Myrtle** (*Ceanothus thyrsiflorus*, Esch.), is related to the shrubby New Jersey tea, or redroot of the eastern half of the continent. But it is a California species, and there we shall find it in all stages from a small shrub on the bleak lower coast to a towering tree 40 feet high among the redwoods, and on the hillsides of Mendocino County. It keeps to the western part of the state. The most striking feature of this plant is the inflorescence. The twigs end in clusters of small, blue, fragrant flowers (rarely white), which suggest nothing more than our garden lilac blooms, in miniature. The leaves are small with peculiar venation, having three midribs instead of one. From this native species have been derived forms of showier bloom, which are extensively planted. These California lilacs do poorly in the Eastern States, but much better in Europe.

The **Spiny Lilac** (*Ceanothus spinosus*, Nutt.) grows in cañon sides in southern California, and a velvety-branched species (*C. arboreus*, Greene) is found only on the Santa Barbara Islands.

CHAPTER LI: THE LINDENS

Family Tiliaceæ

Genus TILIA, Linn.

Trees with mucilaginous sap, tough inner bark and broad, dense head. *Wood* soft, white. *Leaves* alternate, deciduous, broad, unsymmetrical, toothed, with veins branching strongly on side next to petiole. *Flowers* creamy, fragrant, perfect, clustered in cymes; borne on narrow leaf-like blades. *Fruit* a dry, 1 to 2-seeded, globular nut.

KEY TO SPECIES

A. Leaves green on both sides.
    B. Linings of leaves nearly, or quite, smooth; fruit ovoid.
                (*T. Americana*) AMERICAN LINDEN
    BB. Linings of leaves pubescent; fruit globose.
                (*T. pubescens*) DOWNY BASSWOOD
AA. Leaves pale below; fruit globose.
                (*T. heterophylla*) WHITE BASSWOOD

The genus Tilia, comprising sixteen recognised species, ranges widely in the Northern Hemisphere, omitting only central Asia, the Himalaya district, and western America. It belongs to a tropical family of which it is the only northern representative. America has three Eastern species and one confined to Mexico. Three other little-known forms have been recently admitted to the rank of species by Professor Sargent.

In classical literature and in folk lore the lindens have an honoured place. In the south of Europe the impressionable Greeks and Romans loved them for their beauty and their honey-laden flowers. The hives of Hybla were sung by poets, and the honey from the linden trees in the Lithuanian forests brought a price three times as large as any other. Linnæus had his name, Carl Linnè (afterward Carolus Linnæus), from a favourite linden tree that stood by his peasant father's house.

Scarcely a part has a linden tree that is not turned to good use. Its fagots make the best of charcoal. The leaves are used, fresh and dry, as fodder for cattle. The flowers furnish nectar to bees, and are distilled by makers of perfumes. An infusion of fresh flowers has long been used as a remedy for indigestion, nervousness, and for coughs and hoarseness. The seed balls are full of oil which is esteemed equal to olive oil for cooking and table use. This oil is also used in perfumeries. The bark of young trees makes the shoes of the Russian peasant. Ropes, fishnets and mats are made of this tough "bast fibre" of the inner bark. It was a favourite tying material in nurseries and greenhouses until the more adaptable raffia came in to replace it. Basswood is second only to "tulip poplar" in the wood carver's esteem. The wood is uniform in colour and texture, does not split easily, and is free from hard knots and minor imperfections. Dryden describes it as

" Smooth grained and proper for the turner's trade,
Which curious hands may carve and steel with ease invade."

Sometimes basswood is sawed by holding a short section of a log so that it revolves against a saw blade. The wood is thus spirally sawed; that is, a thin, continuous board is made as long as the log, and as wide as the spiral path of the saw from bark to pith. Sometimes this sheet of wood is 100 feet wide. Steaming and pressing prepare these curved sheets for veneer work. This method practically eliminates waste, both in the sawmill and in the cabinet shop.

Famous old trees in Europe include the Neustadt Linden in Würtemburg. Its sheltering boughs formed a temple of justice in the Middle Ages. Public questions were discussed under it. It lived to be almost a thousand years old, with a crown over 100 feet in diameter and a trunk 42 feet in circumference. Nearly 200 columns supported it in its dotage.

American Linden, Basswood (*Tilia Americana*, Linn.)— Tall, stately tree with spreading round top, 75 to 125 feet high; trunk 2 to 4 feet in diameter. *Bark* brown, deeply furrowed, scaly; inner layer tough; branches grey, twigs reddish. *Wood* white or pale brown, soft, tough, close grained, free of knots; hard to split. *Winter buds* smooth, plump, pointed, dark red. *Leaves* alternate, obliquely heart shaped, serrate, with prominent veins and paler lining, veins branching mainly on the side next the petiole; rusty hairy in axils of side veins underneath. Petioles 3 to 4 inches long, slender; blades 6 to 8 inches long, 3 to 4 inches wide. *Flowers*, June, July; small, perfect, yellowish white, very fragrant, full of nectar, clustered on end of flower stalk borne on narrow leaf-like blade. Peculiar petal-like scale opposite each petal. *Fruit* a cluster of woody, pea-like balls, grey, rather woolly, round or ovoid; seeds 2 to 3. *Preferred habitat,* moist, rich woodlands. *Distribution*, New Brunswick to Dakota; south to Virginia, along mountains to Alabama; west to Texas. *Uses:* An ornamental and shade tree; planted for bee pasture. Wood used for carriage bodies, bureaus, chair seats, shoe soles, cooperage, wood carving, paper pulp, charcoal and fuel.

No American tree has more abundant foliage than the linden. The branches subdivide into very many twigs, all set with plump buds in winter. These develop into leafy shoots that lengthen rapidly, carrying the broad leaves out where there is room for them to expand fully. A dense shade is cast by this roof of green, and cattle ranging in mixed and open woods are likely to choose this tree as the best shelter from the heat and glare of dog days.

The linden's roots are large and fibrous, penetrating deeply and widely in the soil. The vigour of its growth is not to be wondered at. It is not dependent on transient soil conditions: it draws its sustenance from the deeper sources. Its smooth bark and the lusty symmetry of its frame are revealed in winter. Its lines are gentle curves; its twigs are stout but supple. Its whole character suggests the quality of its wood, which the axe cuts like cheese. Just so the hickory tells by its winter "expression" of the tough fibres its shaggy bark conceals.

The linden opens late in spring. But watch how it makes up time, when the ruby buds do stir, and the inner scales lengthen and reveal the succulent shoots. The flowers wait until the flood of pink and white has subsided in the orchard. Then they open by the hundreds, creamy white and honey laden, and we enjoy them with the bees. Only catalpa and chestnuts will bid for our attention, and the appeal of the fragrance alone is strong enough to lead us to the tree. The blossoms are clustered on dainty pale-green blades. The tree is illuminated, the broad leaf platforms lined with the delicate inflorescence. A bird flying over

395

looks down upon a tree covered with shingled leaves. It is from underneath that the full beauty of these trees must now be seen.

In midsummer the linden grows coarse. The great leaves are soft and attract hordes of insect enemies. Plant lice cover them with patches of honey dew, and the sticky surfaces catch dust and smoke. Riddled with holes and torn by the wind, they fall in desultory fashion. The faded yellow does not please as does the gold of beech and hickory leaves.

Before they lose their spring freshness, note the linden leaf, so you will always recognise it. The heart-shaped blade is unsymmetrical—one half is bigger than the other. The bases do not match, if you fold a leaf on its midrib. Then look at the veining. The main side ribs have large branches only on the lower sides. Those on the other side are simple and small. This is noticeable on no other tree as it is in this one. This peculiarity is seen in the basal half of the leaf, where the side veins are of good size. All lindens show this characteristic. It is one of the marked family traits.

In the virgin forests of the Ohio Valley basswoods vastly outnumbered all other trees. The reasons are easy to discover. Vigorous seeds, winged for flight, are borne in profusion by these trees. Their seedlings are content to grow in the shade. Suckers grow up from the roots of a tree that falls, and every twig the wind tears off is likely to strike root, and soon to become a tree. Only man can interfere with the triumph of such a species in the unceasing battle in the forest. He has distributed Nature's equilibrium. The giant lindens, hundreds of years old, fell under the pioneer's axe, and it will take centuries for the second-growth trees to reach their full stature. Let us hope some of them may be permitted to live their lives undisturbed, just to show to coming generations what the linden trees of the Ohio Valley were in the old days.

The **White Basswood,** or **Bee Tree** of the South (*Tilia heterophylla*, Vent.), is an exceptionally handsome tree, for its bright leaves are pale beneath, often lined with fine, silvery down. As they flutter in the breeze they make a dazzling play of white and pale green against a background usually sombre with hemlocks and mountain laurel.

The white basswood is a lusty forest tree with a preference

for the sides of mountain streams. It occurs at Ithaca, New York, and following the Alleghanies south from Pennsylvania, extends to Florida and Alabama, and west to Illinois, Kentucky and Tennessee. The leaves are narrower in most cases than those of the Northern species, but they vary in size and form, averaging somewhat larger than those of *T. Americana*. The fruits are globular, with two seeds in each.

The **Downy Basswood** (*T. pubescens*, Ait.), like the Northern species, has leaves that are green on both sides, but this species is distinguished by the rusty hairs that line its leaves and coat its young shoots. It is a small tree, with leaves, flowers and fruits reduced in size. It is a basswood in every character, and need not be confused with the other native species. Its flower blade is rounded at its base, while the others taper narrowly to the short stem.

This little basswood follows the coast from the Carolinas to Texas. It occurs also in Long Island. It is too rare to have any importance as a lumber tree, and it is not a desirable species for cultivation.

A large tree, with pubescent leaf linings and flower stalks, has been discovered growing in various localities from Montreal to Georgia and Texas. Collectors have assigned it to *Tilia pubescens*, because it is a hairy species. It does not fit the description, having larger features throughout, and the seed bract being narrowly obovate, tapering to the base. These may be merely variations from the type species. Professor Sargent accepts Nuttall's name, *Tilia Michauxii*, in his Manual. The tree is little known as yet.

European Lindens

Under the Linnæan and trade name, *Tilia Europæa*, many different species of lindens have been imported by American nurserymen, and these trees are widely planted, especially in the Eastern States. *Tilia vulgaris*, with small leaves green on both sides, is a favourite avenue tree, beside which the American basswood looks coarse indeed. This is the linden that lines the famous Berlin thoroughfare, "Unter den Linden"—which so disappoints the average tourist. To judge the lindens of the Continent by these trees would be like judging American trees by specimens that grow along Broadway in New York. The splendid lime trees in the rural sections of France and Germany and in the parks show the linden in its best estate.

In America some fine avenues of this species have attained great age and size. The season of 1904 found these trees loaded with flowers and fruit, under a leaf crown of unusual density and beauty. The lower limbs lie on the ground when the tree makes a natural growth, and the platforms of foliage, each lined with the pendant cluster of flowers, fairly dripping with nectar, form a symmetrical cone worth going miles to see. The ground under these trees was covered with discarded petals and the weakest of the flower clusters, but the limbs above still bent under the burden of the ripening seed balls. The leaves remain much later than those of the native basswoods.

There are many fine specimens of *Tilia tomentosa* and *Tilia argentea*, from eastern Europe, now coming into American gardens and parks. These species deserve more extended cultivation. Each has its foliage lightened with silky leaf linings. The weeping silver linden, *Tilia petiolaris*, is an elegant tree with white-lined leaves.

The **Broad-leaved Linden** (*Tilia platyphyllos*), very common in European parks and avenues, soon loses its foliage in dry weather and is less desirable than other species for America. It is clipped to form hedges in Europe; the alleys of the Tuilleries gardens were made of it.

Because lindens submit patiently to pruning, they have long been clipped into grotesque figures, along with yew and box. They had a tremendous vogue while the formal garden was approaching its most elaborate development. A more lasting popularity was vouchsafed them as avenue and park trees, a popularity which dates from remote times and is still unchecked. "The Linden spreadeth forth his branches wide and farre abroad, being a tree which yieldeth a most pleasant shadow, under and within whose boughs may be made brave summer houses and banquetting arbours."

CHAPTER LII: THE GORDONIAS

FAMILY THEACEÆ

Genus GORDONIA, Ell.

Two very interesting and beautiful species of this genus grow in the South Atlantic States. They are flowering trees that rank in beauty with the magnolias which they resemble. They belong, in fact, to the camellia family, whose flowers are famous in horticulture. The tea plant, *Camillia Thea*, of commerce, itself a beautiful flowering shrub, is a member of the family, and a relative of our gordonias.

The **Loblolly Bay** (*Gordonia Lasianthus*, Ell.) grows to be a tree of 70 feet in height, with slender, straight trunk and narrow, compact head, in swampy land from tidewater Virginia along the coast to the delta of the Mississippi. It is most frequent in eastern Florida and Georgia. Its leaves are evergreen, leathery and shining, lanceolate in form and serrate on the margins. Its flowers are perfect, with fleshy white petals spreading out like great wild roses often two to three inches across. They begin to bloom in July and continue several weeks. A dry, woody, ovoid capsule succeeds the flower. In it are 2 to 8 square, winged seeds.

The tree thrives in cultivation, though at best it is short lived. A handsome specimen blossoms freely in the Arnold Arboretum at Boston.

The **Franklinia** (*G. Altamaha*, Sarg.) is a tree rarely seen over 15 to 20 feet high now. Its flowers, larger than those of the loblolly bay, open in September. The leaves resemble those of the other species in form, but are deciduous, and notable for their splendid scarlet in autumn. The fruit is globular and the seeds not winged.

In 1790 William Bartram found this tree growing in groves along the Altamaha River. Specimens were sent to John Bartram's garden in Philadelphia, and from there were introduced into cultivation. Strangely, no succeeding explorer has ever found the trees growing wild, though careful search has been made to rediscover them. The only specimens known are in gardens, lineal descendants and sole representatives of those Bartram described.

THE AMERICAN LINDEN (*Tilia Americana*)

The broad leaves are unsymmetrical and the side veins branch only on the side next to the base of the leaf. The flower clusters spring in June and July out of pale-green, leafy bracts. The dry seed balls are scattered by wind in winter. The leathery bracts give them wings. The outer twig is of *Tilia heterophylla*

THE RED MANGROVE (*Rhizophora Mangle*)

This Floridian tree spreads over marshy coast plains, forming almost impassable stretches of arching roots. It throws down aerial roots that bind the treetop to the soil in all directions. The seeds germinate on the tree, then fall and immediately become established.

THE WHITE MANGROVE (*Laguncularia racemosa*)

This tree mingles with the others of its name, but is not a true mangrove at all. It is the buttonwood. It has no aerial nor arching roots, but relies on its dry, flask-shaped seeds for multiplication

THE BLACK MANGROVE (*Avicennia nitida*)

It has grey-green, thick leaves, and bears continuously its small white flowers. The seeds germinate before falling. There are no aerial roots, but a grove of erect, leafless, often much-branched, projections arise from the roots. These aerating organs hold the débris and thus make soil

CHAPTER LIII: THE MANGROVES

THE true mangrove family, *Rhizophoraceæ*, of fifteen genera, is chiefly confined to the tropical regions of the Old World. One genus with a single species reaches the extreme end of Florida. Two other species of the genus Rhizophora are found in tide pools and marshes of Asiatic and African equatorial waters. The remarkable habit of throwing out aerial roots from trunks and limbs, and of germinating its seeds before they fall enable the mangrove to extend its range on all sides, encroaching upon the surrounding water slowly but surely. The secondary roots fasten themselves in the soil, and the young plantlets, as they fall, strike root at varying distances from the parent tree. The flotsam and jetsam brought in and out by tides lodge among the network of roots and stems, and thus new soil is formed.

Red Mangrove (*Rhizophora Mangle*, Linn.)—A round-topped tree, 15 to 25 feet high, with drooping, aerial roots. Occasionally 75 feet high, with small, narrow head. *Bark* reddish brown or grey, irregularly broken by shallow fissures; branches smooth. *Wood* reddish brown, streaked with paler brown, hard, heavy, close grained. *Leaves* persistent, thick, oval, blunt, 3 to 5 inches long, dark green and shining above, paler beneath; margins entire. *Flowers*, axillary, perfect, 2 to 3 on short stalk, petals 4, yellow, hairy inside; ever-blooming. *Fruit* berry-like, 1 inch long, with leathery, rough, brown skin; 4 calyx lobes curl back from base, and tube of developing cotyledon of germinating seed protrudes from apex. *Preferred habitat*, along coasts and rivers in wet soil. *Distribution*, Florida from Mosquito Inlet to Cedar Keys, rounding the southern end of the peninsula, and outlying islands. *Uses:* Wood for wharf piles and fuel. Bark yields tannin, and a decoction of it is used as a febrifuge.

This is the true mangrove of the West Indies and the Florida coast, found also along the Pacific coast of Mexico and Lower California. With the coral polyp it co-operates to extend the borders of island and mainland. It spreads in monotonous green thickets over marshy coast plains and in the estuaries of rivers, forming almost impassable stretches of arching roots, accumulating rubbish of all sorts that finally lifts the level above the tide and makes solid ground that is soon covered with the characteristic vegetation of the tropics. Mangrove islands of varying sizes now dot the surface of shallow bays which a few years ago were quite destitute of islands.

The tree reaches its greatest height on dry ground back from the coast. Here the trees grow tall and bare of limbs for two-thirds of their height, and almost abandon the habit of throwing down aerial roots. The wood is used for fuel and built into wharfs. It is not counted a valuable tree.

The **White Mangrove**, or **Buttonwood** (*Laguncularia racemosa*, Gærtn.), is not a true mangrove at all; it belongs in a different botanical family, and is related to the aralias. It mingles with the mangroves, but lacks the aerial roots characteristic of the latter. The foliage is red when it unfolds, becoming dark green and glossy. The flowers are small, in axillary spikes. The fruit is a flask-shaped, 1-seeded drupe with corky flesh and leathery skin. The wood is hard and dark brown, except for the wide white sap wood. The bark is rich in tannic acid, and were the trees located in less miasmic regions they would soon be cut down for the bark alone.

The buttonwood the Floridian esteems as a fuel tree is *Conocarpus erecta*, Linn., whose flowers and fruits are button-like. It is also esteemed for its bark which yields tannin and a tonic drug.

The **Black Mangrove** (*Avicennia nitida*, Jacq.) is an ever-blooming tree, with inconspicuous white flowers and a dry, 1-seeded capsule, 1 to $1\frac{1}{2}$ inches long. The leaves resemble those of the true mangrove in form, but have a grey-green colour. The tree's habit enables it to make soil in much the same way. The seeds germinate before they fall, and are ready to root as soon as they lodge in the mud. The roots of the adult trees extend far out and, branching, send up a grove of leafless projections a foot or two above the tide level, thus forming a network that holds the soil, and soon makes land out of what was a tide-swept marsh. No aerial roots strike downward from the branches of this tree.

The bark of the black mangrove exceeds that of *Laguncularia racemosa* in value to tanners. It is certain that were the trees located in more accessible regions, on solid ground instead of bottomless swamps, they would fall a prey to the peeler's axe. The Floridian depends upon a smudge of punky black mangrove to rid him of mosquitoes and sandflies, the twin scourge of the summer nights. The range of this tree reaches north to St. Augustine and Cedar Keys. From the southern end of the peninsula and the neighbouring keys it extends into the West Indies, the Bahamas, and on to Brazil.

The black mangrove is a tropical member of the verbena family, well known to us in its herbaceous representatives that grow in Northern gardens. The fiddlewood of lower Florida (*Citheraxylon villosum*) is its nearest relative. The most important timber tree in the family is the teak, *Tectoria grandis*, which grows in tropical Asia and the East Indies. The catalpas in the bignonia family are also close tree kin of the black mangrove.

CHAPTER XLIV: THE HERCULES' CLUB

FAMILY ARALIACEÆ

Genus ARALIA, Linn.

FIFTY genera of aralias compose a great tropical family. The well-known English ivy (genus Hedera) is perhaps the most familiar representative. Of the five native species of aralia the spikenards and sarsaparillas are pretty generally known, having a striking luxuriance of growth and a reputation for medicinal properties. There is a single arborescent species. One tree aralia, the angelica tree of China and Japan, is cultivated in the Northeastern States, where it proves hardy, and our native tree is not. In appearance the two species are much alike, though thornless varieties of the Chinese tree are oftenest met in cultivation.

Hercules' Club (*Aralia spinosa*, Linn.)—A spreading, aromatic, spiny tree, with club-like branches, 25 to 35 feet high, or an unbranched shrubby cluster of shoots from underground stems, 6 to 15 feet high in one season. *Bark* dark brown, furrowed by wide, shallow cracks between rounded ridges. *Wood* light, brittle, pale brown, soft. *Buds*: terminal, large, blunt; lateral, flat, small, triangular. *Leaves* clustered near top of branch, 3 to 4 feet long, 1 to 2½ feet wide, twice compound, on stout, spiny petioles; leaflets oval, pointed, with toothed margins; yellow in autumn. *Flowers* white, minute, in many-flowered umbels, forming compound panicles often 3 to 4 feet high above the leaves in midsummer. *Fruits* few, berry-like, juicy, purplish. Nutlets 5, hard, flattened. *Preferred habitat*, deep, moist soil near water courses. *Distribution*, Pennsylvania to southern Missouri, south to Florida and Texas. *Uses:* Handsome and quick-growing ornamental tree. Berries and fleshy roots have medicinal properties, used in home remedies.

The Hercules' club certainly earns its name when an underground stem, stored with plant food, sends up its lusty shoots in spring. The ailanthus, in its most ambitious efforts, never threw up such tall, thick sprouts. Fifteen to twenty feet these unbranched shoots grow, and crown themselves with umbrellas of leaves, twice compound like those of the Kentucky coffee-tree, but much larger. In fact, no temperate zone tree has leaves of such dimensions, though the oval leaflets are moderate in size, and people are likely to mistake the strong, spiny petiole of this leaf for a branch.

These leaves deserve more than a passing comment. They come out with a rich, silky bronze sheen in spring, and turn to red and gold in autumn. They sway in the summer winds, giving the tree the look of a royal palm transplanted from the land of the orange and citron. I have seen a vacant lot overrun by these headstrong yearlings, and there is no such sight outside the tropics for unrestrained vegetable exuberance. It would be a hardy person who succeeded in getting a piece of land away from these outlaws, for the stems though soft and brittle inside, have a tough, horny covering, and spines which though but skin deep are formidable weapons of defence.

The Hercules' club is very late about its blooming, which makes it horticulturally more valuable. There are few trees and shrubs in flower to compete with this one when the cloud of minute white flowers settles above its crown of leaves. What they lack in size as individuals they make up in numbers. The flower cluster matches the leaves in its dimensions. The purplish berries make a fine showing in the fall and winter.

This tree strongly reminds us of the wild sarsaparilla and the spikenard of our woodland rambles; and for the best of reasons. They are all members of the ginseng family, and all have the most extravagant habits, though but one is arborescent. All have a well-earned reputation for medicinal properties. The little plant from which the family name comes is noted the world over. The Chinese reverence its "man-shaped" root, and pay fabulous prices for it, believing that it cures all human ills. Since collectors have almost exterminated our wild ginseng, it is profitably cultivated for export. If it but grew as do the roots of *Aralia spinosa*—but then, the price would shrink accordingly, and people would still have to work for a living!

The name, Hercules' club, is also applied to the prickly ash, *Fagara clava-herculis*, with which this tree may become confused. Comparison of descriptions of the two will enable one to distinguish them without difficulty.

THE HERCULES CLUB (*Aralia spinosa*)

This aromatic, spiny relative cf sarsaparilla and ginseng has club-like branches, leaves a yard long, and a flower cluster four feet high. In the North it is a rampant shrub; in the South it is a little tree

THE TUPELO (*Nyssa sylvatica*)

Short, twiggy branches at the top of a tall trunk make a very picturesque tree. It ranges from swamp borders to high mountain
slopes, and from Maine to Florida and Texas

CHAPTER LV: THE TUPELOS AND THE DOGWOODS

FAMILY CORNACEÆ

THE cornel family is a large temperate zone group comprising fifteen genera, a few of which are tropical. Comparatively few species are arborescent. Two genera in the United States have species of tree habit. They both include ornamental trees with showy flowers and fruit, and foliage of exceptional beauty. The wood of all is extremely hard and close textured.

KEY TO GENERA

A. Leaves alternate; flowers and fruits inconspicuous.
    1. Genus NYSSA, Linn.

THE TUPELOS

AA. Leaves opposite (except *alternifolia*); flowers and fruits showy.
    2. Genus CORNUS, Linn.

THE DOGWOODS

THE TUPELOS

Genus NYSSA, Linn.

Trees of picturesque habit, with twiggy, contorted branches; growing in wet soil. *Wood* cross grained, tough. *Leaves* alternate, simple, deciduous, leathery. *Flowers* minute, greenish, in short racemes or heads. *Fruit*, a fleshy drupe.

KEY TO SPECIES

A. Stones of fruit with rounded ridges; leaves broad, blunt at apex; fruit small.   (*N. sylvatica*) TUPELO
AA. Stones of fruit with sharp, winged ridges; fruit large.

407

B. Leaves blunt pointed; fruit red.

(*N. Ogeche*) OGEECHEE LIME

BB. Leaves sharp pointed; fruit purple.

(*N. aquatica*) COTTON GUM

Tupelo, Pepperidge, Sour or **Black Gum** (*Nyssa sylvatica*, Marsh.)—A medium-sized tree of variable shape, 50 to 100 feet high, with short, rigid, twiggy, horizontal branches. *Bark* rough, dark grey, broken into many-sided plates; on younger trees, pale brown or grey; branches brown; twigs green to orange, often downy. *Wood* heavy, tough, cross grained, soft, not durable in contact with the soil, hard to work. *Buds* small, brown, with hairy scales. *Leaves* alternate, entire, 2 to 4 inches long, oval, leathery, shining above, pale, often hairy beneath, turning scarlet above in autumn. *Flowers*, May, after leaves, yellowish green, inconspicuous, polygamo-diœcious; staminate in loose, pendant heads; pistillate larger, 2 or more in a cluster. *Fruits*, October, 1 to 3 in cluster; fleshy drupes ovoid, blue-black, sour, ⅔ inch long; stone ridged. *Preferred habitat*, low, wet soil, borders of swamps, rivers and ponds. *Distribution*, Maine to Florida; west to southern Ontario, Michigan, Missouri and Texas. *Uses:* Handsome, hardy ornamental trees. Wood used for mauls, pulleys, hubs, rollers, ox yokes and woodenware.

In early fall the rambler in the woods is often startled to see on the mossy carpet in front of him a thick, shining leaf, part of which is still deep green and part as red as blood. It is the tupelo's signal that winter is on the way. Look up, my friend, and the branches above show only a few leaves coloured like the one you found. Come again in a week or two and the tree is ablaze with reds of every shade. It is a pillar of fire, indeed, among the yellowing ashes and hickories; only the reds of the swamp maples and sumachs compare with it in brilliancy. Who can fail to know the tupelo in the glory of its dying foliage? Certainly no rational being, if he has eyes in his head, and the tree in his neighbourhood. The sight of one, and a few sprays of its lustrous leaves to put up behind the picture frames at home, are well worth a Sabbath day's journey.

"Tupelo" is the pretty Indian name. "Pepperidge" cannot be accounted for. It is probable that the fiery foliage first led people to suppose this tree to be a relative of the sweet gum. They grow together—both large trees in the bottom lands of the

South. This "black gum" can be readily distinguished from the red gum, or liquidambar, as far as the colour of the trunks can be made out. The name, "sour gum," refers to the fruit. Linnæus gave to this water-loving genus the name of Nyssa, the water nymph who reared the infant Bacchus. It was the fashion for the old botanists to give new plants names derived from classical mythology, without much thought of appropriateness.

The foliage of the tupelo is without question its chiefest charm, but there are others which the leaves partially conceal. The winter aspect of the tree is strikingly picturesque. There is a central axis, such as we see commonly among evergreens but seldom among broad-leaved trees. From this tapering shaft the slender branches spread in level platforms that subdivide into wiry, angular branchlets and end in a dense, flat twig system. A young tupelo in winter has as much rigidity of mien as a young honey locust.

With advancing years the tupelo loses the symmetry of its youth. The lower branches droop dejectedly. The top is likely to die. When the wreck blows over it often shows a hollow butt, for the wood, though tough, is soft and quick to decay. Where the vitality of the tree is low, agencies of deterioration are quick to follow up their advantage. Wood-destroying fungi in the soil rot the trunk off in an incredibly short time. An artist studying the expression of trees in winter will look in vain for a more melancholy figure than an aged tupelo, smitten by untoward fates—the very King Lear of the forest.

In the ponds of the pine barrens in the Carolinas a two-flowered tupelo is found, variety *biflora*. It is smaller than the parent species, and has a much swollen base, with large roots that hump themselves out of the water. Its leaves are smaller than those the tupelo bears in the North.

The **Ogeechee Lime,** or **Sour Tupelo** (*Nyssa Ogeche*, Marsh.), grows in the river swamps that line the coasts of South Carolina, Georgia and northern Florida. It takes its name from the Ogeechee Valley, which is the centre of its limited range. The trees are small, with bushy tops and hoary grey twigs, which when young are coated with silky red tomentum. The leaves are 4 to 6 inches long, oval, and firm in texture. The tree is a striking figure when laden with its red fruits, about the size and shape of pecan nuts. They hang in profuse clusters from August till late autumn, long after they are ripe and the leaves are fallen. These juicy fruits are sour, and make excellent preserves. It must be difficult business to get them, for the trees stand in water. Nevertheless, the demand for them is good, and justifies the necessary exertion.

The **Cotton Gum** (*Nyssa aquatica*, Marsh.) is the large tupelo of the swamps, a tree with an unusually broad base, an abundance of corky roots, and a superb pyramidal crown. Trunks 3 to 4 feet in diameter and 80 to 100 feet high are not at all unusual. White cottony down is noticeable throughout the treetop as spring growth begins. The young leaves divest themselves of this covering as they mature, except as a lining. These leaves are large, oval, often remotely toothed or lobed. The fruit is purple, and hangs on long, flexible stalks among the gay-coloured leaves in autumn. It has not the popularity of the Ogeechee limes, for the flesh is thin and the skin is tough. The lumber is largely used for fruit crates, broom handles and other cheap articles. The tree is seen at its best in the cypress swamps of Louisiana and Texas.

THE DOGWOODS

Genus CORNUS, Linn.

Small, slender-twigged trees, with very hard wood. *Leaves* simple, entire, opposite (except one). *Flowers* small, in dense cymes; perfect. *Fruit* a berry-like, 2-celled drupe.

KEY TO SPECIES

A. Leaves opposite.
  B. Fruit red.
    C. Flower buds covered; bracts 4, notched.
          (*C. florida*) FLOWERING DOGWOOD
    CC. Flower buds naked; bracts 4 to 6, not notched.
          (*C. Nuttallii*) WESTERN DOGWOOD
  BB. Fruit white (rarely dark blue); leaves rough above.
          (*C. asperifolia*) DOGWOOD
AA. Leaves alternate; fruit blue.
      (*C. alternifolia*) ALTERNATE-LEAVED DOGWOOD

The dogwoods include about thirty species distributed over the Northern Hemisphere, with a single species in Peru. They

B. Staminate flower   A. Pistillate flower

THE TUPELO or Pepperidge (*Nyssa sylvatica*)

Flowers appear after the leaves in May. They are greenish and very small. Staminate trees bear crowded heads of stamens only. Pistillate trees bear perfect flowers, 1 to 3 in a cluster. The sour, blue berries ripen in October. The foliage is the glory of the tree, dark-green and glossy all summer, scarlet in autumn. The wood is especially dense and heavy

Upper plate, fruit   Lower plate, winter bud

THE FLOWERING DOGWOOD (*Cornus florida*,

    The showy white flowers are but the expanded outer scales that enclosed the winter buds. The true flowers cluster in the centre. The shining red berries in October rival the brilliance of the foliage. The grey, checkered bark looks like rough alligator skin. The tree is beautiful, winter or summer

are chiefly shrubs, a few small trees, and all hardy and ornamental, with handsome foliage, flowers and fruits. An attractive character is the vivid autumn foliage.

From ancient times dogwoods have been planted as ornamentals about homes, and in parks and pleasure grounds; tonic drugs, dyes and inks have been derived from their bark; and the wood has been used for engravers' blocks, tool handles, and in turnery. The name *Cornus* (from *cornu*, a horn) calls attention to the hardness and toughness of the wood. "Dogwood" is one of those unfortunate popular names fastened without reason upon a family of beautiful trees and shrubs. In the good old times it was the practice in England to steep the bark of a certain species and wash mangy dogs with the astringent decoction. Perhaps the dogs were as indignant at this treatment as we are to be persistently reminded of it.

There are eighteen American species in the genus Cornus; one is the little herbaceous bunchberry, scarcely six inches high, but distinctly a near relative of the tree dogwoods, as anyone can see.

Flowering Dogwood (*Cornus florida*, Linn.)—A small, flat-topped, bushy tree, 15 to 40 feet high. *Bark* dark grey or brown, broken into squarish plates; branches grey; twigs velvety, purplish green. *Wood* heavy, strong, hard, tough; brown, fine grained. *Buds* conical; flower buds vertically flattened. *Leaves* opposite, simple, 3 to 5 inches long, oval, with midrib and parallel side ribs indented above; whitish. *Flowers*, March to May, before the leaves, in close clusters at ends of branches; greenish, small, tubular; 4 white or pink involucral bracts, notched at tip, surround the flower cluster. *Fruit*, October, ovoid, scarlet drupes, ½ inch long, few in a cluster; seeds 2. *Preferred habitat*, woodlands and rocky hillsides. *Distribution*, Massachusetts to Florida; west to Michigan, Missouri and Texas. *Uses:* Hardy and handsome ornamental trees. Wood used for bearings in machinery, hubs, tool handles; also for wood engravings and wood carving. Bark yields a drug like quinine; also a red dye.

The striking thing about the flowering dogwood in winter is the alligator-skin appearance of its grey, checkered bark. This identifies it in any stretch of woodland without further aid to the observer. One notices, too, the greyness and the platformed stratification of its bushy top, from whose larger branches the twigs rise with curious bendings so as to hold their clustering buds into the light. The tree has a picturesque waywardness of habit in the woods: it crouches in the shadows of tall trees, and leans out to reach the sunshine that sifts through the forest cover. The twigs are thickly set with buds, formed in midsummer, for the flowering dogwood is a thrifty, far-sighted tree. The slim leaf buds are inconspicuous among the squat, box-like buds that contain the flowers.

I need not tell anyone how beautiful a dogwood tree is when the thick cloud of white or pink-flushed blossoms covers its bare branches to their utmost twig. It is a sight to remember to the end of one's days. Perhaps it may seem pedantic, and even unkind, to say here that the beauty of the tree is not in its flowers, but in the four large petal-like scales, or bracts, that surround the greenish bunch of small, tubular, true flowers. In winter these four bracts enfold the flowers. They are the outer envelope of the little flattened and pointed buds. In spring these bud scales do not fall, but grow at an amazing rate. Only the very tips of them are too dry to grow. They form the peculiar notch at the apex, and give the bract an artistic, if rather irregular, twist.

These bracts are merely leaves changed for the special purpose of notifying the little mining bee, Andrena, and other insects of like appetites, that there is nectar in the flower tubes they guard. Leafy in texture, though white and delicately tinted, these bracts develop before the flowers, and last beyond their fading; so we enjoy the dogwood bloom for weeks in spring instead of days, merely. This is the fact that counts, after all, and the added one that we may go out again and again and bring home sprays of the flowers, and yet leave the tree in better state than it was before, if only we cut judiciously, where the top is thickest. Dogwood trees suffer from lack of pruning; their flowers are stunted by crowding.

The grace and beauty of the leaves, with their channelled, curving, parallel veins, must strike one in summertime. Before they change colour the clustered fruits, standing where the flowers stood, burn bright against the leafy background. These shining, waxy berries are never lost to view, even when the foliage takes on shades of crimson and scarlet. They deepen and intensify these royal colours until the hungry birds have taken the last one.

The leaves have fallen, and left behind a bare grey tree, set with multitudes of buds, pledge of next year's flowers and leaves and fruit. The artist will tell you, if you press him (for he doesn't force his notions upon his friends), that the dogwood wears its finest colours in the winter time! Go out into the woods in late February or early March, just when willows and aspens show green—just a hint of it!—through their telltale bark. All the other early trees wear that "rapt, expectant look" that precedes the bold casting off of bud scales. The silky twigs and velvety buds of the dogwood, alive and thrilling with the stir of the sap, show marvellous tones of olive and grey and lavender, with deeper purple shadows and warm hints of red. These are the colours that Japanese artists revel in.

Most people miss all of the loveliness of graceful line and delicate colour harmony revealed by leafless trees. I am happy to say it is a curable form of blindness. By taking thought, one can learn to see the beauty of balance and symmetry that give strength and grace to the frame of a tree, and beauty of form to the dead teazel and mullein stalks under it. One can learn to see the purple with the dun in the autumn grain fields, and the blue in the hemlock shadows on the snow. We may not all be painters, but we may enter into some of the joys the artist finds in the common things about us. Next spring will be a good time to watch the grey bud scales expand, turn green, then pink and white. From April on we may see the steps by which the miracle progresses.

Flowering dogwoods do not grow wild in any country but ours. They are being exterminated in many places. They are cut for the paltry bit of lumber yielded by their spindling trunks. It ought to be a capital crime to cut a single one. They are destroyed for less cause. Here is an example. A hermit lived alone in a strip of woods along a little Michigan lake. He loved trees and plants, and kept this area a veritable Nature's garden, and willed it to the nearby city on his death. The park commissioners, when they had spread their thanks upon the records, took immediate steps "to put the grounds in shape." Two strong labourers were sent in to clear it up. *They cut out all the dogwoods*—"because they didn't trim up straight!" Lower limbs, small trees and underbrush were all sacrificed to make straight the paths of picnic parties; and to get a nice sod started,

413

and have a *park!* The gentle donor of this tract would have broken his heart over the look of it when these improvements (?) were completed. Though he "leaned out from the gold bar of heaven," I think he must have hurled imprecations down upon the stupidity which undid all he had so lovingly and intelligently done, but chiefly upon the slothful and incompetent commissioners who trusted such work to such hands. Only the people themselves, intelligent and vigilant, can defend themselves from such maltreatment, and save from destruction natural beauty which belongs to all.

The **Dogwood** (*Cornus Nuttallii*, Aud.), of the Pacific coast, occasionally reaches 100 feet in height in the forest opposite Vancouver Island. It grows tall and slim, and thus does not commend itself to gardeners as its Eastern relative does. Its flowers are very much like it in colouring and form, though much more conspicuous because twice as large. The bracts do not cover the flowers in the buds, and are not notched at the tip when developed. There are often six instead of four of them.

This dogwood seems not to thrive outside its native woods, on the mountain slopes from British Columbia to southern California. But here it is easily first in a land of splendid flowering trees, leaning upon the sombre evergreens, in its snowy spring robes and its rich scarlet autumnal garb—a spectacle never to be forgotten once it is seen.

The **Rough-leaved Dogwood** (*C. asperifolia*, Michx.) has long been classed among the shrubby species. It becomes tree-like in southern Arkansas and eastern Texas, sometimes reaching a height of 50 feet. As a shrub it is distributed from Ontario to Minnesota and Nebraska, and south into the Gulf States.

The leaves are dark green, paler below and often softly pubescent, but made rough above by stubby white hairs. This is the only tree dogwood with white berries, so it is easily identified by leaf and fruit.

Alternate-leaved Dogwood (*Cornus alternifolia*, Linn.)— A small tree or shrub, 15 to 30 feet high, with low, round head made of layers of horizontal branches. *Bark* smooth, reddish brown; twigs reddish green. *Wood* heavy, hard, fine textured, brown. *Buds* pale brown, acute, scaly. *Leaves* alternate, 3 to 5 inches long, oval, pointed, entire, whitish beneath, on slim petioles. *Flowers* in May, creamy white, small, in flat cymes, $1\frac{1}{2}$ to 3 inches across, on short lateral branches. *Fruits*, October, dark blue, berry-like, $\frac{1}{3}$ inch across, on red peduncles; nutlets 1 to 2, grooved. *Preferred habitat*, moist, well-drained soil. *Distribution*, Nova Scotia to Minnesota; south to Georgia and Alabama. *Uses:* Handsome ornamental tree.

Dogwoods are among the few native trees with simple and opposite leaves—this is a fact well worth remembering. It is a key to many secrets of the woods. The most uninformed person can know by this simple means that a certain tree he never saw before is likely a viburnum, a maple or a dogwood. The ashes and buckeyes have opposite leaves, too, but they are compound. The dogwood we are now considering is an exception to the rule of its family; it has alternate, instead of opposite, leaves. The blades have the general characteristics of the other dogwood leaves, but hang on longer stems. They turn in autumn to the soft, melancholy blue-reds, which seem to belong to the shadowy places the tree commonly frequents. An open situation is required to bring out the tints of scarlet and orange—the colours with sunshine and laughter in them.

On the margins of woods this platform dogwood shows to best advantage its shelving mode of branch arrangement. These striking and beautiful tiers or platforms of branches, leafy to the trunk, considered alone would make this tree popular as an ornamental. The flowers are showy by their numbers, though they lack the coloured bracts that belong to the other two dogwood trees. The black fruits also are profuse and noticeable upon their coral-red branching stems.

Shrubby Dogwoods

Our American woods are rich in shrubby dogwoods, whose beauty earns them places in our gardens and shrubbery borders. There is the white-berried red-osier dogwood (*C. stolonifera*), whose many smooth stems gleam like red-hot pokers in the winter sunlight against the background of an evergreen hedge. The little kinnikinick, or silky cornel (*C. Amomum*), adds to its purplish stems the charm of silky leaves, with white flowers and pale-blue berries in broad, loose cymes. Bailey's dogwood (*C. Baileyi*) looks grey because of the upturning of the silk-lined leaves. The rich red of its twigs in winter and the colours of its

415

autumn foliage are uncommonly fine, even for a dogwood. This species is not quite constant in its characters outside of Michigan.

The **European Dogwood**, or **Cornel** (*Cornus mas*), is the carnelian cherry of our parks and gardens. Its button-like clusters of tiny yellow blossoms cover the bare branches in earliest spring, preceding even the forsythia and the spice bush. The scarlet fruits, as large as olives, make a brave show against the glossy foliage in late summer. Dogwoods of exceeding beauty come from Japan and from the Himalayas. But the average American turns from all exotic species, no matter what their charms, to his own *Cornus florida*, and in May votes it the most beautiful of flowering trees.

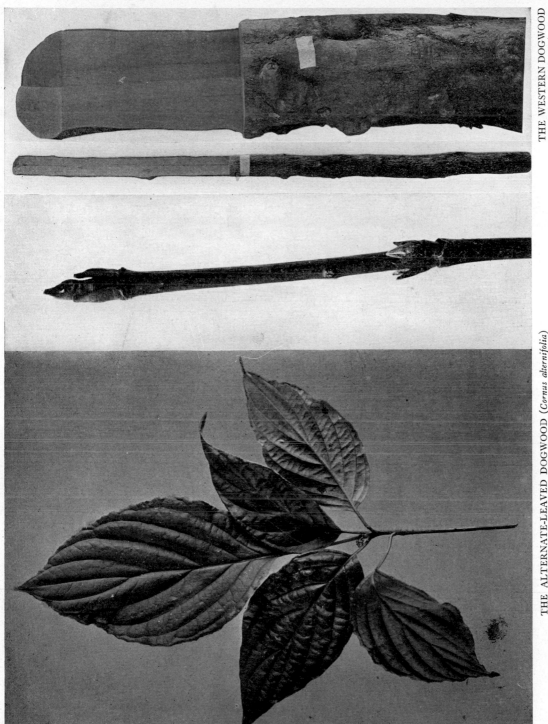

THE ALTERNATE-LEAVED DOGWOOD (*Cornus alternifolia*)

Opposite leaves are habitual with dogwoods. But here is the exception. This little tree more often has but one leaf at a joint, though not always, as this twig shows. The strongly ribbed leaves are crowded only at the end of the twig. The flowers are white and they are small, though the flat cyme is conspicuous in May and June. The berries are dark-blue on coral-red branching pedicels in October

THE WESTERN DOGWOOD
(*Cornus Nuttallii*)

THE SOURWOOD (*Oxydendrum arboreum*)

This is a heath, as the long compound raceme of prim little flower bells and the dry little seed capsules prove. The foliage is a beautiful bronze-green in spring and becomes a vivid scarlet in autumn. The sour twigs and leaves allay the thirst of hunters lost in southern woods. Hardy to Boston, this little-known species deserves wide cultivation

CHAPTER LVI: THE HEATHS

THE RHODODENDRON AND THE MOUNTAIN LAUREL

FAMILY ERICACEÆ

TREES usually of small size and high ornamental value. *Leaves* simple, alternate, mostly evergreen. *Flowers* perfect, regular, in many-flowered clusters. *Fruits*, dry capsules or berry-like drupes.

KEY TO GENERA AND SPECIES

A. Leaves evergreen or sub-evergreen.
   B. Flowers large, showy; fruit a 5-celled capsule.
      C. Capsules conical; flower clusters terminal.

        1. Genus RHODODENDRON, Linn.

            (*R. maximum*) GREAT RHODODENDRON
      CC. Capsules globular; flower clusters axillary.

        2. Genus KALMIA, Linn.

            (*K. latifolia*) MOUNTAIN LAUREL
   BB. Flowers small, in compound racemes; fruit a fleshy drupe; bark shed in thin scales.

        3. Genus ARBUTUS, Linn.
      C. Bark red to brown; leaves oval.
         D. Fruit orange red, $\frac{1}{2}$ inch in diameter.
            (*A. Menziesii*) MADROÑA
        DD. Fruit dark red, $\frac{1}{3}$ inch in diameter.
           (*A. Xalapensis*) MEXICAN MADROÑA
      CC. Bark red to pale grey; leaves lanceolate.
          (*A. Arizonica*) ARIZONA MADROÑA
AA. Leaves deciduous; flowers small, numerous, in terminal compound racemes; fruit a conical 5-celled capsule.

      4. Genus OXYDENDRUM, DC.

         (*O. arboreum*) SOURWOOD

The heath family is world-wide in distribution, consisting of more than fifty genera, with over a thousand species, and modified through centuries of cultivation into unnumbered horticultural varieties. Heaths are perennials, usually woody, with a tendency to profuse and showy bloom. The type of the family is the Scotch heather, immortalised in song and story. A very few genera are represented by tree forms.

In the first quarter of the nineteenth century, when the English first took possession of the Cape of Good Hope, they introduced into England heaths from Australia and South Africa. Their popularity was instant. People went wild over them. They became the dominant feature of the indoor horticulture of the day—the pride of the English gardener. The heydey of these heaths is past. But even now, in London, half a million little potted plants of a single species, *Erica hyemalis*, are sold each Christmas. An average plant a foot high bears a thousand tiny flowers, rosy and tipped with white. It is good for a month of bloom, and costs from twenty-five to fifty cents. It is the poor man's Christmas flower. The azaleas, which the Belgian gardeners have brought to such perfection and variety, also belong to this family.

1. Genus RHODODENDRON, Linn.

Rhododendrons have a hard reputation. Their juice is considered poisonous to man and beast. Honey made from these flowers was believed to have crazed Xenophon's retreating host. Browsing animals were hurt by tasting the leaves and shoots. In his Herbal, Turner wrote of the Italian rhododendron: "I care not if it neuer com into England, seyng it in all poyntes is lyke a Pharesy; that is, beauteus without, and within a rauenus wolf and murderer."

The American rhododendrons are our most ornamental evergreen shrubs. Only one becomes tree-like in size and habit. It attains its greatest height on the mountain slopes of the Carolinas and eastern Tennessee. Here it spreads over considerable areas, often forming impenetrable jungles of great beauty, winter and summer.

Great Rhododendron, Rose Bay (*Rhododendron maximum*, Linn.)—Evergreen shrub or small tree, becoming 35 feet high, with dense, broad head of twisted branches. *Bark* reddish brown, scaly; branches rusty tomentose at first, becoming greyish.

Wood light brown, hard, heavy, fine. *Buds* scaly, prominent; leaf buds small, axillary, on flowerless branches; flower buds large, conical, terminal. *Leaves* narrow oblong, tapering to a short petiole; apex abruptly pointed; margin entire, leathery, stiff, dark green, shining above, dull whitish beneath, 4 to 10 inches long. *Flowers,* June, in large umbels, on viscid stems; corollas irregular, bell shaped, 5-lobed, 1½ inches across, rosy, purplish or white, with hairy and spotted throat; stamens 8 to 12, curved; pistil simple, with 5-celled ovary and elongated style with 5-lobed red stigma. *Fruit* a woody, 5-celled many-seeded capsule. *Preferred habitat,* sandy, peaty or loamy soil, in somewhat shady situations. *Distribution,* New Brunswick to Florida; west to Lake Erie, through Gulf States to Louisiana and Arkansas. Mainly along mountains. Rare north of Pennsylvania. *Uses:* Valuable hardy ornamental evergreen. Forced for winter bloom as potted plants.

Rhododendron means "rose tree"—and we wisely cling to the long, sonorous Greek name. The common English name, rose bay, seems trivial applied to so beautiful a plant. The traveller who visits the southern Appalachian Mountains in early summer sees *Rhododendron maximum* in its best estate. Above each umbrella-like whorl of glossy evergreen leaves appears a rounded cluster of white or rosy blossoms, dimmed only by the bright green of the new leafy shoots that stand out between the flower clusters. For miles these tree-like growths illuminate the woods, as their shrubby relatives, the azaleas, do in woods farther north, where the rhododendrons dwindle in size and in numbers.

Through late summer the green capsules, each with its curving style atop, mark the place where the blossoms were. They hang on all winter, though the seeds fall in autumn. Against the snow the broad leaves shine brighter than all other evergreens, and a large scaly bud in the centre of the young shoots conceals and promises flowers in profusion for the coming summer.

R. Catawbiense, a more brilliant species in bloom, but always a shrub, is brought by the carload from the high Alleghanies, and planted on great estates in the North, where it passes *R. maximum* in hardiness. The transplanting of these rhododendrons is accomplished with a loss of scarcely 1 per cent. if done by responsible nurserymen.

419

2. Genus KALMIA, Linn.

Mountain Laurel (*Kalmia latifolia*, Linn.)—Evergreen shrub or tree, becoming 30 feet high, with dense, round head and crooked branches. *Bark* dark brown with tinge of red, scaly, branches red or yellow, smooth. *Wood* reddish brown, heavy, fine grained. *Buds* large, scaly, sub-terminal ones contain flowers; leaf buds small, naked, axillary. *Leaves* alternate or irregularly whorled, oblong, tapering at both ends, leathery, stiff, dark green and shining above, yellow-green below; 3 to 4 inches long, on short petioles; evergreen, falling during second summer. *Flowers* in large terminal compound corymbs, on viscid peduncles; perfect in June; calyx 5-parted, on 10-lobed disc; corolla, saucer shaped, rosy or white with purple markings in short tube, 10 tiny pouches below 5-parted border; stamens 10, with anthers in pouches, and filaments bent over until time to discharge pollen, when they straighten; pistil 1, with head on long style; ovary 5-celled. *Fruit* a globular, woody, 5-celled, many-seeded capsule. *Preferred habitat*, cool, moist, well-drained soil that contains no lime. Sheltered situations in the North. *Distribution*, Nova Scotia to Lake Erie (north shore); southward through New England and New York, and along Alleghanies to northern Georgia. *Uses:* Hardy ornamental evergreen. Foliage used for winter decoration of houses and churches, and to trim fruit stands in city markets.

Along with the rhododendrons in June and July the mountain laurel hides its shining evergreen leaves with flower clusters larger than any the rhododendron bears. At least it seems so, for the clusters lie close, cheek by cheek, quite subordinating the foliage, making often a great mass a foot across, upon a single slender branch.

Smaller than the rhododendron in blooms, the laurel shows more exquisite colouring, and more interesting and beautiful forms from bud to seed. First, the buds, little fluted cones of vivid pink, make with the green of the new leaves one of the finest colour combinations to be found in any shrub. The largest ones open first, spreading into wide, 5-lobed corollas with ten pockets in a circle around the base of each. Ten stamens stand about the free central pistil, and the anther of each is hid in a pocket, its filament bent back. This is a curious contrivance,

MOUNTAIN LAUREL (*Kalmia latifolia*)

and well worth looking into. There is a bee lighting on the border, and probing the tube of the corolla for honey. Her clumsiness makes her Nature's agent for the fertilising of these flowers. As she steps on a bent filament, it straightens itself with a spring, the hidden anther is drawn forth and bangs against her furry body, dusting her well with the pollen, which comes in a jet out of a small pore at the top of the anther. The mountain laurel is not self-fertile. Only insects, gathering nectar by the hour, fertilise these flowers. They brush their pollen-laden bodies against the erect pistils, thus bringing about cross-fertilisation wherever they go. A net tied over a mass of blossoms, excluding the bees, will defeat Nature, for the stamens are never released, though the pollen cells are ripe and waiting, as is the sticky stigma in their midst. No seed will be set, though all about, on branches not covered, little flattened green capsules, each waving a curved green wand aloft, ripen their seeds and cast them in the fall.

The mountain laurel is being stripped from its native hills in wholesale quantities: first, by the nurserymen, for the decorative planting of private estates; second, by collectors of Christmas greens. In the blossoming season the bushes are mutilated by thoughtless persons—collectors who will sell the flowers, and thoughtless, greedy persons who "can't stop picking because they are so beautiful." The present moment is the only portion of time these people consider.

The makers of wooden spoons, ladles, rustic furniture and pipes are despoiling the Southern woods of rhododendron and laurel. The end of these beautiful heaths is not so far off, unless the ruthless destruction of them in the wild woods can be checked. There is no more beautiful garden shrub than Kalmia. It is easily propagated from seed in nurseries, and should be obtained from these sources. It is hardy and thrifty farther north than rhododendron. Transplanting from the wild is precarious business with heaths, and the average person fails utterly.

In the name of this genus, Linnæus commemorates the devoted labours of Peter Kalm, the Swedish traveller and botanist, through whose eyes "the father of botany" saw the wonderfully rich and varied flora of the New World.

3. Genus ARBUTUS, Linn.

Madroña (*Arbutus Menziesii*, Pursh.)—Evergreen shrub or tree 40 to 100 feet high, with smooth, reddish brown bark, and smooth red branches. *Wood* heavy, hard, strong, reddish brown, close grained. *Leaves* alternate, persistent, entire, rounded or heart shaped at base, oval or oblong, 3 to 4 inches long, smooth, shining above, glaucous beneath. *Flowers* white, in erect panicles, 5 to 6 inches long, monopetalous, ovate, $\frac{1}{3}$ inch long, perfect. *Fruit* a globular, many-seeded berry, $\frac{1}{2}$ inch long, orange red, edible. *Preferred habitat,* well-drained soil in situations protected from dry winds. *Distribution,* coast region, British Columbia to California; on mountain slopes becoming shrubby. *Uses:* Valuable ornamental tree in warm-temperate climates. Wood used for furniture, charcoal, and bark for tanning leather.

"The Madroña, clad in thin, smooth, red and yellow bark and big glossy leaves, seems in the dark coniferous forests of Washington and Vancouver Island, like some lost wanderer from the magnolia groves of the South."

No American tree of considerable size equals this one in beauty the year around. It bears large conical clusters of white flowers, above the vivid green of its leathery leaves. The tree is further lightened by silvery leaf linings. The red-brown trunk and bright red branches add a rich colour note, which is intensified when the copious scarlet fruits appear and the two-year-old leaves turn to scarlet or orange in the autumn. Even among the redwoods this arbutus is a tree that commands attention and admiration at every season. The wood tempts the charcoal burner to chop down trees whose beauty ought to save them from destruction. The Japan Current makes them hardy in the west coast regions, and they thrive in the gardens of western and southern Europe.

The **Mexican Madroña** (*Arbutus Xalapensis*, H. B. K.), similar to the previous species in essential characters, but small in stature, has wandered up along the mountains from Mexico, and grows scattered along the limestone hillsides of western Texas. Handsome as it is, this tree is not yet known in cultivation. The Mexicans use its wood to make stirrups. It is also used for tool handles and mathematical instruments.

The **Arizona Madroña** (*Arbutus Arizonica*, Sarg.) is strikingly beautiful in the contrast of its white trunk, red branches, and lustrous pale green leaves, to which are added in spring feathery plumes of white flowers, and in the fall clusters of deep orange-red berries. It grows on high mountain slopes, but has been introduced into cultivation.

The **Strawberry Tree** (*Arbutus Unedo*, Linn.), related to our Madroñas, is cultivated in Southern gardens. This brilliant little European tree bears in the fall its rosy flowers in nodding clusters along with its large scarlet fruits. It is hardy in warm-temperate regions, but requires shelter from the wind. It is also offered by dealers in red-flowered varieties.

4. Genus OXYDENDRUM, D.C.

Sourwood, Sorrel Tree (*Oxydendrum arboreum*, DC.)—A slender-stemmed tree, 15 to 60 feet high, with oblong, round-topped head. *Bark* smooth, reddish grey, scaly. *Wood* reddish brown, heavy, fine grained, hard. *Buds* axillary, small, partly hidden, red. *Leaves* alternate, deciduous, membraneous, oblong or lanceolate, entire, 3 to 6 inches long, smooth. *Flowers*, June or July, perfect, in panicles, 7 or 8 inches long, of racemed white bells, narrowed and frilled at the tops. *Fruit* a downy capsule, 5-celled; seeds numerous, needle-like. *Preferred habitat*, moist woods. *Distribution*, Pennsylvania, Ohio and Indiana; south to Florida, Alabama, Louisiana and Arkansas. *Uses:* Ornamental tree, valued for its flowers and vivid scarlet autumn foliage.

This little deciduous tree, whose sour-tasting twigs and leaves temporarily assuage the thirst of the hunter lost in Southern woods, deserves mention for this, even if it had no other redeeming traits. Besides, the tree is beautiful in its bronze-green spring foliage and its long compound racemes of tiny, bell-shaped flowers, and later, in its autumnal robes of vivid scarlet. It is a heath in all its characters recognisable by its prim little flower bells and the dry little capsules that succeed them. Hardy as far north as Boston, it is occasionally seen in American gardens, and in western and central Europe.

CHAPTER LVII: THE PERSIMMONS

Family Ebenaceæ

Genus DIOSPYROS, Linn.

ROUND-HEADED trees, with zigzag branchlets and no terminal buds; wood hard and close grained. *Leaves* leathery, entire, simple, alternate, deciduous. *Flowers* diœcious, axillary; staminate in cymes, pistillate solitary or paired. *Fruit* a large, juicy berry, 1 to 10-seeded.

KEY TO SPECIES

A. Leaves 4 to 6 inches long, pointed; fruit 1 to 2 inches in diameter, orange to brown when ripe.
    (*D. Virginiana*) PERSIMMON
AA. Leaves ¾ to 1½ inches long, blunt; fruit ½ to 1 inch in diameter, black when ripe.
    (*D. Texana*) BLACK PERSIMMON

The ebony family has five genera, the most important of which is Diospyros. This genus contains 180 species, including among them the two temperate zone trees in America, and others of horticultural importance in Japan and China. The ebony of commerce comes from different tropical species. *D. Ebenum*, native of Ceylon and the East Indies, produces the most valuable wood. Beside lumber, ebonies furnish fruit trees and ornamentals planted for their lustrous foliage and decorative fruits. Some of the tropical species are grown in Northern greenhouses.

Persimmon (*Diospyros Virginiana*, Linn.)—A slender, tall tree with handsome round head, rarely over 50 feet high; twigs angular, often hollow. *Bark* broken into thick scaly plates, dark grey or brown; twigs reddish, pubescent, becoming grey. *Wood* very hard, dark brown, with pale sap wood, fine grained, tough, like hickory; not durable in soil. *Buds* small, pointed, reddish. *Leaves* alternate, simple. oval, pointed, 4 to 6

424

inches long, thick, shining above, paler beneath; petioles short, stout. *Flowers*, June, after leaves, diœcious, small, yellowish green; staminate in 3-flowered cymes, scarcely opening; pistillate solitary, wide open, with imperfect stamens. *Fruit* a reddish-yellow berry 1 to 1½ inches in diameter, pulpy, sweet, edible when ripe; astringent when green. *Preferred habitat*, light, sandy soil, or moist woodlands, fence rows and abandoned fields. *Distribution*, Rhode Island to Florida; west to Kansas and Texas. *Uses:* Worthy of planting for its rich green foliage in late summer, and its graceful habit. Comes readily from seed, but is transplanted with difficulty. Fruit shows little improvement in cultivation. Wood is used in turnery, for shoe lasts, plane stocks and shuttles.

There is no better way to fix the persimmon tree indelibly in the mind than to yield to the importunities of Southern friends and taste the fruit before it is ripe. You will be quite willing after that to wait until the frost (or whatever influence it is) mellows the puckery little plum. A traveller in the colony of Virginia wrote his friends in England about "the pessemins that grow on a most high tree." He describes them, with a fervency born of experience, as "harsh and choakie and furre in a man's mouth like allam!" Some of us say, "Amen!"

Possibly some part of the persimmon's popularity is due to its exclusiveness. Certainly no other tree keeps its fruit so far out of reach of eager hands and thirsty lips. "*The longest pole takes the persimmon*," is a proverb that has passed the bounds of the Southern States, and taken on a much broader significance than its originator probably intended.

The persimmon tree is not confined to the South, though its finest proportions are reached in Oklahoma forests, and it "feels the cold" in Ohio and New York. Northerners are likely to content themselves with a taste even when the fruit is at its best. It is strangely different from other things. But the Southerner born and bred knows and delights in this native fruit. The Negro revels in it, and begrudges the opossum all he steals, forgetting that a 'simmon tree when fruit is ripe belongs to the first comer. "'Possums an' 'simmons come together, an' bofe is good fruit." This statement sums up the feelings of the Negro on two vital topics. The opossum camps down in the neighbourhood of a well-laden persimmon tree and fattens on its fruit; but the defrauded darkey who marked that tree for his own can afford to keep his temper. The fat 'possum on his table on Thanksgiving day is especially delicate for this 'simmon feast, with which it tops off the season. So there is no question but that he laughs best who laughs last.

The 'possum is a nocturnal beast, and he likes company. It is not unusual for three or four to be found by night up a persimmon tree, hanging on with their bare, prehensible tails, or bracing themselves in crotches of limbs, within reach of the soft sugar lumps of fruit. They are lazy, and do not climb up if enough fruit is to be found under the tree to satisfy their appetites. In a near-by rail heap or a hollow tree the opossums sleep off the effects of heavy feeding, and return to their quest with zeal the following night.

The following, from high authority, is conclusive: "Anyone who has hunted quail through the Carolinas in January or February, when the fruit still hangs on the trees (as it occasionally does in the woods on young trees only six to eight feet high), knows that toward the end of a long day's tramp no more delicious or refreshing morsel can be imagined than these persimmons. They are thoroughly ripe then, entirely without bitterness or astringency, sweet, rich and juicy."

It is tannin in the fruit that gives it its astringency. This is gradually withdrawn, probably quite independent of the action of frost. The orange colour comes to it long before the fruit is ripe.

The **Black Persimmon**, or **Chapote** (*Diospyros Texana*, Scheele), is a scrubby tree that covers its matted top from February till the following midwinter with dark, leathery leaves, which are narrow and scarcely an inch long. The black, insipid fruit ripens in August, and its juice is used as a black dye. The wood is black, often streaked with yellow, and handsome when polished. It is sometimes used for engravers' blocks. The tree grows in western Texas, and south to the Gulf of Mexico.

The wood of our two persimmon trees somewhat resembles that of their esteemed tropical relatives, the ebony trees of the East and West Indies. But, as often is true of temperate-zone species, the quality is inferior.

In Japan, the native persimmon, *Kaki*, in the Japanese language, has been improved, until there are numberless horti-

THE PERSIMMON (*Diospyros Virginiana*)

This may be a broad tree of wayward habit or a tall one with handsome, round head. The bark is broken by deep furrows into small thick plates. Winter buds are small and red. The yellow flowers are borne in axils of leaves in June. The pistillate trees bear orange-coloured berries, 1 to 1½ inches in diameter. They are astringent and inedible until dead ripe; after heavy frosts they are sweet and luscious. The Negro and the opossum are devoted to this fruit, and are its most ardent collectors

1 Winter bud   2 Fruiting branch   3 Fruit: A, stone   4 Bark and wood   5 (*Symplocos tinctoria*)

THE SILVER BELL TREE (*Mohrodendron tetraptera*)

The pale-green 4-winged seed cases cluster behind the leafy shoots in summer—the wonder of all observers. The bark is coarser and the trunk larger than in the Sweet Leaf, *Symplocos tinctoria*

cultural varieties. They bear large, luscious fruits, much better in all respects than those of the American species. The Department of Agriculture at Washington has successfully introduced several varieties of Kaki into the Southern States. They do best when grafted upon our own trees.

Prejudice against persimmons results when a stranger to the fruit attempts to eat it before it is ripe. The handsome Japanese sorts are often ripe-looking before the tannin has left them. The experienced person knows that there is no fruit more delicate than a thoroughly ripe Kaki, so soft it must be eaten with a spoon.

CHAPTER LVIII: THE SILVER BELL TREE AND THE SWEET LEAF

FAMILY STYRACEÆ

THERE are seven genera in the storax family, and few species, scattered over the warmer sections of the north temperate zone. Benzoin and storax, valuable balsams of commerce, are obtained from two species, one in the Molucca Islands, the other in Asia Minor and Europe.

1. Genus MOHRODENDRON, Britt.

Small trees with slender, pithy, pubescent branchlets and no terminal buds. *Leaves* simple, alternate, deciduous. *Flowers* white, bell-shaped, conspicuous. *Fruit* corky, 2 to 4-winged, 2 to 4-celled, with 1 seed in each cell.

KEY TO SPECIES

A. Fruit 2-winged; corolla deeply lobed.
(*M. dipterum*) SNOWDROP TREE
AA. Fruit 4-winged; corolla shallowly lobed.
(*M. tetraptera*) SILVER BELL TREE

Silver Bell Tree, Snowdrop Tree (*Mohrodendron tetraptera*, Britt.)—Tree or shrub to 80 feet high, with erect branches and narrow head. *Bark* scaly, brown, with shallow furrows and broad ridges, new shoots pubescent; twigs smooth. *Wood* pale brownish, soft, light, close. *Buds* hairy, small, reddish, blunt. *Leaves* ovate, oblong, acuminate entire, 2 to 4 inches long, dark green above, paler and stellate pubescent beneath, pale yellow in fall. *Flowers* in May, white, bell shaped, in lateral clusters of 2 to 4, perfect; stamens 8 to 16, pistil 2 to 4-celled, 4 ovules in each cell. *Fruit* 4-winged, dry, oblong drupe. *Preferred habitat*, well-drained, rich soil in sheltered situations. *Distribution*, mountains of West Virginia to Illinois; south to Florida, northern Alabama and Mississippi to Arkansas, Louisiana and eastern Texas. *Uses:* A beautiful ornamental tree for parks and private grounds.

If the snowdrops from the garden should suddenly quit their sunny corner and take to the woods and you went out to find them, you would be sure they had climbed a tree and were looking down at you with that same meek expression, though you never looked into their faces before. The little mohrodendron tree knows better than you do where these white bells come from that whiten her ruddy twigs so completely that even the tuft of opening leaves on the end of the shoot is forgotten. With the opening of the buds little flesh-coloured flowers appear and hang inconspicuously down for a considerable time. There are rosy tones in the opening leaf buds and a ruddy glow on the twigs themselves. Sun and rain work slowly but surely. The corolla grows to full size, and bleaches, surrendering its colour and its leathery texture. The sun comes out, and on some fine morning the carriages that have driven by the tree each day, perhaps for weeks, are stopped, while the occupants exclaim upon the magic which has clothed the little tree in a bridal veil—

"Has turned it white
In a single night,"

some will insist, for "we would never have missed it." Yet the truth is, the miracle has been gradually unfolding, and people in carriages do miss all but the dénouement of such miracles. They view Nature from afar off, and miss a great deal of good fun that the pedestrian finds for himself.

The white bells fade and fall, and a queer little green, tapering thing, with four thin wings in lengthwise lines, ripens into the seed case. Among the leaves these pale-green fruits are distinctly ornamental throughout the season.

"The snowdrop tree" is a favourite in gardens, and is perfectly hardy north to the Great Lakes. It is easily transplanted and grows in bush or tree form, according to the pruning it receives. A variety, *Meehani*, of handsome, bushy habit and copious bloom, grows about 12 feet high. It looks in full bloom somewhat like an apple tree. The flowers are smaller but more numerous than on the parent tree, and the corollas are more open and bowl shaped. The variety has thus far failed to set perfect seed.

429

A **Snowdrop Tree** (*M. diptera*, Britt.) inhabits swampy land along the south Atlantic and Gulf coasts and follows the Mississippi to Arkansas. It is hardy in cultivation no farther north than Philadelphia. It is smaller in stature than the silver bell tree, but has larger leaves and more showy flowers. Between the two species the chief difference is that two of the seed's wings in this one have become obsolete, leaving it two winged, *di-ptera*. The other species has four-winged seeds, expressed in the Greek word *tetra-ptera*.

2. Genus SYMPLOCOS, L'Her.

Trees with pithy branchlets, forming open, round head. *Leaves* half evergreen, simple, alternate, entire, oval. *Flowers* small, perfect, white, bell shaped in axillary clusters. *Fruit* a brown berry. · (*S. tinctoria*) SWEET LEAF

Symplocos is a large genus of trees that grow wild in Australia and in the tropics of Asia and America. Many species belonging to British India yield important dyes and drugs. A species from Japan has recently created a stir in horticultural circles in this country. It has profuse white flowers that look like those of the hawthorns, hence its name, *S. cratægoides*. These racemed flowers give place to berries which turn on ripening to a brilliant blue, which make the shrubby tree a most striking and beautiful object in a garden in the fall. The only American representative of this genus is a little tree.

Sweet Leaf, Horse Sugar (*Symplocos tinctoria*, L'Her.)— A small, open-headed tree, 10 to 30 feet high, with short trunk and slim, ascending branches. *Bark* ashy grey with reddish cast, warty. *Buds* ovate, with triangular scales. *Leaves* leathery, dark green and lustrous above; paler and pubescent beneath; 5 to 6 inches long, 1 to 2 inches wide, tapering at base and apex; entire or remotely toothed on margins; petioles short, winged. *Flowers* white, fragrant, in close axillary clusters; March to May. *Fruit*, a brown, nut-like drupe with 1 seed. *Preferred habitat*, moist, shady woodlands. *Distribution*, Delaware to Florida; west to Blue Ridge Mountains, and in Gulf States to Louisiana and southern Arkansas. *Uses:* Rare in gardens, though it deserves attention for its handsome, sweet-tasting foliage. Bark of stems and roots, bitter and aromatic, yields yellow dye and has tonic medicinal properties. Horses and cattle browse the foliage.

FLOWERS OF THE SILVER BELL TREE (*Mohrodendron tetraptera*)

CHAPTER LIX: THE ASHES AND THE FRINGE TREE

Family Oleaceæ

1. Genus FRAXINUS, Linn.

VALUABLE timber and ornamental trees. *Leaves* deciduous, pinnately compound, opposite. *Flowers* small, inconspicuous, in compound panicles; the two kinds, except in A, borne on separate trees. *Fruit* a dry seed, winged like a dart.

KEY TO MOST IMPORTANT SPECIES

A. Twigs 4-angled; flowers perfect.
(F. quadrangulata) BLUE ASH
AA. Twigs round; flowers diœcious.
  B. Branchlets, petioles and leaf linings smooth.
    C. Buds brown; leaflets stalked.
      D. Leaves whitish beneath.
        E. Wings of fruit broad; leaflets blunt.
(F. Caroliniana) SWAMP ASH
        EE. Wings of fruit narrow; leaflets taper pointed.
(F. Americana) WHITE ASH
      DD. Leaves green beneath. (<i>F. lanceolata</i>) GREEN ASH
    CC. Buds black; leaflets sessile.   (<i>F. nigra</i>) BLACK ASH
  BB. Branchlets, petioles and leaf linings downy.
    C. Twigs slender; keys very long and slender.
(F. Pennsylvanica) RED ASH
    CC. Twigs stout; leaves pale green.
      D. Trunk cylindrical.   (<i>F. Oregona</i>) OREGON ASH
      DD. Trunk bulging at base. (<i>F. profunda</i>) PUMPKIN ASH

Ash trees are easily distinguished in the woods by the opposite arrangement of their pinnately compound leaves. Hickories, walnuts, and other trees with similar leaves will be found to have an alternate arrangement. The snugly fitting bark, broken into small, often diamond-shaped plates, gives the trunk of an ash a trim, handsome appearance in the winter woods. The seeds, winged and shaped like darts, are borne profusely, and are quite sufficient identification. No other tree bears a fruit that can be confused with this one.

There are thirty known species in the genus Fraxinus, half of which inhabit North America, covering all sections except the coldest. The Northern Hemisphere in the Old World is as well supplied. Cuba, northern Africa and the Orient have tropical species.

It is not so clear to ordinary people as it is to the botanists that the ashes belong to the olive family. If we knew all the tropical members of the group we might not be surprised. The relationship is established by morphological characters obvious only to trained observers.

The name *ash* is applied to several other kinds of trees. Mountain ashes belong to the rose family. Prickly ash belongs with the sumachs in the rue family. "Yellow ash" is a Tennessee name for *Cladrastis lutea*, the virgilia, a member of the locust family. The "hoop ash" of Vermont is the hackberry, a close relative of the elms.

White Ash (*Fraxinus Americana*, Linn.)—A tall, stately tree, 75 to 125 feet high, with straight, columnar trunk reaching 6 feet in diameter, and high pyramidal or round head of erect, stout branches. *Bark* closely furrowed into many deep, diamond-shaped ridges and hollows, dark brown or grey, thick. *Wood* reddish brown, with paler sap wood, tough, elastic, coarse, heavy, hard, not durable in soil, becoming brittle with age. *Buds* smooth, dark brown, plump, leathery, on pale twigs. *Leaves*, opposite, pinnate, 8 to 12 inches long, of 5 to 9 leaflets, usually 7, appearing late, falling early; autumn colour purple or yellow; leaflets stalked, smooth when mature, dark green above, pale, often silvery beneath, oblong-lanceolate, with entire or wavy margins. *Flowers*, May before leaves, diœcious, in panicles, at first compact, later long and loose; staminate purple, later yellow, stamens 3 on short filaments; pistillate purple, vase shaped, with elongated style and spreading, divided stigma. *Fruit*, September, slender, dart-like keys, 1 to 2 inches long, pointed, wing twice the length of the round, tapering body. *Preferred habitat*, rich, moist soil. *Distribution*, Newfoundland and Nova Scotia to Florida; west to Ontario, Minnesota and Texas. *Uses:* An admirable park and street tree. Wood used for agricultural implements, frames of vehicles, tool handles, oars, furniture, interior finish of houses, stairs, and fuel.

The white ash is one of the trees that holds its own in our Eastern forests, the peer of the loftiest oak or sycamore or black walnut. Narrow as its head is when crowded in the company of other trees, it can broaden out into a canopy of benignant shade when it has room to grow naturally. The *white* of its leaf linings enters into its name. The pale twigs and bark also justify its name.

The tree is a column of grey in winter, topped by upright branches and erect, rigid twigs, set with mathematical accuracy in opposite pairs. There is little grace in such a tree until June has covered it with supple new shoots, and the leaves droop and flutter in sun and wind. Then the white ash stands transformed, and all through the summer the pistillate trees are hung with bountiful clusters of pale or rosy keys that dance and gleam and fairly dazzle the eyes of the beholder.

Staminate trees ordinarily shed their flowers as soon as the bursting pollen cells have turned their purple to gold. A little mite has discovered some virtue in these flower clusters, and mite families innumerable are raised therein, causing the distorted blossoms to remain in place, though withered. I once found an old man carefully gathering these bunches in winter, thinking them to be seed of the tree. He looked incredulous when I tried to dispel his illusion, and a moment later resumed his task.

In the South the white ash languishes, is undersized, and its wood is of poor quality. In the Northeastern and Central States it is at its best, and is counted one of the most important of our American timber trees. It is probably put to more uses than any other species.

In cultivation, the small-fruited white ash (var. *microcarpa*, Gray) is often met with. The clustered darts are scarce one-half inch long.

Black Ash (*Fraxinus nigra*, Marsh.)—Slender, upright tree with narrow head, 50 to 90 feet high; twigs stout. *Bark* close textured, dark grey, with interlacing furrows; twigs smooth, grey, with pale lenticels. *Wood* brown, soft, heavy, tough, splitting into annual layers along the porous spring wood. *Buds* broadly ovate, almost black, granular-pubescent; inner scales becoming

433

leaf-like. *Leaves* in May, 12 to 16 inches long, of 7 to 11 oblong-lanceolate leaflets, all but terminal one sessile; margins with incurving teeth, upper surfaces dark green, smooth; lower pale with rufous hairs in tufts along pale midribs; fall early, after turning rusty brown. *Flowers*, May, before leaves, diœcious, in axillary panicles; stamens dark purple with short filaments; pistils with long cleft purple stigmas, often with abortive stamens below. *Fruit* winged keys in open panicles, 8 to 10 inches long; seed flat, short, surrounded by wing which is broad, thin and conspicuously notched. *Preferred habitat*, deep, cold swamps and stream borders. *Distribution*, Newfoundland and north shore of Gulf of St. Lawrence to Manitoba; south to Delaware and the mountains of Virginia, southern Illinois, central Missouri, and northwestern Arkansas. *Uses:* Wood especially suited for baskets, chair bottoms and barrel hoops; also used for fencing and fuel, for cabinet work and furniture. Saplings used for hop and bean poles.

If you have learned to recognise an ash tree at sight, it is an easy matter to distinguish the black ash at any time of year. It is the slenderest of them all, rarely more than a foot in diameter, even though its height be over 50 feet. The trunk looks like a dark grey granite column, so even and close textured is its bark. In winter the blue-black buds are our best identification sign. They are only "exceeded in blackness" by the buds of the European ash (*F. excelsior*). Tennyson, describing the eyes of the gardener's daughter, uses this striking simile: "Black as ash buds in the front of March." The foliage is so dark green it looks black at a distance and the side leaflets have no stalks.

Like its European cousin, the black ash is unusually late in coming out in the spring. Often it is the middle of May before the black outer pair of bud scales fall, and the two inner pairs broaden and lengthen and turn green to help for a short season the opening leaves. As a rule the staminate flowers are on different trees from those bearing the pistillate, and rarely a few perfect ones.

The black ash is not a tree for the lawn. It loves to stand with its roots submerged, and often dies of thirst in the rich loam of a garden. It is a short-lived tree, at best, and very slow of growth; it keeps its foliage but a short time, turning a dull, rusty hue in early autumn. So we shall not wish to plant it anywhere unless perhaps in swampy land. The roots range far and wide

Winter buds　　　　　Pistillate flowers　　　　　Staminate flowers

THE WHITE ASH (*Fraxinus Americana*)

　　Winter shows the framework of its fine, rounded dome.　The stout twigs bear rusty blunt buds set opposite in pairs, above crescentic leaf scars.　The flowers are small.　Clustered purple stamens appear with the leaves in May on the sterile trees.　They turn to yellow when the pollen is ripe.　Racemes of greenish pistillate flowers are borne on the fertile trees.　These become the clustered key fruits, which are pale-green in summer, but turn brown, and are gradually shed in winter

THE BLACK ASH (*Fraxinus nigra*)

Black, blunt buds, dark brown wood and grey bark, furrowed into irregular plates, are characters of this species. Dull, dark green leaflets, all sessile but the terminal one. make the foliage mass gloomy

THE RED ASH (*Fraxinus Pennsylvanica*)

The very slender fruits distinguish this species. The leaf linings, stems and the youngest shoots are velvety. The bark is reddish brown

Flowers

THE BLUE ASH (*Fraxinus quadrangulata*)

Perfect flowers and 4-angled twigs set this ash apart from all other species

and drink up the moisture at a marvellous rate. A few trees will soon cover such a tract, sending their seeds broadcast, and throwing up suckers from their roots.

It was the Indians who taught our forefathers to weave baskets of black-ash splints. The wood is split into sticks an inch or so wide and two or three inches thick. These are bent over a block, and the strain breaks the loose tissue that forms the spring wood, and separates the bands of dense, tough summer wood into thin strips suitable for basket weaving.

The grain of black ash is normally straight, but warty excrescences called "burls" form on the trunk sometimes, and these show wonderful contortions of the grain. Innumerable radiating pins, or abortive branches, keep on growing within the wood, each the centre of a set of circles or wavy lines, which show when a "burl" is cut across. Bowls hollowed out of single burls and polished show exquisitely waved lines as delicate as those in a banded agate.

European ash sometimes shows a twisted and warped condition of the fibres known to woodworkers as "ram's-horn" and "fiddle-back" ash. Knotty parts of stems and roots once went under the trade name of "green ebony," and fancy boxes and other articles made of it and polished brought extravagant prices. "When our woodmen light upon it, they make what money they will of it," says Evelyn. And he tells of a famous table made of an old ash tree on whose polished surface "divers strange figures of fish, men and beasts" were discernible in the grain of the wood! Another enthusiast, with still livelier imagination, saw in the cleft trunk of an ash tree, before it was polished even, "the various vestments of a priest, with the rosary and other symbols of his office!"

Red Ash (*Fraxinus Pennsylvanica*, Marsh.)—A small, spreading tree, 40 to 60 feet high, with irregular, compact head of twiggy branches. *Bark* reddish, closely furrowed, scaly; young twigs pubescent. *Buds* small, dark brown, nodes close together. *Leaves* 10 to 12 inches long, of 7 to 9 leaflets, lanceolate, coarsely serrate, on short stalks, smooth, yellow-green above, silvery pubescence on petioles and leaf linings; yellow in fall. *Flowers*, May, with leaves; diœcious, in hairy panicles; pistillate greenish, inconspicuous. *Fruit* slender, clustered keys, 1 to 2 inches long, on hairy stems; wing 1 inch long and extending half way

435

around the body. *Preferred habitat*, moist soil near streams or lakes. *Distribution*, New Brunswick to Ontario and the Black Hills in Dakota; south to Florida, Alabama and Nebraska. *Uses:* Inferior to white ash in all ways. Often planted in eastern United States for shade and ornament.

The red ash thrives best in the Northeastern States, especially in Pennsylvania. West of the Alleghanies it is an inferior tree. Its lumber is of poor quality compared with white ash, but being of the same colour it is often substituted for the latter by unscrupulous lumber dealers.

The common name of this species probably refers to the red inner layer of the outer bark of the branches. This trait alone is not a distinguishing one, however, for white ash sometimes shows the same character. The red ash has velvety down that invests its new shoots. Winter and summer, this sign never fails. The tree has slimmer twigs and branches than most of the ashes, and crowds its buds and twigs much more closely. The silky leaf linings lighten and soften the yellow-green foliage mass. Red-ash seeds are extremely slender, and vary in size and form, the most graceful in outline of all the darts the various ash trees bear. Lingeringly the tree gives up its seeds in winter. A breeze strong enough to tear off a few from the cluster will carry them a considerable distance. The heavy body or seed end of a key pitches downward, but the thin wing gives the wind a chance to lift it. So on its dainty sail the seed is borne away to plant an ash far from the parent tree, if by chance it fall in good ground. It is easy to understand why ash trees always grow scattered here and there through the woods. Go out on a winter day when the wind blows a gale and see the pistillate tree launching its seeds. It is worth a journey and some discomfort to see it.

Green Ash (*Fraxinus lanceolata*, Borkh.)—A handsome, round-headed tree, 50 to 60 feet high, with slender spreading branches and grey twigs. *Bark* grey, furrowed, branches smooth. *Wood* heavy, hard, strong, brown, coarse grained, brittle. *Buds* rusty brown, very small, blunt. *Leaves* smooth, 5 to 9 leaflets on short stalks; ovate or lanceolate, acuminate at apex, sharply serrate, bright green on both sides, lustrous above. *Flowers*, April to May, before leaves, diœcious. *Fruit* in thick clusters, $1\frac{1}{2}$ inches long, oblanceolate, body round. *Preferred habitat*, rich soil on banks of streams. *Distribution*, Lake Champlain to Florida; west to Utah, Arizona and Texas. *Uses:* A beautiful shade tree, especially adapted to the regions of scant rainfall. Lumber inferior to white ash, but used for the same purposes.

The green ash has its name from the dark, lustrous foliage which is intensified in its greenness by linings of the same colour, undimmed by any pubescence or pale bloom. The planter on the treeless stretches of Nebraska and Dakota loves this ash which grows with the commoner willow and cottonwood, where many trees utterly fail. A tree it is that not only lives but flourishes, showing that it suffers no homesick pangs for a greener land.

In the East, the green ash and the red are distinct enough, the latter having velvety, the former smooth, new shoots. In the western part of the Mississippi basin are ash trees that appear to be intermediate between the two species. Professor Sargent ranks the green ash as a variety of the red. Other authorities give it rank as a species; and it would not be surprising if further study of the intergrading forms would justify the tree student in making of these a distinct species, co-ordinate with the two older ones.

The most important thing, after all, about the green ash is that it is one of the agencies which is by degrees turning the Great American Desert into a land of shady roads and comfortable, protected homesteads. East of the Alleghanies the tree is little known. West of this range the tree is one among many shade trees where variety of planting is unlimited. In the West the tree comes into its own—and has few rivals. Here people have a sort of affectionate regard for it.

The **Blue Ash** (*Fraxinus quadrangulata*, Michx.) conceals its bluing in its inner bark. Crush a bit of it in water and the dye appears. But this is not always a convenient way to identify a tree. There is a simpler and more satisfactory way. Take a look at the twigs. Are they 4-sided toward the tips? *Quadrangulata* means 4-angled. This obvious trait and the perfect flowers set the blue ash apart from all the others. The leaves and seeds might easily be confused with those of the black ash if form alone were considered. But the foliage mass of a blue ash is yellow-green, much lighter in colour than that of its sombre cousin of the swamps.

437

Blue-ash trees are common in the rich bottom lands of the Wabash River in Illinois, and along other tributaries of the Mississippi from southern Michigan, through Iowa and Missouri to Kansas and into Arkansas. It reaches south to the upper part of Alabama and east to the highlands of Tennessee. Some of the finest specimens grow on the limestone hills of the Big Smoky Mountains. The exact range of this tree is not known at present.

The French botanist, Michaux, fell in love with this tall, graceful grey-stemmed ash when he found it growing among the Alleghany Mountains. He named it for its angled twigs, and sent seeds, and young trees, perhaps, to be planted in European gardens. We can do no better than to follow his example, and plant the blue ash for shade and ornament in America. It is hardy, quick of growth, and unusually free from the ills that beset trees. A well-grown specimen is a constant joy to the tree lover.

The blue ash ranks high as a timber tree. It is fully the equal of white ash, and in one particular is better even than this one. It is more durable than any other ash wood when exposed alternately to wet and dry conditions. It is used for vehicles, for flooring, and for tool handles, especially pitchforks.

Oregon Ash (*Fraxinus Oregona*, Nutt.)—A broad-crowned, shapely tree, 75 to 80 feet high, with stout trunk and erect, stout branches. *Bark* reddish grey or brown, deeply fissured, with ridges interlacing and shedding papery scales. *Wood* brown, coarse, hard, light, porous. *Buds* small, acute, with rusty or pale pubescence. *Leaves* compound, 5 to 14 inches long, of 5 to 7 pinnate leaflets, firm, thick, pale green above, lighter and pubescent beneath; terminal leaflet on stalk 1 inch long, lateral ones on shorter stalks or sessile; leaflets oblong or oval, obscurely serrate, abruptly pointed; autumn colour yellow or russet brown. *Flowers*, April with leaves, diœcious, in smooth, dense panicles. *Fruit* in crowded clusters, each obovate, $1\frac{1}{2}$ to 2 inches long; body fusiform, about length of wing. *Preferred habitat*, rich, moist soil, near streams. *Distribution*, Pacific coast from Puget Sound to Bay of San Francisco, and back to foothills of Sierras. *Uses:* A valuable shade tree. Wood used for furniture, interior finishing of houses, frames of vehicles, cooperage and fuel.

This tree has the ash habit of unfolding its leaves late in

the spring, and "making up for it," as Oliver Goldsmith would say, by losing them early in the fall. From the standpoint of the landscape gardener, this is a double fault. But the cleanly habit of the tree, its graceful head during the summer season, and its valuable lumber, which is counted equal to white ash, commend it to planters. It has been successfully introduced into European gardens, and is hardy in the Arnold Arboretum in Boston.

It is interesting to note that an old tradition recorded by Pliny has arisen, as if spontaneously, among the Indians of the Pacific coast. Nuttall wrote after his visit to this region about the time of the exodus to California in 1849: "An opinion prevails in Oregon among the hunters and Indians that poisonous serpents are unknown in the same tract of country where this Ash grows, and stories are related of a stick of it causing the Rattle Snake to retire with every mark of fear and trepidation, and that it would sooner go into the fire than creep over it." We certainly suspect that the hunters above mentioned, or perhaps earlier white men visiting the region, imported the Old-World tradition.

The **Pumpkin Ash** (*Fraxinus profunda*, Bush.) is one of the largest and most beautiful of our ash trees, and leads all the others in the size of its leaves and keys. The velvety pubescence of its young shoots and leaf linings might confuse it with the red ash, but that its branchlets are stout. The leaves are 10 to 18 inches long, with broadly lanceolate leaflets, pointed and wavy margined, leathery, with downy linings and leaf stalks. The keys are $2\frac{1}{2}$ to 3 inches long, with wings that broaden and round at the tips. They are borne in large, pendulous and very profuse clusters.

This tree grows in deep river swamps in southeastern Missouri and eastern Arkansas, and also in western Florida along the Appalachicola River. It will probably be found in swamps intermediate between these two regions. It has only been discovered and named within the past eight years. Mr. Bush found it first in 1893, and four years later gave it a name, *profunda*, which probably refers to the almost bottomless bayous in which it often grows. The common name, pumpkin ash, refers to the bulging and ridged or buttressed base of the tree from which the straight trunk rises. This is a character shared by other trees (the tupelos, for instance,) that grow in land subject to inundation.

The **Water,** or **Swamp Ash** (*F. Caroliniana*, Mill.) grows to 40 feet high in swampy lands skirting the coast from Virginia to middle Florida, and west to the Sabine River in Texas. It follows the deep river swamps of the Mississippi north to Arkansas. It is as well that the white wood of this tree has less value than that of the other ashes, for it grows in inaccessible places. The leaves are small, and the little seeds have exceptionally broad wings.

Some Little Ashes

There are species of ash of small size and limited area that may be named in passing, but which do not rank among the important species. *Fraxinus anomala*, in the corner where Colorado, Nevada and Utah meet, is interesting because its leaf is reduced to one leaflet, rarely two or three. The winged seed declares it an ash. *Fraxinus Greggii*, a little ash on the rocky bluffs of western Texas, has its leaves and fruits reduced to miniature size, and exhibits peculiarly webbed or winged petioles.

The **Biltmore Ash** (*Fraxinus Biltmoreana*, Beadl.) is a small tree quite common about Biltmore, North Carolina. It is closely allied to the white ash, but its leaves and young twigs are densely coated with fine hairs. Very strangely the seedling trees are smooth until four or five years old, after which the young growth is pubescent.

Another little ash (*Fraxinus velutina*, Torr.) grows in the Southwest, extending from Texas to California, climbing to the tops of dry mesas and the walls of cañons, or lending itself to husbandry by shading irrigation ditches and village streets. Its leaflets are narrow and tapering, becoming thick and leathery and occasionally velvety in the hottest, dryest regions. It is distinctly the friend of man in a region where trees are most appreciated. Its wood is good for axe-handles and wagons.

The **Mountain Ash** (*F. Texensis*, Sarg.) grows on the limestone hills and gravelly ridges of western Texas, a small or medium-sized tree with broadly oval leaflets, and small broad-winged seeds. Its wood makes excellent flooring, but is chiefly used as fuel, as it rarely attains sufficient size for lumber.

The **Flowering Ash** (*F. Ornus*) of southern Europe and

Asia Minor, yields the manna of commerce, a medicinal wax which exudes from the leaves and trunk. Chinese white wax comes from a species in eastern Asia.

The **European Ash** (*F. excelsior*) is a large timber tree, native also to western Asia. Evelyn ranked its wood next to oak in universal usefulness. Scholars wrote on its inner bark before paper was invented. Lances and spears, shields, pikes and bows of it armed the soldier in days of old. Implements of all sorts were made of ash from the infancy of agriculture and mechanics. "The husbandman's tree," it was called, for "ploughs, axle-trees, wheel-rings, harrows, balls; . . . oars, blocks for pulleys, tenons and mortises, poles, spars, handles and stocks for tools, spade trees, carts, ladders. . . . In short so good and profitable is this tree that every prudent Lord of a Manor should employ one acre of ground with Ash to every twenty acres of other land, since in as many years it would be more worth than the land itself."

William Cobbett gives the ash a good character. He commends the keys for fattening hogs. "The seeds of ash are very full of oil, and a pig that is put to his shifts will pick the seeds very nicely out from the husks." He says further: "The ash will grow anywhere." "It is the hardiest of our large trees." "On the coasts the trees all, even the firs, lean from the sea breeze, except the ash. It stands upright, as if in a warm, wooded dell. We have no tree that attains greater height or bears pruning better, none that equals the ash in beauty of leaf or usefulness of timber. It is ready for the wheelwright at twenty years or less."

Young ash saplings are cut when only five or six years old and used in making crates for chinaware. When steamed the wood may be bent to any shape, which makes it valuable for hoops. An ash tree 3 inches in diameter is as valuable for spade and fork handles as it will ever be. Walking sticks and whip handles use up still smaller stuff, the very tough second growth, or "stooled" shoots.

The ash is a tree of great reputation in Europe, aside from its lumber value. It is the World Tree—*Igdrasil*—of the Norse mythology, out of which sprung the race of men. It dominated the whole universe. Did not its roots penetrating the earth reach even to the cold and darkness of the Under World? Its giant top supported the Heavens. The Fount of Wisdom and Knowledge was at its base—so were the abodes of the Gods and the Giants. The Fates, also, dwelt there, who held in their hands the destinies of men. There were the Nornies "continually watering the roots of this world-shadowing tree with honey-dew." Hesiod in the South declares that a race of brazen men sprung from the ash tree. In those days, when the world was new, men sprang from oak trees, or from the soil, or the rifted rock, according to the legends and fables handed down to us.

Superstitious parents in rural England used to pass a poor little babe suffering from rupture through the cleft stem of a growing ash. Twice the stem must be sprung apart, and the child passed through. The trunk was then tightly bound, and when its halves were firmly knit, they believed that the child would also be whole. An oil distilled from ash chips was counted a sovereign remedy for many ailments, especially earache. John Gerarde writes: "It is excellent to recover the hearing, some drops of it being distilled warm into the ears"

The kernels of ash seeds were credited with having medicinal value. English apothecaries of Evelyn's time had stock of "*Lingua avis*" on their shelves, calling them this because they were "like almost to divers birds' tongues." Gerarde, citing the authority of Pliny, says: "Serpents dare not so much as touch the morning and evening shadows of the tree, but shun them afar off. . . . Being penned with boughes laid round about [they] will sooner go into the fire than come near the boughes of the ash." And he adds: "It is a wonderful courtesie in nature that the ash should floure before the Serpents appeare, and not cast his leaves before they be gon again."

As for lightning, the ash is said to attract it. Various warnings are current:

"Beware the oak, it draws the stroke;
Avoid the ash, it courts the flash;
Creep under the thorn—it will save you from harm."

The unfortunate rustic, caught in a shower, probably knows that beech is the safest tree to stand under, for experience and tradition both hold that "a beech is never struck by lightning." The early settlers had this saying from the Indians, and proved its truth. A quaint recipe from Gerarde may interest some of my readers, though certain makers of nostrums may frown upon

442

THE RED ASH (*Fraxinus Pennsylvanica*)

The slenderest key and the longest belongs to this species. The wing is as long as the pencil-like body, and extends half-way around it. The winter buds are brown and set above prominent leaf scars

THE GREEN ASH (*Fraxinus lanceolata*)

The taper-pointed leaflets are green on both sides. The slender keys are broader at the top, an inch or more long, and borne in copious clusters; ripe in autumn

THE FRINGE TREE (*Chionanthus Virginica*)

The tree is transformed by the shower of delicate white flowers that every twig supports in June. In September there are blue plums on the tree. They are striking in appearance among the large, yellow-green leaves

me for quoting it. "Three or four leaves of the ash taken in wine each morning doe make those lean that are fat." Parkinson indorses this as "a singular good medicine—with fasting a small quantity—for those already fat or tending thereunto, to abate their greatnesse, and cause them to be lancke and gaunt." Who disbelieves in this will do well to remember that Gerarde was no mean authority in his day, and Parkinson—was he not the King's own Apothecarye? I make no doubt, however, that the conclusion will be drawn by many that the "fasting a small quantity" was the effective part of the treatment prescribed.

"Bee-sucken ash," black at the heart, was counted tougher and harder than the wood of sound trees, and especially desirable for making mallets. Bees were credited (or blamed) with a cankered condition produced by a tree-destroying fungus.

Finally, ash wood makes excellent fuel, and its ashes, rich in potash, make an excellent fertiliser. Certainly the genus as a whole deserves the good word of the poet Spenser, who, enumerating trees and their special uses, closes the list with—"the ash, for nothing ill."

2. Genus CHIONANTHUS, Linn.

Fringe Tree (*Chionanthus Virginica*, Linn.)—A slender, narrow-headed tree, 20 to 30 feet high, or less. *Bark* reddish, scaly; branches grey or brown. *Wood* light brown, close, heavy, hard. *Buds* small, brown, ovate; inner scales becoming leaf-like. *Leaves* opposite, simple, 4 to 8 inches long, 1 to 4 inches broad, smooth, except on veins below, dark green, paler below, oval or oblong on short petioles; yellow in early autumn. *Flowers*, May and June, perfect, white, each with 4 slender, curving petals 1 inch long, in graceful, pendulous clusters. *Fruit* in September, clustered 1-seeded drupes, 1 inch long, dark blue, with slight bloom; flesh dry; skin thick. *Preferred habitat*, rich, moist soil on banks of streams. *Distribution*, southern Pennsylvania to Florida; west to Arkansas and Texas. *Uses:* Admirable ornamental tree, hardy to New England. Much planted in parks and gardens.

The fringe tree's beauty when its belated leaves unfold, and the delicate fringe-like flowers cover it like a bridal veil, is quite sufficient justification for the tree's existence. I do not know but that it adds to its charm to wait till the orchard has done blooming and lilacs and all the early things have passed, making us long for something new and different to come and take their places. A delicate fragrance comes out of the purple-dotted hearts of these drooping blossoms and the daintiness of the whole tree at this supreme moment of its life history is something to be seen and felt—one cannot put it into words. Later the leaves broaden and the blue fruits are unusual and quite ornamental in late summer. But the tree has become substantial looking, and somewhat commonplace. Its ethereal beauty belongs to its blooming period.

Chion means snow, *anthos*, a flower. There is as much beauty in this Greek name as in the flowers it describes. The light and graceful clusters of snow-white petals are indeed like feathery masses of snowflakes. The elegance and singularity of its flowers and fruit give the fringe tree high rank among the native flowering trees suitable for lawn and garden. In Europe it is planted as a beautiful exotic from America. Because it grows wild Americans have been slower to introduce it into cultivation. A species with shorter, broader petals in erect, compact clusters has been found in China. This cannot compare with our own species in grace and beauty.

CHAPTER LX: THE CATALPAS

Family Bignoniaceæ

Genus CATALPA, Scop.

Trees with soft coarse-grained, durable wood. *Leaves* large, simple, heart shaped, opposite or whorled. *Flowers* large, white, showy, perfect, in panicles. *Fruit* long, cylindrical pods full of compressed winged and tufted seeds.

KEY TO SPECIES

A. Flowers many in clusters; leaves thin; pods slender, thin walled.   (*C. Catalpa*) CATALPA

AA. Flowers few in clusters; leaves thick; pods stout, thick walled.   (*C. speciosa*) WESTERN CATALPA

The bignonia family includes among its hundred genera of tropical plants three of arborescent habit in the United States. Large flowers and conspicuous fruits are family traits. The most important timber and ornamental trees are in the genus Catalpa, which has in all seven species. Two of these are found in the United States.

Catalpa, Indian Bean (*Catalpa Catalpa*, Karst.)—Low, spreading tree, 25 to 50 feet high, with broad, irregular head of coarse twigs. *Bark* light brown, reddish, smooth. *Wood* coarse grained, soft, light brown, durable in contact with the ground. *Buds* all lateral, above circular leaf scar, minute, globular; inner scales grow to 2 inches long. *Leaves* bright green, opposite or in three's, 6 to 8 inches long, half as wide, ovate, entire, or sometimes lobed and wavy margined, pubescent beneath; of unpleasant odour; petioles stout, long, terete. *Flowers*, June or July, perfect; large, white, irregular, the frilled corolla marked with two yellow stripes and numerous purplish dots; pedicels downy; panicles loose, 6 to 10 inches long. *Fruit* a green, cylindrical pod, 6 to 20 inches long, 2-valved, filled with flat, tufted seeds.

445

Preferred habitat, moist, rich soil of river banks or shady woods. *Distribution,* Georgia and Florida to Mississippi, but naturalised in many other states. *Uses:* A hardy ornamental tree; wood valuable for inside finish in houses, for posts and railroad ties.

The horse chestnut with its thousand pyramids of bloom is scarcely past its prime when a rival of surpassing loveliness appears. Out of the deadest-looking branches, which show no sign of life until spring has sown meadow and wood with blossoms, a luxuriant crown of bright foliage comes, and with a rush, as if to make up lost time, the tree bursts into bloom.

Now the awkwardness of its frame is forgotten, and the tree looks like a plant from the tropics. The flower clusters are often 10 inches high, loosely conical and blooming from the base upward.

A single flower deserves close scrutiny. The green calyx that enclosed the bud splits in two and the white corolla, with its spreading, scalloped and ruffled border, unfolds. There are five lobes turning out from the deep throat of the flower, where groups and rows of yellow and purple dots adorn the lining. The bumblebees recognise these markings as an invitation to explore the nectaries of the flower, and the fragrance further reassures them. The two stamens are ripe before the stigma that rises between them. A bee that alights on the broad platform and pushes into the flower's depths for nectar is well brushed with pollen as she passes. This she loses to the sticky stigmas of other blossoms as she pursues her vocation in the honey-laden treetops. A later comer to that first blossom might note, if she were observant, that the stamens had wilted in the few hours just past, and it is the erect stigma that is brushed with pollen from her hairy body. Thus Nature prevents self-pollination in this species, and sends the unconscious bees to cross-fertilise catalpa flowers.

The pods that hang on the trees in late summer look like long green pencils. The tree is as much a wonder in fruit as in flower. In winter time, the two thin valves split, and out tumbles a multitude of seeds! There is nothing to them—just thin, papery flakes an inch long, fraying at both ends into silvery hairs. The wind scatters them far and near, and the streams float them toward the seas. So the catalpa seeds are spread. The trees have also the habit of sprouting from the stump; and lower branches, lying on the ground, often strike root.

The **Western Catalpa** (*C. speciosa*, Engelm.) is hardier than the Southern species, and it grows in more upright form, promising more and better timber in a given time. It has stout, thick-walled fruits, thicker, more pointed leaves, and fewer flowers, less gaily spotted, in a cluster.

This tree ranges in bottom lands from lower Indiana and Illinois to Missouri, Arkansas and Texas. It occurs in western Kentucky and Tennessee. This is the best species for the West, where plantations are becoming more and more common and profitable. Railroad companies are interested in these enterprises. The Bureau of Forestry is investigating the possibilities and the limitations of catalpa groves as a source of lumber in the prairie states. The disappearance of American forests has brought into prominence trees of quick growth and durable wood. The railroad men are asking where the ties of the future are to come from. Before the famine comes is the time to lay up stores. Catalpa trees are large enough for ties in a dozen years of growth. They often lay on an inch of wood annually. They come quickly from seed, so that nursery stock is very cheap. A plantation of 50,000 trees was set out by a Western railroad at a cost of one cent per tree. In six years catalpa trunks are big enough for fence posts.

As to durability, tests give very satisfactory results. A forest was inundated in Missouri by the earthquake of 1811. Sixty-seven years after, the catalpas stood perfectly sound, while all other trees had utterly disappeared. Catalpa ties, selected at random, are sound after a dozen years of use. Fence posts known to have been set fifty years look as if they were good for the rest of the century.

The **Desert Willow** (*Chilopsis linearis*, DC.), a little tree on the boundary between Texas and Mexico, is a member of the bignonia family. It has white flowers and pods, somewhat like those of the catalpas, but its leaves are often a foot long, and narrow as a blade of grass. It is sometimes planted in Southern gardens. The only species in the genus, it will not be confused with other trees.

The **Black Calabash Tree** (*Crescentia cucurbitina*, Linn.) is the only other native tree that belongs in the family with the

447

catalpas. The shores of Bay Biscayne, in southeastern Florida, form the outpost of its extensive West Indian and Central American range. Its flower is a solitary, purplish-yellow tube with a flaring border. The leaf is obovate, leathery, dark green, with perfectly plain margin. The fruit is a berry, 3 or 4 inches long, and shaped like a peach or plum. Its hard, shiny shell encloses many flattish seeds.

The gourd-like fruit of the West Indian calabash tree (*C. Cujete*, Linn.) is made into drinking-cups and a great variety of culinary utensils. It is much larger than that of the preceding species.

The **Paulownia** (*Paulownia imperialis*, Sieb. & Zucc.) is a member of the spurge family, not so far away from the catalpa, botanically speaking. Indeed, an untrained eye detects the similarity in foliage, flowers and general habit of the two trees. In lustiness of growth each excels in many regions where tropical profusion of leafage and bloom is exceptional.

The paulownia blossoms before the leaves; its clustered violet flowers hung out on the ends of twigs look like foxgloves. Showy as these are, they need the leaf background—the lack of it scores against them among critical admirers of ornamental trees. The clustered seed balls, too, are unsightly in winter, requiring to be cut off.

A very satisfying screen of verdure is renewed every season by cutting back to one or two stalks seedlings of paulownia. The heart-shaped leaves are often a foot across. The hardiness of the tree commends it. Even as far north as Montreal it comes up from roots every year, forming long shoots which bear leaves astonishingly large compared with trees indigenous to the region.

In spite of the drawbacks named, this tree enjoys a growing popularity in the eastern half of the country. Its flowers are deliciously fragrant, and no tree blossom has more delicate colour. Blue is unusual among tree blossoms, and these trees, like great blue-flowered catalpas, are striking objects in parks and along avenues. Native of Japan and China, the paulownia feels enough at home already in America to run wild in some places. A splendid evergreen species has been found in the Himalayas.

448

CHAPTER LXI: THE VIBURNUMS AND THE ELDERS

Family Caprifoliaceæ

1. Genus VIBURNUM, A. L. de Juss.

SMALL trees with ill-smelling wood, and tough, slender branches. *Leaves* simple, opposite, ovate, 2 to 4 inches long, with margined petioles. *Flowers* white, in broad terminal cymes. *Fruit* a blue, berry-like drupe with flat stone.

KEY TO SPECIES

A. Branches slender; winter buds long pointed; petiole margins wavy, broad.   (*V. Lentago*) SHEEPBERRY
AA. Branches stout; winter buds stout; petiole margins narrow, not wavy.
   B. Leaves and petioles rusty pubescent.
               (*V. rufidulum*) RUSTY NANNYBERRY
  BB. Leaves and petioles smooth.
               (*V. prunifolium*) BLACK HAW

Viburnums are related to the elders and belong in the honeysuckle family. They include a multitude of ornamental shrubs, evergreen and deciduous, grown in gardens and shrubberies the world over for their showy flowers and decorative fruits as well as their handsome foliage which often colours brilliantly in the fall. Not all viburnums combine all these desirable horticultural qualities. There are about one hundred species known. They are distributed in the continents of the Northern Hemisphere and extend south to Central America, North Africa and Java. The old-fashioned snowball bush is perhaps the most familiar representative of the genus. The Japanese snowball, with much more handsome foliage and flowers, followed by red berries, is rapidly succeeding the other in popularity.

Sheepberry (*Viburnum Lentago*, Linn.)—A small. round-headed tree, of many slender, pendulous branches. Twigs pubescent, becoming smooth. *Bark* brown, broken into thick,

449

scaly plates. *Wood* heavy, hard, brownish yellow, close textured, bad smelling. *Buds* red; axillary long pointed, in two pubescent scales; terminal, button-like, with long, abruptly tapering scales. *Leaves* 2 to 3 inches long, ovate, with tapering apex and base, serrate, shining, leathery, opposite, pitted with black underneath; autumn colours orange and red; petioles stout, short, with wavy, winged margins. *Flowers*, April to June, in flat cymes, 3 to 5 inches across; white, perfect. *Fruit*, September, oval, dark blue drupes, sweetish, juicy, smooth, with pale bloom on red pedicels, few in a cluster. *Preferred habitat*, moist soil of rocky stream borders or edges of swamps. *Distribution*, Quebec to Saskatchewan; south to Alabama along Appalachian Mountains; west to Nebraska, Kansas and Wyoming. *Uses:* Ornamental shrubs or trees in Eastern States.

The sheepberry, with its shining leaves set opposite, is likely to be mistaken for a dogwood. But the prominent, wavy-winged margins of the petioles are the best distinguishing character. The multitudinous tiny flowers are in cymes like the elders, and after them come a few oval berries of fair size, dark blue, looking not unlike those of a dogwood, for they hang on coral-red branching stems. They are good to eat—if one is very hungry.

The chief merit of this little tree is its beauty, and because of this it finds its way into many Eastern parks and gardens. There is no season when it is not good to look upon. It is a familiar inhabitant of fence rows and the edges of woodlands. It blooms in late May, and holds its ripe fruits over winter for birds to feed upon.

The **Rusty Nannyberry** (*V. rufidulum*, Raf.) is easily distinguished by the rusty hairs on its winter buds, petioles, and the veins on the lower side of the leaf. It is quite as handsome (though not yet as well known) as the smooth species just described. It has white flowers and large, bright blue berries. It grows from Virginia to Florida, and west to Illinois and Texas. In gardens it has proved hardy in Boston.

The **Black Haw** (*V. prunifolium*, Linn.), with leaves like a plum's, and the narrow petiole margin smooth, has flowers and fruits very much like those of the others. The berries are a trifle smaller, perhaps, and a shade darker. This species is smaller throughout than the other two; it blooms earlier, and has

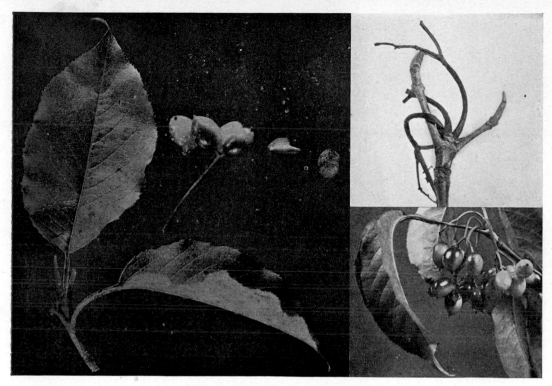

THE SHEEPBERRY (*Viburnum Lentago*)

The wavy-winged petioles distinguish the viburnums. The blue-black berries hang on coral red pedicels until the birds take the last one. The leaf buds are long and slender; the large, plump terminal bud contains a flower cluster. Leaves are rusty-downy on the veins

THE RUSTY NANNYBERRY (*Viburnum rufidulum*)

The rusty hairs that cover winter buds, petioles and veins of leaf linings distinguish this tree. The leaves are lustrous and the fruit bright blue

THE BLACK HAW (*Viburnum prunifolium*)

Flower buds are large and blunt; leaf buds small and slim. The twigs are reddish in winter

THE RED-BERRIED ELDER (*Sambucus pubens*)

The pithy twigs, showy flower cluster and opposite, compound leaves of this shrubby roadside elder are typical of all the elders. Two tree forms occur in the West

THE HOP TREE (*Ptelea trifoliata*)

Pale-green fruits in clusters, the seeds with circular wings all around, remind us of the elm fruits. They illuminate the glossy dark foliage all summer. There are few daintier, cooler-looking trees that grow in shade

stout branches, like *V. rufidulum*. It is found from Connecticut to Georgia, and west to Michigan, Kansas, and Texas. In European parks and gardens and in those of our Eastern States this little "stag bush" is often cultivated for its handsome flowers and foliage and its persistent fruit.

2. Genus SAMBUCUS, Linn.

Quick-growing, stout-branched trees and shrubs, with pithy branchlets and ill-smelling sap. *Wood* dense. light brown, soft. *Leaves* pinnate, of 5 leaflets, opposite, deciduous. *Flowers* small, perfect, white, in broad compound cymes. *Fruits* small, blue or black, juicy, berry-like, each with 3 to 5 nutlets.

KEY TO SPECIES

A. Leaves and young shoots pubescent; fruit destitute of bloom.   (*S. Mexicana*) MEXICAN ELDER
AA. Leaves and young shoots smooth; fruit covered with a pale bloom.   (*S. glauca*) PALE ELDER

Our two arborescent species of the genus Sambucus are found west of the Mississippi, but the family traits are familiar to Eastern people through their acquaintance with the two shrubby species, the red-berried and the black-berried elders.

There are twenty species, all told, in the genus. The golden elder is a yellow-leaved form of the European species, *Sambucus nigra*, Linn. Two other species have produced *golden* varieties. These are altogether too much planted, and the handsome shrubby native species, above mentioned, have not been fully appreciated.

The fruit of the common elder is used in making elderberry wine, and elderberry pie is a staple viand in many country districts in the season of the ripening fruit. In fact, the idea of the improvement of this species as a small fruit has taken hold upon some plant breeders. The Brainerd elderberry with fruit as big as cherries was introduced into the trade in 1890.

Elder shoots are used in toy making and for "spiles" to draw sap from maple trees. The name of the genus is from the Greek, *Sambuke*, a musical wind instrument made of the hollow stems of the elder.

The **Mexican Elder** (*S. Mexicana*, DC.) grows to 30 feet

451

high in the river bottoms of western Texas, and west to California, and south through Mexico and Central America. It is a squat, round-headed tree, with its short trunk bulging suddenly at the base. A soft pubescence covers leaves and twigs. The shiny, black fruit, borne in loose clusters, is eaten by Indians and Mexicans. The tree is often planted near homes for its shade and fruit.

The **Pale Elder** (*S. glauca*, Nutt.) is smooth throughout, and gets its name from the whitish floury covering of the berries. The leaves are pale beneath. The berries are edible. This elder grows from British Columbia to southern California, and east scantily and reduced in stature as far as Montana and Utah. It is sometimes planted as an ornamental. Trees from 30 to 50 feet high are seen in dry, gravelly soil in the coast region, especially in Oregon.

FRUIT OF THE ELDER-LEAVED MOUNTAIN ASH (*Sorbus sambucifolia*)

PART II
FORESTRY

CHAPTER I: FORESTRY IN THE UNITED STATES

FORESTRY is the intelligent management of woodlands to serve some definite purpose. Three distinct types of forests result from working toward as many different objects, each legitimate, and serving the country's needs.

1. *The Supply Forest* is managed upon a commercial basis. Its object is the production of wood, and Nature's resources are bent to this end. How to get the highest grade of lumber of the best kinds, in the greatest quantity and at the lowest cost on a given area and in a given time—these are the problems of the supply forest. At the same time, the aim is to improve the condition of the forest and to make it permanent and self-sustaining in a physical as well as a commercial sense, paying good returns for the cost of its maintenance. Such complex problems tax the judgment of the wisest men. Action, positive and aggressive, is demanded in the supply forest. Beside it, other types of forestry seem negative.

2. *The Protective Forest* is maintained to regulate waterflow on mountain slopes—the headwaters of streams upon which the fertility of the lowlands depends. These forests check tendencies to flooding in the early spring and consequent drought in summer. They prevent destructive erosion of sloping ground and damaging soil deposits in the valleys. Such are many of the state and national reserve forests, including those that hoard the water for irrigation ditches in California and other Western states. Water companies of great cities maintain such forest covers over the sources of their supplies.

Protective forests may be maintained especially as windbreaks in regions subject to damaging winds, hot or cold. Bodies of trees that drink up stagnant water, thus draining swamps and reducing malarial troubles, may also properly be designated as protective. Those whose balsamic exhalations improve climate are in this class.

3. *The Luxury Forest* ministers to the æsthetic and spiritual

455

needs of humanity and to their love of sport. It furnishes recreation, physical and mental, to all. *The Park Reservations* belonging to city, state and nation are such. The Yosemite, Grand Cañon and Yellowstone are our most famous national parks. In the lower Appalachians there will soon be set aside another to be kept as Nature will keep it for the people of the whole country. The Adirondacks contain a New York state park, and other states have similar reserves belonging to all the people. The Metropolitan Park System of Boston is the best illustration in this country of a chain of parks and timber reservations belonging to a city, and devoted to the recreation and uplifting of its whole population. These parks are a refuge for wild flowers that agriculture has exterminated, and for wild birds that towns have driven out. They are the precious heritage of the people and should never pass out of their hands.

The Game Preserve is a second type of recreation forest. It ministers to primitive human instincts—love of pure wildness and the freedom of outdoor life, and that stronger love for hunting and fishing.

National parks and reservations are open to hunters, with certain restrictions. Smaller tracts are owned and maintained by clubs or individuals. Such game preserves, fenced against the public, and in charge of wardens the year around, are found in the Adirondacks and in other Eastern mountains, and along the coast where wild fowl are the chief attraction. In the shooting and fishing season these tracts are visited by the owners and their friends. For the joys of this period great preparations are made. Lakes and streams are stocked with fish, and not uncommonly big game and wild fowl are introduced to increase the number and variety of game in the park.

Mixed forests are best for game of all kinds. Broad-leaved trees furnish better coverts for beasts and birds than conifers do. They have denser undergrowth, and they sprout from stumps and from the roots—a rare thing among evergreens. This young growth furnishes important forage for herbivorous animals in winter and summer. Browsing is their chief living. They do not like the resin of the evergreens, as they do the succulent twigs and inner bark of poplar and birch and maples. The buds and the various tree fruits—berries and oily nuts and starchy seeds—are the winter store of birds and many of the smaller woods folk.

Noxious animals, including dogs, the worst enemy of deer, are exterminated by the wardens, who also keep off poachers, and do all they can to promote the well-being of big game and small. In winters of deep snows it is necessary to cut down trees so that the ruminants may be kept from starvation. Ear corn and fodder are often scattered on the snow that covers the natural food supply. The animal mortality in the North Woods is sometimes appalling in severe winters.

It is most common to find a single forest serving two, or even all three of these different purposes. Lumbering may be profitably carried on in protective forests without damaging them as conservers of the water supply, or interfering to a great extent with hunting. It takes a long time and very thorough clearing to overcome the wildness and to expose the floor of our American forests. Young growth from seed and stumps covers the scars made by lumbermen who, as a rule, want nothing but good-sized logs. Fire and grazing are much more effective agents of deforestation than lumbering, but lumbering fosters fires by the "slash" it leaves behind.

When forestry is mentioned, commercial forestry is usually meant. Wood is necessary to civilised life, and the production of it is a problem that becomes graver as population becomes denser. The history of European countries may eventually be repeated in ours. First came the cutting down of trees for use and for the clearing of land. Then experimental work of a vague and general nature to check wastefulness, and provide for the future productiveness of woodlands. Then more definite plans, more generally effective in their workings, toward the same end. Last, the growing of wood as a crop, seriously, laboriously, profitably, as a general farmer may at last take to celery culture or to strawberries or melons, and make a fortune out of a few acres. Such forestry and such farming are *intensive*. They are specialised to a high degree.

Intensive forestry at its best can be seen in Germany. State and private forests can be found in which tree crops are grown as carefully as any agricultural crop. The land is prepared, the seed selected, the young trees protected, cultivated, pruned and thinned. Such a forest is as clean and as thickly set as a field of grain, and its value when cut and marketed is beyond belief to us whose standard of heavy production has been "the virgin forest."

The plan followed in the administration of these highly specialised forests is to cut a certain acreage clean every year, and replant it. The years required for a crop to mature is the basis of the rotation system. By the time the whole forest is cut over the first plot has a second crop ready to harvest. Most of the German forests are of pine and spruce, with an average rotation period of eighty to one hundred years.

One-quarter of the land in Germany is forest. Not much of this land is continuous in one great wooded section of the country, but is scattered in smaller forests among the thickly settled districts. Each has its force of workers, its sawmill and a ready market for all the forest products. It is said that the thinnings and prunings of these forests pay most of the cost of the labour put upon them while they are growing. Even twigs are used, bound into fagots or made into charcoal and sold as fuel. Mushrooms and truffles are gathered in these forests. The leafage furnishes fodder for cattle in certain broad-leaf woods, as those of linden and maple.

The city of Zurich in Switzerland has owned a forest for one thousand years. It has been so carefully regulated that it has furnished a definite amount of timber each year for six hundred years and is to-day in better condition than ever before. Its plan of management has not changed in all that time. As early as the year 1300 the peoples of northern Europe applied to their forests the principles of rational forestry, while southern Europe ignored these principles, and is still suffering from this folly.

Extensive forestry, adopting improved methods of handling wooded tracts, without greatly increasing the cost of management, is the type of forestry American conditions call for at present, in most sections. In special regions intensive forestry in conjunction with agriculture is justified. The experimental stage will gradually bring us to more intensive methods, but it will be a long, slow evolution. We have seen much destructive lumbering, but forestry is just begun, here and there. Over the bulk of the country, people have never heard of forestry.

The Government has 60,000,000 acres of land in national parks and reservations, set apart since 1890. In parks all lumbering is suspended, game is protected, and troops are stationed along its borders to insure the carrying out of the laws. In reservations no such surveillance is maintained; the laws permit lumbering, hunting and grazing, as the tracts, once open to settlers, are sprinkled over with privately owned areas. It is the President's right to withdraw public lands from sale and settlement at his discretion. This he does to protect the headwaters of streams and to save valuable timber lands and wild scenery. Much land now merely reserved by presidential proclamation will eventually be made by acts of Congress into national parks.

The Yellowstone, over 2,000,000 acres in the northwest corner of Wyoming, is our greatest national park. California has three: the Yosemite, over 160,000 acres of the most beautiful and rugged scenery in the world; Sequoia and General Grant parks, both preserving some fine groves of the Big Trees. All three parks lie in the great Sierra reservation of 4,000,000 acres, which, with a southern chain of reservations, occupy one-tenth of the area of the state. Arizona has four large reserves, one of which includes the famous Grand Cañon of the Colorado. Some of the best of the Pacific coast forests are in the Mount Ranier, Olympic and Washington reservations in Washington, and the Cascade Reservation in Oregon. The tract of over 200,000 acres, including Mount Tacoma, is now a national park.

Great areas of forest reserves check the map of the Rocky Mountain states, extending east to the Dakotas and Oklahoma, and including parks of comparatively small size. State forest reservations are not so common. New York has set a good example by providing in 1885 a pleasure ground of 1,000,000 acres for the people in the wilds of the Adirondacks. It is also a health resort, especially for consumptives. Since 1895, Pennsylvania has acquired 300,000 acres on which practical forestry is to be begun. Many states, spurred to action by the falling off of the timber supply, have established forestry experiment stations. California has two such stations. State universities and agricultural colleges now offer courses in forestry, and have forest laboratories. The state of Michigan set aside a 57,000 acre tract for this purpose when its course in forestry was established. Even the prairie states have followed suit. Land that has been deforested and then abandoned by lumber companies becomes public property in default of taxes. Such lands to a large extent should belong to the state, and should maintain protective forests, as they include watersheds, the sources of streams.

Five years ago the Division of Forestry was an insignificant branch of the Department of Agriculture, with $10,000 a year to spend. Now it is a Bureau, with nearly half a million a year. A large body of forestry specialists trained in the best forestry centres of the Old World, are at work on special American problems, as members of the staff of the Bureau. Co-operation with landowners has brought under the Bureau's management almost 10,000,000 acres of privately owned forest. Experts size up the problems on the ground, and the owners follow the Bureau's advice. The International Paper Company, controlling over 100,000,000 acres of spruce, are introducing reproductive forestry under Government direction. Twenty-six thousand acres in farmers' woodlots are being managed under expert direction.

Teaching forestry in this country has seriously begun. In 1898 the New York State College of Forestry was established at Cornell University, with Dr. B. E. Fernow, ex-chief of the Division of Forestry, at its head. The four years' course provided for broad as well as technical training. A tract of 30,000 acres, the forest laboratory, was at Axton, in the Adirondacks. After five years of healthy growth, this college was extinguished through state politics, and the hundred undergraduate students scattered to other schools to finish their studies.

The Yale School of Forestry, established in 1900, offers at present the most thorough forestry training obtainable. The Universities of Minnesota and Michigan have very strong courses. Berea College, Kentucky, and a large number of other colleges and state universities offer a year or more in forestry. In 1898 the Biltmore Forest School was opened on the Vanderbilt estate near Asheville, North Carolina, for the instruction and training of students.

Outside of the schools, a great power for the upbuilding of public sentiment is vested in the state and national forestry organisations. The American Forestry Association, formed in 1882, binds together all interests. The official organ of this association is the monthly publication, *Forestry and Irrigation.*

A significant meeting was the coming together in Washington, D. C., of the destructive and constructive interests—the lumbermen and the foresters—in friendly council, each recognising the claims of the other, and their interdependence and need of co-operation. The American Forest Congress, of January, 1905, was an epoch-making event.

The Bureau of Forestry is the efficient head of all our forest interests. It has places to put all students who are well trained for the profession of forestry. A large body of strong young men are entering it. The outlook is extremely encouraging.

The public mind is vague when it encounters the nomenclature of a new science. Forestry, its subdivisions and synonyms, and its relation to other sciences, may be briefly set forth.

Forestry is one grand division of the great art of *Agriculture*, "the cultivation of the field." *Silviculture* and *forestry* are used as synonyms. *Arboriculture* includes beside forest trees those that are grown for their fruit, and for ornament. Hence it includes a large part of horticulture and landscape gardening— the growing of trees for any purpose. *Silviculture* is, properly speaking, that branch of forestry which deals with the scientific production of a crop of trees. *Forest regulation* is the business branch, which manages the annual outlay and returns of the forest. It has the lumbering and marketing of the crop in charge. *Dendrology* is one of the fundamental sciences upon which forestry rests. It is the botany of trees, and has three distinct branches of equal importance to the forester: (1) *Tree physiology* and *pathology*, life processes of trees in health and disease; (2) *tree anatomy* and *histology*, the structure, gross and minute, of trees; (3) *systematic* botany, a study of the kinds of trees in order to know them by name.

CHAPTER II: A LUMBER CAMP OF TO-DAY

In a mountainous corner of one of the thirteen original states is a "patch" of white pine, one of the last remnants of the forest primeval, Here is a lumber camp with a hundred men working throughout the year. It is estimated that at the present rate the cutting will be finished in about fifteen years. The company is an old, conservative one whose name has been familiar in the lumber trade for three generations. It owns large tracts on the Pacific coast, whose forests wait until this Eastern harvest is done.

Not large, like the great lumbering enterprises that have stripped the pine from northern Michigan, nor small, like the patchy lumbering jobs left here and there in neighbouring states, this busy camp combines the best and most interesting phases of each. The characteristic activities of the lumbering industry are all carried forward with modern appliances and modern methods.

The sawmills are the nucleus of a little community composed of the families of all the mill folks, from the resident partner who lives like a feudal lord among his vassals, to the day labourer. Nobody lives here except those employed by the company. Beside the houses, there is a general store, with postoffice and express office, a church and school, a barber shop, carpenter shop, and blacksmith shop, and two boarding houses for the men without families. All real estate is the company's property and is under company management.

A stage carries mail, express and passengers between the village and the railroad station three miles down the valley. There the mountain stream that floats logs down to the mills in the spring freshets joins the river, which is deep enough for big flat-bottomed lumber barges. A stub of the railroad runs up to the mills, and switches run conveniently among the piles of lumber.

A private railroad climbs the hills, through hard woods and scattering second growth of pine and hemlock, to the upper camp eight miles away, where the "fallers" are at work cutting pine trees that count their years by centuries. The road gives off a branch half way up, that goes into the hemlock woods.

There is no higher land in the vicinity than these pine-crowned hills, which looks down benignantly on the landscape that slopes away on every side. A cluster of rude cabins about the end of the railroad house the families that form this ever-shifting temporary upper camp. There is wood to burn and water from the springs, and supplies are sent up from the store. The men keep their axes and saws sharp and use them eleven hours a day. They get $1.75 a day—more if they furnish a team. There is a "head faller" set over the men who cut the timber. Another "boss" manages the loading of the logs into the skidways and from them into the cars.

Having read "The Blazed Trail," I was ready to embrace with fervour the invitation to spend three days at the upper camp. Accommodations were ample, if primitive ways were no objection. So the day was set and transportation bespoken, though this is an unnecessary formality. At 4:30 A. M. the mill whistle screamed in the ears of the sleeping settlement, and the little engine began puffing and snorting to get up steam for its toilsome uphill drag of the empty log cars. It was well we had dressed for inclement weather, for a drizzling rain dampened our clothing, if not our zeal. We attached ourselves like leaches to the trucks of the bottomless cars, with a determination to enjoy the ride.

The road followed the course of a brook which twisted like an agitated garter snake. The rails made only gentle curves, so that the train crossed the water more than fifty times in the eight miles.

The one bark car was switched off on a siding half way up, and its passengers, mostly berry pickers bound for the higher valleys, had to follow our example and chose seats on the running gears of the log cars, to which we all clung with some apprehension as they lurched and joggled over the uneven road bed. At intervals great gridiron-like "skids," built of logs and worn smooth by long use, ran alongside the track. The lower ones had fallen into disuse—abandoned when the woods were cleared of pine. The higher ones we passed were still in working order, the last ones piled with fresh logs waiting for the cars.

The panting little engine reached the camp and rested from its labours. The engineer, posing as a good-natured Santa Claus, handed out parcels to those who came expecting them. A scarlet sweater to one burly chopper, a double-bitted axe to another, a new pair of brogans to a third. There were canned and boxed provisions for the boarding house, and papers and letters from the postoffice.

Off in the woods I heard a sound as of an explosion. Leaving our superfluous belongings on the engine we set out toward the big noise, following a "skid road" down which logs were being dragged. We soon came within the sound of a saw. Two men knelt on opposite sides of a giant pine whose fall we had heard. They were sawing it into lengths according to marks chipped by the axe of a third man who carried also a measuring stick. He had in his hand orders for bridge timbers—the "bill" for the day— and this log, being as he had judged it, a sound tree, about three feet in diameter, had furnished the seventy-foot "stick" requisite to "fill the bill," and two or three twelve-foot logs beside. The top was a mere rosette of leafy branches, above the clear, straight trunk. Such a tree is worth a dollar for each one of its three hundred years, if no defects are discovered as it goes through the mill.

There are trees standing among these with a trunk diameter exceeding four feet. These venerable pines do not make the best lumber. They are over ripe, and almost certain to be hollow at the base and to show "punky" spots of cheesy unsound wood, which has to be discarded in the mill.

This head faller is a man of long experience and ripe judgment. He must choose the trees most likely to fill the orders sent him by the manager from the office. His eye measures the standing tree, selects one, and decides which way it shall fall. While his two sawyers are busy cutting the last one into proper lengths, he chops a long notch low on the butt of the next to fall. It is as deep as his axe head—a smooth, two-lipped trough, whose angle is a straight line terminating in the bark each way. As the tree falls the two lips meet. There must be no log nor stump across its path,. or the falling tree breaks. Often a tree is broken by the impact of its fall on boggy ground, but this usually is due to decay that has weakened its trunk in certain spots.

The tree must fall where the "skidders" who come with horses to "snake" its logs to the railroad can get at it with least

464

troubl of clearing away other obstructions. It must lie, if possible, with its butt toward a skid road. Young trees, especially pines, are saved as far as possible. But I saw a cucumber tree fifty feet high shattered to kindling wood by a falling pine.

The axe of the head faller chips the thick bark off in a circle around the tree, joining the ends of the wedge. This bark is full of dirt that would dull the saw much more than the hard wood. Now the sawyers come and kneel to their task. Men with horses and massive log chains come to get the fresh logs.

The long cross-cut saw has ragged teeth and a handle on each end. Its blade was sprayed well with kerosene before work began, for the resin of the bleeding tree has to be "cut" with oil, or it binds the saw and stops the work. The saw began on the side opposite the notch, and fared steadily toward it. The rhythm of its song and the perfect co-operation of the two men were good to hear and see. Once or twice they stopped, took off one handle, drew the saw out and oiled it on both sides. When half way through they drove in a wedge, that gave the saw more room.

There was no anxiety on the part of the crouching men, no least tremour of the tree, until the trunk was almost severed. Then the sawing suddenly doubled its speed. When within a few inches of the notch it ceased, the men sprang away, the tree trembled, swayed, and fell, its top sweeping through the air with a mighty sigh. The lips of the notch closed with crushing impact as the shaft shook the earth that shuddered under the blow.

The men stood aside, oiling their saw, and set it into the fallen trunk as the marker indicated the place. The absence of conversation was oppressive—the understanding of each sawyer with the other made talk unnecessary. Were they overcome by the presence of visitors? "No," the head faller told us, "they are always quiet." The work among the pines has this strange effect upon the men. They do not raise their voices when they speak, even to their horses. The hemlock peelers are a noisy, quarrelsome crew, given to profanity and coarse joking; but the fallers in the upper camp are thoughtful and pensive, while at their work. In that cathedral woods we felt the presence of something that discouraged speech. We did not understand it—any more than the labourers did. Three days we spent among the pines, each day repeating the events of the first, and deepening its impressions.

The nights in camp were full of new sights and sounds. A rasping sound as of something gnawing off the very foundations of the house was silenced by the gun of the householder. Next morning we heard it was "nawthin' but a couple o' porkypines that come around chawin' on the sills." The housewife bewailed the invasion of her turnip patch by wild deer. A black bear had recently contested the claims of berry pickers in one of the upland spaces cleared of timber.

The logs are piled in order down on the skidways by men who scamper over them like ants, teasing them into parallel position, fitting them into solid phalanx, with peavy and cant hook—difficult and dangerous tools to the learner, but wonderfully effective when mastered.

From early morning till two o'clock the gang is loading cars from the skids. Three long logs rest on two trucks set far enough apart to support the two ends of the load, which are solidly chained to prevent any slipping. Short logs are fitted in pyramidal piles on regular cars. They usually bind each other, the upper logs fitting into the troughs between the lower ones. If the fit does not suffice, a chain binds them into a solid unit.

A warning whistle after dinner gave notice that in an hour the train started for the valley. We found the cars all full, and I looked inquiringly into the engineer's little cubby. It had scarcely room for himself and various boxes and bundles. "On top of the logs?" It seemed incredible. But there were women with berry baskets—*and babies*—perched on those wooden pinnacles. There is no other way of getting down to the settlement, not even a trail.

It wasn't bad at all. We perched on a round log terrace and leaned luxuriously back against another which formed the keystone of the arch of the load. Berry pickers gathered in, the manager himself joined us, introducing the Catholic priest, who had spent the day among his isolated parishioners. A jovial, if scattered, company of passengers waved a farewell to the camp.

The long logs went first, making the curves safely, though their chains groaned. A man with a peavy rode erect upon them, watching anxiously for trouble. It was a silly short car behind that ran one wheel off the track over a boggy spot where the

466

track sagged. The passengers kept their seats, even on that car. A short length of rail was laid under the offending wheels, the little engine at the upper end of the train pulled suddenly and the wheel got back to the rail. There was just time to pick a bunch of scarlet hobble berries which the kindly genius of the short rail heard me crave; then the descent began again, the little engine halting violently to overcome and to gauge properly the mighty force of gravitation, in whose power we were hurrying to the valley. And we drew in alongside the mill slough while the autumnal sun still shone through the hemlocks on the western hill.

There was one stop at a siding to attach a car piled high and solid with sheets of dry hemlock bark, and to add a number of extra passengers from the woods and berry patches. This hemlock furnishes a valuable side line to the main lumbering business. The wood is not highly rated, but the bark is valuable for tanning. All through the summer, work is active among the hemlocks. The bark slips until September, and a gang of peelers works through the growing season. Then it disbands. There is only the bark to market, and the logs to get to the mills.

The bark is checked into uniform sheets four feet long before it is stripped from the fresh-cut log. It is stacked and loaded on cars by the stripper, who gets $2 per cord for his work. The tanneries pay $10 or more per cord for it. The force of 150 men get out 10,000 cords of bark in a summer.

The hemlock logs, too slippery for handling by men, are loaded on cars by machinery. A big iron thumb and finger— a derrick—lifts them and places them on the cars. They are sawed into building timbers of the cheaper sorts, and the small stuff goes to the shingle mill. Most of the bark is consumed by a tannery in the neighbourhood. Green hides from the Argentine Republic are shipped to this establishment, which does also a great business with Western hides.

It is the proud boast of the owners that in their mills there is no waste. It is indeed remarkable how little good pine goes out over the dam to feed the ever-burning slab pile on the other side of the river. The course of one log is easily followed in the great open mill.

The pine logs, bleeding red at both ends, are rolled from the cars into the mill slough. A man on a raft with a long pike leads a leviathan to the bottom of an inclined plane at the door-way of the mill. An endless chain set with sharp teeth drags it to the elevated skidway on a level with the saw. In its turn it rolls down, and is clamped solidly to the carrier on the side of a car that runs back and forward past the saw, and lays the whole log, a slice at a time, on a table beyond. The saw itself is a slender, flexible ribbon of steel with one toothed edge, thirty feet long, its ends joined, and hung between two cylinders of steel, one above, the other below the floor level, that keep it in a state of high tension and tremendous speed, about these two revolving axes. This saw slices a log as easily as if it were a potato. The eye can hardly follow the car as it races forward and the saw takes off a board. It fairly leaps back to position, and then as swiftly forward, as if eager for the game.

They had shut down the mill activities for two minutes—the exact time required to replace a dull saw with a sharp one. Everybody relaxed, except the five men who hung the saw. The machinery was all out of gear. But at a signal everyone was alert again. The car springs forward, the saw takes a slab from the long log and lays it on the table beyond. Next a two-inch plank comes off, and follows the slab. Then the log is flopped over and the opposite side loses a slab and a plank. The two remaining sides are similarly treated, the carrier lets go its burden, and a vast squared timber, 20 by 20 inches by 70 feet, rides forward on the moving table, and trucks carry it on to the freight car.

It is the pale, thin man whom I took for an onlooker who cut this timber to order. The peg under his foot and the lever in his hand controlled that powerful machinery. A short log is next. It is sawed into two-inch planks, but a punky spot is revealed, and the balance is cut into inch lumber. All planks and boards go through the edger, which removes the bark and all unevenness, making the edges true and parallel. Rip saws set by foot cut the wide boards into the desired widths. These boards are later sorted as to length and width in the yards. The inferior qualities are piled to season outdoors. The best stock goes to the kiln, where it is dried by artificial heat in forty-eight hours. This process checks decay, and seasons the wood without the warping and checking which the slow and variable open-air process involves.

The course of the slabs is interesting. To the slab pile to

burn? Not yet, and not all. They are cut into six-foot lengths on the table, by saws that jump up in response to foot pressure. Then they are ripped into 2 by 2 inch sticks and descend to the lath mill on the lower floor. The fragments left behind follow two paths. The bark and rotten stuff go by a shute to the bonfire. The good wood fragments are dropped into a hopper—the cavernous maw of "the hawg." An awful roar issues from this beast's throat whenever it is fed. It is the noise of grinding wood into sawdust. A stream of it flows to the furnace room, where it accumulates above two doors that open into the fire boxes. Tilting the lid lets this light fuel slide into the fire. A man lies on the hot sawdust here operating the two circular lids and so regulating the heating of the engines. His is the vision of Dante all day long.

In summer hemlock logs cut near the main stream are piled into it. The freshets bring them down in spring to the mills. The streams are but brooks up where the pine stands, and the railroad, which follows the camp of the "fallers," carries logs to mill without delay and without the inevitable deterioration that water transportation involves.

There is no atmosphere of hurry in the woods nor about the mills. The hum of industry is heard from seven o'clock until six. Then the night watchmen go on duty, and the day men enjoy the library and reading room above the main office, or talk things over in the store or barber shop, or go home to rest for the next day's work. No liquor is sold in the place, and a case of drunkenness means a workman's discharge. Each day's work is the quiet filling of orders from the mill or the yards. Supply and demand are at proper tension and prices keep strong. Big timbers for bridge work are a paying specialty. Fair treatmen and good wages keep a good class of workers in permanent employ, and it is the boast of the company that it has never had a strike.

CHAPTER III : PROFITABLE TREE PLANTING

THE establishment of the date palm in Arizona is one of the latest triumphs of the Department of Agriculture. Out of the oases of Arabian and African Saharas—out of antiquity itself—this Old-World "tree of life" has been set down in the irrigated oases of the Great American Desert, in the dawn of the twentieth century. It thrives and fruits in its new home, and gives every promise of continued prosperity. Behind the date palm is a list, indefinitely long, of fruit and ornamental trees introduced from other countries. Distant parts of America have exchanged species through seed distribution and otherwise. The result is infinite variety in our planting—vast fortunes in orchard and garden products every year and in the enhanced values of land well planted. There is no doubt that where horticulture is concerned, tree planting has proved profitable, in spite of losses that experimentation has involved.

DOES IT PAY TO PLANT TREES FOR TIMBER?

This is another question. Fifty years ago it would generally have been answered in the negative. The pioneer was still clearing land for his farm, the great lumber companies were but beginning their work, and the Great Plains were not yet peopled. Conditions have changed. The virgin forests are about gone. The question is no longer: "How can we get rid of this superfluous timber?" It is now: "Where is the lumber supply of the immediate future to come from?" It is no longer a problem for children's children. It concerns us all to-day. The man who builds a fence, a house or a railroad reads the warning in the price list of the lumber dealer.

The forests of the country are not gone yet, nor nearly gone. In regions originally in woods Nature is the great planter. Land lying idle "goes back to forest" in a few years. Local wants are supplied from the woodlots of farmers. No general alarm over shortage in the lumber supply will break out in such communities.

The Bureau of Forestry has a "Co-operative Tree-planting Plan," simple as the Woodlot Plan, in fact a phase of it, by which owners of land who wish to put some acres into a wood crop can have expert advice as to selection of kinds, and care of the crop. An agent of the Bureau visits the neighbourhood, and meets in a conference all who may be interested in planting. Advice is based on examination of soil, drainage, exposure, climatic conditions, and a study of the experience of planters in like regions and under like conditions.

Of the many plans now in force the majority are on the prairies, but many are in the "abandoned farm" regions of New England. The great treeless belt from the Dakotas to Texas has been the inevitable centre of activity in general tree planting. Forty acres planted to trees entitled a man to a quarter section of land under the Homestead Law. Failure marked much of this "tree-claim" work, some honestly, some dishonestly done. Cottonwoods, box elders, silver maples and willows, quick-growing but short-lived trees, were generally planted because they could be depended upon to grow. Gradually better trees were introduced, with higher timber and fuel value, as well as ability to stand against the winds and to give shade and protection to homes, orchards and crops. Altogether, tree planting has been vague and unsystematic but persistent in the treeless belt. It has been an evolution and an education to the people, and it is going to become a financial success.

The forests of the Mississippi Valley are giving out, but the demand for posts and railroad ties and telegraph poles increases as the country develops. Telephone and trolley lines are threading the country, doubling the demand for poles and cross ties. The Kansas farmer cannot afford to buy fence posts grown in Canada, Oregon or Maine. Neither can he do without. His shrewdest move is to raise his posts as he would any other crop, and sell the surplus to his less provident neighbours.

The growing of wood crops for profit is the logical outcome of Western experimentation. Railroad companies have begun to raise their own ties. Landowners have put some of their best land into tree crops. Among the latter are many farmers. The quickest crop is fuel; the next, posts; next, cross ties; and last, poles for telegraph, telephone and trolley lines.

The search has been for a tree that can stand hot, dry winds

471

and occasional drought, and produce in the shortest possible time wood that is durable in contact with the soil. The tree that comes nearest to fulfilling all these requirements is the hardy catalpa, native of the Mississippi Valley, which reaches its best development in the Ohio Valley and in Arkansas. It needs a porous soil, for its root system is large, ranging widely for food and water, and anchoring the trees securely against wind. On tough clay soil these trees are a failure.

RAISING CATALPA TIMBER

The Yaggy plantation of 440 acres of catalpa trees is the best example of what a Kansas farmer's woodlot can yield. It is reported in Bulletin 39 of the Bureau of Forestry, and from this source the following facts are taken:

The land lies in Reno County, near Hutchinson, Kansas, in the valley of the Arkansas River. It is a rich, deep, sandy loam, underlaid by soft, sandy clay. Both surface soil and subsoil are several feet thick, and give free range to water and tree roots. The water table is from four to six feet below the surface.

In this excellent cultivated farm land seedling catalpas one year old were set in rows, three and a half feet apart east and west, six feet apart north and south. Mr. Yaggy grew his own stock from seed. The planting covered three years: 120 acres in 1890, eighty acres in 1891, and 240 acres in 1892. Corn was planted between the rows the first year, and the cultivation of the corn three times served the growing trees. They branched and made bushy tops and good root growth. Next year they were cut off at the ground, except strips of three rows each, for each twenty rows, reserved for windbreaks throughout the plantation. Strong unbranched shoots six to twelve feet high came up the second year, with no cultivation. All but the best one of these sprouts were cut off at the end of the second season—this one to become the trunk. Cultivation was thorough the third summer. The trees branched at eight to twelve feet high, shading the ground and keeping out grass. The leaves formed a mulch this third winter, and cultivation was thereafter discontinued.

After six years of growth thinning was begun, the largest trees being taken out; in the winter of 1897–8 one-eighth of the total number of trees were removed. These trees made two

Fruit

Winter bud

THE CATALPA (*Catalpa Catalpa*)

The tree is unusual and beautiful in its large leaves and pendant green pods all summer and autumn. The supreme moment is the time of flowering—June and early July. The buds are minute, three at a joint, each set above a circular leaf scar. The rattling pods discharge their thin seeds all winter. The tree looks dead in winter.

THE EUCALYPTUS (*Eucalyptus viminalis*)

This tree's drooping habit and narrow leaves suggest the willow family. In bark shedding it resembles the sycamores. It grows with astonishing rapidity and to great size. In southern California and Arizona it is an important tree in the exacting semi-arid regions

Upper: *Eucalyptus robusta*—leaves, flowers and fruits. Lower: *Eucalyptus globulus*

posts each, the larger one four to six inches in diameter, the smaller one two to four inches. There were 15,500 trees cut on the eighty-acre tract in these two years, making twice that number of posts. The lower posts brought ten cents each, the upper cuts four to six cents. The tops yielded some fuel.

The Division of Forestry made some measurements of typical half-acre blocks on Mr. Yaggy's farm, in 1900. The plantation was eight to ten years old, and a part had been yielding posts and fuel for four years. Careful records of the height, diameter, number and condition of all the trees on the tracts were made. These were reduced to terms of posts, stakes and fuel, at current market prices. To this record was added the results of four years of thinning, and the total showed a gross value of $267.15 per acre for the crop produced in ten years.

An equally careful record was kept of the cost of every step in the development of the plantation. To the expense list was added rent of the land and compound interest on the investment of each year. The cost per acre by this record is shown to have been $69.90 for the ten years. This deduction from the gross value leaves a net gain of $197.55 per acre, at ten years.

The cutting off of all the trees would bring in this handsome return, but it would be the greatest folly. As posts bring better prices than fuel, so railroad ties are better than posts, and telegraph poles than ties. Trees big enough for cross ties are salable for general lumber purposes. A post worth ten cents can be grown in six years. At fifteen years the same trunk makes a tie worth fifty cents and two or three posts besides. At twenty-five years it is fit for a telegraph pole, at not less than a dollar. The general market quotations run from $1 to $50 per pole. The wise owner of a catalpa plantation thins his stand for posts and stakes, holding his best trees until they command the prices of ties or telegraph poles. The wood is as durable as any timber known. It is not inferior when most rapidly grown, as many woods are. While the large trees are maturing, young ones are coming on from stumps. The plantation is thus a permanent forest.

Hardy catalpa is successfully grown on the deep, porous soil of eastern Kansas and Nebraska, south into Arkansas, and east to the Wabash Valley. Outside of this catalpa belt, locust, osage orange and Russian mulberry, all quick-growing post and tie timbers, are beginning to be commercially grown. Tamarack,

473

bur oak, white and green ash, grow farther north. Black walnut, post and white oak, and the red juniper are all worth growing for profit in the states bordering the Missouri. In fact, the whole upper valley of the Mississippi is in need of tree planting to supply the local needs in the next two or three decades, until a definite forest policy is adopted. There will be demand for all such tree crops, as long as wooden posts and ties and poles are used.

EUCALYPTUS PLANTATIONS

The "blue gum" is but one of forty species of the Australian genus, Eucalyptus, which have been naturalised in this country. In the tree-planting experiments of California and the semi-arid Southwestern States these immigrant trees are comparable to the catalpa in Kansas. They are propagated from seeds, which are light and abundant. They grow with astonishing vigour and rapidity, sprouting from the stump indefinitely. Most of them have very hard wood, and its durability under water and in the soil justifies the growing of it for paving blocks, railroad ties, posts, telegraph poles and piles for wharves. Some species have wood like hickory, used for tool handles, implements of agriculture and vehicles. Much is consumed as fuel.

Added to the wood value of these trees are such products as gums and resins useful in medicine and in the arts. The oil expressed from the leaves is exceptionally valuable in the drug trade. The flowers of many species furnish copious bee pasturage. The trees have beautiful evergreen leaves, graceful habit, handsome bark, and finally, curious, nut-like fruits—all characters that give the trees popularity among available ornamental kinds. As a forest cover and a windbreak the eucalypts have a serious work to do. Denuded slopes that threatened the exhaus-of water supply have been planted with these trees with most gratifying results. They have drained swamps, thus removing miasma and, as many believe, improving the climate in other tangible ways.

Waste land planted to blue gum (*Eucalyptus globosus*) is transformed in five years into a beautiful grove from which fuel may be cut. Successive clean cuttings, six to eight years apart. are followed by sprouting from the stumps. An average yield of an acre in this wood harvest is sixty cords of four-foot wood. "One seventeen-acre grove near Los Angeles, set in 1880 and cut for the third time in June, 1900, produced 1,360 cords, an average of eighty cords per acre. On poor land the yield is only a third to a half the above amount. In a grove near Pasadena set in 1885 and cut for fuel in 1893, there were in July, 1900, some trees two feet in diameter and many over one hundred feet in height."—*Bulletin No. 35, Bureau of Forestry.*

Hon. Elwood Cooper has 200 acres of broken land planted to several species of gums. He estimates that he can cut 1,000 cords a year indefinitely without detracting from the appearance of his groves or from their usefulness in other ways. Fuel brings $3 to $5 per cord in the local markets. The depletion of the natural forests in many sections of the Southwest has made a fuel famine, which the Eucalyptus has averted. In some places the oily leaves, pressed into bricks with crude oil, have proved an acceptable fuel for cooking. It is as timber that these trees bring the highest prices. Masts, piles, bridge timbers and telegraph poles, tall, straight, hard and durable—these are in demand at good prices. The best Eucalyptus produces in but twenty years a log equal to an oak that takes 200 years to grow. Blue gum lasts twice as long as redwood and Douglas spruce in the piers of Santa Barbara and other coast cities.

Eucalyptus oil and eucalyptol, distilled from the fresh leaves, form important by-products when trees are cut down. One ton of leaves yield 500 ounces of oil. This is extensively used in lung and throat troubles, and is proving beneficial in the treatment of many other disorders.

WHITE-PINE PLANTATIONS

"Between the years 1820 and 1880 was a period of enthusiastic white-pine planting in New England. Men were then able to foresee the time when the marketable native white pine would be gone, and the rise in prices would make the planted timber of economic importance. . . . At the end of this period there were said to be in Massachusetts alone forest plantations of white pine to the extent of 10,000 acres. About 1880 the interest began to decline, largely because it was found possible to bring lumber from the immense supply in the region of the Great

475

Lakes at a lower transportation rate than was expected."—
Bulletin 45, Bureau of Forestry, 1903.

It will be noticed that pine planting in New England has
been going on for almost a century. The Bureau of Forestry
has made careful investigations of various tracts, and publishes
facts and figures which prove that land that is worthless for
ordinary agriculture has yielded valuable crops of timber, and
this in from thirty-five to fifty years after planting. Individual
plantations in various states have furnished the data embodied
in the bulletins, published for the guidance and encouragement
of landowners who are uncertain as to the best way of employing
unproductive tracts.

The planting of pine has proved profitable on five types
of land: (1) watersheds, (2) sand barrens and dunes along
the seashore, (3) bare and worn-out land, (4) cut-over forest
land, and (5) woodlots. Water companies and the state at large
are benefited by the planting of trees at the headwaters of streams.
Shifting sand held by tree roots and accumulating the leaves
and other debris of tree growth, is converted into good soil. So
is worn-out land of any kind. Growing trees enrich the soil
that feeds them. These types of reforestation are justified,
even if the trees do nothing but hold the soil and restore it to
fertility.

The raising of a crop of trees has been the main object in
planting the last two types of ground. In the three species
before mentioned examples are numerous to prove that trees
set out for other purposes have served these purposes well, and
yielded a valuable lumber crop beside. There have been failures,
many of them, but they are traceable in most cases to ignorance
or neglect. White pine grows in a white-pine country if it has
half a chance.

An encouraging fact for the planter to contemplate is that
he may reap the harvest of his own sowing. It takes only thirty-
five years to grow marketable pine. If the land is good and well
prepared the trees grow faster and are of better quality in a given
time. Better timber is produced by pruning the trees, thinning
them and cutting when the trees are big enough for first-class
lumber. For this they must grow sixty years or more. The
father must plant for his sons to reap this harvest. No
better legacy, no more judicious investment could be made

476

than this. A few years doubles the value of a plantation thus coming on.

About 1835 Mr. F. A. Cutter, of Pelham, New Hampshire, took charge of a farm on which there was a forty-acre tract seeded to white pine by a few old trees. He determined to care for it properly. As need was, the trees were thinned, the weakest removed to give room for the others to grow. A close forest crown of foliage was maintained to prevent the trees from spreading by side branches. Every year an acre was gone over and the trees pruned of their branches as high as the hand axe could reach. This prevented the formation of large knots, and enhanced the value of the timber. A second pruning all around, and continuous thinning kept the tract in good health and growth.

That tract has recently yielded a harvest which averages 25,000 feet, B. M., per acre. The father sowed and his son reaped 1,000,000 feet of prime white-pine lumber from forty acres! This is five times the average yield in the Michigan pineries. It proves that husbandry in a crop of trees is rewarded as certainly as in a crop of corn.

Another lot on the same farm has a stand of white pine on it about sixty years old that experts estimate will cut 200,000 feet of lumber. The average log measures over sixty feet.

In the Massachusetts town of Tyngsborough is a plot of fifty-three acres that was a rye field within the memory of men now living. It grew up to young white pine, and was bought for $400. The timber is not yet of marketable age, though by selection the owner has taken out over 600,000 feet of lumber during his life. His estate was recently appraised, and the stand of pine estimated at 100,000 feet. As white pine is becoming scarcer and the demand for it urgent, the price has risen steadily.

Hon. J. D. Lyman, of Exeter, New Hampshire, gives the reasons for his success with white pine. He gathers cones in early September, spreads them in a dry, airy room, and when they open beats out the seeds. This is about a fortnight after they are gathered. He prefers to sow the seed at once in beds. For three years the young seedlings are cultivated, lath screens protecting them from the hot sun. Then they are ready to set out. If they are to grow unpruned and be cut at forty years or so for boxboards they are set nine or ten feet apart each way. If clear timber of the best quality is desired, they are set four feet apart each way so that they will grow tall and lose their lower limbs. This kind of timber requires longer time to grow, and it must be pruned and thinned as it needs it. The price it brings is higher. Access to market and cost of the necessary labour determine which course to pursue. Mr. Lyman believes that a thickly planted young forest properly thinned will in fifty years produce as much lumber as it would produce in twice that time if left unthinned.

Hon. Augustus Pratt of Massachusetts once planted thirteen acres of blueberry thicket to white pines. It took one man eight days to do it. Forty years later he went in and cut from eight acres between forty and forty-five cords of box-board logs which he sold at the mill for $6 per cord. He got considerable fuel out of the tops. The five acres remaining he held untouched for a few years—then sold them for more than $1,000.

A small pine forest in Enfield, Connecticut, is noteworthy. Two quarts of pine seed per acre were sown in September broadcast with rye on the worn-out sand plain, which had been first ploughed and harrowed, then rolled. No further attention was paid to either crop. The rye shaded the seedlings as long as they required shade. The slow, imperfect growth achieved is not what it would have been if Mr. Cutter had had it in his care. But the soil has been enriched by the litter of the forest, and there is considerable good timber. Desert land has been reclaimed.

Certain facts have been learned from the study of white-pine plantations. They are worth bringing together and emphasising.

1. Cleared land is the best for a pine plantation.

2. Hilly, rolling or level land, moderately dry, with not too dense a ground cover, is best.

3. Swampy land will not do at all.

4. Land with scattering brush gives young seedling pines the shade they need.

5. Land thickly set with stumps of hardwoods which produce dense coppice growth will kill out the young pines.

6. White pine grows well in sandy and exposed situations if protected from the direct influence of salt winds.

7. Seedlings may be successfully taken from the forest.

8. Planted white pine uncrowded grows faster than native pine for twenty years, perhaps longer.

9. Trees set 4 x 4 feet apart should be thinned by removing half of them at fifteen years. Set 4 x 6 feet, remove half at thirty years.

10. Pruning lower limbs as high as axe can be used converts third-grade pine trees into first grade. It should be done in midsummer, when resin will cover the wounds completely. The trees need pruning ten years after planting. They will be fifteen feet high, with lower limbs still alive. The cut should be clean and close to the bark.

11. It pays to prune only trees intended for first-class lumber—trees to grow at least sixty years. Knots do not lower the price of trees cut at thirty to forty years for box boards.

12. Chestnut, rock maple and red oak are first-class trees to plant with white pine. They furnish protection to growing seedlings, they prune the pines by rubbing lower limbs, and are ready for removal when they begin to crowd. They are then big enough for posts and fuel.

13. The best way to fix shifting sand or gravel is to get tree roots established in it. Washing and gullying of the soil of farms is best remedied by the same means. Worn-out soil is best restored to fertility by growing a crop of trees on it.

An estimate, summarising the facts obtained by the special agent of the Bureau of Forestry, and averaging the actual cost and profits of intelligent white-pine culture in various parts of New England, is herewith set down:

Average cost of land per acre $4.00
Average cost of raising seedlings and planting . . 4.84
Average taxes at 2 per cent. for 40 years 3.20
_____
Total $12.04

Compounding interest on each item for forty years brings the total cost per acre to $50.99. An average yield is forty cords of box-board timber worth $4 per cord from each acre. This is worth on the stump $160. Deducting the cost, $50.99, a balance of $109.01 remains as net profit. This is a net annual return of $1.15 per acre, with 4 per cent. compound interest computed for forty years.   Twenty years added greatly increases the profits.

The New England farmer cannot help the Kansas farmer, except to prove that principles are universal in application.   Forestry is not alone for the corporation and the state.   It is practicable also on a limited area, and the smaller the woodlot the more simple the problem and the more perfectly it may be solved.

FRUIT AND AUTUMN LEAVES OF FLOWERING DOGWOOD (*Cornus florida*)

CHAPTER IV: THE WOODLOT THAT PAYS

ONE might think the farmer's woodlot unworthy of mention in a grave conference over the forest problems which now confront the American people. Yet a recent census report gives 630,000,000 acres of land in farms in the United States. Of this, 200,000,000 acres is wooded, almost one-third of the whole.

From this vast acreage the farmers get cordwood to burn and to sell. They haul logs to the sawmills and get cash or lumber in return. Telegraph and telephone poles, posts, railroad ties, nuts, Christmas trees—all these are sold from the woodlot. Beside fuel and fencing, the farmers get timbers for their barns, sheds and corn cribs. Their wagon tongues, axe handles and whiffletrees are largely made from sticks of seasoned timber, furnished by the woodlots. If strict account of sales were kept and credit were given for things sold and used at home, the woodlot would often prove itself the most profitable part of the farm.

The passing of the virgin forests is but a matter of a few years. The work of the big lumber companies is about done. Dearth of lumber is already felt in a marked rise of prices. The supply of pine in North and East is practically exhausted. The South is sacrificing its pine forests at a suicidal rate. White oak, black walnut and other valuable hardwoods are alarmingly scarce. The question of the lumber supply for the future has reached a critical stage.

The reservation of public lands began in 1891, when Congress authorised the President to withdraw tracts of forest from sale and occupation by settlers. Fifty million acres of Western lands have thus been set apart. States, too, have reserved lands, with the aim of saving forests on mountains where rivers take their rise. They have undertaken to reforest denuded areas. Pennsylvania furnishes a notable instance of this.

It is not surprising that the Department of Agriculture, fully realising the close relation between agriculture and forestry, and the dependence of the farm upon its woodlot, has, through the Bureau of Forestry, attacked the problem strongly on this side. It is proposed to prove in a very practical, convincing way that it pays a farmer to raise wood. No radical change, such as introducing the intensive forestry methods of European countries, is contemplated. The gradual introduction of improved methods suited to varied American conditions is the plan. This means an educative process that must move slowly. Every woodlot is a miniature forest. The smaller the forest the more simple and definite the problem of making it pay. That forest husbandry pays in America is proved by numberless examples of farmers working out plans of their own devising. Large profits have been realised on very slight investments of time and money, often by people who did not know that they were practising scientific forestry. The plan is to substitute good for bad methods, to make the wood harvest pay a good interest on the plot as an investment, and at the same time to keep the forest in good condition, and year by year to increase its productivity.

Any farmer, or other owner of a woodlot, may place it under the supervision of the Bureau of Forestry, *free of cost*. The Bureau sends an expert forester to go over the land carefully. With data thus obtained, a working plan is formulated and submitted to the owner. If it is accepted, the owner carries it out under the supervision of the forester who has it in charge. The owner does the work, or hires men to do it. He receives all money returns. The Bureau asks only that the plan be carried out and accurate records kept. It pays the expenses of its agent's visit, and asks nothing for his services.

The agreement entered into is very simple, and may be abandoned on ten days' notice by either party. It is binding, therefore, only as long as it is perfectly satisfactory to both.

The owners of woodlands need instruction in the management of their property, down to the least detail. They need definite, typical examples of what has been accomplished in their own section of the country. A balance sheet is a very convincing argument. The forester's method of tackling the problem is an eye-opener and an inspiration to the average farmer of intelligence.

In exchange for the making and supervising of these woodlot plans the Department obtains a body of facts of inestimable value. The various sections of the country are represented by typical woodlot problems. These results will be published in bulletins. Failures will teach no less than successes. The response to the government offer has been most gratifying. As fast as the Bureau of Forestry is able to get to them the applications have been taken up. From woodlots to state forests, the plans include tracts of widely divergent types and sizes. They promise to help to tide over the expensive experimental stage of a vast national forest policy.

Bulletin 42 of the Bureau of Forestry, 1903, is "A Handbook for Owners of Woodlands in Southern New England." It is full of practical, every-day advice for practical, every-day men. It is based on extensive investigations in this region. It urges that the following steps be taken:

I. Thinning in woods not yet mature to improve the conditions for growth, and to utilise material, much of which would otherwise be wasted.

II. Cutting in mature woods in such a way that the succeeding growth will follow quickly, will be composed of good species, and will be dense enough to produce not only trees with clear trunks, but also the greatest possible amount of wood and timber.

III. Pruning which is only practicable under certain special conditions.

IV. Protecting forest property against fire and, in some cases, against grazing.

V. Re-stocking waste land by planting, or sowing.

These are practices that fit any region and any woodlot. Under them, a forest is returned to health and efficiency of production, from a state of poverty wherein every cutting harms rather than improves it.

"The virgin forest" is often understood to be a synonym of the best possible stand of timber. In fact, Nature is a wasteful forester, as all second-growth woods show when left to themselves. Such a forest as the state of Saxony grows for paper pulp reminds one of a field of grain. The spruces stand, tall and slim and close, and without a weed, bearing at eighty years a tree crop beside which a patch of second-growth trees here would look like volunteer grain come up by chance in a fallow field. Gradually we shall come to imitate the European foresters and demand of our forest lands the highest possible yield and quantity of timber.

The following suggestions are for the correction of abuses that commonly keep woodlots in a bad condition. Not one of them is hard to follow:

1. *Don't let the woodlot be grazed.* Browsing destroys young growth, gnawing injures older trees, trampling packs and hardens the leaf mould, kills seedlings and prevents seed germination.

2. *Don't burn the wood's floor over.* It destroys the rich leaf mould, main food of trees; it causes the soil to cake and dry; it injures the old trees and kills the young ones; it makes inroads of fungi and insects easy.

3. *Destroy dead and dying trees and rubbish.* They are full of diseases that infect sound timber. They harbour insects. They invite and spread fires.

4. *Remove gnarled and otherwise imperfect trees* that over-shadow young growth.

5. *Take out undesirable kinds* of trees and give better kinds their places.

6. *Plan to have a tree fall* so as to injure as little as possible the surrounding trees. "Brushing out" around a tree and its final fall often destroy its natural successors.

7. *Cut with low stumps.* This is economy, and with trees that sprout from the stump it gives the sprout close connection with the root system which in time becomes its own.

8. *Make smooth, slanting cuts for stump reproduction.* If the cut is ragged (through wood or bark) or trough-shaped, it accumulates water which induces decay. Sprout timber after such cutting is mostly unsound at the butt, and useless except as fuel.

9. *Plant young trees* raised in the garden or transplanted from the woods in open spaces in the woodlot.

10. *Sow seeds of desirable kinds* where they will improve the stand. Pick up white-oak acorns and walnuts and hickory nuts, push them into the leaf mould, one here, one there, and step on them. Treat thus the thinly planted parts of your woods. It takes thought but very slight expense of time or work, to do a great deal of this supplementary forest planting.

11. *Leave seed trees of good kinds,* when cutting logs or cord-wood. They will save you a great deal of work.

12. *Plant waste land with trees.* On almost every farm is some land that is non-productive. It may wash in rainy weather.

484

Or it may be too rocky to plough, or too sandy, or have too much clay. It will always grow trees. Stop trying to farm it. Let Nature clothe it and make good soil of it. It will add to the value of the place in the eyes of any prospective buyer, in addition to the timber it produces. It will convert a blemish into a beauty spot.

13. *Study local lumber markets.* Is there a pulp mill or a tannery in your neighbourhood? Then spruce and hemlock are paying crops. Poplars and basswood bring good prices at paper mills. Birches pay near a toy or spool factory. Hickory and ash are in great demand in vehicle and implement factories. Walnut, maple, oak and cherry bring good prices where furniture is manufactured. Fuel commands good prices near large cities; so do Christmas trees. In a newly developing country, telegraph poles, fence posts and railroad ties are in brisk demand. Pine and many other staple lumber trees are a safe crop at any time.

It is almost as easy to grow good trees as poor ones, to cut out the right ones as the wrong ones, to cut down a tree properly as to do it improperly. A bit more time and thought, only, and the result is a vast improvement. Leave a sprout forest to itself and you get defective, crooked trees unfit for any use but fuel. Take out some of the sprouts and the rest grow at greatly accelerated speed into straight trees bringing much higher prices. An increased yield of 20 per cent. to 40 per cent. is recorded in experiments made by farmers working at odd days with no outside help. The farmer's great advantage is that during the winter he has leisure to improve his woodland, and with boys to help him, need hire no labour. Then, too, a series of improvements may extend over a period of years. Harvesting is always to be done as a part of the maintenance of the woodlot. This means a constant income. It is the man who goes to his woodlot only to chop and haul out poles and firewood that gets the lowest rate of interest on his investment, and who declares truthfully that his woodlot doesn't pay.

CHAPTER V: TRANSPLANTING TREES

FROM THE WOODS

PERHAPS it is a primitive instinct, though it is a defensible and lovable one, that impels the home-maker to straighten his back after digging an ample hole in the ground and betake him to the woods to get a tree to set out in it. The handsomest and the most grotesque of cultivated trees came originally from the wilds, somewhere and at some time.

Competition is sharp, and growth slow in thickly settled places. A little tree that grows in the open has the best chance for symmetry and normal development. The roots are not tangled with others. Choose it, unless it be one of those tap-rooted kinds whose probings extend deeper than strength and patience can dig. If it is one of the fibrous-rooted tribe, dig on, in all carefulness and faith. Cut a circle as wide as the tree's crown. This will leave most of the roots in the earth ball. There is tough sod above, which you will discard when the planting is finished. It helps to hold the earth intact now. It is a long job, but at last the tree is loose, and an extra bucketful of its familiar earth may be dug out for use in planting. A wheelbarrow or a stone boat brings the tree home; and, if equal care surrounds the ceremonial of planting, it need never know of the change. Most trees submit to transplanting as if it were no ordeal. The safest way is to move them in their sleep—before the spring awakening, and while the earth is still solid and dry about the roots.

The capricious ones with long tap roots and few bushy side branches must have special treatment. Small trees only are safely moved. It is wise to select the tree a year beforehand, and to cut off its tap root by a thrust of a sharp spade at a moderate depth. It is thus forced to branch above the cut, and the next spring you know just how deep to dig to get this new root system.

The magnolias and the tulip tree have fleshy, brittle roots which are easily bruised and broken if carelessly handled. Most

486

evergreens die if their roots are exposed to the air. Yet all are successfully transplanted if pains are taken. The rhododendrons on Southern mountains are brought by carloads to Northern estates where they are set out with a loss of less than one per cent. Evergreens of middle age and large size are successfully transplanted in the growing season. It requires careful work and proper mechanical appliances to do these things, but there is no secret method. Whatever grows in the neighbouring woods may be safely trusted to thrive in home grounds unless violent changes in soil, shade and moisture conditions are made. Even then, some surprises are in store for the experimenting planter. Such water-loving trees as black ash, cottonwood, willow, sycamore and red maple do well in upland soil. Where transplanting from the wild is practicable, one is justified in experimenting at the cost of occasional failure. It is a part of wild gardening; it has a piquant charm that can't be bought with money. "Cheaper at the nursery," calls a neighbour, but the man with the spade and wheelbarrow goes along to the woods. This is his heart's holiday.

Trees differ by families and species in the tenacity of their hold on life. Those with a tendency to strike root from joints of the stem bear much abuse of roots. Such are most willows and poplars, basswood, osage orange and mulberry. In general, trees with many fibrous roots are most successfully transplanted. If the main branches are short and extend laterally, making a shallow but dense root system, the chances are best. If there is a long tap root going straight down, with but sparse side branches for feeding roots, difficulties and danger beset the transplanting. The maples and elms illustrate the first class; hickories and white oaks the second. "You can't transplant an oak too early nor an elm too late," is Evelyn's assurance, very old but still true.

A comparatively recent discovery is that certain families of plants depend for their soil food upon the ministrations of fungi, whose threads invest the rootlets completely, and have long been mistaken for the root hairs themselves. So intimate is the contact of this *mycorhiza* with the rootlets that the crude sap absorbed by the fungus from the soil is conducted to the leaves for manufacture into sugar and starch. The return current of sap nourishes not only the plant above ground and its root system, but also the mycorhiza, which has no green tissues, and therefore no way of elaborating plant food taken in the raw state. Each organism

487

serves the other's vital need. Without the fungus the tree would probably die, and vice versa.

The beech exhibits this notably among trees. So do the oaks, most of the conifers, and even certain of the willows and poplars. The great heath family, including laurels, rhododendrons, wintergreen and trailing arbutus, are believed to exhibit this "*symbiosis*," or interdependence between fungi and roots.

Moving such trees is precarious work, because the welfare of both tree and fungus must be looked after. If the mycorhiza dries out, the tree dies. If the tree is planted in soil destitute of this fungus, that brought in the earth ball often proves inadequate to the demands of the treetop. Most trees of this type grow naturally in great colonies, crowding out other kinds. The soil under beech woods is one great network of delicate fungous threads. An isolated beech tree taken to your garden sustains a great shock and a trying deprivation. No wonder trailing arbutus usually dies in domestication. The range of species exhibiting symbiosis is not very definitely known yet. It is certainly very large, and students are busy upon the problem. Many plants, however, feed with their own roots, and are therefore independent of organisms in the soil. So far as we know, most trees belong to the latter class.

The whole philosophy of transplanting is the keeping of the root system in ignorance of the change. The ideal way is to save all the roots. The practical way is to save as many as possible.

The trunk roots and their branches are important as a framework to support the tree in the ground and the rootlets at their extremities. But only the season's rootlets absorb plant food. Next year they, too, will pass the feeding function on to newer filaments of more delicate structure. The year-old roots become conductors but no longer gatherers of food. Each year's growth underground has had its turn, since the main branches were the tender first branchings of the radicle of the germinating seed.

FROM THE NURSERY

Nursery trees have been grown in rich soil and cultivated as they grew. Their root systems are, or should be, compact because the trees have been transplanted yearly in the nursery rows.

First-class trees cost a little more than second-class, but are cheaper in the end.

Nursery trees are delivered for fall or spring planting. If in fall, they should come early enough for the roots to become established in the ground before winter. For spring planting they should arrive early enough to be planted and have the advantages of early sunshine and shower in getting a good start during this first year in their permanent places.

Nurserymen ship trees in boxes or bundles, tied securely, their roots wrapped in damp straw or other protective covering. It is too expensive to ship much dirt. Trees often arrive before it is fit weather to plant them. The care of them during this interval is important. They should be "puddled" and "heeled in." Before the boxes are unpacked, and the bundles loosened by cutting their cords, a trench is dug with a sloping side away from prevailing winds. A pot hole is dug and a thin batter of mud prepared in it. Into this puddle the trees are dipped, a few at a time, and stirred about until every root has a mud coating. Now they are laid in the trench, their tops away from the wind, and a cover of earth shovelled over the roots. In this trench they are safe and comfortable until planting time comes.

Below are some rules for tree planting. They apply to all trees, and involve considerable more painstaking than some trees demand. But it is doubtful whether the man who expects the best results will dare to take less time and trouble than is here advised. After all, it is almost as easy to plant a tree right as to plant it wrong. If it is worth while to invest in a tree at all it is worth while to plant it well, inasmuch as tree planting is a job which if done well need not be done over for a century or two.

HOW TO PLANT A TREE

I. *Dig the hole wider and deeper than the tree requires.* The root tips are the feeders, and they cover the periphery of the root system. They will reach out during the growing season, forming a new set of feeding roots. They should find only mellow, rich soil in all directions. If the tree just fits into the socket, its roots will meet a hard wall which the delicate tips cannot penetrate and hold fast to, nor feed in. The first year is the critical one.

489

II. *Be sure that the surface soil is hoarded at one side when the hole is dug.* This soil is mellow and full of plant food. The under soil is more barren and harder. Some rich garden soil can well be brought over and used instead of this subsoil.

III. *Take up as large a root system as possible with the tree you dig.* The smaller the ball of earth, the greater the loss of feeding roots and the danger of starvation to the tree.

Prevent the drying of the exposed roots. When root hairs once shrivel they never revive. This is the general rule. A tree may survive but be greatly debilitated by careless handling in this particular.

IV. *Trim all torn and broken roots with a sharp knife.* A ragged wound above or below ground is slow and uncertain in healing. A clean, slanting cut heals soonest and surest.

V. *Set the tree on a bed of mellow soil with all its roots spread naturally.*

VI. *Let the level be the same as before.* The tree's roots must be planted, but not buried too deep to breathe. A stick laid across the hole at the ground level will indicate where the tree "collar" should be.

VII. *Sift rich earth, free from clods, among the roots.* Hold the tree erect and firm. Lift it a little to make sure the spaces are well filled underneath. Pack it well down with your foot.

VIII. *If in the growing season, pour in water and let it settle away.* This establishes contact between root hairs and soil particles, and dissolves plant food for absorption. If the tree is dormant, do not water it.

IX. *Fill the hole with dirt.* Tramp in well as filling goes on. Heap it somewhat to allow for settling. If subsoil is used, put it on last. Make the tree firm in its place.

X. *Prune the top to a few main branches and shorten these.* This applies to a sapling of a few years whose head you are able to form. Older trees should also be pruned to balance the loss of roots. Otherwise transpiration of water from the foliage would be so great as to overtax the roots, not yet established in the new place. Many trees die from this abuse. People cannot bear to cut back the handsome top, though a handsomer one is so soon supplied by following this reasonable rule.

XI. *Water the tree frequently as it first starts.* A thorough soaking of all the roots, not a mere sprinkling of the surface soil, is needed. Continuous growth depends on moisture in the soil. Drainage will remove the surplus water.

XII. *Keep the surface soil free from cakes and cracks.* This prevents excessive evaporation.   Do not stir the soil deep enough to disturb the roots.   Keep out grass and weeds.

CHAPTER VI: HOW TREES ARE MULTIPLIED

NATURE begrudges man all the land he has cleared of forests, and if he relaxes his vigilance—lets a field lie fallow a year or two— the forest begins to encroach, and takes it back. Every year trees flower and fruit, and young saplings come up wherever there is room and a chance in the woods. But here there is crowding and struggling even among the large trees, and the saplings die unless they can live under the shade of larger trees.

I. THE NATURAL WAY

The fortunate trees are those with abundant seeds, so light or so winged that they can sail off on the winds and fall in new places less crowded than the forest. The birches have such seeds—little heart-shaped discs with thin, papery webs on their edges all around. The pencil-like cones are packed with hundreds of these seeds, and the trees hang full of cones. What wonder, then, that birches so often follow in the wake of the lumbermen in New England woods. Pines and the other narrow-leaved evergreens are known by their cones. Have you ever shaken or beaten the seeds out of an opening cone of white pine? This is a typical conifer. The heavy brown seed has a wing by which the wind carries it. That very field now grown up to birches was once covered with virgin forests of pine. The neighbouring woods scatter pine seeds with birch and many other kinds. The birch gets the start. But in a few years you will see the little pines coming up in the shade of the birches. The "nurse trees" are short lived; they give way in time, and a pine forest follows the brief sway of the birches.

Why does poplar follow pine woods in many places? Note the poplar trees in early June. They are discharging seeds from long strings of green beads, burst open and turning brown. A puff of cottony substance, light as down, encloses each minute seed. There are millions on every tree. Wafted forth, these seeds lodge all over the neighbourhood. The cleared ground offers an opportunity. They spring up vigorously—a poplar forest. But under them are other slower, longer-lived trees loving the shade in their first years, but prepared to replace their poplar nurses in due season.

Look at the thin, round disc of the elm seed and you will see how the trees cater to their distributing friend, the wind. How copiously the tree sheds its seeds in early summer! Notice the young elms that come up about the neighbourhood, if Nature is let alone. Observe the keen-pointed, winged dart an ash tree bears. What a burden of seeds one tree yields! Watch the tree on a windy day in October and on into winter. Study the winged key of the maples, the catalpa's thousands of thin, papery seeds in its hundreds of long pods that the wintry breezes shake and loosen and scatter every year. How much the willows' fuzzy seeds look like the poplars'—for willows and poplars are own cousins!

How different is the wing on the basswood's cluster of woody balls. The wind whirls them abroad and basswoods come up unexpectedly here and there. Sycamores bang their balls, and every loosened seed sails away on its own hairy parachute. The abundant ailanthus seed is balanced on a tipsy raft, that the wind carries long distances. The hornbeam seed sails in a shallop. The hop hornbeam seed is shut into an inflated balloon. The wind is the staunch ally of the forest in its policy of expansion.

So are the birds. The trees with fleshy fruits depend upon them. All the berries with small seeds, the sassafras, haws, Juneberries, hackberries, dogwoods, mountain ash, hollies and the cedars are in this group; cherries, too, and apples are distributed by birds to some extent. The larger fruits must wait for the larger creatures of the woods; they carry off the plums for the flesh and thin nut-like pits. There are the acorns and nuts that fall heavily, rolling down hillsides, if the parent tree is on the slope, but lodging soon, and waiting for squirrels and their kin to come and carry them off. The animals are selfish in this hoarding of nuts. They do not mean to leave one. But those that are hidden in the runways and not eaten, after all, sprout the next spring, and so the old nut tree is parent to scattered offspring, as well as to many that come up under its own shadow. The locusts fling their pods abroad to go careening over snow-banks in winter, and so to break open at length and spill their

493

flinty seeds. The witch hazel bursts open its woody pods in October and the seeds are shot out like bullets from a gun.

Thousands of tree seeds are sown where but tens may hope to germinate and grow. Some seeds (e. g., willow) must germinate at once or they lose their vitality and die. Most of these cannot start unless they fall in very moist soil. So each has its peculiar limitations, and these keep the number of seedlings down. Fortunate kinds are not particular as to soil. This is especially true of those whose seeds will wait till a second year if the first does not offer them a chance to grow.

The willows illustrate better than other trees another method of reproduction. They rise superior to the limitations of their feeble seeds, and cast off twigs which strike root and grow into trees. Many willows have twigs that are brittle at the base. Touch one lightly and off it snaps in your hand. Every wind breaks off these natural willow cuttings and scatters them. Stream banks are lined for miles with trees of one kind. The twigs floating down stream lodged and grew. Sandbanks are covered by the same means. Even willow posts set green follow the twig habit and grow into trees. Osage orange and mulberry, poplar and basswood root quickly as cuttings. Theoretically, any plant will do the same. In practice, few trees are economically propagated in this way.

Young chestnut and oak trees follow old ones by the sprouting of the old stumps. It is not uncommon to find an ancient stump with a whorl of young trees circling its base—from five to a dozen of them. Foresters call this the coppice method of renewing woodlands. It is a cheap way to reproduce timber. These "suckers" grow rapidly, for they have the whole root system of the parent tree to feed them. Such trees, however, are short lived. Most of the familiar hardwoods sprout from the stump— maples, elms, beech, ashes and locusts. Also the softer-wooded birches, basswoods, willows and poplars. The only conifers that do this are the redwood and the pitch pine.

It is common to see a white poplar or a Lombardy poplar or a garden plum tree growing neglected in the midst of a crowd of youngsters. These are not seedling trees, but suckers from the parent roots. They resemble coppice growth where they spring out close to the tree's "collar," but they have not waited for the removal of the old trunks. Such trees are nuisances on a

494

lawn or in a fence row. However, they illustrate one more of the methods that trees resort to to insure the perpetuation of their kind. In the race for life the trees with these secondary means of propagation, reinforcing the seed, are winners. Consider, for instance, the pines. The one species in the East which comes up from the stump is the pitch pine. It rises like the Phœnix, from devastating fires, and after the sawmill has departed, when other species must rely on seeds alone. The result is marked. Though not the most valuable Eastern pine, it is the one best able to hold its own in the race for life.

By seeds, by sprouts and by cast-off twigs the forest has ever renewed its youth and extended its boundaries. By these means it has resisted the forces which work toward its extermination.

II. THE ARTIFICIAL WAY

From Nature man learned the three ways of propagating plants: by seeds, by sprouts and by cuttings; and he invented grafting, for which there is little suggestion in Nature. In all these he improved upon Nature, for he threw his energies into one single enterprise, sacrificing everything to its success. Look at the wild fruit trees in the woods; then look at the orchards, their lineal descendants. Look at the wild grasses scattered over the earth; the fields of grain have come from them. Look at the scattered cedars in an old pasture; then consider the serried ranks of them in the forests of Germany, standing close like rye in a field, waiting for the harvest that converts their wood into cedar pencils. The forester replants the ground, cultivates, weeds, thins and prunes the young trees for another harvest a century hence.

The growing of young trees from seed makes a large nursery business in all civilised countries. The seed is selected to discard the inferior qualities. The growing is in rows that are cultivated. Again the poorest are discarded, and only the thrifty seedlings transplanted. When set in their permanent places they are tended and defended against anything that encroaches upon their rights. So they thrive, and yield vastly better returns than their wild relatives, whose life is a long fight for mere existence.

A fallen willow twig strikes root. Why not strip the tree to its trunk and plant every bit? It is done. The old stump

495

covers itself again with a thicket of suckers, and every twig it lost is a hale yearling tree on its own roots. This is the way to get willows and poplars in the nursery rows. It is quicker and surer and easier than planting the seed.

Any tree that sends up suckers from the root will yield young trees as fast as you can dig them up. Loss stimulates the parent tree to greater feats of production.

The highest form of tree multiplication is *grafting*, and its kindred practice, *budding*. It is among the oldest arts, discoursed upon by writers since the dawn of literature. It consists in setting a part of one plant upon another in order that the two may become united by growth into one living structure. The rooted plant is the *stock;* the added part, a piece of a twig with one or more buds, is called the *cion*.

Grafting is the act of making this union. The *graft* is the union, or joint, thus formed. *Budding* is essentially the same process. The difference is that instead of a cion a single bud is joined to the stock, only enough of the twig being used to give the bud a foundation.

The object of grafting and budding is to produce a tree whose character shall be twofold. The top that grows above the graft or bud shall have the better fruit or other characteristics of the tree from which the cion or bud came. The stock retains its own character, for example, straight growth, deep root system or resistance to diseases. The stock is the nurse tree, feeding the top, which flowers and fruits after its own kind. Its leaves and mode of branching are characteristic of the new, ingrafted variety, else the process would be useless.

Cultivated trees rarely "come true" from seed. They "revert" to the original wild species from which varieties have so recently sprung. For seedlings change their natures very gradually, and the forming of varieties in plants is a modern innovation, compared with the unnumbered centuries during which seed bearing has gone on in the wilds.

Grafting and budding serve four purposes: 1. The perpetuation of a desired variety. 2. The multiplying of its numbers. 3. The production of dwarfs. 4. The production of hardy varieties.

A nurseryman's business is largely the accomplishment of these ends, and the supplying of planters with the results of his labours. Flowers and fruits and ornamental plants are his products. Let us consider an illustration of each: 1. The bellflower apple is a choice variety. Mixed seeds from a cider mill are planted in the nursery rows. They come up as little whips, and are budded with buds from bellflower trees. Whatever their lineage, these trees will be bellflowers when they come into bearing, for the whole treetop came out of that one bellflower bud. 2. The number of young trees of bellflower a nurseryman can supply depends on the number of seedlings he buds successfully. An old tree spares hundreds of buds, so the multiplication is wonderfully rapid. 3. It is possible to dwarf a variety by budding or grafting it upon a slow-growing stock. Thus, the stunted quince is used as a stock for varieties of pears, and dwarfs result. The law of its growth enables the stock to curb the ambitions of the top. 4. Tender-rooted varieties that are winter killed in cold climates are often made hardy by grafting them upon stocks of native kinds. For instance, the wild plum and the sand cherry of Dakota and Nebraska are successfully grafted with varieties of peaches, apricots and Japanese plums, which have failed repeatedly in this dry, cold region "on their own roots." Native crabs have proved good stocks for imported varieties of apples. Nursery stock is oftener budded than grafted, the trees being but yearling whips, as a rule. Stone fruits are generally budded. Apple trees are commonly budded in the East, but root grafting is the rule in Western nurseries. Older trees are grafted, to save time and labour.

"There are as many ways of grafting as there are of whittling," a wise horticulturist has remarked. The object in each case is to fit the cion (or bud) to the stock with the cambium of the two in close contact. A tied band of raffia or a covering of grafting wax, or both, excludes the air and injurious substances and holds the parts securely.

Cleft grafting is very common in changing the variety of a fruit tree. For other methods see Bailey's "Nursery Book," or any other horticulturist's guide. Cleft grafting is typical. The end of a branch is sawed squarely off. It should be less than two inches in diameter. A special grafting knife is used next. Its blade, set across the stub, is driven in by the stroke of a mallet. A tooth on the end of the knife is inserted in the split thus made, to hold the cleft open. A cion is inserted at each end of the split, so that there may be two chances for it to "stick" fast and grow, instead of one. Each cion is a bit of a twig, bearing two or three buds, and sharpened by two slanting cuts to fit the cleft stub. When set, there should be a bud on a level with the top of the stub. It should be held tight between the lips of the cleft, by the "spring" of the two sides (the tooth being removed now), and the green cambium of cion and stock should pinch. Now grafting wax is moulded about the graft and the work is complete.

The best time to graft is just before the buds swell in the spring. If all is well, leaves will shoot upon the cions as April comes on; if one fails, no matter. By grafting one-third of the limbs each year for three years the whole treetop can be changed from one variety to another. Several varieties may be grafted on one tree.

Budding is usually done in summer or early fall. *Shield budding* is the common nursery method. A T-shaped cut through the bark of the slender whip is made on the north side just above the ground. A twist of the knife loosens the four corners of the bark. An oval bit of bark with a bud in its centre is cut from a twig of the desired variety; a leaf stem serves as a convenient handle. The disc of bark bearing the bud is slipped down under the thin flaps of bark on the stock. They hold the bud in place against the cambium of the stock. A wrapping of raffia protects and binds the wound. It is cut as soon as the bud "sticks," or it would impede the growth. The stem above is cut off, so that the treetop formed later may be the outgrowth of this bud. Budding is usually done upon seedlings of one season's growth, and is ordinarily intrusted to an expert, with a helper to tie the buds he sets. A record of three thousand buds a day is not unusual.

Weeping forms are propagated by grafting cions from weeping trees upon erect stocks. The popular notion that they are produced by inserting the buds upside down is entirely false. Horticultural varieties are all grafted, e. g., cut-leaved, variegated, pyramidal and double-flowered varieties of standard species. These peculiarities are originally discovered as seedling variations in the nursery rows or "freak" branches on normal trees. A good character is hoarded, emphasised and multiplied; then exploited as a new variety. It would not come true from seed, even if it appeared first in a seedling. It is too new to be fixed, except by grafting cions from the original tree.

The extent to which grafting and budding can be practised was at first much exaggerated. Virgil prophesied thus:

"Thou shalt lend
Grafts of rude arbute unto the walnut tree:
Shalt bid the unfruitful plane sound apples bear,
Chestnuts the beech, the ash blow white with the pear,
And under the elm, the sow on acorns fare."

Pliny's report of "cherry growing upon the willow, the plane upon the laurel, the laurel upon the cherry, and fruits of various tints and hues all springing from the same tree at once," is like other of his vain imaginings.

Abram Cowley, in 1666, comes nearer the truth, as he should with centuries of experience to lean upon, in these lines:

"We nowhere Art do so triumphant see,
As when it Grafts or Buds the Tree;

He bids the ill-natur'd Crab produce
The gentle Apple's Winy Juice

He does the savage Hawthorn teach
To bear the Medlar and the Pear
He bids the rustic Plum to rear
A noble Trunk and be a Peach."

The modern rule of "seed on seed and pit on pit' is embodied in this account. The species named are all in the same botanical family at least. Plums are budded upon peach stocks in the South. Peach-rooted trees thrive better in the hot, sandy soil than plum-rooted trees do. In the Northern States peaches are budded on plum stocks which are hardier in the native kinds. Crab apples, native to various regions, prove good stocks for introduced varieties of apples.

The limits of grafting are not very well defined yet. The safest and most practicable method is to inter-graft varieties of one species. Remoter relationships admit of union sometimes, as the peach and plum, which are of different species; by some authorities these are considered of different genera. The mountain ash has served as a stock for apples—again, two different genera. But these instances are plainly beyond safe limits.

The origination of new varieties by hybridisation is an entirely different subject. Its variations come through the seeds. Here the pollen, scattered in various ways when plants blossom, falls on the pistils of flowers somewhat indiscriminately. Especially is this true of wind-fertilised flowers which produce pollen in abundance and of a dry, powdery sort. The pollen lies inert on the stigmas of alien species. It fertilises those of its own kind. There are intermediate varietal relationships and very closely related species in certain families. In these cases natural crosses occur, flowers being fertilised by pollen of another species. Seeds thus set produce hybrid plants, new kinds having characters of their two parents. Thus the species of willows are hopelessly intermixed. Natural crosses between oaks are frequently discernible in the woods. The white oak crosses with several species in its own (annual) group. The biennial or black oaks also intercross among themselves. But black and white oaks do not cross.

Artificial crosses are frequently made by plant breeders for scientific and economic reasons. Some of the best horticultural varieties of fruits and flowers are artificial hybrids. Among these are the Kieffer pear, the wild goose plum, and various roses, grapes, begonias, cannas and pelargoniums. Hybrids are propagated by division.

CHAPTER VII: HOW TREES ARE MEASURED

I was walking one day with a forester trained in the Black Forest. A beautiful shagbark of unusual height attracted my attention. I asked how tall he thought it was. Imagine my surprise when he shut up like a jack-knife—his hips the hinge, his head between his knees, his back to the tree. Not satisfied with the first inverted glimpse he thus obtained, he moved a step or two nearer to the tree and looked again. Then he straightened up, smiled at my bewilderment, paced the distance to the foot of the tree, and said that it was about ninety feet high.

MEASURING HEIGHT

This method of estimating the heights of trees is common among German foresters. At a distance just equal to the tree's height, the observer, with his head between his knees, sees the top of the tree and no higher. To get this location is very easy; then there is left nothing to do but to pace off the distance.

The tree's shadow on bright days may be measured, then the shadow of any short object standing erect—a man, a fence post or a sapling. As the man's shadow is to his height, so is the tree's shadow to its height. Suppose a six-foot man casts a ten-foot shadow, and the tree's shadow is seventy feet. The proportion reads:

$10:6::70:x$; then $\dfrac{6 \times 70}{10}=x$. The tree is forty-two feet high.

A third simple method is interesting. Set a perpendicular pole about five feet high in the ground at a distance about equal to the tree's height from the base of it. Between this short pole and the tree, in line with both, set a taller pole, near enough so that, sighting from the top of the short pole to the top of the tree, the line of vision crosses the tall pole. Have this point marked. Now sight the base of the tree, and mark the place where the line of vision crosses the taller pole. Measure now the distance between the poles, the distance between the short pole and the tree, and the distance between the two marks on the tall pole. Suppose the marks on the pole to be six feet apart, the poles five feet apart, and the short pole forty feet from the tree. Then we have two similar triangles and a proportion with three known quantities. The distance between the poles is to the distance from the short pole to the tree as the distance between the marks on the tall pole is to height of the tree. $5 : 40 :: 6 : x.$

Solved, $\dfrac{40 \times 6}{5} = 48$. The tree is forty-eight feet high.

A fourth method involves a right-angled isosceles triangle and a plumb line, but it is extremely simple, and is in common use by men who go out to estimate standing timber in terms of board measure. Take a square of pasteboard or shingle, and cut it in two diagonally. One of these halves is your tool. To the square corner hang a plumb line—a string with a weight attached—to indicate when you hold the triangle so that its sides are exactly vertical and horizontal. Sight along the diagonal, stepping backward or forward until the top of the tree is in line with the diagonal and your eye. Now sight along the horizontal base line of the triangle to get the point on the tree trunk at the height of your eye. The tree's height above this point is equal to your distance from the tree, for it is one base of an isosceles right-angled triangle similar to your tool. Pace the distance to the tree, add your height, and you have the tree's height. In this method of measurement, level ground is necessary to the amateur. The practised eye makes due allowance for inequalities, which must be taken as they come in the woods.

The Faustman "mirror hypsometer" is a clever little instrument by which the observer may get the height of trees by simply pacing the distance from its base to the point where the treetop is in line with an eye piece and a hair line set six inches away. The treetop appears to the observer, a slide is moved up to the figure corresponding to the distance, a plummet swings over a scale, and the figure it covers, reflected by a mirror to the observer's eye, is the tree's height. This convenient tool does away with computations, and enables the user to accomplish much in a short time.

MEASURING DIAMETER

A tree's diameter is measured by calipers, which consist of a graduated rule, marked in inches and fractions, a fixed arm forming a right angle at one end, and a movable arm, parallel with the first one, sliding on the rule. The rule is set against a tree above the bulge of the base. The fixed arm touches it at one point, and the sliding arm comes up to a point on the bark diametrically opposite. The base of this arm indicates the diameter of the tree on the scale of inches.

Logs and standing timber are measured by this tool. Calipers for ordinary work have rules four to five feet long. Few trees require longer ones.

MEASURING VOLUME

Standing trees are assumed to be regular geometrical solids, resting on a circular base and tapering to the limbs, a compromise between a cone and a cylinder.

To get the solid contents of a trunk, the area of the base is multiplied by one-half the altitude. With a pair of calipers and any one of the four methods of obtaining the tree's height its cubical contents are easily computed. The forester cannot stop to multiply and compute the circular base on which the tree rests. He uses a table where these are worked out.

Timber is measured in board feet oftener than by volume. A board foot is a foot square and one inch thick; there are twelve board feet in one cubic foot. It is generally estimated that one-third to one-half of a log is sawdust, slabs and defective wood. Allowance is therefore made for these losses. Much depends upon how the logs are sawed.

A "cruiser" was an old-time woodsman who went into the forest with a compass, and, pacing off the distances, located and estimated the timber in tracts with obscure boundaries. Once is was saw stuff only that he calculated. Now not only sawlogs, but ties and poles and fuel are taken account of in these estimates.

By tables known as "Log Scales" the number of feet, board measure, a given tree will yield is quickly found. Height and diameter being known, the table gives the contents. In measuring standing timber it is customary for two measurers to go ahead

503

and a tally keeper to record their work. Each tree is marked to prevent counting it twice. Sheets for different kinds of trees and columns and lines for different heights and diameters of trees are provided in the record book. From this notebook and its tally marks the solid contents of a tract of woods is easily estimated at home or in the field, in terms of board measure or by cord measure. A cord is 128 cubic feet.

"Log scalers" or measurers record how many board feet a log will cut. These men carry a scale rule, which they apply to the small end of the log. From the diameter it measures four inches are deducted. The square of the balance is the log's contents in board feet, provided the length is sixteen feet. Allowance is made for logs longer or shorter than the standard. The table with these results worked out for logs from ten to sixty inches in diameter, and for twelve, fourteen and sixteen feet in length, constitute the Doyle-Scribner Log Scale in common use. It is a compact table, containing in four columns, of fifty lines depth, results that save much toilsome multiplying. It is so simple, however, that any intelligent woodchopper can reconstruct his own table in an evening, if he loses one. The four inches deducted allow for ordinary waste in sawing. Very crooked, knotty or otherwise defective logs have a greater deduction made at the discretion of the scaler.

MEASURING ANNUAL GROWTH

Cut down a tree, measure the diameter of its stump and count the rings in the outside inch of wood—the first inch inside the bark. Multiply the diameter by the number of rings to this inch. Divide 400 by the product obtained by this multiplication. The quotient is the percentage of yearly increase of the tree.

This seems like an arbitrary formula, and it is not accurate to a hair. But it is a practical method for estimating the yearly accretion that a tree makes. It is the method used by the Bureau of Forestry in estimating the annual growth of woodlots, and it is so simple that anyone can use it. Farmers can tell how much interest they are getting by letting their trees grow, and when they are cutting into their wood principal in harvesting the crop. It replaces guesswork by knowledge.

One tree does not make a forest, nor a woodlot. But one

tree is a key to the rest. Take each kind of tree by itself. Cut sixteen or twenty white oaks of different sizes and grown under varying conditions at different places on the woodlot. Their average will fairly represent the individuals of this species. Take the tulip trees in the same way, and get the increase of the average tree. When the different species have been considered separately, they may be averaged to get the general per cent. of growth for all. Then the owner knows about what amount of wood cut in a winter will be replaced by the growth of the following summer. The secret of success in the best-kept forests of Germany and France is the management that does not cut more than the annual increase will restore. It explains the perennial vigour and productiveness of these secular forests.

CHAPTER VIII : THE PRUNING OF TREES

PRUNING is the cutting out of parts of a tree for the improvement of the parts that remain. *Cleaning* might better designate the removal of dead wood. *Trimming* is the shaping of the outline, as the shearing of hedges and individuals of box and yew into formal or grotesque figures. *Training* is the bringing of the tree to some desired arrangement of its limbs, as the espalier fruit trees, that lie flat against a wall in European gardens.

All green plants need sun and air, as well as room for roots. Trees crowd out other plants in close forests. Where thousands of saplings start in a plot of woodland, only hundreds reach middle life, and only tens, maturity. In every treetop the story of continuous thinning is repeated. The trunk and limbs are full of knots which the bark has healed over. They are records of twigs and large branches that failed. A dozen apple blossoms make up a single cluster. Two or three apples at most mature, and they are inferior to the apple that grows alone, sole survivor of the dozen May promises. Every well-grown leaf nurses a bud at its base. Next year these buds send out shoots, each with leaves that nurture other buds. These twigs are stifled by the crowding. The weaklings die. On the stronger ones the leaves in the shade turn yellow and fall. The weak buds fail even to start in spring. As the tree's crown grows larger, many branches are overshadowed. Their leaves languish and die. The whole bough declines, and at length snaps off. Nature sacrifices the many to the few—the weak for the good of the strong. It is the law of the survival of the fittest.

Pruning is a practice we learn directly from Nature. Yet there are those who decry it as "unnatural"! The difference is that man does a much better job—where he knows what he is about. The quack tree doctor, alas! too often takes the case, and then it were far better to have let Nature manage the affair herself. The peripatetic tree pruner is almost always a tree butcher, a menace to the well-being of any self-respecting, tree-loving community. He preys upon the good intentions and the credulity of the public.   His glibness passes for scientific knowledge with people who are themselves ignorant of the life and the needs of their trees.   Too often they succumb to his arguments and let him scrape and hack and doctor the trees as he sees fit.   It is probably an indignant neighbour who expatiates on the havoc wrought.   The dazed owner, with flattened purse and a sense of failure and disillusion, bewails what cannot be undone.   The tree pruner is gone, so the vengeance that should cut short his profitable career follows him afar off.

This is plain justice to the family and to the community and to the trees:—If a tree is worth pruning at all it is worth the owner's while to inform himself as to the best method and then stand by and see that his directions are carried out, unless there is some man of well-known intelligence who can be trusted to do it properly.   We shall come to recognise one day that the trees of a community are common property in the best sense, and no man has a right to prune them or cut them down unless he acts as a duly appointed representative of all the people.

HOW TO CUT OFF A LIMB

"The best pruning tool is the thumb and finger."   So it is, even for trees in their infantile stages.   Pinching back tender shoots forms the tree's head to the owner's liking, and yearly attention keeps it under control.   This is the ideal way.   In practice, however, limbs must be cut off—sometimes very large ones. Pruning knives and shears and the long-armed, strong-jawed pruners will easily cut limbs to an inch or a little more in thickness. After this, a good saw is the right tool.   Axes and hatchets are unfit for use in pruning, as they leave the cut surface uneven and tear the bark.

The limb should be sawed off smooth and clean on a level with the surrounding bark.   There will be some projection, inevitably, for the limb has a flaring base.   But no projecting stub of the branch itself should be permitted to remain.   Better far a larger wound made by sawing well down in the enlarged basal part. If any tearing of the bark has occurred, unevennesses should be trimmed with a sharp knife.

The healing of the wound must be a slow process, for the inner bark has to form a layer of new tissue that gradually rolls in and closes over the solid wood at the centre. There is no union between the wood and the healing bark, for the former is practically dead. Being porous, it absorbs rain that follows down its tubular wood fibres. Germs of wood-destroying fungi, afloat in the air from rotting trees and twigs in the neighbourhood, lodge in the exposed wound, germinate, and send their filamentous hyphæ down into the stub and on toward the heart of the tree. Sugary, starchy cell contents moistened by the rain make the best possible soil for such fungi. Better leave the tree unpruned than to expose the inert heart wood by careless work.

A covering of any waterproof substance protects the helpless tree against invasion by its worst enemies. A cheap oil paint like linseed oil and white lead fills the surface pores and lasts a long time. It should be generously applied, so that no entrance is left for disease. It likewise checks the bleeding, or flow of sap, which dries the exposed stub and makes more room for rain to enter with its accumulation of dirt and disease spores. Meanwhile, the new bark rolls in, and when it meets over the wound the paint has served its purpose. The covered wood has been kept sound. It is often years before the process is complete, depending on the size of the wound and the rate of the tree's growth. In many cases the paint needs renewing.

THAT VICIOUS LONG STUB

Hired men set to pruning trees are almost sure to leave stubs. They will argue that this is the best way. Go for your answer to trees thus pruned in previous years. They are plenty in any neighbourhood. The stub decays, its bark sloughs off at length, and the bark at the base can never hope to heal the wound until it swallows the stub entire, or the latter rots off at the base. In the first case it is a delay of years. In the last, it means the invasion of rot into the heart of the tree. A long stub, therefore, always threatens the health of the tree, is a blot upon its beauty, and a monument to the laziness and ignorance or dishonesty of the man who pruned by this pernicious method.

TEN PRINCIPLES OF PRUNING

1. Pruning the roots lessens the food supply, and so retards top growth.

2. Pruning the top invigorates the branches that remain, the root system being unchanged.

3. Removing terminal buds induces forking, thus thickening the branching system. It checks wood production, and encourages the production of flowers and fruit.

4. Unpruned trees tend to wood production.

5. Summer pruning reduces the struggle among leaves and twigs for light and produces stronger buds for spring.

6. Winter pruning removes superfluous buds, inducing greater vigour in those that are left to develop.

7. Dead wood should be taken out at any season and burned.

8. The best time to prune, generally speaking, is just before growth starts in spring.

9. Early winter pruning is undesirable because the healing of wounds must wait till spring.

10. Yearly pruning is better than pruning at less frequent intervals.

PRUNING SHADE TREES

An ideal shade tree has the character of its species or variety, as the oval of the hard maple or the broad dome of the white oak or the fan top of the elm. It has the greatest possible foliage mass on a sturdy framework of trunk and limbs. To keep this dome intact, losing just enough for the health of the leaves, is the object of pruning. It needs only the removal of dead and broken limbs and of those that interfere and crowd. Wayward limbs are cut back to preserve the tree's symmetry. Long, heavy limbs that threaten to split away from the trunk by their weight are cut back.

In fact, shade trees take care of themselves almost altogether. Accidents to their limbs are usually responsible for conditions that make pruning necessary.

PRUNING ORNAMENTAL TREES

Here is a wide range of choice. If foliage is the ornamental feature, or a multitude of flowers, no matter how small, little thinning of branches will be required. If size of flowers is more important than numbers, thinning should be thorough. Late-blooming kinds are best pruned in spring; early-blooming kinds, directly after the fading of the flowers. The energies of bud formation are thus concentrated on the branches that remain.

Dwarf forms of trees are kept in trim by pruning the roots with a sharp spade, and by "heading in" the branches severely. Shearing keeps a tree in formal shape. Weeping trees and others of peculiar habits are trimmed to preserve their characteristics.

In all ornamental trees care must be taken to cut off shoots that start below the bud or graft. The stock is of a different kind, and these low shoots therefore introduce a false note into the top grown from the cion or bud.

PRUNING EVERGREENS

The best form a conifer can have is its natural, pyramidal one, tapering to the sky. The end bud, or leader, should never be cut. When this is destroyed the central shaft branches, and the tree's beauty gives place to oddity. The lower limbs of evergreens should lie upon the ground, if they can be kept green and healthy. Spruces especially hold these branches late. If limbs are sparse, pinching out terminal buds on the lateral branches will force out new shoots from side buds, soon producing a compact dome of foliage. Symmetry should be preserved by heading in wayward branches. Formal shapes are produced by clipping and shearing. Evergreens generally have resinous sap which covers wounds. Such need no paint to prevent inoculation by fungous diseases while healing.

PRUNING FRUIT TREES

This is a very large and special subject. Methods depend upon the aims of the owners. While the trees are young they are pruned to shape and thinned to induce vigour. As fruiting age comes on they are checked by heading back terminal buds. This diverts the tree's forces from wood production to fruiting. If the best fruit is desired, thinning of twigs and especially of fruit clusters while green is practised.

Pruning is an annual practice with the best fruit growers. A fruit tree left to its own devices for years produces firewood. The severe pruning that follows this neglect produces a forest of "water sprouts" or "suckers" the next year. It takes a long time to get such a tree checked and back into bearing.

The cutting off of lower limbs to overcome the interfering of neighbouring trees in an orchard is a bad practice. It elevates the bearing area, until ladders are necessary to reach the lowest fruit. Better take out alternate trees, or best of all, plant originally at the proper distances, setting short-lived fruits between.

Yearly pruning will prevent interference by training the orchard trees to a narrower habit. By the "thumb-and-finger" pruning mentioned before, a tree may be shaped to the low, round head, or sent upward into a tall, narrow one. It takes the heaviest tools to convert them into the Japanese parasol form. Such an orchard tree makes life miserable for the pickers and is a living witness of the obtuse and neglectful character of the owner.

PRUNING FOREST TREES

This is a practice that belongs to intensive forestry. It is a part of a type of silviculture that crops land with trees as the careful farmer does with grain. If a dense stand does not "clean itself" of lower limbs by Nature's pruning, there is cheap labour to do the work, and sale for the limbs as fagots, or as charcoal. Thus in various European forests it pays to prune trees. In America it rarely pays yet. The illustration of pruning white-pine seedlings in small woodlots (see page 477) is a notable exception. White pine does not clean itself of branches, even dead ones, as most trees do. This fact greatly impairs the quality of the timber, for dead knots abound in it. Only trees intended for a mature first-grade crop can be pruned with profit.

Judicious selective cuttings which keep the forest cover intact bring about natural pruning by the choking out and chafing of lower limbs.

GENERAL TREE SURGERY

Capital operations in tree surgery are performed with notable success nowadays. When a great limb cracks away from the trunk, threatening the admission of water and disease germs into the cleft, an iron bolt of proper length and strength is provided. An auger hole is bored through the limb a foot or two above its base, and another in line with it through the main trunk. Inserting the bolt, through both limb and trunk, the nut is

511

screwed on as tight as possible. This brings the lips of the crack together and holds them. A wise precaution is to wash the wound with some antiseptic, as coal tar or paint, or a mixture of both.

Lightning often tears away part of a tree, exposing the heart wood over an area so large that the tree cannot be expected to heal it. When it is desirable to save the tree, several methods are possible. Thorough painting of the wound is effectual if repeated as the paint wears off. A hollow, as of a limb torn out, may be filled with cement after an antiseptic dressing. The outer bark has to bring its edges together over the cement. A very successful protection is tar. Sheet iron, tar paper, etc., tacked on over wounds that have not been treated to check invasion of tree diseases, are of doubtful advantage. Outside they look snug and neat, but underneath insects harbour and fungi thrive in the moist darkness which is the most favourable condition for their development. A tree thus protected (?) often goes over in a storm, revealing a rotten heart that has developed since the accident that tore off its limb.

A hollow tree, or one with a cheesy heart, may be opened (if there is no opening on the side), scraped clean of its corrupt interior substance, and filled with cement. With this pillar of stone fitted inside it, the tree is no longer a hollow shell weak enough for wind to overthrow it. Its disease checked, it may take on a new lease of life. Historic trees, especially, justify thorough renovation and bolstering inside; but the average old tree, weakened by accident and disease, is best cut down and a young one given its place.

TULIP TREE (*Liriodendron Tulipifera*)

CHAPTER IX: THE ENEMIES OF TREES

In every treetop we can read the story of a long fight. Leaf, flower and fruit, bud, twig and branch, contest unceasingly for room and food and sun. Underground, the roots have their own struggle for the bounty of the soil. Always the struggle is unequal, the weak succumbing to the strong. Where tens succeed, hundreds and thousands fail.

In the woods the story is the same. Neighbour trees contend as do neighbour branches. Nature thins and prunes, discarding all but the fittest. Many people understand that the best forests are those in which Nature has her own way. But only from Nature's point of view. She is the great impartial all-Mother, and is as much interested in the well-being of a fungus that destroys a tree as in the tree itself. A virgin forest is a battleground where varied and multitudinous natural forces meet and fight for supremacy.

The noble forests of the Cascade range in Washington and Oregon best illustrate the victory of trees over all other forms of vegetation. The pine forests of the Great Lakes and of the South, the broad-leaved forests of the Ohio and lower Mississippi Valleys, all showed how trees triumphed in days gone by over inimical forces of Nature. The meagre fringe of trees along streams in the arid West, the stunted growth of northernmost woods, show how trees are affected by drought and cold. The distribution of forests and their condition are traceable to well-known causes.

Some of the enemies of the forest are natural; some are attributable to man and his civilisation. In many instances responsibility is divided. One enters and leaves the door open for others.

The chief enemies of forests are fires and insects. Winds, frost, lightning, snow, hail, ice, drought and flood are atmospheric in origin. Fungi decompose dead wood, doing the forest a service by enriching the soil. But many of them menace sound trees wherever their bark is broken. Grazing and wasteful lumbering are two abuses of the first magnitude. Beside these, man is responsible for most forest fires.

Cold is the barrier that sets a limit to each species of trees at a certain degree of latitude and at a certain altitude above the sea. Few species are hardy enough to reach into British America, or to climb high up on mountains.

Frost damages forests by nipping the buds and tender shoots, by actually causing tree trunks as well as branches to burst open after the freezing of sap in spring, and by heaving the porous soil so that saplings of all ages are uprooted. Frost often destroys seeds before they are ripe, and while they are germinating.

Snow and ice burden trees in winter time, doing great damage to their tops—often maiming young trees for life. Broad-leaved trees avoid much injury by their deciduous habit, but evergreens suffer where snows are heavy and winters long. Extreme toughness and flexibility of limb characterise trees that successfully throw off their snow burdens spring after spring. The Western mountain hemlock, crouching on the most exposed ridges of the coast mountains, is a good example.

Hail beats off the leaves and tender shoots of trees, especially in the warmer states. It destroys flowers and unripe fruits, and bruises young growth.

Lightning shatters trees, and leaves them a prey to the attacks of insects and fungi. The chief harm caused by it is the starting of forest fires. Compared with this, the other damage it does is slight.

Winds lash the trees, breaking and maiming them. Hurricanes plough their paths through the woods. This exposes the trees left on the border of the swath to a new danger. Their support on the open side is gone; they fall by reason of the inadequacy of their roots to hold them securely in the ground. Roots do not go deep unless they must. Winds fan small fires into conflagrations. Beneficent carriers of pollen and distributors of seed, they also carry infection from diseased trees to sound ones, lodging spores in fresh wounds to eat down to the tree's heart or to prey upon leaf or twig or bark. Each species finds its habitat.

Fungi are flowerless vegetable organisms that multiply by spores. The mushrooms are the familiar fruiting organs of underground species. Rust, mildew, blight and rot of fruit or of wood are also among the well-known fungous growths that disfigure trees. The shelf fungi are the largest. Many kinds of destroying fungi may attack a single tree. Every enfeebled tree is increasingly vulnerable. Dead trees are gradually devoured by fungous organisms.

Protection against fungous diseases is not practicable yet in the forests. In orchards and home grounds and parks spraying is used as a preventive. Compounds of copper destroy the spores of fungi. It is asserted that one part of copper sulphate in ten thousand parts of water will prevent the germination of a spore of apple scab or pear-leaf blight. Lime water is added to keep the copper sulphate from burning the foliage. Copper, lime, and a large proportion of water make the so-called "Bordeaux mixture"— the standard fungicide in the orchards and vineyards of Europe and America. Two or three sprayings a year, the first just before the leaves open, will keep a healthy forest tree free from fungous troubles, while neighbour trees and their fruit are badly damaged by rot and other fungous attacks.

Bacterial diseases that enter the growing shoots of trees and develop within them are well illustrated by the "fire blight" of the pear. No fungicide can reach and check this disorder. The affected parts should be cut off and burned. Often burning the whole tree is the only safe method, as otherwise contagion will spread to other trees.

Constitutional diseases are found among trees, as well as in the human family, and no explanation of their causes nor hint of proper treatment has been discovered. "Peach yellows" is an example. It is the moral, if not the legal, obligation of every owner of a tree thus afflicted to dig it out and burn it, root and branch, in order that the disease may be kept from spreading. Tree diseases are not all disseminated by the wind. Some live underground, carrying infection by contact of root tips from unsound to sound trees.

Insects form a large body of the enemies of trees, inflicting untold damage each year upon orchards and forests, and upon trees everywhere. Each species has its insect enemies, not one, but more—often many. There are *borers* that infest the solid wood, channelling it and ruining it for timber, or working just under the bark, sapping the cambium, which is the tree's life. Some borers work in the twigs, causing the young shoots to die

515

and snap off. Black locust, one of the most valuable post timbers, is ruined wherever it grows now in the East by the locust borer.

Sucking insects are a vast aggregation of species whose bond of similarity is the beak or proboscis, by means of which they puncture the skin of fruits, leaves, twigs or roots and suck the juices there found. To this class belong the deadly scale insects, the plant lice, bark lice, true bugs, weevils, etc.

Chewing insects eat the substance of the leaf or other parts. The caterpillars of many butterflies, moths and beetles are chewers. Borers belong to this class.

It is quite out of the question to attempt in this volume a discussion of a subject so vast as the insect enemies of trees and the methods science has devised to combat them. Horticulture has led the way, of course. Publications covering all that is known on the subject are issued by the Department of Agriculture. Experiment stations in the different states are investigating this subject and reporting progress in bulletins, which anyone within the state may have for the asking. Besides, a growing body of literature on the subject is being issued by various publishers of scientific books.

Spraying and fumigation are the two methods now in use for the wholesale destruction of insects. They are developed to a high degree by fruit growers. Power spraying has been introduced by park commissioners in a few large cities for the protection of shade trees. It promises to grow in popularity wherever public spirit is strong and trees are threatened, as they are with the gypsy-moth plague near Boston. Study of the life history of different insects and fungi reveals their various weak points and helpless stages. The principles and practice of spraying depend for success upon this intimate knowledge.

Boring insects cannot be reached by spraying. They are dug out of fruit trees or destroyed by running a wire up the burrows. It is the grub that does the damage.

Chewing insects that live on trees are killed by spraying poison on their food. Paris green, dissolved in water, and arsenate of lead are commonly used. The younger insects are sprayed the better.

Sucking insects are killed by spraying with kerosene and water, or with an emulsion of whale-oil soap, and with lime and sulphur washes. The oil chokes the breathing tubes which are along the sides of the body. The whale-oil soap chokes and is also injurious to the delicate body wall. So is the lime and sulphur solution. Scale insects, plant lice and all soft-bodied insects of whatever eating habits are thus treated.

Fumigation chokes the insects with poisonous gas. Hydro-cyanic-acid gas, confined by a canvas tent that completely covers a tree, destroys all insect life in a few minutes. This is an expensive method, but it is used in orange groves in California as the best means of checking scale insects. As these insects do not fly nor walk, but settle down after birth, a tree once cleared of the nuisance is not likely to become infested again for some time.

MAN'S DAMAGE TO THE FORESTS

Clearing of wooded lands was the pioneer's duty and necessity. He had to make room for the civilisation that followed him. The Eastern country was so generally covered with forests that farms could be made only by clearing the land. This made trees the chief enemy to be overthrown—the greatest of all the weeds that the farmer battled against.

Wasteful lumbering came next, and took the best logs from the virgin forests, leaving all the "slash" behind to dry and feed terrible forest fires. An unreasonable rate of taxation discouraged the buying and holding of lands by lumber companies. When the sawmills left, the land was waste, unfit for the use of man.

Fire is the greatest enemy of forests in this country. Hunters carelessly leave their campfires still alive; cinders from locomotives ignite dry rubbish; farmers burning brush over cleared land let the fires get beyond control. Spite against the owners sometimes finds expression in firing a forest. Lightning sets fires and winds spread them.

Fortunes are swept away each year in standing timber; lives and property are destroyed in the track of the fire. Young growth of seedling trees, the forests of the future, are wiped out. Tree seeds are consumed, and the leaf mould, that precious porous blanket that holds the food and drink for all the trees, that is the nursery of seedlings and the anchorage of the old trees—this is reduced to an ash heap. All the organisms of the soil that converted the forest litter into loam are killed; and the litter is also gone, so that there is no means of restoring promptly the supply of humus necessary for seed to germinate.

Trees fall over in such a "burn." Grass, one of the forest's ancient enemies, creeps in. The sun and wind steal the soil water: it runs off as floods in spring rains, overflowing streams that run dry in summer. Gullies are formed where the cracked soil washes. Insects and fungi attack trees, young and old, which were crippled but not killed by the fire. A severe fire destroys the forest equilibrium utterly, reducing the area to a desert state.

Fires under control are sometimes justified in forests of indifferent quality. Tracts covered with blueberry and blackberry are systematically burned in Maine and other states because the new growth fruits better than the old canes. In other regions forests are fired to open them and improve the grazing. A great many fires are set for this purpose by sheep men in remote mountainous woodlands belonging to the Government or to private parties who know nothing of this systematic wholesale stealing.

PROTECTION AGAINST FIRE

Practically no attention has been given to providing fire lanes through American forests for the checking of fires when they start. This belongs to intensive forestry, and we have not come to that yet. Consequently fires find us unprepared. A small ground fire can usually be put out near its beginning by beating it with branches bearing mops of green leaves. A narrow track of dirt or sand thrown about the burning area will help to keep it within bounds. Throwing earth or sand on the smouldering leaf mould is one of the best means of choking out fire. If there is time, a belt can be burned across the path of the fire which will end it. Digging narrow trenches is also effective.

Fires that sweep the forest crown can be stayed only by openings that they cannot bridge—broad, natural fire lanes. With a wind blowing, such a conflagration flings firebrands in all directions, lighting new fires in the rubbish that litters the forest floor.

Fighting a forest fire is almost hopeless after it once gets under way. A ground fire may be impossible to locate, though the smoke indicates its existence, and approximately its place. Slash makes progress and fire fighting in the woods very toilsome work. After a fire is believed to be extinguished it often smoulders and breaks out with renewed violence later on. Or it may seem under control over most of its area, and by suddenly climbing a dead tree be out of reach, start a fresh blaze among the treetops and threaten a much larger territory. The broad-leaved trees are less likely to spread a fire than the inflammable, resinous conifers.

Grazing as practised in this country is sometimes as destructive to forests as fire. *Over-grazing* is the proper term, for a flock of sheep is generally kept in a section of woods until everything green within reach has disappeared. Sheep nibble and gnaw and crop roots and saplings, and their little feet pack and tear open the leaf mould, trampling out the life of all young growth they do not eat. They are especially destructive to young coniferous growth. A lease of a tract for grazing generally means desolation in the wake of the flock, as far as all undergrowth is concerned. Government lands have been grazed to their lasting damage by sheep men without leave from any authority. This is being stopped wherever reservations are patrolled.

Cattle do less harm in grazing than sheep and goats. They do not keep so close together, their feet do not cut into the soil so deep, nor do they strip all growths clean as they go, unless driven to it by drought. Horses do less harm than cattle. Hogs prevent much young growth by eating tree seeds, especially those of beech, oak and other nut trees.

Grazing should be prohibited in young woods, and permitted but sparingly in old forests. In fact, a forest should have no openings in its roof, and so no grass on the forest floor.

ENEMIES OF CITY TREES

Trees in cities lead a hard life. The air is charged with smoke, soot and noxious gases. These clog the leaf doorways, thus interfering with the tree's life processes. Paved streets and sidewalks prevent the proper ventilation and watering of the soil. The roots need to breathe as well as the leaves. Leaks in sewer pipes and gas mains often suffocate a tree through its roots.

Regrading and filling in change the ground level, and trees are left with roots exposed or buried deeper than before. Either

519

is a distinct damage, which lowers the tree's vitality, and in extreme cases kills it outright. The soil of towns is often "made," containing refuse, such as tin cans, glass bottles, ashes and cinders —anything but good soil. Roots obliged to batten on such pasturage can hardly be expected to keep the top growing well.

Excavations for buildings and for the laying of sewer pipes, water and gas mains generally ignore the trees whose roots lie in the way. Whatever interferes is cut out without thought of the rights of the community in the trees that give beauty and shade to its streets.

Horses gnaw the bark and kill by girdling unguarded trees used as hitching posts in front of stores. This may be seen in small towns where no public sentiment in defense of street trees has been aroused. Bruising and scraping of the bark by contact with loaded wagons and other heavy vehicles produce the disabled, ugly trees one sees along streets and in congested market places.

GUARDS FOR STREET TREES

The cheap and effective roll of heavy woven wire is often seen in this country. The wooden boxing of erect slats is strong but ugly. Iron rods secured by iron hoops are developed in ornamental designs in many of the parks of European cities, and oftenest in connection with an iron grill or circular openwork plate that lies under the tree in paved streets that have had their grade raised. The tree has its old level for the space of the diameter of the grill, through which air and water are admitted to the soil about the roots. It is common in more obscure streets to use wicker guards or to make jackets of small upright poles wired securely together around young trees. Old trees are often merely set around with short stone pillars to keep vehicles away. Grills and guards of iron around park trees are sometimes made less conspicuous by a seat that encircles the tree protected. On country roads in France thorn branches are tied on young trees as guards.

In all cases guards should be roomy enough to allow of many years of growth before they could fit snugly. As these protections are permanent necessities to exposed trees they should be strongly made, and secured to the trees so that they will not work loose.

INJURIES TO TREES FROM ELECTRIC WIRES

The damage done to roadside trees offsets to an alarming degree the benefits derived by the public from the telephone and the trolley. The poles are set in the line of the trees, and the wires threaded between them. The limbs that might strike the wire when the wind is high are hacked off. Miles of road are lined with trees ruthlessly beheaded and utterly ruined under the direction of the foreman in charge of the pole setting. The workmen proceed rapidly through a section of country, passing from one property to another. They keep an eye out for objections; the owners could make them a great deal of trouble. But rarely is there concerted action, unless it be a mass meeting to bewail the damage *after* it is done. Then things settle down, and the poor maimed trees do their best to heal their wounds and to grow new tops. As they reach up they encounter the wires, and this interferes with the service. The offending trees are shorn again. They finally become stunted old pollards, throwing up groves of straight water sprouts, year by year, if they are by nature inclined to sprout from stubs.

"Burns" that cost the lives of large limbs are proved to result from contact with electric wires passing through treetops. Proofs are also indubitable that trees are killed by the same cause. Investigations made by the Experiment Station of the Massachusetts Agricultural College in 1903 led to the following conclusions (Bulletin No. 91):

1. The high resistance offered by trees serves as a protection against death from an electrical contact.*

2. There are cases where the direct current, used in operating street railways, has killed large shade trees.

3. Electrical currents act as stimulants to growth up to a certain degree of intensity. Beyond that degree, growth is retarded, and the death current is the maximum.

4. The greatest damage caused by alternating and direct currents is by local burnings. The stronger the voltage the greater the injury.

5. There is practically little or no leakage from wires during

* Wood is a non-conductor when dry, but when wet it is a partial conductor. After a rain one often sees sparks in trees caused by electric wires that touch the branches.

521

dry weather. In wet weather a film of water covers the tree and leakage is likely to occur. If insulation is defective and contact between wire and tree exists, grounding results, and the tree is burned where the wire touches it.

6. While no instance has shown death produced by alternating current, yet the proofs are absolute that this cause maims and disfigures young trees so badly that it amounts to their destruction.

7. Arc lights in close proximity to trees cannot be discovered to be accountable for any sickliness these trees exhibit. Poverty of the soil, paving, etc., are generally the causes.

8. Linemen's spurs do great damage to the bark of young trees.

9. Wounds caused by climbing and ill-advised pruning and by burning leave trees an easy prey to insect and fungous enemies.

10. There is no permanent recovery possible to the trees while the wires remain in place and in use.

What will mitigate this trouble?

1. In cities, the laying of wires underground.

2. In villages, carrying the wires across the back of lots instead of the front.

3. Lifting wires higher by using taller poles.

4. Giving a competent committee power to act for the community to prevent the defacing of roadside trees by corporations owning franchises, and ignoring the law and the rights of property owners along their rights of way.

5. Forcing corporations to put necessary pruning in the hands of competent men.

6. Forcing trolley and electric light companies to preserve the beauty of the highway, even at a sacrifice of short cuts and conveniences they customarily exact without payment from a long-suffering public.

7. Organising in every community in the interests of civic beauty, with a strong, fearless committee to defend the trees against the vandalism of pole-setting, wire-stringing corporations. Let them be well informed on the legal side of their cause, and vigilant to have the law enforced.

8. Emphasising in and out of season the fact that the beautifying of grounds adds to the market value of real estate. Ordering their rights of way well planted and well kept is not mere philanthropy on the part of railway corporations. It is paying business. Trolley companies may eventually learn to count avenues of trees as valuable assets.

PART III
THE USES OF WOOD

CHAPTER I: THE USES OF WOOD

"It is certain and demonstrable that all arts and artisans whatsoever must fail and cease, if there were no timber and wood in a nation (for he that shall take his pen, and begin to set down what art, mystery, or trade belonging any way to human life, could be maintained and exercised without wood, will quickly find that I speak no paradox). . . . We had better be without gold than without timber."—*John Evelyn.*

THIS is the age of steel. Yet it is not to be expected that metal will take the place of wood much more than now. Although steel frames have replaced timbers in ships, bridges and many-storied buildings, the demand for wood in the bulk of the world's industries grows stronger and prices are rising. The fires of factory, mill and household in this country are more than half of them fed to-day with wood. Coal (a fossil wood), oil and gas, happily come in to check the too rapid consumption of our forests for fuel.

Trees grow, therefore wood is cheaper than metals. It is easily worked with tools into desired shapes and sizes. It is held securely by nails and by glue. It is practically permanent when protected by paint; under water or in the ground it outlasts metal. Its strength and lightness adapt it to varied uses. Its lightness makes it easy to handle. It preserves the flavour of wines as no other material can do. It is a non-conductor of heat and electricity. Many woods are marked by patterns of infinite variety and beauty, whose very irregularities constitute an abiding charm. To this is added a fine blending of colours and a lustre when polished that give woods a place in the decorative arts that can be taken by no other substance.

Precious woods, worth their weight in gold, are not unknown to-day. A wagonload of satinwood worth $75,000 was delivered to an English furniture manufactory recently. It was cut for veneer work, sixteen thin sheets to the inch. The price paid per square foot was one pound sterling. Peacocks' feathers, arabesques, and wonderful mythological beasts are revealed by the saw that cuts through the gnarled butts of maple, birch and

527

yew, and through the burls that stand out like excrescenses on ash and other trees. Imperfections in the normal grain are responsible for these figures and colouring. It is the sawing that makes the most of these good points. In woods like oak there are broad, radial bands of "medullary rays," which quarter-sawing reveals. They are fully exposed by sawing through the centre of a log, and when polished gleam with "mirrors," the cabinetmaker's delight. The larger the log the larger proportion of this valuable mirrored wood it will yield.

White oak, which contains a large percentage of pith rays and reveals these mirrors to perfection when "quarter-sawed," is now largely used in veneering. So are the curly and bird's-eye maples and birches, and the exotic woods, mahogany, rosewood and satinwood. The layer glued on the cheap frames of piano cases and all manner of furniture is often but a sixteenth of an inch in thickness. Black-walnut stumps are bought for veneer wherever they can be found.

It is hopeless to try to list the uses of wood—even of our native kinds—with fulness and accuracy. The lumber trade is in unstable equilibrium. Certain kinds of lumber are giving out— the black walnut, for instance. Substitution of cheaper woods by furniture factories is a symptom that the supply of good lumber is running low and prices high. A few years ago red oak was discarded. Only white oak was suitable for furniture and oak interior finish. To-day no distinction is made between these two species. White oak is scarce and is used for the most expensive work. Red oak is the bulk of the supply. To the general public oak is oak, and the manufacturer and retailer are not inclined to bother the buyer with hair-splitting distinctions. In fact, most "oak" furniture that sells at low prices is elm, whose coarse, muddy grain is a poor imitation of oak.

Spruce forests were ignored by lumbermen and esteemed worthless by the general public twenty-five years ago. Then the pulp industry sprung up, and spruce wood made the best paper. The pulp men bought tracts of spruce forests, and the mills now consume thousands of acres a year. So great has been the drain upon these forests that already pulp makers are looking to Canada as the source of future supplies. Regenerative forestry is being put into force in many thousand acres to maintain the spruce crop on the same land. Spruce wood brings $6 to $7 per cord at the pulp mills, and even spruce stumps are bought at \$15 per thousand feet. This revolution of values brings spruce up until it costs more than Southern pine in the market—a condition of affairs unthinkable in the lumber trade a few years ago.

Paper making has raised cottonwood and other soft, white woods to a rank above ordinary hardwoods, among which they were counted by foresters as mere nurse trees and forest weeds. A state forester recently said: "If I could change all the trees in the state forests to poplars I would add greatly to the wealth these acres represent. The pulp and paper mills would take every stick we could cut and beg for more. We could set our own price."

Twenty years ago white pine was still king of soft-wood lumbers. Its day is past, partly owing to the exhaustion of the virgin growth in great Northern pineries, partly by reason of the exploitation of Southern pines. The "black sap" of Southern pines, seasoned slowly in the lumber pile, darkened the wood and made it impossible as a competitor of white pine in the markets. But kiln-drying makes yellow pine white, so that the yellow pines of the South now furnish handsome flooring, interior finish and general building material in vast quantities. It is also used for furniture and for ties.

FOREST BY-PRODUCTS

The Naval-Stores Industry. Turpentine gathering in the longleaf pine woods began with the settlement of the country, and forms one of its greatest forest industries. Vast quantities of tar, rosin and turpentine have been consumed, chiefly in shipyards in this and other countries, until the steel craft replaced the wooden. Now other industries consume the surplus output of these turpentine orchards.

A pocket several inches wide and deep is cut near the base of a tree. It holds two or three pints of the resin.* The bark and the outer wood to the depth of an inch are chipped off for a considerable distance above the pocket. The exposed wood bleeds resin, which is regularly dipped from the pocket by a man with a ladle

---

Resin is the crude liquid ; *rosin* is the hard, brittle substance left after the turpentine is extracted.

and a pail, who gathers the flow and carries it in barrels to the still. Once a week from March till November the chipping is repeated, and two inches are added to the height of the chipped area. If this fresh wounding did not occur, the flow would cease by the hardening of the resin.

One man tends ten thousand "boxes," and should get forty barrels at each round, or "dip." Eight to ten circuits are made for collecting in the thirty-two weeks the resin flows. The hard gum that accumulates in cold weather is also gathered. The yield of "dip" to "scrape" in this first season is as four to one. As the trees are drained, the surface exposed, becoming larger, yields more of the hardened gum, and the grade of the products deteriorates. The fourth year the orchard is abandoned by the largest operators, who move to pastures new. Small owners box their trees much longer, rest them a few years, then box again on bark before untouched.

In the still, the resin is melted and the volatile turpentine driven off and collected in barrels. The fire goes out and the residue in the retort is drawn off through strainers into barrels, where it solidifies when cool into rosin. The price of turpentine varies from twenty-eight cents to forty cents per gallon; that of rosin is about $2 per barrel.

The wastefulness of the old boxing methods shocks every intelligent observer. Better ways are being introduced, which, while more expensive, yet pay for the trouble in the generous increase in yield and the improving of the quality of the turpentine and rosin. The cup devised by Mr. Schuler (see Bulletin 13, Division of Forestry) takes the place of the deep, injurious pocket made in old-fashioned boxing and does away with dirt and chips in the crude turpentine.

While the timber is not directly injured by the boxing, the pine orchards fall a prey to fungi and insects, the trunks are weakened by deep boxes, and the wounds destroy the cambium, semi-girdling the trees and necessarily lowering their vitality. The demoralised condition of an abandoned orchard under the ordinary careless management points to the trees' early death.

Pine tar has long been extracted from the longleaf by piling dry wood, limbs, roots, and stumps, cut in small sizes, closely in a clay-lined pit, covering it with sods and earth, and burning it with smouldering fires lit below at small apertures. A passageway provided from the pit leads the oozing resin to the barrels. After a week or more this pine tar begins to flow and continues for several weeks. The quality is much lower than that produced in retorts, for it is mixed with dirt. Boiling down pine tar until it loses one-third its weight makes a sticky mass called pitch. The wood in the pit is transformed into charcoal.

This pit method of extracting tar and making charcoal is a crude prototype of the process of dry or destructive distillation of wood.

The Dry-Distillation Process.—What the oil mill is to the cotton field the still is to the forest. Its work is to dispose of the refuse and to turn it into gold. Crooked branches, knots, root stubs—sound wood the lumberman ignores—is cut up and packed into a retort. A furnace underneath heats this air-tight chamber to 600°–800° F. The water goes off as steam in a coil or worm, upon which cold water is played in order to cool and condense its contents. A wood gas is next driven off. Then a brownish liquid flows out. This contains wood vinegar, used extensively in dyeworks, and acetic acid, which is made into vinegar. There is also present wood alcohol, useful to the manufacturing chemist, and in many other industries. Tar and creosote are also yielded by maple, beech, and birch, the preferred woods at the regular acid mills. After twelve hours, the retort is emptied and refilled. The wood is found to be transformed into charcoal. Many acid mills are located in New York and Pennsylvania.

In the longleaf pine woods the crooked, knotty top stuff and root stubs are the richest in resin. These yield in distillation the greatest quantity of tar and turpentine and the highest qualities of these products, also the best charcoal. Beside this process the old method of burning the wood in kilns or pits in hillsides and ladling the tar into barrels was most slovenly and wasteful. Many valuable volatile substances that are now captured in the coil formerly escaped in smoke.

The most remarkable invention is a method by which ethyl-alcohol, the highest grade known, is derived by distillation from sawdust, and an equally high grade of charcoal is left. It is the Classen method, introduced from Germany a year ago, and it promises to utilise the greatest nuisances of the sawmill, the sawdust and slabs.

531

SOME INTERESTING MINOR INDUSTRIES

"Top stuff" in European forests is cut and bound in neat bundles of fagots. Even small twigs are utilised as fuel. In the Southern pineries a similar industry has cut "fat pine" into small kindling wood for use in Northern cities.

Brushwood is used in the construction of earthworks and jetties to keep the channels of rivers narrow and deep. The lower course of the Mississippi has been improved by sinking out from shore latticework of limbs bound together. These sink, become loaded with silt, and act as a barrier to prevent the crumbling of the banks. The force of great waves, striking a latticework of branches, is broken into innumerable harmless ripples. Jetties are much cheaper to build than retaining walls.

The great wickerware industry of Europe, now beginning to establish itself in this country, consumes only the year's growth on certain supple varieties of willow.

Young growth of white birch that springs up in low ground in New England is being consumed in quantities by spool factories and manufactories of toys and other small wares. The trees are used when scarcely larger than cornstalks in some of these factories.

Christmas trees for cities of the East strip hundreds of acres of young hemlock and balsam firs each year. In the South young longleaf pines are shipped North, and hollies and magnolias of all sizes are cut and stripped of their branches for Christmas decoration.

In all this we see that the lumberman has left behind much forest wealth, and people are learning to gather up the refuse and turn it to account. The small sawmill is having its day in many wooded regions of the country, making money in ways which the big mill overlooked. There is much good stuff in slabs, albeit sap wood is less sound and harder to season than heart wood. Lath and shingles can be got out of logs unfit for first-class boards. Tops of trees contain posts, stakes and hop and bean poles. There is no better firewood than limbs from one to two inches in diameter. Fuel which consumes much crooked hardwood-stuff yields at last one of the best of fertilisers.

Tanbark comes from many oaks and from hemlock in this country. Chestnut and the black oaks are richest in tannin.

The tanbark oak of California is exceptionally rich, and its extermination by peelers is inevitable unless protective measures are adopted soon. The same may be said of hemlock in many regions, though hemlock has a much more extensive range. In sections of Pennsylvania and New England hillsides are covered with peeled hemlocks of all ages, the trees being destroyed for their bark alone.

There are many tropical trees and other plants that yield tannin. Quebracho wood, a South American tree, is the source of tannin extract that is imported by American tanneries to a considerable extent. Our native black mangrove or blackwood, on the Florida coast and neighbouring keys and in the delta of the Mississipi, is a valuable source of tannin, though it grows in inaccessible swamps, full of fever and other dangers.

The method of getting out hemlock bark is described in the chapter: "A Lumber Camp of To-day."

Among the products of native trees the nuts are important. Their food value is coming to be appreciated at home and abroad. The hickories include the pecan and two shagbarks, both nuts of commercial importance. Walnuts and chestnuts are secondary. Beech and acorn mast fatten hogs and furnish a living to innumerable birds and wild game, as also do berries, plums and other tree fruits. Flowers of locust and basswood, plum and cherry pasture honey bees. So do many trees of less conspicuous inflorescence.

Gums of balsam fir and other conifers, sweet gum and wax myrtle, berries of buckthorns, wild cherry and holly, roots of sassafras, twigs of witch hazel, all yield drugs. Our Southern silva furnishes valuable dyewoods. Sugar from the sap of maples forms an important and delicious food product.

In the Old World and in the tropics are trees whose great value to the human race is suggested by the mere mention of their names. The cinchona tree yields quinine from its bark. The juice of certain trees hardens into rubber. Para, the Brazilian seaport, is the great distributor of rubber to the world, and the silvas of the Amazon the great producers. Lacquer varnish is the juice of a sumach in Japan. Nutmeg and mace and cloves and allspice grow on trees in tropical countries. The palms feed, clothe and house people.

It is an endless story—the useful products of trees, cultivated

533

and growing wild on the earth. The tropical woods are full of undiscovered possibilities. Our own rich forest flora has but begun to show its value to man.

THE FOREST AS A UNIT

In a literal and an emphatic sense the wooden walls of a nation are its forests. The trees on mountain slopes restrain the waterflow in the valleys, preventing flood and drought, and thereby hoarding for cities their supply of water. Trees temper climate, drain swamps, add a stimulating tonic to the air, and take from it the poisonous carbonic-acid gas. The pine forests are sought by invalids for the healing of lung troubles in every country. Our Adirondacks and the Colorado mountains have their proto-types in the pine-clad health resorts of southwestern France and the region around Baden in Germany, whose famous Black Forest has a balsamic breath.

European nations that have cut down their forests and failed to store them have proved their national weakness and their dependence upon wiser neighbours. The Mediterranean countries are among the foolish—buying lumber continually from Norway, Sweden and Germany, and suffering in climate, water supply and in the poverty of the peasant class, the results of having no home forests.

Tree roots are rock breakers, able to make their way even through granite boulders. The root hairs excrete an acid that eats away limestone and disintegrates rock particles, while the mighty pressure of growth is crowding the sides of cracks apart. In time, with water and frost and other forces co-operating, the forbidding rock ledges have a crumbling layer kept from blowing away by the falling leaves and sheltering undergrowth. The leaf carpet rots, earthworms mingle its substance with this "rock meal," and the name of the mixture is *soil*—broken-down vegetable and mineral substance yielding plant food to the hungry roots of trees.

Thus a forest makes soil, deepening and enriching it the more the roots take from it. "Virgin soil" is that which has been covered with trees for hundreds of years. Waste land moist enough to grow trees may be reclaimed by this agency in a few years. Even semi-arid regions will grow trees if only the proper ones are chosen. This is the lesson Kansas and Nebraska are learning after long experiment and repeated failure.

The meaning of trees in a landscape—the beauty value of them—is oftenest overlooked by those who have always seen them. When crossing such a monotonous stretch of treeless country as the plains of Arizona that wait for irrigation, the Easterner for the first time has a full appreciation of the beauty of his familiar wooded hillsides, and tree-lined streets. Out of homesickness for forest scenery, as well as the necessity for protection and wood supply, came the great tree-planting crusade that swept over the Middle West and will yet dot every state with homes surrounded by groves.

It is proper to recognise here the influence that men have unconsciously drunk in from trees. Myth and song have remembered and repeated the feelings of primitive races to whom trees gave shelter and raiment and food. The old Druids worshipping the oak expressed a veneration which we all inherit, whatever our race and line. Contact with trees is a purifying, uplifting experience. Work in the woods develops a hardy, clean and intelligent race. When we lose our wonted strength of mind and body go to to the woods to find it.

CHAPTER II: WOOD PRESERVATION

THE tendency of wood to rot when exposed to the weather, and especially when placed in contact with the soil, and when partially submerged in water, fresh or salt, is something everybody knows. Season a stick of timber, then build it into your house where it never gets damp and it is practically imperishable. But lay it in the sill, and unless the foundation is exceptionally high, dampness may creep up and fungous disease attack and ultimately destroy the timbers upon which your house rests. No matter how long the albuminous substance in the cells of sap wood has been dry and inert, moisture softens it and it becomes a favourable soil for wood-destroying fungi. Rot is the result. Every decayed twig in the woods is a menace to the healthy trees. In time it scatters disease far and wide.

A telegraph pole a few years old breaks off at the ground in a stiff wind storm. It is rotten to the heart. But the wood above ground is sound; so it is below the surface. This is not a marvel. Rot is an organism that breathes while it grows. Oxygen available for growth is not found far below the entrance. Rot is dependent on moisture; the wind keeps the exposed parts of the pole dry. Hence the rot is restricted to a narrow zone—the surface of the soil—and the broken ends show how far its growth has proceeded. Posts break off at the ground for like cause. Piles in wharves rot off at some point between high and low water mark. Railroad ties and paving blocks suffer a more general decadence. Mine timbers fall a prey to their own particular subterranean fungi.

Weathering boards turn grey in the alternation of sun and rain, heat and cold. The outer fibres weaken and disintegrate. Oak can be scraped off with the finger nail. Hornets chew it into pulp to build their paper castles.

The protection and preservation of wood has been one of the problems of civilisation. A vast body of experience has accumulated, and we are nearer to-day to a satisfactory, a trium-

536

phant, solution of the problem than ever before. Decay is something that enters wood from the outside, at some time. To prevent the entrance of the spores of the disease into sound timber is to save it. A protective covering that will effectively do this is the quest of science and of all the wood-consuming industries. One of the earliest hints came to men before the days of Plato and Aristotle. The lasting qualities of charred wood were observed. So they learned to char the lower parts of all stakes, posts and poles before setting them in the ground. The ancient practice is still held to in many regions. The timbers in salt mines last indefinitely. So the suggestion to soak posts in brine has been eagerly followed. But the salt soon leaches out in contact with soil water. Impregnation of timbers with chemicals has been practised commercially for about one hundred years. Numerous preparations and processes have been tried with varying success. Chloride of zinc and of mercury, sulphate of iron and of copper, and other things have had their advocates. Most of them fail because the preservatives are lost to the surrounding soil or water, in a short time. Some are too expensive to be practical. Impregnation by soaking, steeping, boiling and pressure has been tried. High temperature, while it produces thorough impregnation, has a disintegrating effect upon the wood fibres as a whole. Soaking takes too much time. Pressure requires elaborate and expensive machinery. Each seems to have its drawbacks.

Creosote oil, a by-product of illuminating gas, is believed now to be the best substance available for impregnation, and the following the best method of treating the timbers. Seasoned railroad ties are placed in a tank in the hot oil until a high temperature is reached. The oil is drawn off, and a cold supply pumped in. The sudden cooling and condensing of gases and vapour in the wood cells produce a vacuum suction, to which is added the force of capillarity. Thus oil is *forced* into the wood.

Creosote oil has the following good points: (1) It fills the cells with oil, thus keeping water out. (2) It does not leach or lose strength in water or soil. (3) It is a fungicide, and is also poisonous to boring insects and crustaceans, like the white ants, the ship worm, and the Limnoria, creatures that honeycomb furniture, ship bottoms and wharves, giving no visible warning until the structure is a wreck. Creosote prevents the rusting of spikes and nails driven into timbers treated. They remain tight whatever happens. Creosote can be thoroughly applied with moderate cheapness. It can be had in large quantities from gas works. The average tie of white oak costs sixty cents and thirty cents to lay it. Creosoting costs but twenty cents additional. Treated ties are still sound after untreated ones have been replaced several times.

A very fortunate coincidence was discovered in the course of the investigations on wood preservation. Hard woods, like white oak and longleaf pine, do not absorb preservatives as rapidly nor as thoroughly as cheaper, more porous woods, with thicker sap wood, like red oak and Cuban pine. Therefore, the cheap woods, well saturated, outlive the dear ones. White oak, for which railroads offer fifty cents a tie, will bring double that sum at the furniture factory. Railroads cannot longer afford to use white oak. Beech, properly impregnated, will outlast white oak. Its normal life of five years can be extended to twenty-five years.

The Bureau of Forestry, with the co-operation of railroad corporations in different sections of the country, has elaborate experiments in progress bearing upon the preservation of wood. The work is disinterested and scientific, and creosoting is the method that has proved best. The important railroad systems of England and the Continent have reached the same conclusion. Creosoting ties is there as much a matter of course as laying them. The higher prices and greater scarcity of timber in Europe explain why they are so far in advance of us in the practice of wood preservation.

The importance of thoroughly seasoning wood before impregnating it with chemicals cannot be over-estimated. Green wood, full of sap, resists the entrance of any substance, especially oils. Even if this difficulty could be surmounted, the seasoning of wood produces cracks through which decay gets in, and impregnation counts for naught. Before treating, railroad ties are bored with holes for the entrance of the spikes, so that even these small apertures offer no untreated surfaces for water containing disease spores to enter.

Creosoting paving blocks, piles for bridges, wharves and cribs and the exposed hulls of wooden vessels is successfully and extensively done nowadays. The ship worm does not like the taste of treated wood, though this attenuated crustacean bores his way through the hardest of wood (except green heart) that is not medicated to discourage him.

Trees that fall in bogs and lakes lie too far down for destruction by fungous organisms. The water-soaked fibres have their protoplasmic contents dissolved out, and mineral substances held in the water are deposited by slow degrees. Bog oak of Ireland is black as ebony from bark to pith. It is also heavy by the weight of the mineral substance that impregnates its cells. Wood impregnation by natural processes reaches its highest perfection in the petrifactions that occur. The petrified forest of Arizona contains trees which preserve their form and structure, even to wood rings, but silica has been infiltrated to the utmost cell, turning the whole tree into agate, chalcedony or other forms of quartz. Montana has an extensive forest of trees turned to stone of a translucent, opaline character. The colours are blue, white and smoky black. Doctor Merrill of the National Museum found this forest in 1903, and his report wisely withholds its location. It is scarcely desirable that this remarkable opalised wood should be nabbed by a syndicate and cut up into paper weights—a fate that has overtaken the fossil forest of Arizona.

Paint gives effectual protection to wood exposed to the weather, with its alternation of heat and cold, sun and rain. It needs renewing every few years. The basis of paint is oil—pure linseed oil being the best. Ground pigments mixed into the oil until it has the consistency of rich cream supply colour and filling. The paint applied, the oil soaks in and fills the wood cells, while the pigments form a protective layer, or film, over the surface. When this layer cracks and scales off, a fresh painting is needed. Oil alone is a protective covering. Or oil may be left out, and pigments dissolved in other liquids may be applied. Whitewash is a familiar example of this treatment. All such applications last but a short time. In the chapter that follows some account is given of the processes that preserve wood and at the same time beautify it.

CHAPTER III: THE FINISHING OF WOODS

THE various processes to which wood is treated under this head accomplish one or more of these results: (1) They preserve it; (2) they make it easy to keep clean; (3) they beautify it, by bringing out the grain or by covering it with a uniform colour.

Paint has long been the standard finish for woods of cheap quality exposed to the air, for inside and outside work. It is a preservative, filling the pores of the wood with pigments mixed with oil; and it satisfies the tastes of all, being made in an infinite variety of colours, shades and tints. It conceals knots, cracks and other defects, producing a smooth, shining, uniform surface.

"Graining" is a base imitation of the natural grain of oak and other woods. As a child I watched a man at this work. Yellow paint had dried fairly on a cheap, white-pine door. A light brushing of brown paint was spread unevenly over one panel. Then one thumb, wrapped with a rag, was dipped into the brown paint, and a knot with radiating brown streaks was set in each end of the panel. One or two scattered little knots were thrown in for good measure. Then the artistic thumb retired, and a comb came into commission. The blade of it drawn over the plain brown field scraped off narrow lines of the dark colour and left the yellow showing through in parallel, alternating lines. An agitated sidewise motion of the comb produced a "curly" patch on a field intended to imitate the grain of oak with its spring and summer wood of alternating yellow and brown.

There may be such a thing as *good* graining. I can see only ugly, insincere imitation in it. A painted door makes no pretence to be a hard wood, therefore it is honest. A grained door is not.

Staining. Pigments dissolved in water or in other liquids stain wood to any desired colour. Nut galls and various dyestuffs are used for this purpose. Creosote oil, properly coloured, is a popular stain for shingles. It is a preservative, and gives a soft, dull finish, being absorbed without concealing the texture of the wood. This sort of staining is a far more artistic colour process than painting, when the outside finish of houses is considered. Being a rough finish, it is not employed on interiors unless a rustic scheme is being followed.

Staining is also an important part of the finishing of expensive hardwood interiors. Even the best white oak is treated to a little yellow to give it a creamier colour. "Weathered oak" owes its age to fumes of ammonia or to burnt umber as a rule, and Flemish oak to darker dyes. The bog oak of Ireland is black as soot, but an imitation is produced by staining any of our oaks black. It takes a connoisseur to tell the genuine from the bogus. Ebony and teak are easily imitated. Elm masquerades as oak, birch as mahogany. Yet staining is a legitimate practice. The handsomest of mahogany has had a little Venetian red worked into its pores to brighten the grain and make the colour even.

Filling. Coarse grained woods are very porous and easily dented, and do not take a good polish unless a filler is used. A great many different substances are used to replace the air in these wood cells. In fact there are very few woods that are not both filled and stained before they are ready to be polished. "White fillers" are tinted before they are applied. Some woods are filled with plaster of Paris, moistened with water or spirits after being rubbed into the surface as a powder. Whiting and pumice are also used. Glue and patent wood sizings, even tallow with plaster of Paris, are used. A popular filler is ordinary varnish. When the filler is dry the surface is hard and ready for the finishing process.

Varnishing. Varnish is made by dissolving shellac in spirits. The volatile liquid elements dry away, and a shiny, hard coating of the shellac remains. It shows white lines when scratched with a pin. Varnish combined with stain is a popular finish for cheap woodwork. The best varnish is made of white shellac; through it the grain of the wood shows as if through a pane of polished glass.

After the filler, which raises the grain into a rough surface, there is a rubbing down with pumice or fine sandpaper. Otherwise the varnish emphasises the roughness.

Polishing. Every fine piece of furniture or of woodwork is polished to bring out the beauty of its grain and colouring. The marvellous lustre of piano cases and rich furniture is due as much to the faithful rubbing with an old rag as to any other trick

541

of the trade. Not just *any* old rag, but one specialised and mellowed by long years of use. "French polish" is the highest art in the finishing of woods.

Good taste prefers the soft, waxy lustre to the gleaming surface of new varnish. A rag. with rotten stone to dip it in occasionally, and patient, long-continued rubbing, eliminates "the vulgar shine." Soft pine, stained red, varnished, then "pummied" (rubbed with powdered pumice stone), gives a very satisfactory cherry finish.

Wax polishing is a dull finish, made simply by saturating the surface of coarse-grained woods with melted beeswax mixed with turpentine. Rosin added makes a harder surface. One rag rubs in the polish. Another wipes off all excess. A third rag polishes the surface. It is a laborious method, but it pays in utility and looks. Oak dining tables, if varnished, turn white where hot dishes touch them. Wax polishing is not discoloured by heat, so it is preferable.

Oil polishing is very often seen in the finishing of handsome hard pine. As much pure linseed oil as the smoothed surface will absorb; then rub, rub, rub! This brightens the rich orange red of the grain and makes the intricate and beautiful patterns of it stand out with striking clearness through the transparent dressing. A soft lustre follows persistent rubbing. This process is by no means restricted to pine. Any wood with handsome grain warrants the oil finish.

Glazing is a process used in finishing fretwork which cannot be reached by the polishing rag or that is too frail to be rubbed. Spindles of fancy chairs and cabinets, grilled archways and the like require it, while the rest of the article is polished. Inlay work is often glazed. The preparation is made of some choice gum dissolved in methylated spirits. This enamelling of wood to a china-like finish is comparable to the lacquer work of the Japanese artisans, a secret process which produces, from the milky juice of a tree closely related to our own poison sumach, a coating that resembles patent leather on boxes and innumerable fancy articles made out of the soft, white magnolia wood.

FLOWER AND BUD OF GREAT RHODODENDRON (*Rhododendron maximum*)

CHAPTER IV: WOODEN PAPER

ONCE upon a time paper grew on trees, and within the past quarter of a century the world has turned again to the forests as the source of its supply. Thin sheets of the inner bark of birch in America and Europe, and of the paper mulberry in Asiatic countries preserved the crude characters by which primitive peoples expressed themselves. The names—*beech, beece, boc, bok, buch, book*—link the past with the present in the races sprung from Teutonic stock. They sent messages from tribe to tribe written in symbols on thin beechen boards—their first written communications. Afterward, the old Scandinavian and Icelandic runes were written on the same sort of wood, and many boards constituted a *book*. The word *"liber,"* Latin for "book," is the name of the inner bark of trees; in botany the term has always been used. The word "library," therefore, has a long and interesting pedigree.

The reed, papyrus, was harvested for paper in the days of antiquity, along the banks of the river Nile. Thin sheets of the pith of this slender plant formed the books of early Egypt. Libraries of these ancient writings were preserved in the Pyramids. The narrow, thin strips of pith were joined by overlapping their margins and by lining each sheet thus formed with a similar one whose strips were at right angles with the strips of the first one. The two sheets, made one by pressure, formed a page beside which the boards of the beechen books seem very clumsy indeed.

The fibres of cotton, wool, flax, and silk, gathered as rags, cleaned, bleached and shredded, furnished the better qualities of paper in later times. They still do. But such paper is expensive. The crude materials cannot be gathered in sufficient quantity to supply the demand for it. Straw, hemp and other grass fibres serve for paper of coarse grades.

To-day, as of old, our paper grows on trees, for nothing has been discovered to substitute for rags; so wooden paper, not so good, but the best thing so far to be had, has come to fill the demand. No longer the *liber*, merely, but the whole bulk of the wood substance is used.

The first manufacturers of paper from wood pulp were the white-faced hornets, whose grey nests are sedulously let alone by the sophisticated roamer of the woods in summer, and often ignorantly, in winter, too, though the citadel is empty and might be taken. The wavy lines of shaded colour, each about an inch long and one-eighth of an inch wide, are mouthfuls of wood fibre gathered from the surface of unpainted posts or rails, or dead limbs weatherworn but not decayed. Chewed into a ball by the tireless wasp, this pulp is skilfully spread and attached to the thin edge of the wall that is building. It dries into tough paper, whose texture and colour vary with the species of wood the insect collects from. Men were slow to learn of the hornet, but they were driven to it. The immense increase in the demand for paper has had to be met. Forests of spruce are raised in Europe like any other crop for the supplying of the paper mills. The trees grow uniform like corn in a field. They are thinned and tended throughout their lives. A certain part of the forests are cut clean each year and the land reset with seedling trees. By the time its turn comes round again, this area has another crop ready for harvest. The limbs even, and the trees taken out by the thinning process, go to the pulp factory.

In America great quantities of spruce and other woods are yearly cut for pulp. A single large New York daily newspaper consumes 180 tons of spruce paper in a single issue. It takes 250 cords of wood to make this much paper. In course of a year this one order will clear 18,000 acres of spruce timber, as it averages among our Northern mountain forests. When we consider the newspapers and books each day brings forth, the paper used in other ways—the manifold uses to which paper pulp is put beside paper making—we are not surprised that the pulp makers are concerned as to the future sources of the raw materials that feed their mills.

PAPER FROM GROUND WOOD

Ordinary news paper is made by grinding the wood, cleared of bark and knots, and pressing it into thin sheets. It is not strong nor durable, but it outlasts the interest of the reader who buys it. It goes from the rubbish heap in vast quantities back to the paper mill, to be bleached and used over and over again.

THE MAKING OF SULPHITE

There is a new process of separating the wood fibres from other organic substance by chemicals. Everything but the tough cellulose is removed, and it makes a strong paper. I visited one of these mills. The chemicals used produce a pulp called in trade "sulphite."

The Wood. This mill, on the bank of the Delaware, soon consumed all the available wood on the hill slopes of the neighbourhood. Now the supply comes in on cars from regions more remote. Hemlock and spruce are the only kinds used here. They are sound and green and cost at the mill about $6 per cord. The sticks average six inches to eight inches in diameter, and are sawed in two-foot lengths. The smaller the sticks, the greater the bulk of clear stock per cord and the less waste in bark.

The blocks of wood are stored in the basement and go in their turn to the peeling machine, whose knives remove the bark in thin slivers, leaving the blocks white and smooth. The bark is carried into the furnace, for it has considerable fuel value, and must be put out of the way. The blocks next pass to a machine where they are chipped into flakes, much like chips on a woodpile. These are carried to a great cauldron called the "Digester," with capacity of four or five tons of chips.

The Acid Solution. In the end of the building farthest away from the stored blocks of wood are the raw materials that combine to convert wood into sulphite. In one bin is dry sulphur, or brimstone, shovelled in by the ton. In another is air-slacked lime. Into a large tank of lime water the fumes of burning sulphur are introduced. The acid solution thus produced is the liquor poured over the chips in the digester. Under a pressure of eighty pounds of steam the chips cook for about twelve hours or longer. The judgment of an experienced tester is needed to decide when the cooking is done.

To scoop out this mass of hot pulp, reeking with strong chemicals, would seem a dangerous as well as difficult operation. On the contrary, it is very simply done. A tube at the bottom of the digester is now opened. It leads to an empty receiving

545

vat. The steam pressure is increased above, and the mass is driven out by the blast, leaving the walls of the digester as clean as if they had been scrubbed.

The cooking has chemically freed the wood fibre from everything else. It remains to get the delicate white threads separated from the mass of waste with which they are now associated in the vat. Washing and screening are the means of freeing the fibres. The processes now are purely mechanical. Water is introduced, and by churning and draining alternately the acid solution is washed out. Then the pulp passes, thinly spread, over sets of screens that take out the coarsest of the impurities, brown flakes of pith rays, uncooked knots, and bits of foreign matter.

Water streams over and through the screens, carrying the fine white fibres with it. There is a wide, endless apron of linen, like a gigantic roller towel, that revolves at right angles with the screening tables. As the water pours over this the fibres lodge on the cloth, and as the dripping, tightly stretched sheet of linen passes between the two big steel rollers at the end the filmy layer of fibres has most of the water squeezed out, and adheres as a damp, matted sheet of cotton wool to the upper wheel.

A continual winding of this coating of fibres thickens the roll on the steel cylinder until it is like table felt of heavy quality. The machinery need not stop while it is removed. A pocket knife is run from end to end of the cylinder of steel. The next revolution lays the white sheet of sulphite on the table in front of the machine. The thin film on the steel is the beginning of another.

This is *sulphite*. It has the colour of unbleached linen or muslin. In fact, it looks much like felt, its fibres being merely pressed together—not woven. It is folded clumsily and stacked for the present. In this form it dries gradually for use or shipment later, or it may be used at once.

The Making of Paper. In this mill manufacture goes further than in many. Sulphite is made into paper. Not the highest grades, for the refuse of a woollen mill up stream pollutes the water, so that an expensive system of filters would be required if the manufacture of the better papers were attempted.

The first step in the process of paper making is to bring out the rolls of sulphite and throw them into a tank with plenty of water. A central revolving shaft bears heavy arms under water that mix the contents of the tank into a uniform, pulpy consistency. The motion is continuous and vigorous, giving the tank its name—"the beater." This is the stage in paper making where the character of the product is determined. Usually a definite order limits both quality and quantity. Here colouring is put in. "Fillers" of clay, talc or starch add consistency and weight. "Sizing" of alum and rosin or of animal glue bind the fibres and make the paper take a higher polish. There is a recipe for each paper in the sample book. The beater corresponds to the cook's mixing bowl in the kitchen.

From the beater the pulp is drawn off into the "stock chest," another vat with a slowly moving paddle that keeps the ingredients thoroughly mixed. This is close to the paper machine, and the liquid contents of it are screened again to take out still smaller impurities, if the paper is required to be free from specks and other small blemishes.

The Mill. The paper mill is long and narrow, with many cylindrical rollers, some covered with revolving bands of cloth that act as carriers—others of bare, shining steel. The fluid pulp that drains through the screens falls on a moving sheet of bronze wire netting, woven so fine that only the water goes through. This netting is like the linen roller towel under the first screens—it is an endless apron, and leads around the lower one of a pair of rollers, bringing to them a thin but continuous layer of wet wood fibre. The upper roller is wrapped with cloth, to which the film of fibres sticks while the wire net turns back clean to the point of beginning. Its sole duty is to bring the pulp to the first pair of rollers, and there, giving it up, return for more. Pressed into a sheet by the close-set rollers, the fibres cling to each other and give up more water to the absorbent cloth. The sheet may now be called paper. It gains strength and compactness as it is drawn from one set of rollers to another; it ceases to drip water into the trough below. Taut and firm it winds through a maze of a dozen hot rollers, and the last sign of moisture rises in steam. Next it goes through rollers called calendars, whose high pressure gives the paper a polished surface almost equal to their own. Now knives trim the margins, cut the sheet into required widths, and wind it on wooden spools for market. The machine relinquishes these to men who weigh and mark the spools and stack them aside.

There is need of but few men in a mill where the machinery

547

is so intelligent. They are needed when the sheet breaks, which occasionally happen. Ordinarily the machine makes pulp into paper in an incredibly short time, and without help or guidance.

There seems to be no waste in this mill. The first screenings are made into coarse wrapping paper such as hardware and furniture are done up in. Though ugly and spotted, it is fairly strong. The second screenings make a finer grade of paper. The trimmings and broken sheets go back into the beater, and come to the mill again as pulp. Each sort of waste accumulates, waits its turn, and is in time converted into paper that matches it in quality.

There is much paper making along our northern border, and much grief that there is a duty that restricts the importation of wood from the ample spruce forests of Canada. The American paper makers would have the duty taken off their wood supplies and laid on Canadian paper, sulphite, etc. This is "human nature"—self interest.

The mills of northern New York are often highly specialised. Paper mills all about Carthage get their sulphite and ground wood from a single factory. A firm in Watertown makes exclusively the coloured, super-calendered paper used for the covers of magazines. There is a mill in Carthage which makes nothing but tissue paper. It is a new mill and a growing business, but its daily output already averages seventeen tons of marketable product. Some of the largest mills make only wall papers. Others make in vast quantities the paper on which the great dailies are printed.

Certain woods are adapted to special uses. Our postal cards are all made of the soft yellowish wood of the tulip tree, also known as the tulip poplar or whitewood. Cottonwoods and their relatives—the true poplars—likewise the basswoods or lindens, make excellent paper. Their wood is white and soft and the fibres are small and uniform in size.

A pulp mill or paper plant cannot be shifted from place to place as a sawmill can. It is too elaborate and expensive. The forests about it are soon stripped of suitable material, and then the item of transportation of wood enters the expense account, and adds greatly to the cost of pulp and paper. A Fond du Lac, Wisconsin, mill, having exhausted its own woods, is now making pulp out of spruce that grows on the mountains of Virginia.

PART IV
THE LIFE OF THE TREES

CHAPTER I: THE WORK OF THE LEAVES

THE swift unfolding of the leaves in spring is always a miracle. One day the budded twigs are still wrapped in the deep sleep of winter. A trace of green appears about the edges of the bud scales—they loosen and fall, and the tender green shoot looks timidly out and begins to unfold its crumpled leaves. Soon the delicate blade broadens and takes on the texture and familiar appearance of the grown-up leaf. Behold! while we watched the single shoot the bare tree has clothed itself in the green canopy of summer.

How can this miracle take place? How does the tree come into full leaf, sometimes within a fraction of a week? It could never happen except for the store of concentrated food that the sap dissolves in spring and carries to the buds, and for the remarkable activity of the cambium cells within the buds.

What is a bud? It is a shoot in miniature—its leaves or flowers, or both, formed with wondrous completeness in the previous summer. About its base are crowded leaves so hardened and overlapped as to cover and protect the tender shoot. All the tree can ever express of beauty or of energy comes out of these precious little "growing points," wrapped up all winter, but impatient, as spring approaches, to accept the invitation of the south wind and sun.

The protective scale-leaves fall when they are no longer needed. This vernal leaf fall makes little show on the forest floor, but it greatly exceeds in number of leaves the autumnal defoliation.

Sometimes these bud scales lengthen before the shoot spares them. The silky, brown scales of the beech buds sometimes add twice their length, thus protecting the lengthening shoot which seems more delicate than most kinds, less ready to encounter unguarded the wind and the sun. The hickories, shagbark and mockernut, show scales more than three inches long.

Many leaves are rosy, or lilac tinted, when they open—the waxy granules of their precious "leaf green" screened by these colored pigments from the full glare of the sun. Some leaves have wool or silk growing like the pile of velvet on their surfaces. These hairs are protective also. They shrivel or blow away when the leaf comes to its full development. Occasionally a species retains the down on the lower surface of its leaves, or, oftener, merely in the angles of its veins.

The folding and plaiting of the leaves bring the ribs and veins into prominence. The delicate green web sinks into folds between and is therefore protected from the weather. Young leaves hang limp, never presenting their perpendicular surfaces to the sun.

Another protection to the infant leaf is the pair of stipules at its base. Such stipules enclose the leaves of tulip and magnolia trees. The beech leaf has two long strap-like stipules. Linden stipules are green and red—two concave, oblong leaves, like the two valves of a pea pod. Elm stipules are conspicuous. The black willow has large, leaf-like, heart-shaped stipules, green as the leaf and saw-toothed.

Most stipules shield the tender leaf during the hours of its helplessness, and fall away as the leaf matures. Others persist, as is often seen in the black willows.

With this second vernal leaf fall (for stipules are leaves) the leaves assume independence, and take up their serious work. They are ready to make the living for the whole tree. Nothing contributed by soil or atmosphere—no matter how rich it is—can become available for the tree's use until the leaves receive and prepare it.

Every leaf that spreads its green blade to the sun is a laboratory, devoted to the manufacture of starch. It is, in fact, an outward extension of the living cambium, thrust out beyond the thick, hampering bark, and specialised to do its specific work rapidly and effectively.

The structure of the leaves must be studied with a microscope. This laboratory has a delicate, transparent, enclosing wall, with doors, called stomates, scattered over the lower surface. The "leaf pulp" is inside, so is the framework of ribs and veins, that not only supports the soft tissues but furnishes the vascular system by which an incoming and outgoing current of sap is kept in constant circulation. In the upper half of the leaf, facing the sun, the pulp is in "palisade cells," regular, oblong, crowded together, and perpendicular to the flat surface. There are sometimes more than one layer of these cells.

In the lower half of the leaf's thickness, between the palisade cells and the under surface, the tissue is spongy. There is no crowding of cells here. They are irregularly spherical, and cohere loosely, being separated by ample air spaces, which communicate with the outside world by the doorways mentioned above. An ordinary apple leaf has about one hundred thousand of these stomates to each square inch of its under surface. So the ventilation of the leaf is provided for.

The food of trees comes from two sources—the air and the soil. Dry a stick of wood, and the water leaves it. Burn it now, and ashes remain. The water and the ashes came from the soil. That which came from the air passed off in gaseous form with the burning. Some elements from the soil also were converted by the heat into gases, and escaped by the chimneys.

Take that same stick of wood, and, instead of burning it in an open fireplace or stove, smother it in a pit and burn it slowly, and it comes out a stick of charcoal, having its shape and size and grain preserved. It is carbon, its only impurity being a trace of ashes. What would have escaped up a chimney as carbonic-acid gas is confined here as a solid, and fire can yet liberate it.

The vast amount of carbon which the body of a tree contains came into its leaves as a gas, carbon dioxide. The soil furnished various minerals, which were brought up in the "crude sap." Most of these remain as ashes when the wood is burned. Water comes from the soil. So the list of raw materials of tree food is complete, and the next question is: How are they prepared for the tree's use?

The ascent of the sap from roots to leaves brings water with mineral salts dissolved in it. Thus potassium, calcium, magnesium, iron, sulphur, nitrogen and phosphorus are brought to the leaf laboratories—some are useful, some useless. The stream of water contributes of itself to the laboratory whatever the leaf cells demand to keep their own substance sufficiently moist, and those molecules that are necessary to furnish hydrogen and oxygen for the making of starch. Water is needed also to keep full the channels of the returning streams, but the great bulk of water that the roots send up escapes by evaporation through the curtained doorways of the leaves.

Starch contains carbon, hydrogen and oxygen, the last two in the exact proportion that they bear to each other in water, H_2O. The carbon comes in as carbon dioxide, CO_2. There is no lack of this familiar gas in the air. It is exhaled constantly from the lungs of every animal, from chimneys and from all decaying substances. It is diffused through the air, and, entering the leaves by the stomates, comes in contact with other food elements in the palisade cells.

The power that runs this starch factory is the sun. The chlorophyll, or leaf green, which colours the clear protoplasm of the cells, is able to absorb in daylight (and especially on warm, sunny days) some of the energy of sunlight, and to enable the protoplasm to use the energy thus captured to the chemical breaking down of water and carbon dioxide, and the re-uniting of their free atoms into new and more complex molecules. These are molecules of starch, $C_6H_{10}O_5$.

The new product in soluble form makes its way into the current of nutritious sap that sets back into the tree. This is the one product of the factory—the source of all the tree's growth—for it is the elaborated sap, the food which nourishes every living cell from leaf to root tip. It builds new wood layers, extends both twigs and roots, and perfects the buds for the coming year.

Sunset puts a stop to starch making. The power is turned off till another day. The distribution of starch goes on. The surplus is unloaded, and the way is cleared for work next day. On a sunless day less starch is made than on a bright one.

Excess of water and of free oxygen is noticeable in this making of starch. Both escape in invisible gaseous form through the stomates. No carbon escapes, for it is all used up, and a continual supply of CO_2 sets in from outside. We find it at last in the form of solid wood fibres. So it is the leaf's high calling to take the crude elements brought to it, and convert them into food ready for assimilation.

There are little elastic curtains on the doors of leaves, and in dry weather they are closely drawn. This is to prevent the free escape of water, which might debilitate the starch-making cells. In a moist atmosphere the doors stand wide open. Evaporation does not draw water so hard in such weather, and there is no danger of excessive loss. "The average oak tree in its five

554

active months evaporates about 28,000 gallons of water"—an average of about 187 gallons a day.

In the making of starch there is oxygen left over—just the amount there is left of the carbon dioxide when the carbon is seized for starch making. This accumulating gas passes into the air as free oxygen, "purifying" it for the use of all animal life, even as the absorption of carbon dioxide does.

When daylight is gone, the exchange of these two gases ceases. There is no excess of oxygen nor demand for carbon dioxide until business begins in the morning. But now a process is detected that the day's activities had obscured.

The living tree breathes—inhales oxygen and exhales carbonic-acid gas. Because the leaves exercise the function of respiration, they may properly be called the lungs of trees. For the respiration of animals differs in no essential from that of plants.

The bulk of the work of the leaves is accomplished before midsummer. They are damaged by whipping in the wind, by the ravages of fungi and insects of many kinds. Soot and dust clog the stomates. Mineral deposits cumber the working cells. Finally they become sere and russet or "die like the dolphin," passing in all the splendour of sunset skies to oblivion on the leaf mould under the trees.

CHAPTER II: THE GROWTH OF A TREE

THE great chestnut tree on the hillside has cast its burden of ripe nuts, flung down the empty burs, and given its yellow leaves to the autumn winds. Now the owner has cut down its twin, which was too near a neighbour for the well-being of either, and is converting it into lumber. The lopped limbs have gone to the woodpile, and the boards will be dressed and polished and used for the woodwork of the new house. Here is our opportunity to see what the bark of the living tree conceals—to study the anatomy of the tree—to learn something of grain, and wood rings and knots.

The most amazing fact is that this "too, too solid flesh" of the tree body was all made of dirty water and carbonic-acid gas. Well may we feel a kind of awe and reverence for the leaves and the cambium—the builders of this wooden structure we call a tree. The bark, or outer garment, covers the tree completely, from tip of farthest root to tip of highest twig. Under the bark is the slimy, colourless living layer, the *cambium*, which we may define as the separation between wood and bark. It seems to have no perceptible diameter, though it impregnates with its substance the wood and bark next to it. This cambium is a continuous under garment, lining the bark everywhere, covering the wood of every root and every twig as well as of the trunk and all its larger divisions.

Under the cambium is the wood, which forms the real body of the tree. It is a hard and fibrous substance, which in cross section of root or trunk or limb or twig is seen to be in fine, but distinctly marked, concentric rings about a central pith. This pith is most conspicuous in the twigs.

Now, what does the chestnut tree accomplish in a single growing season? We have seen its buds open in early spring and watched the leafy shoots unfold. Many of these bore clusters of blossoms in midsummer, long yellow spikes, shaking out a mist of pollen, and falling away at length, while the inconspicuous green flowers developed into spiny, velvet-lined burs that gave up in their own good time the nuts which are the seeds of the tree.

The new shoots, having formed buds in the angles of their leaves, rest from their labours. The tree had added to the height and breadth of its crown the exact measure of its new shoots. There has been no lengthening of limb or trunk. But underground the roots have made a season's growth by extending their tips. These fresh rootlets clothed with the velvety root hairs are new, just as the shoots are new that bear the leaves on the ends of the branches.

There is a general popular impression that trees grow in height by the gradual lengthening of trunk and limbs. If this were true, nails driven into the trunk in a vertical line would gradually become farther apart. They do not, as observation proves. Fence wires stapled to growing trees are not spread apart nor carried upward, though the trees may serve as posts for years, and the growth in diameter may swallow up staple and wire in a short time. Normal wood fibres are inert and do not lengthen. Only the season's rootlets and leafy shoots are soft and alive and capable of lengthening by cell division.

The work of the leaves has already been described. The return current, bearing starch in soluble form, flows freely among the cells of the cambium. Oxygen is there also. The cambium cell in the growing season fulfils its life mission by absorbing food and dividing. This is growth—and the power to grow comes only to the cell attacked by oxygen. The rebuilding of its tissues multiplies the substance of the cambium at a rapid rate. A cell divides, producing two "daughter cells." Each is soon as large as its parent, and ready to divide in the same way. A cambium cell is a microscopic object, but in a tree there are millions upon millions of them. Consider how large an area of cambium a large tree has. It is exactly equivalent to the total area of its bark. Two cells by dividing make four. The next division produces eight, then sixteen, thirty-two, sixty-four, in geometric proportion. The cell's power and disposition to divide seems limited only by the food and oxygen supply. The cambium layer itself remains a very narrow zone of the newest, most active cells. The margins of the cambium are crowded with cells whose walls are thickened and whose protoplasm is no longer active. The accumulation of these worn-out cells forms the total of the season's growth, the annual ring of wood on one side of the cambium and the annual layer of bark on the other.

What was once a delicate cell now becomes a hollow wood fibre, thin walled, but becoming thickened as it gets older. For a few years the superannuated cell is a part of the sap wood and is used as a tube in the system through which the crude sap mounts to the leaves. Later it may be stored full of starch, and the sap will flow up through newer tubes. At last the walls of the old cell harden and darken with mineral deposits. Many annual rings lie between it and the cambium. It has become a part of the heart wood of the tree.

The cells of its own generation that were crowded in the other direction made part of an annual layer of bark. As new layers formed beneath them, and the bark stretched and cracked, they lost their moisture by contact with the outer air. Finally they became thin, loose bark fibres, and scaled off.

The years of a tree's life are recorded with fair accuracy in the rings of its wood. The bark tells the same story, but the record is lost by its habit of sloughing off the outer layers. Occasionally a tree makes two layers of wood in a single season, but this is exceptional. Sometimes, as in a year of drought, the wood ring is so small as to be hardly distinguishable.

Each annual ring in the chestnut stump is distinct from its neighbouring ring. The wood gradually merges from a dark band full of large pores to one paler in colour and of denser texture. It is very distinct in oak and ash. The coarser belt was formed first. The spring wood, being so open, discolours by the accumulation of dust when exposed to the air. The closer summer wood is paler in colour and harder, the pores almost invisible to the unaided eye. The best timber has the highest percentage of summer wood.

If a tree had no limbs, and merely laid on each year a layer of wood made of parallel fibres fitted on each other like pencils in a box, wood splitting would be child's play and carpenters would have less care to look after their tools. But woods differ in structure, and all fall short of the woodworker's ideal. The fibres of oak vary in shape and size. They taper and overlap their ends, making the wood less easily split than soft pine, for instance, whose fibres are regular cylinders, which lie parallel, and meet end to end without "breaking joints."

Fibres of oak are also bound together by flattened bundles of horizontal fibres that extend from pith to cambium, insinuated between the vertical fibres. These are seen on a cross section of a log as narrow, radiating lines starting from the pith and cutting straight through heart wood and sap wood to the bark. A tangential section of a log (the surface exposed by the removal of a slab on any side) shows these "pith rays," or "medullary rays" as long, tapering streaks. A longitudinal section made from bark to centre, as when a log is "quarter-sawed" shows a full side view of the "medullary rays." They are often an inch wide or more in oak; these wavy, irregular, gleaming fibre bands are known in the furniture trade as the "mirrors" of oak. They take a beautiful polish, and are highly esteemed in cabinet work. The best white oak has 20 per cent. to 25 per cent. of its substance made up of these pith rays. The horny texture of its wood, together with its strength and durability, give white oak an enviable place among timber trees, while the beauty of its pith rays ranks it high among ornamental woods.

The grain of wood is its texture. Wide annual rings with large pores mark coarse-grained woods. They need "filling" with varnish or other substance before they can be satisfactorily polished. Fine-grained woods, if hard, polish best. Trees of slow growth usually have fine-grained wood, though the rule is not universal.

Ordinarily wood fibres are parallel with their pith. They are straight grained. Exceptions to this rule are constantly encountered. The chief cause of variation is the fact that tree trunks branch. Limbs have their origin in the pith of the stems that bear them. Any stem is normally one year older than the branch it bears. So the base of any branch is a cone quite buried in the parent stem. A cross section of this cone in a board sawed from the trunk is a *knot*. Its size and number of rings indicate its age. If the knot is diseased and loose, it will fall out, leaving a *knot hole*. The fibres of the wood of a branch are extensions of those just below it on the main stem. They spread out so as to meet around the twig and continue in parallel lines to its extremity. The fibres contiguous to those which were diverted from the main stem to clothe the branch must spread so as to meet above the branch, else the parent stem would be bare in this quarter. The union of stem and branch is weak

559

above, as is shown by the clean break made above a twig when it is torn off, and the stubborn tearing of the fibres below down into the older stem. A half hour spent at the woodpile or among the trees with a jack-knife will demonstrate the laws by which the straight grain of wood is diverted by the insertion of limbs. The careful picking up and tearing back of the fibres of bark and wood will answer all our questions. Basswood whose fibres are tough is excellent for illustration.

When a twig breaks off, the bark heals the wound and the grain becomes straight over the place. Trees crowded in a forest early divest themselves of their lower branches. These die for lack of sun and air, and the trunk covers their stubs with layers of straight-grained wood. Such timbers are the masts of ships, telegraph poles and the best bridge timbers. Yet buried in their heart wood are the roots of every twig, great or small, that started out to grow when the tree was young. These knots are mostly small and sound, so they do not detract from the value of the lumber. It is a pleasure to work upon such a "stick of timber."

A tree that grows in the open is clothed to the ground with branches, and its grain is found to be warped by hundreds of knots when it reaches the sawmill. Such a tree is an ornament to the landscape, but it makes inferior, unreliable lumber. The carpenter and the wood chopper despise it, for it ruins tools and tempers.

Beside the natural diversion of straight grain by knots, there are some abnormal forms to notice. Wood sometimes shows wavy grain under its bark. Certain trees twist in growing, so as to throw the grain into spiral lines. Cypresses and gum trees often exhibit in old stumps a veering of the grain to the left for a few years, then suddenly to the right, producing a "cross grain" that defies attempts to split it.

"Bird's-eye" and "curly maple" are prizes for the furniture maker. Occasionally a tree of swamp or sugar maple keeps alive the crowded twigs of its sapling for years, and forms adventitious buds as well. These dwarfed shoots persist, never getting ahead further than a few inches outside the bark. Each is the centre of a wood swelling on the tree body. The annual layers preserve all the inequalities. Dots surrounded by wavy rings are scattered over the boards when the tree is sawed. This is bird's-eye grain, beautiful in pattern and in sheen and colouring when polished. It is cut thin for veneer work. Extreme irregularity of grain adds to the value of woods, if they are capable of a high polish. The fine texture and colouring, combined with the beautiful patterns they display, give woods a place in the decorative arts that can be taken by no other material.

CHAPTER III: THE FALL OF THE LEAVES

It is November, and the glory of the woods is departed. Dull browns and purples show where oaks still hold their leaves. Beech trees in sheltered places are still dressed in pale yellow. The elfin flowers of the witch hazel shine like threads of gold against the dull leaves that still cling. The trees lapse into their winter sleep.

Last week a strange thing happened. The wind tore the red robes from our swamp maples and sassafras and scattered them in tatters over the lawn. But the horse chestnut, decked out in yellow and green, lost scarcely a leaf. Three days later, in the hush of early morning, when there was not a whiff of a breeze perceptible, the signal, "Let go!" came, and with one accord the leaves of the horse chestnut fell. In an hour the tree stood knee deep in a stack of yellow leaves; the few that still clung had considerable traces of green in them. Gradually these are dropping, and the shining buds remain as a pledge that the summer story just ended will be told again next year.

Perhaps such a sight is more impressive if one realises the vast importance of the work the leaves of a summer accomplish for the tree before their surrender.

The shedding of leaves is a habit broad-leaved trees have learned by experience in contact with cold winters. The swamp magnolia is a beautiful evergreen tree in Florida. In Virginia the leaves shrivel, but they cling throughout the season. In New Jersey and north as far as Gloucester, where the tree occurs sparingly, it is frankly deciduous. Certain oaks in the Northern States have a stubborn way of clinging to their dead leaves all winter. Farther south some of these species grow and their leaves do not die in fall, but are practically evergreen, lasting till next year's shoots push them off. The same gradual change in habit is seen as a species is followed up a mountain side.

The horse chestnut will serve as a type of deciduous trees. Its leaves are large, and they write out, as if in capital letters, the story of the fall of the leaf. It is a serial, whose chapters

SUGAR MAPLE   SCARLET OAK   CHESTNUT   YELLOW BIRCH

THE GLORY OF AUTUMN TREES

run from July until November. The tree anticipates the coming of winter. Its buds are well formed by midsummer. Even then signs of preparation for the leaf fall appear. A line around the base of the leaf stem indicates where the break will be. Corky cells form on each side of **this** joint, replacing tissues which in the growing season can only be parted by breaking or tearing them forcibly. A clean-cut zone of separation weakens the hold of the leaf upon its twig, and when the moment arrives the lightest breath of wind—even the weight of the withered leaf itself—causes the natural separation. And the leaflets simultaneously fall away from their common petiole.

There are more important things happening in leaves in late summer than the formation of corky cells. The plump green blades are full of valuable substance that the tree can ill afford to spare. In fact, a leaf is a layer of the precious cambium spread out on a framework of veins and covered with a delicate, transparent skin—a sort of etherealised bark. What a vast quantity of leaf pulp is in the foliage of a large tree!

As summer wanes, and the upward tide of sap begins to fail, starch making in the leaf laboratories declines proportionately. Usually before midsummer the fresh green is dimmed. Dust and heat and insect injuries impair the leaf's capacity for work. The thrifty tree undertakes to withdraw the leaf pulp before winter comes.

But how?

It is not a simple process nor is it fully understood. The tubes that carried the products of the laboratory away are bound up with the fibres of the leaf's skeleton. Through the transparent leaf wall the migration of the pulp may be watched. It leaves the margins and the net veins, and settles around the ribs and mid vein, exactly as we should expect. Dried and shrivelled horse-chestnut leaves are still able to show various stages in this marvellous retreat of the cambium. If moisture fails, the leaf bears some of its green substance with it to the earth. The "breaking down of the chlorophyll" is a chemical change that attends the ripening of a leaf. (Leaf ripening is as natural as the ripening of fruit.) The waxy granules disintegrate, and a yellow liquid shows its colours through the delicate leaf walls. Now other pigments, some curtained from view by the chlorophyll, others the products of decomposition, show themselves. Iron and other minerals the sap brought from the soil contribute reds and yellows and purples to the colour scheme. As drainage proceeds, with the chemical changes that accompany it, the pageant of autumn colours passes over the woodlands. No weed or grass stem but joins in the carnival of the year.

Crisp and dry the leaves fall. Among the crystals and granules that remain in their empty chambers there is little but waste that the tree can well afford to be rid of—substances that have clogged the leaf and impeded its work.

We have been mistaken in attributing the gay colours of autumnal foliage to the action of frost. The ripening of the leaves occurs in the season of warm days and frosty nights, but it does not follow that the two phenomena belong together as cause and effect. Frost no doubt hastens the process. But the chemical changes that attend the migration of the carbohydrates and albuminous materials from the leaf back into twig and trunk and root for safe keeping go on no matter what the weather.

In countries having a moist atmosphere autumn colours are less vivid. England and our own Pacific coast have nothing to compare with the glory of the foliage in the forests of Canada and the Northeastern States, and with those on the wooded slopes of the Swiss Alps, and along the Rhine and the Danube. Long, dry autumns produce the finest succession of colours. The most brilliant reds and yellows often appear long before the first frost. Cold rains of long duration wash the colours out of the landscape, sometimes spoiling everything before October. A sharp freeze before the leaves expect it often cuts them off before they are ripe. They stiffen and fall, and are wet and limp next day, as if they had been scalded; all their rich cell substance lost to the tree, except as they form a mulch about its roots. But no tree can afford so expensive a fertiliser, and happily they are not often caught unawares.

Under the trees the dead leaves lie, forming with the snow a protective blanket for the roots. In spring the rains will leach out their mineral substance and add it to the soil. The abundant lime in dead leaves is active in the formation of *humus*, which is decayed vegetable matter. We call it "leaf mould." So even the waste portions have their effectual work to do for the tree's good.

The leaves of certain trees in regions of mild winters persist until they are pushed off by the swelling buds in spring. Others cling a year longer, in sorry contrast with the new foliage. We may believe that this is an indolent habit induced by climatic conditions.

Leaves of evergreens cling from three to five years. Families and individuals differ; altitude and latitude produce variations. An evergreen in winter is a dull-looking object, if we could compare it with its summer foliage. Its chlorophyll granules withdraw from the surface of the leaf. They seek the lower ends of the palisade cells, as far as they can get from the leaf surface, assume a dull reddish-brown or brownish-yellow colour, huddle in clumps, their water content greatly reduced, and thus hibernate, much as the cells of the cambium are doing under the bark. In this condition, alternate freezing and thawing seem to do no harm, and the leaves are ready in spring to resume the starch-making function if they are still young. Naturally, the oldest leaves are least capable of this work, and least is expected of them. Gradually they die and drop as new ones come on. As among broad-leaved trees, the zone of foliage in evergreens is an outer dome of newest shoots; the framework of large limbs is practically destitute of leaves.

CHAPTER IV: HOW TREES SPEND THE WINTER

Nine out of every ten intelligent people will see nothing of interest in a row of bare trees. They casually state that buds are made in the early spring. They miss seeing the strength and beauty of tree architecture which the foliage conceals in summertime. The close-knit, alive-looking bark of a living tree they do not distinguish from the dull, loose-hung garment worn by the dead tree in the row. All trees look alike to them in winter.

Yet there is so much to see if only one will take time to look. Even the most heedless are struck at times with the mystery of the winter trance of the trees. They know that each spring re-enacts the vernal miracle. Thoughtful people have put questions to these Sphinx-like trees. Secrets the bark and bud scales hide have been revealed to those who have patiently and importunately inquired. A keen pair of eyes used upon a single elm in the dooryard for a whole year will surprise and inform the observer. It will be indeed the year of miracle.

A tree has no centre of life, no vital organs corresponding to those of animals. It is made up, from twig to root, of annual, concentric layers of wood around a central pith. It is completely covered with a close garment of bark, also made of annual layers. Between bark and wood is a delicate undergarment of living tissue called *cambium*. This is disappointing when one comes to look for it, for all there is of it is a colourless, slimy substance that moistens the youngest layers of wood and bark, and forms the layer of separation between them. This cambium is the life of the tree. A hollow trunk seems scarcely a disability. The loss of limbs a tree can survive and start afresh. But girdle its trunk, exposing a ring of the cambium to the air, and the tree dies. The vital connection of leaves and roots is destroyed by the girdling; nothing can save the tree's life. Girdle a limb or a twig and all above the injury suffers practical amputation.

The bark protects the cambium, and the cambium is the tissue which by cell multiplication in the growing season produces the yearly additions of wood and bark. Buds are growing points set along the twigs. They produce leafy shoots, as a rule. Some are specialised to produce flowers and subsequently fruits. Leaves are extensions of cambium spread in the sun and air in the season when there is no danger from frosts. The leaves have been called the stomachs of a tree. They receive crude materials from the soil and the air and transmute them into starch under the action of sunlight. This elaborated sap supplies the hungry cambium cells during the growing season, and the excess of starch made in the leaf laboratories is stored away in empty wood cells and in every available space from bud to root tip, from bark to pith.

The tree's period of greatest activity is the early summer. It is the time of growth and of preparation for the coming winter and for the spring that follows it. Winter is the time of rest—of sleep, or hibernation. A bear digs a hollow under the tree's roots and sleeps in it all winter, waking in the spring. In many ways the tree imitates the bear. Dangerous as are analogies between plants and animals, it is literally true that the sleeping bear and the dormant tree have each ceased to feed. The sole activity of each seems to be the quiet breathing.

Do trees really breathe? As truly and as incessantly as you do, but not as actively. Other processes are intermittent, but breathing must go on, day and night, winter and summer, as long as life lasts. Breathing is low in winter. The tree is not growing. There is only the necessity of keeping it alive.

Leaves are the lungs of plants. In the growing season respiration goes on at a vigorous rate. The leaves also throw off in insensible vapour a vast quantity of water. This is called *transpiration* in plants; in animals the term used is *perspiration*. They are one and the same process. An average white-oak tree throws off 150 gallons of water in a single summer day. With the cutting off of the water supply at the roots in late fall, transpiration is also cut off.

The skin is the efficient "third lung" of animals. The closing of its pores causes immediate suffocation. The bark of trees carries on the work of respiration in the absence of the leaves. Bark is porous, even where it is thickest.

Look at the twigs of half a dozen kinds of trees, and find the little raised dots on the smooth surface. They usually vary in colour from the bark. These are *lenticels,* or breathing pores— not holes, likely to become clogged with dust, but porous, corky tissue that filters the air as it comes in. In most trees the smooth epidermis of twigs is shed as the bark thickens and breaks into furrows. This obscures, though it does not obliterate, the air passages. Cherry and birch trees retain the silky epidermal bark on limbs, and in patches, at least, on the trunks of old trees. Here the lenticels are seen as parallel, horizontal slits, open sometimes, but usually filled with the characteristic corky substance. They admit air to the cambium.

There is a popular fallacy that trees have no buds until spring. Some trees have very small buds. But there is no tree in our winter woods that will not freely show its buds to anyone who wishes to see them. A very important part of the summer work of a tree is the forming of buds for next spring. Even when the leaves are just unfolding, on the tender shoots a bud will be found in each angle between leaf and stem. All summer long its bud is the especial charge of each particular leaf. If accident destroys the leaf, the bud dies of neglect. When midsummer comes the bud is full grown, or nearly so, and the fall of the leaf is anticipated. The thrifty tree withdraws as much as possible of the rich green leaf pulp, and stores it in the twig to feed the opening buds in spring.

What is there inside the wrappings of a winter bud? "A leaf," is the usual reply—and it is not a true one. A bud is an embryo shoot—one would better say, a shoot in miniature. It has very little length or diameter when the scales are stripped off. But with care the leaves can be spread open, and their shape and venation seen. The exact number the shoot was to bear are there to be counted. Take a horse-chestnut bud —one of the biggest ones—and you will unpack a cluster of flowers distinct in number and in parts. The bud of the tulip tree is smaller, but it holds a single blossom, and petals, stamens and pistil are easily recognisable. Some buds contain flowers and no leaves. Some have shoots with both upon them. If we know the tree, we may guess accurately about its buds.

There is another popular notion, very pretty and sentimental, but untrue, that study of buds is bound to overthrow. It is the belief that the woolly and silky linings of bud scales, and the scales themselves, and the wax that seals up many buds are all for the purpose of keeping the bud warm through the cold winter. The bark, according to the same notion, is to keep the tree warm. This idea is equally untenable. There is but feeble analogy between a warm-blooded animal wrapped in fur, its bodily heat kept up by fires within (the rapid oxidation of fats and carbohydrates in the tissues), and the winter condition of a tree. Hardy plants are of all things the most cold blooded. They are defended against injuries from cold in an effective but entirely different way.

Exposure to the air and consequent loss of its moisture by evaporation is the death of the cambium—that which lies under the thick bark and in the tender tissues of the bud, sealed up in its layers of protecting scales.

The cells of the cambium are plump little masses of protoplasm, semi-fluid in consistency in the growing season. They have plenty of room for expansion and division. Freezing would rupture their walls, and this would mean disintegration and death. Nature prepares the cells to be frozen without any harm. The water of the protoplasm is withdrawn by osmosis into the spaces between the cells. The mucilaginous substance left behind is loosely enclosed by the crumpled cell wall. Thus we see that a tree has about as much water in it in winter as in summer. Green wood cut in winter burns slowly and oozes water at the ends in the same discouraging way as it does in summertime.

A tree takes on in winter the temperature of the surrounding air. In cold weather the water in buds and trunk and cambium freezes solid. Ice crystals form in the intercellular spaces where they have ample room, and so they do no damage in their alternate freezing and thawing. The protoplasm stiffens in excessive cold, but when the thermometer rises, life stirs again. Motion, breathing and feeding are essential to cell life.

It is hard to believe that buds freeze solid. But cut one open in a freezing cold room, and before you breathe upon it take a good look with a magnifier, and you should make out the ice crystals. The bark is actually frozen upon a stick of green stove wood. The sap that oozes out of the pith and heart wood was frozen, and dripped not at all until it was brought indoors.

What is meant by the freezing of fruit buds in winter, by which the peach crop is so often lost in Northern States? When spring opens, the warmth of the air wakes the sleeping buds. It thaws the ice in the intercellular spaces, and the cells are quick to absorb the water they gave up when winter approached. The thawing of the ground surrounds the roots with moisture. Sap rises and flows into the utmost twig. Warm days in January or February are able to deceive the tree to this extent. The sudden change back to winter again catches them. The plump cells are ruptured and killed by the "frost bite."

It is a bad plan to plant a tender kind of tree on the south side of a house or a wall. The direct and the reflected warmth of the sun forces its buds out too soon, and the late frosts cut them off. There is rarely a good yield on a tree so situated.

There is no miracle like "the burst of spring." Who has watched a tree by the window as its twigs began to shine in early March, and the buds to swell and show edges of green as their scales lengthened? Then the little shoot struggled out, casting off the hindering scales with the scandalous ingratitude characteristic of infancy. Feeble and very appealing are the limp baby leaves on the shoot, as tender and pale green as asparagus tips. But all that store of rich nutritive material is backing the enterprise. The palms are lifted into the air; they broaden and take on the texture of the perfect, mature leaf. Scarcely a day is required to outgrow the hesitation and inexperience of youth. The tree stands decked in its canopy of leaves, every one of which is ready and eager to assume the responsibilities it faces. The season of starch making has opened.

Cut some twigs of convenient trees in winter. Let them be good ones, with vigorous buds, and have them at least two feet long. You may test this statement I have made about the storing of food in the twigs, and the one about the unfolding of the leafy shoots. Get a number of them from the orchard—samples from cherry, plum and apple trees; from maple and elm and any other familiar tree. Put them in jars of water and set them where they get the sun on a convenient window shelf. Give them plenty of water, and do not crowd them. It is not necessary to change the water, but cutting the ends slanting and under water every few days insures the unimpeded flow of the water up the stems and the more rapid development of the buds you are watching. When spring comes there are too many things that demand attention. The forcing of winter buds while yet it is winter is the ideal way to discover the trees' most precious secrets.

APPENDIX

APPENDIX

Giant Eucalyptus—*Eucalyptus amyg-
dalina*—Australia. . . . . .470 feet

Big Tree—*Sequoia Wellingtonia*—
W. Am. . . . . 350 "

Redwood—*Sequoia sempervirens*—
California . . . . 325 "

Sugar Pine—*Pinus Lambertiana*—
Pacific Coast . . . . 300 "

Douglas Spruce—*Psudotsuga mucro-
nata*—Pacific Coast . . . . 300 "

Western Hemlock—*Tsuga hetero-
phylla*—Pacific Coast. . . . . 250 "

Western Larch—*Larix occidentalis*
—Pacific Coast . . . . 250 "

Western Arbor Vitae—*Thuya gigan-
tea*—Pacific Coast. . . . . 200 "

Buttonwood—*Platanus occidentalis*
—E. Am. . . . . 160 "

Red Oak—*Quercus rubra*—E. Am. . 150 "

Tulip Tree—*Liriodendron Tulipifera* 150 "

THE OLDEST TREES IN THE WORLD
(Probable age limit)

Dragon Tree—*Dracæna Draco*—
Canaries. . . . . 6,000 years

Baobab Tree—*Adansonia digitata*
—Africa. . . . . 5,000 "

Bald Cypress—*Taxodium mucro-
natum*—Mexico. . . . . 4,000 "

Oriental Plane—*Platanus orien-
talis*—Europe and Asia . . . . 4,000 "

Eastern Cypress—*Cupressus sempervirens*—Europe and Asia. . . 3,000 "

European Yew—*Taxus baccata*—
Europe, Asia and Africa . . . . 3,000 "

European Chestnut—*Castanea
sativa*—Europe . . . . 2,000 "

English Oak—*Quercus peduncu-
lata*—Europe. . . . . 2,000 "

Big Tree—*Sequoia Wellingtonia*—
California . . . . 2,000 "

Cedar of Lebanon—*Cedrus Lebani*
Asia Minor . . . . 2,000 "

APPROXIMATE AGES AT WHICH TREES MATURE

White Pine—*Pinus Strobus*. . . . . . . 250 years

White Oak—*Quercus alba*. . . . . 200 "

Chestnut—*Castanea dentata* . . . . . . 200 "

Elms—*Ulmus* spp. . . . . 90 "

Beech—*Fagus Americana*. . . . . 100 "

Poplars—*Populus* spp. . . . . 50 "

Birches—*Betula* spp. . . . . 50 "

Willows—*Salix* spp. . . . . 50 "

Basswoods—*Tilia* spp . . . . 100 "

Catalpa—*Catalpa speciosa* . . . . 25 "

White Ash—*Fraxinus Americana* . 80 "

RELATIVE RAPIDITY OF GROWTH OF FAMILIAR TREES

[From report of W. F. Fox, Superintend-
ent of State Forests, New York]

Three-inch saplings, in favourable situations, will, in twenty years, have diameters of:

Silver Maple—*Acer saccharinum* . . 21 inches

Box Elder—*Acer Negundo*. . . . . . . 21 "

American Elm—*Ulnus Americana* 19 "

Tulip Tree—*Liriodendron Tulipi-
fera* . . . . 18 "

Sycamore—*Platanus occidentalis*. . 18 "

Basswood—*Tilia Americana* . . . . . 17 "

Catalpa—*Catalpa speciosa* . . . . 16 "

Red Maple—*Acer rubrum*. . . . . 16 "

Ailanthus—*Ailanthus glandulosa*. . 16 "

Cucumber Tree—*Magnolia acumi-
nata* . . . . 15 "

Chestnut—*Castanea dentata* . . . . . . 14 "

Yellow Locust—*Robinia Pseuduca-
cia*. . . . . 14 "

Hard Maple—*Acer Saccharum*. . . . 13 "

Horse Chestnut—*Æsculus Hippo-
castanum* . . . . 13 "

Honey Locust—*Gleditsia triacan-
thos*. . . . . 13 "

Red Oak—*Quercus rubra*. . . . . 13 "

Pin Oak—*Quercus palustris* . . . . . . 13 "

Scarlet Oak—*Quercus coccinea*. . . . 13 "

White Ash—*Fraxinus Americana*. . 12 "

White Oak—*Quercus alba*. . . . . 11 "

Hackberry—*Celtis occidentalis*. . . . . 10 "

TREES THAT SPROUT FROM THE STUMP

Black Locust—*Robinia Pseudacacia*

Chestnut—*Castanea dentata*

Oaks—*Quercus* spp.

Ashes—*Fraxinus* spp.

Elms—*Ulmus* spp.

Maples—*Acer rubrum* and *saccharinum*

Beech—*Fagus Americana*

Birches—*Betula* spp.

Basswood—*Tilia* spp.

Willows—*Salix* spp.

Appendix

Poplars—*Populus* spp.
Eucalyptus—*Eucalyptus* spp.
Catalpa—*Catalpa* spp.
Osage Orange—*Toxylon pomiferum*
Pitch Pine—*Pinus rigida*
Shortleaf Pine—*Pinus echinata*
Hickory (shagbark) *Hicoria ovata*
Walnut (black) *Juglans nigra*
Redwood—*Sequoia sempervirens*
Ailanthus—*Ailanthus glandulosa*

TREES PREFERRING WET SOIL

Red Maple—*Acer rubrum*
Silver Maple—*Acer saccharinum*
Sweet Gum—*Liquidambar Styraciflua*
Red Birch—*Betula nigra*
White Birch—*Betula populifolia*
Big Shell-bark Hickory—*Hicoria laciniosa*
Tupelos—*Nyssa* spp.
Bald Cypress—*Taxodium distichum*
Pin Oak—*Quercus palustris*
Swamp White Oak—*Quercus platanoides*
Willow Oak—*Quercus Phellos*
Poplars—*Populus* spp.
Willows—*Salix* spp.
Alders—*Alnus* spp.
Black Ash—*Fraxinus nigra*
Black Spruce—*Picea Mariana*
Blue Beech—*Carpinus Caroliniana*
Sycamore—*Platanus occidentalis*
Swamp Bay—*Magnolia glauca*
Tamarack—*Larix Americana*

TEN BROAD-LEAVED TREES HAVING WEEPING FORMS

Silver Maple—*Acer saccharinum*, var. *Wieri*
White Birch—*Betula alba*, var. *pendula*
Beech—*Fagus Americana*, var. *pendula*
Ash—*Fraxinus excelsior*, var. *pendula*
Plum—*Prunus pendula*
Cherry—*Prunus serotina*, var. *pendula*
Willow—*Salix Babylonica*
Linden—*Tilia petiolaris*
Elm—*Ulmus scabra*, var. *pendula*
Oak—*Quercus pedunculata*, var. *pendula*

TEN TREES FOR SMOKY CITIES

(Evergreens cannot endure smoke)

Honey Locust—*Gleditsia triacanthos*
American Elm—*Ulmus Americana*
White Ash—*Fraxinus Americana*
Cottonwood—*Populus deltoidea*
Ailanthus—*Ailanthus glandulosa*
Horse Chestnut—*Æsculus Hippocastanum*
Buttonwood—*Platanus occidentalis*.
Lindens—*Tilia* spp.
Maples—*Acer* spp.
Balm of Gilead—*Populus balsamifera*

TREES WITH LARGE SPREADING CROWNS

(Suitable for wide streets and roadways.)

American Elm—*Ulmus Americana*
Silver Maple—*Acer saccharinum*
Honey Locust—*Gleditsia triacanthos*
Tulip Tree—*Liriodendron Tulipifera*
Sycamore—*Platanus occidentalis*
Cottonwood—*Populus deltoidea*
Red Oak—*Quercus rubra*
Black Oak—*Quercus velutina*
Live Oak—*Quercus Virginiana*
White Oak—*Quercus alba*
White Ash—*Fraxinus Americana*
Chestnut—*Castanea dentata*
Horse Chestnut—*Æsculus Hippocastanum*
Silver Poplar—*Populus alba*
Black Walnut—*Juglans nigra*

TEN VERY TALL DECIDUOUS TREES

(Suitable for avenues and parks)

Buttonwood—*Platanus occidentalis*
Black Walnut—*Juglans nigra*
Tulip Tree—*Liriodendron Tulipifera*
Pin Oak—*Quercus palustris*
Red Oak—*Quercus rubra*
Black Oak—*Quercus velutina*
Cottonwood—*Populus deltoidea*
American Elm—*Ulmus Americana*
Bald Cypress—*Taxodium distichum*
Honey Locust—*Gleditsia triacanthos*

TEN VERY NARROW PYRAMIDAL TREES

(Suitable for formal gardens.)

Red Cedar—*Juniperus Virginiana*
Firs—*Abies* spp.
Spruces—*Picea* spp.
Larches—*Larix* spp.
Bald Cypress—*Taxodium distichum*
Arbor Vitae—*Thuya* spp.
Lombardy Poplar—*Populus nigra*, var. *Italica*
Yellow Cypress—*Chamæcyparis Nootkatensis*
Port Orford Cedar — *Chamæcyparis Lawsoniana*
Ginkgo—*Salisburia adiantifolia*

TEN TREES UNDESIRABLE FOR STREET PLANTING

Box Elder—Short-lived; easily broken by wind.
Silver Maple—Short-lived; easily broken by wind.
Virgilia—Low branched; easily broken; flowers stolen.
Carolina Poplar—Short-lived, coarse; easily broken.
Mountain Ash—Too small; branches broken by thieves.

Dogwoods—Too small; branches broken by thieves.

Black Locust—Foliage late and soon falling; frame ugly when bare.

Kentucky Coffee Tree—Needs rich soil; dead looking when bare.

Butternut—Short-lived, branches low, infested by insects.

Evergreens—Give little shade; branches low.

TEN BROAD-LEAVED EVERGREENS

American Holly—*Ilex opaca*
Great Laurel—*Rhododendron maximum*
Swamp Bay—*Magnolia glauca*
Great-flowered Magnolia—*Magnolia fœtida*
Live Oak—*Quercus Virginiana*
California Live Oak—*Quercus agrifolia*
Red Bay—*Persea Borbonia*
Laurel Cherry—*Prunus Caroliniana*
Evergreen Buckthorn—*Rhamnus crocea*
Mountain Laurel—*Kalmia latifolia*

TREES WITH VERY LARGE LEAVES

Magnolias—*Magnolia* spp.
Large-leaved Maple—*Acer macrophyllum*
Hercules' Club—*Aralia spinosa*
Papaw—*Asimina triloba*
Kentucky Coffee Tree—*Gymnocladus dioicus*
Catalpa—*Catalpa speciosa*
Ailanthus—*Ailanthus glandulosa*
Bur Oak—*Quercus macrocarpa*
Paulownia—*Paulownia imperialis*
Walnuts and Hickories—*Juglans* and *Hicoria* spp.

TREES WITH NARROW OR FINELY CUT LEAVES

Willows—*Salix* spp.
Locust—*Robinia Pseudacacia*
Honey Locust—*Gleditsia triacanthos*
Black Cherry—*Prunus serotina*
Bald Cypress—*Taxodium distichum*
Most Evergreens—*Coniferae*
Willow Oak—*Quercus Phellos*
Sumachs—*Rhus* spp.
(Cut-leaf varieties of many other kinds.)

TREES WITH FRAGRANT FLOWERS

Magnolias—*Magnolia* spp.
Plums and Cherries—*Prunus* spp.
Lindens—*Tilia* spp.
Apples—*Malus* spp.
Locusts—*Gleditsia, Robinia* and *Cladrastis,* spp.
Hawthorns—*Cratægus* spp.
Juneberries—*Amelanchier* spp.

TREES WITH SHOWY WHITE FLOWERS

Blooming before the leaves:
Flowering Dogwood—*Cornus florida*
Plums and Cherries—*Prunus* spp.
Shadbush—*Amelanchier* spp.

Blooming after the leaves:
Mountain Ashes—*Sorbus* spp.
Elders—*Sambucus* spp.
Fringe Tree—*Chionanthus Virginica*
Viburnums—*Viburnum* spp.
Sourwood—*Oxydendrum arboreum*
Loblolly Bay—*Gordonia Lasianthus*
Basswoods—*Tilia* spp.
Hercules' Club—*Aralia spinosa*
Magnolias—*Magnolia* spp.
Black Locust—*Robinia Pseudacacia*
Yellowwood—*Cladrastis lutea*
Rhododendrons—*Rhododendron maximum*
Hawthorns—*Cratægus* spp.
Buckeyes and Horse Chestnuts—*Æsculus* spp.
Catalpas—*Catalpa* spp.
Silverbell Trees—*Mohrodendron* spp.

TREES WITH SHOWY YELLOW FLOWERS

Tulip Tree—*Liriodendron Tulipifera*
Cucumber Tree—*Magnolia acuminata*
Yellow Cucumber Tree—*Magnolia cordata*
Chestnut—*Castanea dentata*
Willows—(Staminate)—*Salix* spp.
Sassafras—*Sassafras Sassafras*
Witch Hazel—*Hamamelis Virginiana*
Yellow Buckeye—*Æsculus octandra*
Birches—(Staminate)—*Betula* spp.

TREES WITH SHOWY PINK FLOWERS

Red Bud—*Cercis Canadensis*
Crab Apple—*Malus coronaria*
Clammy Locust—*Robinia viscosa*
Mountain Laurel—*Kalmia latifolia*
Rhododendron—*Rhododendron maximum*

TREES WITH SHOWY RED FLOWERS

Red Maple—*Acer rubrum*
Sumachs—*Rhus* spp.
Papaw—*Asimina triloba*

TREES HAVING ONE OR BOTH KINDS OF FLOWERS IN CATKINS

Both kinds on the same tree:
Chestnuts
Oaks
Hickories
Walnuts
Birches
Alders
Hornbeams
Pines, and other Conifers
Two kinds on separate trees:
Poplars
Willows

TREES WITH SHOWY RED FRUITS

Flowering Dogwood—*Cornus florida*
Viburnum—*Viburnum Lentago*
Mountain Ash—*Sorbus Americana*

577

Appendix

Cherries and Plums—*Prunus* spp.
Hawthorns—*Cratægus* spp.
Sumachs—*Rhus* spp.
Yews—*Taxus* spp.
Hollies—*Ilex* spp.
Red Maple—*Acer rubrum*
Magnolias—*Magnolia* spp.
Burning Bush—*Evonymus atropurpureus*
Red Ailanthus—*Ailanthus glandulosa* var. *erythrocarpa*

TREES WITH BRIGHT AUTUMN FOLIAGE

Leaves turning red:
 Sumachs—*Rhus* spp.
 Red Maple—*Acer rubrum*
 Tupelo—*Nyssa sylvatica*
 Sweet Gum—*Liquidambar Styraciflua*
 Dogwood—*Cornus florida*
 Juneberry—*Amalanchier Canadensis*
 Hawthorn—*Cratægus Crus-galli*
 Scarlet Oak—*Quercus coccinea*
 Red Oak—*Quercus rubra*
 Burning Bush—*Evonymus atropurpureus*
 Sorrel Tree—*Oxydendrum arboreum*
Leaves Turning Yellow:
 White Ash—*Fraxinus Americana*
 Beech—*Fagus Americana*
 White Maple—*Acer saccharinum*
 Tulip Tree—*Liriodendron Tulipifera*
 Larch—*Larix* spp.
 Ginkgo—*Salisburia adiantifolia*
 Hickories—*Hicoria* spp.
 Walnuts—*Juglans* spp.
 Locusts—*Robinia, Cladrastis* and *Gleditsia* spp.
 Willows—*Salix* spp.
 Poplars—*Populus* spp.
 Chestnut—*Castanea dentata*
 Ailanthus—*Ailanthus glandulosa*
 Cucumber Tree—*Magnolia acuminata*
 White Birch—*Betula populifolia*
 Bur Oak—*Quercus macrocarpa*

Leaves Turning to Mixed Red and Yellow:
 Hard Maple—*Acer Saccharum*
 Sweet Gum—*Liquidamber Styraciflua*
 Sassafras—*Sassafras Sassafras*
 Black Birch—*Betula lenta*
Leaves Turning Purple:
 White Ash—*Fraxinus Americana*
 White Oak—*Quercus alba*
 Red Oak—*Quercus rubra*
 Dogwood—*Cornus alternifolia*

EUROPEAN TREES WIDELY PLANTED

White Birch—*Betula alba* (horticultural forms)
Scotch Pine—*Pinus sylvestris*
Austrian Pine—*Pinus Laricio*, var. *Austriaca*
Norway Spruce—*Picea excelsa*
Norway Maple—*Acer platanoides*
Beech—*Fagus sylvatica*
English Walnut—*Juglans regia*
English Oak—*Quercus Robur*
English Hawthorn—*Cratægus Oxyacantha*
European Lindens—*Tilia* spp.
European Plane—*Platanus orientalis*
Fig—*Ficus Carica*

ASIATIC TREES WIDELY PLANTED

Magnolias—*Magnolia* spp. and varieties
China Tree—*Melia Azadarach*
Hercules' Club—*Aralia Chinensis*
Cedars—*Cedrus Deodara* and *Libani*
Japanese Maples—*Acer* spp.
Horse Chestnut—*Æsculus Hippocastanum*
Ginkgo—*Salisburia adiantifolia*
Ailanthus—*Ailanthus glandulosa*
Paulownia—*Paulownia imperialis*
Paper Mulberry—*Broussonetia papyrifera*
Apple—*Malus* spp. and varieties
Pear—*Pyrus communis* in varieties
Peach—*Prunus Persica*
Almond—*Prunus Amygdalus*
Many Conifers

INDEX

Index

Index

Index

Index

Index

588

LILACS

By Amy Lowell

Lilacs,
False blue,
White,
Purple,
Color of lilac,
Your great puffs of bowers
Are everywhere in this my New England.
Among your heart-shaped leaves
Orange orioles hop like music-box birds and sing
Their little weak soft songs;
In the crooks of your branches
The bright eyes of song sparrows sitting on spotted
    eggs
Peer restlessly through the light and shadow
Of all Springs,
Lilacs in dooryards
Holding quiet conversations with an early moon;
Lilacs watching a deserted house
Settling sideways into the grass of an old road;
Lilacs, wind-beaten, staggering under a lopsided
    shock of bloom
Above a cellar dug into a hill.
You are everywhere.
You were everywhere.
You tapped the window when the preacher
    preached his sermon,
And ran along the road beside the boy going to
    school.
You stood by pasture-bars to give the cows good
    milking.
You persuaded the housewife that her dish pan
    was of silver
And her husband an image of pure gold.
You flaunted the fragrance of your blossoms
Through the wide doors of Custom Houses—
You, and sandal wood, and tea,
Charging the noses of quill-driving clerks
When a ship was in from China.
You called to them: " Goose-quill men, goose-quill
    men.
May is a month for flitting."
Until they writhed on their high stools
And wrote poetry on their letter-sheets behind
    the propped-up ledgers.
Paradoxical New England clerks,
Writing inventories in ledgers, reading the " Song
    of Solomon " at night,
So many verses before bedtime,
Because it was the Bible.
The dead fed you
Amid the slant stones of graveyards.
Pale ghosts who planted you
Came in the night-time
And let their thin hair blow through your clustered
    stems.
You are of the green sea.
And of the stone hills which reach a long distance.
You are of elm-shaded streets with little shops
    where they sell kites and marbles.
You are of great parks where every one walks and
    nobody is at home.
You cover the blind sides of greenhouses
And lean over the top to say a hurry word through
    the glass
To your friends, the grapes, inside.
Lilacs,
False blue,
White,
Purple,
Color of lilac,
You have forgotten your Eastern origin,
The veiled women with eyes like panthers,
The swollen aggressive turbans of jeweled Pashas.
Now you are a very decent flower,
A reticent flower,
A curiously clear-cut, candid flower,
Standing beside clean doorways,
Friendly to a house-cat and a pair of spectacles,

Maine knows you,
Has for years and years;
New Hampshire knows you
And Massachusetts
And Vermont.
Cape Cod starts you along the beaches to Rhode
    Island;
Connecticut takes you from a river to the sea.
You are brighter than apples,
Sweeter than tulips,
You are the great flood of our souls
Bursting above the leaf-shapes of our hearts,
You are the smell of all Summers,
The love of wives and children
The recollection of the gardens of little children,
You are State Houses and Charters
And the familiar treading of the foot to and fro
    on a road it knows.
May is lilac here in New Eng.and,
May is a thrush singing "Sun up!" on a tip-top
    ash-tree,
May is white clouds behind pinetrees
Puffed out and marching upon a blue sky.
May is a green as no other,
May is much sun through small leaves,
May is soft earth,
And apple-blossoms,
And windows open to a South wind.
May is a full light wind of lilac
From Canada to Narra. ansett Bay.
Lilacs,
False blue,
White,
Purple,
Color of lilac,
Heart-leaves of lilac all over New England,
Roots of lilac under all the soil of New England,
Lilac in me because I am New England,
Because my roots are in it,
Because my leaves are of it,
Because my flowers are for it,
Because it is my country
And I speak to it of itself
And sing of it with my own voice
Since certainly it is mine.

Trees.

I think that I shall never see

A poem lovely as a tree,

A tree that looks to God all day,

And lifts her leafy arms to pray;

A tree whose hungry mouth is pressed

Close to the earth's sweet-flowing breast;

A tree who may in summer wear

A nest of robins in her hair;

Upon whose breast the snow has lain,

Who intimately lives with rain.

Poems are made by fools like me

But only God can make a tree.

Joyce Kilmer.